ON

Woodworking Technology

WOODWORKING TECHNOLOGY

JAMES J. HAMMOND
President
State College
Fitchburg, Massachusetts

EDWARD T. DONNELLY
Professor and Director of Industrial Arts
State College
Fitchburg, Massachusetts

WALTER F. HARROD
Associate Professor of Industrial Arts
State College
Fitchburg, Massachusetts

NORMAN A. RAYNER
Head of Industrial Arts Department
Wachusett Regional High School
Holden, Massachusetts

McKNIGHT & McKNIGHT

PUBLISHING COMPANY

BLOOMINGTON, ILLINOIS

Foreword

This book has been written for those who have a need or a desire for knowing about the several related factors involved in wood and its fabrication. Both a comprehensive coverage and a reasonable degree of detail have been included. The text ranges from simple, interesting facts to technical and scientific knowledge. It encompasses the theory of wood and woodworking technology in their application in furniture, structures, and patterns.

The underlying assumption of the authors is that the subject of wood and wood fabrication is many-sided. They believe that intelligent and effective work with wood presupposes knowledge of tools, materials, processes, mechanics, and design. Hence the book is divided into *sections*, each dealing with a specific topic. References are made also to *industries* and to *occupations* within the wood industries.

The section on design should be helpful to individuals who wish to design a project or who have a woodworking design problem. Basic principles are suggested, along with dimension ranges, shapes, forms, and decorations.

Facts and principles are given on the general topic of wood (lumber) while the specific properties of more than twenty-five woods are covered.

Each tool and machine is considered as both a unit of precision or mechanical efficiency and as a device for performing a particular kind of work. The outline for each tool includes descriptions of the principal parts and their function, along with safety considerations and information about sizes, attachments, and other pertinent facts. Something of the history and evolution of some tools is also given.

Virtually all of the operations and processes normally covered in woodworking books have been included in this one. However, in addition to outlining and illustrating the steps of procedure, emphasis has been given to the principles underlying the processes involved.

Since no book on woodworking would be complete without some reference to the subject of wood finishing, both modern and traditional finishes and finishing methods have been included.

Each species of wood, each separate material, tool, machine, operation, or process has been handled as a distinct topic. To assist the reader, these topics have been grouped into appropriate sections. Thus the reader may readily find information on topics of interest and concern. The authors did not intend that each topic and section should be studied in the order and sequence by which they have been organized in the book. Rather, they assumed that the reader or student would study the respective topics with reference to some problem or need for information.

The content has been developed and used with industrial arts classes on the senior high and college levels respectively. It is also appropriate for classes in vocational woodworking and (in some cases) manufacturers. The authors were gratified that the previous edition of this text was selected as the woodworking textbook to be translated and printed in the Turkish language.

The authors are indebted to many people for their assistance with this undertaking. The business and industrial firms who provided photographs, cuts, catalogs, and technical information were most cooperative.

We are particularly appreciative of the excellent review of the previous edition and the constructive criticism provided by Dr. John R. Ballard of Southwest Texas State College in San Marcos, Texas. We wish to thank Dr. Harold Gatslick and Dr. Bruce Hoadley of the School of Forestry at the University of Massachusetts for their assistance. We are also indebted to Mr. Howard Rivers and Mr. Dennis Swierad for their assistance in taking photographs, and for the cooperation of Mr. Robert J. Shannon of Stanley Tools. We are especially grateful to our wives and families for their encouragement and forbearance.

Contents

Section One.   Introduction **1**

Section Two.   Design **4**

Topic 1.   Design 4
Dimension Reference Chart.. 12
Topic 2.   Glossary of Furniture Terms................................... 13

Section Three.   Wood **15**

Topic 3.   Wood, Trees, and Lumber 15
Topic 4.   Lumber Terms, Defects, and Grading 27
Topic 5.   Practices of Lumber Computation 32
Topic 6.   Ash 33
Topic 7.   Balsa 34
Topic 8.   Basswood 35
Topic 9.   Beech 36
Topic 10.   Birch 38
Topic 11.   Cedar 39
Topic 12.   Cherry 42
Topic 13.   Cypress 43
Topic 14.   Fir 46
Topic 15.   Gumwood 50
Topic 16.   Hemlock 51
Topic 17.   Hickory 53
Topic 17A.   Limba (Korina) 55
Topic 18.   Mahogany 55
Topic 19.   Philippine Mahogany 57
Topic 20.   Maple 58
Topic 21.   Oak 59
The Deacon's Masterpiece 61
Topic 22.   Eastern Pine 62
Topic 23.   Ponderosa Pine 63
Topic 24.   Yellow Pine or Hard Pine 64
Topic 25.   Yellow Poplar 65
Topic 26.   Redwood 66
Topic 27.   Spruce 67
Topic 27A.   Sycamore 68
Topic 28.   Black Walnut 69
Topic 29.   Black Willow 70
Topic 29A.   Manufactured Board 71
Topic 30.   Plywood 72
Topic 31.   Hardboard 80
Topic 32.   Particle Board 81
Excerpts from The Song of Hiawatha.. 84

Section Four.   Laying Out 85

Topic 33.   Tools 85
Topic 34.   Introduction to Measurement and Layout 88
Topic 34A.   Rules 89
Topic 35.   Gauges 91
Topic 36.   Squares 94
Topic 37.   Laying Out and Testing Angles 97
Topic 38.   Layout 99
Topic 39.   Getting Out Stock 101

Section Five.   Cutting Stock with Saws 103

Topic 40.   Theory Underlying the Design and Action of Cutting Tools 103
Topic 41.   Safety 105
Topic 42.   Hand Saws 107
Topic 43.   Sawing a Board with a Hand Saw 110
Topic 44.   Miter Box 113
Topic 44A.   Motorized Miter Box 114
Topic 45.   Jig Saw or Scroll Saw 115
Topic 46.   Using the Jig Saw 118
Topic 47.   Portable Electric Saber Saw (Bayonet Saw) 121
Topic 48.   Circular Saw — Table Type 122
Topic 48A.   Selecting Blades for the Circular Saw 125
Topic 49.   Using the Circular Saw 128
Topic 50.   Circular Saw Operator 134
Topic 51.   Radial Arm Saw 134
Topic 52.   Using the Radial Arm Saw 136
Topic 53.   Portable Electric Saw 140
Topic 54.   Band Saw 143
Topic 54A.   Band Saw Blades 145
Topic 55.   Using the Band Saw 146
Topic 56.   Replacing a Band Saw Blade 148
Topic 57.   Band Saw Operator 150
Topic 58.   Occupations in the Furniture Industry 150

Section Six.   Hand Cutting to Basic Form 152

Topic 59.   Hand Planes 152
Topic 60.   Special Purpose Planes 154
Topic 61.   Squaring a Board (Hand Process) 158
Topic 62.   Spoke Shave 163
Topic 63.   Drawknife or Drawing Knife 164
Topic 64.   Scrapers — Hand, Cabinet, Hook 165
Topic 65.   Sharpening Hand Scrapers and Cabinet Scrapers 166
Topic 66.   Chisels, Gouges, and Carving Tools 168
Topic 67.   Using Chisels, Gouges, and Carving Tools 170
Topic 68.   Grinder — Bench, Floor Models 174
Topic 69.   Grinding Edge Tools 176

Topic 70.   Oilstone 178
Topic 71.   Whetting or Honing a Cutting Tool 180

Section Seven.   Machine Cutting to Basic Form 184

Topic 72.   Jointer 184
Topic 73.   Setting Knives and Aligning Rear Jointer Table 186
Topic 74.   Smoothing a Surface on the Jointer 187
Topic 74A.   Uniplane 190
Topic 75.   Single Surface Planer 191
Topic 76.   Using the Surface Planer 193
Topic 77.   Squaring a Board by Machine Process 194
Topic 78.   Portable Hand Router 196
Topic 79.   Using a Portable Hand Router 199
Topic 80.   The Shaper 203
Topic 81.   Cutting Moldings, Molding an Edge, Making Special Cuts for
Joining Edges with a Shaper 205

Section Eight.   Filing 209

Topic 82.   Wood File and Rasp 209
Topic 83.   Shaping with a File or Rasp 211

Section Nine.   Sanding 213

Topic 84.   Coated Abrasives 213
Topic 85.   Sanders — Spindle, Belt, Disk 215
Topic 86.   Portable Sanders — Belt, Disk, Finish 218
Topic 87.   Using Sanders — Spindle, Belt, Disk 220

Section Ten.   Drilling, Boring, and Mortising 223

Topic 88.   Selecting the Proper Tool to Cut a Hole 223
Topic 89.   Bit Brace 224
Topic 90.   Wood Bits 226
Topic 91.   Boring a Hole with Bit and Brace 231
Topic 92.   Hand Drill and Breast Drill 234
Topic 93.   Twist Drill 236
Topic 94.   Drilling a Hole 237
Topic 95.   Portable Electric Drill 238
Topic 96.   Drill Press — Floor and Bench Models 239
Topic 97.   Using the Drill Press 242
Topic 98.   Vertical Hollow Chisel Mortiser 247

Section Eleven.   Shaping Circular Forms on the Lathe 250

Topic 99.   Wood Turning 250
Topic 100.   Wood Lathe 252
Topic 101.   Turning Chisels 258

Topic 102.   Spindle or Between-Center Turning 260
Topic 103.   Face-Plate Turning on a Lathe 266
Topic 104.   Industrial Turning 269
Topic 105.   The Wood Turner 271

Section Twelve.   Joinery 272

Topic 106.   Joinery 272
Topic 107.   Common Wood Joints 273
Topic 108.   Making an Edge-to-Edge Spring Joint 276
Topic 109.   Making a Lap Joint 277
Topic 110.   Making a Dado Joint — Hand Process 278
Topic 111.   Making a Rabbet Joint — Hand Process 280
Topic 112.   Dowels — Wood and Metal 281
Topic 113.   Reinforcing Joints with Dowels 282
Topic 114.   Making a Miter Joint 284
Topic 115.   Making a Mortise and Tenon Joint — Hand Process 288
Topic 116.   Making a Mortise and Tenon Joint — Machine Process 291
Topic 117.   Making a Dovetail Joint — Hand Process 294
Topic 118.   Laying Out and Cutting Dovetails on a Pedestal Leg 296
Topic 119.   Making a Coped Joint 298
Topic 120.   Making Finger Joints to Support Table Leaves 299
Topic 121.   Joints Commonly Used in Table Construction 302

Section Thirteen.   Fastening 304

Topic 122.   Wood Glue 304
Topic 123.   Hand Screw 309
Topic 124.   Bar Clamps 310
Topic 125.   C-, Band, Miter, and Spring Clamps 313
Topic 126.   Gluing a Joint 317
Topic 127.   Claw Hammer 319
Topic 128.   Nails 320
Topic 129.   Driving Nails 325
Topic 130.   Screwdrivers 328
Topic 131.   Wood Screws 330
Topic 132.   Driving Wood Screws 332
Topic 133.   Corner Irons, Braces, Flat Corner Irons, Mending Plates, T-Plates....333
Topic 134.   Hinges 335
Topic 135.   Hanging a Cabinet Door with Fixed-Pin Butts..................338

Section Fourteen.   Veneering 340

Topic 136.   Veneer and Transveneer 340
Topic 137.   Veneering a Surface 342
Topic 138.   Inlay and Insets 344
Topic 139.   Applying Inlay and Insets 345

Section Fifteen. **Laminating, Bending, and Molding** **347**

Topic 140.   Plastic Laminates 347
Topic 141.   Contact Cement 348
Topic 142.   Bending Wood to a Form 348

Section Sixteen. **Structures** **353**

Topic 143.   Structures 353
Topic 144.   The Carpenter 355
Topic 145.   Leveling Tools 356
Topic 146.   Laying Out Batter Boards 358
Topic 147.   House Framing 359
Topic 148.   Framing a Wall 369
Topic 149.   Plumbing a Wall or Corner 371
Topic 150.   Roofs 373
Topic 151.   Reading a Rafter Table to Figure the Length of a Common Rafter . . .374
Topic 152.   Reading a Rafter Table to Lay Out the Length of
             Hip and Valley Rafters 376
Topic 153.   Reading a Rafter Table to Lay Out the Length of Jack Rafters 377
Topic 154.   Trusses and Their Use 379
Topic 155.   Sheathing and Siding 382
Topic 156.   Laying Out Straight-Run Stair Jacks 385
Topic 157.   Figuring Board Measure by the Use of the Essex Scale 386
Topic 158.   Fitting and Hanging a Door 387
Topic 159.   Installing a Cylindrical Lockset in a Door 389
Topic 160.   Standards Pertaining to Structural Elements 390
Topic 161.   Boat Construction 391
Topic 162.   Glossary of Structural Terms 393

Section Seventeen. **Patternmaking** **397**

Topic 163.   Patternmaking 397
Topic 164.   Considerations for Laying Out a Pattern 399
Topic 165.   Making a Simple Pattern 400
Topic 166.   Laying Out and Shaping a Cylindrical Split Pattern 401
Topic 167.   Laying Out and Constructing a Simple Cylindrical Core Box 402
Topic 168.   Fillets 403
Topic 169.   Applying Fillets 403
Topic 170.   Glossary of Patternmaking Terms 404
Topic 171.   The Patternmaker 406

Section Eighteen. **Finishing** **407**

Topic 172.   Finishing 407
Topic 173.   Preparing the Surface for Finishing 408
Topic 174.   Paint Brushes 409
Topic 175.   Paints and Enamels 411
Topic 176.   Latex Emulsion Paints 412

Topic 177.	Epoxy Finishes 414
Topic 178.	Oil Stain 415
Topic 179.	Applying Oil Stains 416
Topic 180.	Water Stain 417
Topic 181.	Applying Water Stain — Brush Method 417
Topic 182.	Sealer 419
Topic 183.	Paste Wood Filler 419
Topic 184.	Applying Paste Wood Filler 420
Topic 185.	Shellac 422
Topic 186.	Varnish 423
Topic 187.	Applying Varnish — Brush Method 424
Topic 188.	Polyurethane Varnish 425
Topic 189.	Lacquer 426
Topic 190.	Applying Lacquer 427
Topic 191.	Super Finishes 429
Topic 192.	Spray Gun 430
Topic 193.	Abrasive Flours — Pumice and Rottenstone 432
Topic 194.	Waxes — Liquid, Paste 433
Topic 195.	Preparing and Applying a Wipe-on Gum Finish 434
Topic 196.	Finish Schedules for Close and Open Grain Woods 435
Topic 197.	Decalcomania Transfers — Decals 436
Topic 198.	Glossary of Finishing Terms 437
Reference List 439
Index 449

It is very appropriate that wood—a material with a hundred thousand uses—has been recognized as a medium of instruction as well as of construction. Woodworking is identified with all levels of education and is a standard, well-established area of industrial education.

Scientists and engineers are busily engaged in research and development programs to more efficiently utilize the ingredients of wood as well as wood itself. It is forecast that there will be new equipment, new materials, and new processes — all leading to wood with improved properties and expanded usage, along with greater reduction in waste.

Students need to become familiar with the properties of wood and allied materials, with the equipment, and with the principles underlying wood fabrication.

Wood technology, as all other subjects of education, has a basic structure of its own and can be organized around specific definable patterns. Obviously one subdivision is *wood and its classifications.* A second is the *forms of construction,* including methods of joinery and types of fasteners and hardware. A third subdivision is the classification of *tools and machines,* and a fourth is the *tool and machine operations and processes.*

Woodworking occupations are so numerous that it would serve little purpose to even list them or to attempt to classify them. There are hand and bench operations, work with jigs and fixtures, construction jobs, and machine operations. Even within given trades of woodworking there are craft divisions. Woodworking industries also defy classification, for they are too numerous and varied. There is little point to even attempt to classify wood products, although for instructional purposes, such a classification may be more reasonable. Courses in woodworking can be subdivided into such topics as furniture, structures, patterns or tools, containers, accessories, novelties, toys and playthings.

The major categories of the field of woodworking might well be: wood and allied materials, construction forms, tools and machines, operations and processes, products and applications.

Wood is classified commercially as hard-

Fig. 1-1. Woodworking in Education — Students in School Shop

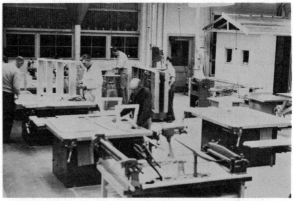

Fig. 1-2. Woodworking in Education — Adults in a School Shop

1

wood, softwood, and manufactured board. In school shops, specific kinds or species of each of these classes of wood should be used and studied. Each kind of wood used may serve as representative of a respective type but woods differ greatly even within their classification. Each wood should be selected because of its particular fitness for the job at hand. A general woodworking program should provide experiences with several kinds of wood in a variety of applications to provide an awareness of the likenesses and differences in properties and uses of various kinds and classifications of wood.

Woodworking construction is classified as *solid, open structure, carcase,* and a combination of all three. The term *solid construction* covers articles which are made of a solid mass of wood. This may be a single solid piece or several pieces glued together. The identifying characteristic is that the object is one solid mass or unit. Examples are: baseball bats, bows, tool handles, split patterns, propellers, newel posts, legs and spindles of furniture, solid seats, and other like pieces.

Open structure is a type of construction where the structural members can be seen; that is, they are open or uncovered. Examples of this type of construction are: wooden wheels, stepladders, chairs, tables, scaffolding, bridges, crates, crutches, and some truck bodies.

Carcase construction, commonly referred to as *case construction,* is the type of work where the structural members are covered. The "carcase" is the box-like body; though it may be divided with sections, doors, drawers, and partitions. The term is used more frequently in furniture and cabinet work, often as "case work." Some examples of carcase construction are found in: bookcases, breakfronts, secretaries, highboys, wardrobes, chests of drawers, clocks, radios, and television cabinets. Some glider wings, surfboards, and framed buildings also may be considered examples of carcase construction.

Most articles of woodwork are composed of a combination of the above mentioned three methods of construction. All experiences that

Fig. 1-3. Woodworking in Industry (Courtesy Heywood Wakefield Co.)

students have in producing articles of wood will serve as examples of one or the other of these types of construction.

Woodworking tools are, in reality, *an extension or amplification of man's muscles and senses,* ingeniously contrived by generations of craftsmen to perform a specific step in the art of working with wood. These tools represent in their present form the most effective design man has been able to develop for the purpose. Some are equally effective for several purposes. Each tool represents not only good, functional design, but also one or more principles of mathematics and/or science. Standard measuring, marking, and layout tools are basic instruments of woodworking, as well as those tools commonly identified with wood industries as the tools and machines used for such operations as cutting, boring, clamping, and driving.

Students of woodworking should know the classification of each tool in terms of its function and the principles of science and mechanics which it utilizes. They should understand the unique design of the particular tools they use, the principles by which such tools are most efficiently operated, and the reasons underlying the methods by which they are used. There are basic tools and processes in woodworking and they apply to all the jobs, trades, and industries in the woodworking field.

Woodworking consists of a great number of different tool operations but fortunately all of them are reducible to a reasonable number of basic processes such as cutting, boring, forming, jointing, and finishing. Upholstery is an allied area, but in it there is no actual processing of wood itself. There is layout in woodworking, but the processes involved are not peculiar to woodworking. Cutting, boring, forming, jointing, and finishing are processes which change the shape, size, form, and appearance of the wood itself. Wood is cut to shape and dimension by shearing, chipping, and abrading. Wood is formed into shape through bending, compressing, and laminating-molding. Wood is built-up or joined by fitting, splicing, and fastening with glue, nails, screws, bolts, and other hardware. It is finished by a number of well-known techniques such as staining, painting, waxing, and the application of covering materials. These processes are basic to all woodwork.

Students should learn the underlying principle of every operation they perform and they should be aware of additional applications of that principle with other tools and materials in different operations. If, through realistic experiences, students achieve reasonable proficiency in processing wood with tools and machines, then the techniques of one or more woodworking jobs will have been learned.

At various stages in the history of civilization man has achieved extraordinary results in his utilization of wood. His attainments have reflected physical, social, economic, esthetic, and religious needs and interests. His material accomplishments have ranged from very simple, practical implements and works of art to complex engineering feats.

Somehow, even the primitives and savages soon learned that wood could be used in numerous ways. They accomplished surprising results in their tools, weapons, implements, statues, totems, and conveyances. Along with their patience and skill they must have gained penetrating insight into the character of wood and how it could be worked.

On occasion an artist or poet expresses his admiration for the artist-craftsman who works in wood. In this book there appear excerpts from "The Song of Hiawatha" and from "The Deacon's Masterpiece." In the former, Longfellow masterfully depicted the high level of practical wisdom the American Indians had about woodcraft. He revealed how they had learned the especial properties of given species of wood and knew how to select and use the proper wood for a given function. In "The Deacon's Masterpiece" Oliver Wendell Holmes cleverly portrays how a discriminating workman analyzed each member of the "One-Horse Shay" and then proceeded to select from the available materials the one whose properties best suited the requirements of that particular part. That he selected well and knew his craft was evidenced in the durability of the creation. Both Holmes and Longfellow demonstrated that they themselves possessed a surprising knowledge of the characteristics and properties of wood.

Topic *1.* Design

Design in the field of wood processing is not reducible to any set of formulae. All that is wood possesses its own design. This is so whether the design is planned or accidental. In shape and size, as well as in grain, figure, texture (or even blemish), wood presents to the craftsman many natural qualities of design. To enhance these natural characteristics, craftsmen and designers have created numerous methods of working and finishing wood to give it character, beauty and distinctiveness.

Fig. 2-1. Pie Crust Tilt-Top Table

Consider how wood products come into being. Generally wood is fabricated into form in response to some need or, at least, with some end use in mind. Style, ornamentation, and motif are considered also.

While most woods are appropriate for numerous applications the selection of the most suitable wood for a given use is based on both scientific findings and traditional practice. Oftentimes a particular wood is known best by some specific use; that is, ash for bats; mahogany, maple, and cherry for furniture; knotty pine for paneling; oak for floors; hickory for handles; and so on. The experienced woodworker is reasonably well informed about the properties of the respective woods and their suitability for particular applications. The student of woodwork or the amateur woodworker should investigate available authentic data about woods and their properties when planning and designing objects to be made of wood.

In addition to functional considerations the woodworker should strive for esthetic effects as well. Wood products can and should be attractive as well as practical or technically sound.

Thus there are many wood products that are considered as objects of beauty because of shapes, styles, grain patterns, finishes, and other qualities. Still, wood as an art medium has not been fully exploited. Though considerable has been done with wood in this regard, ever so much more could be done. Since wood varies so in its many characteristics it contains numerous potentialities for artistic treatment.

Throughout the years imaginative craftsmen have discovered that wood can be fashioned readily into a variety of shapes with

4

innumerable degrees of inside and outside curves, with either sharp or rounded edges and corners, with bevels and tapers, and an almost infinite variety of turnings. Panels, beading, and molding of countless designs are employed to impart a unique character to wood products. Also used are carvings, fretwork, and inlay and marquetry.

In recent times form-fitting molded shapes and laminations have contributed further variety to woodworking designs. Improved types of appliques in the form of decals, transfers, wood tapes, and manufactured panels have added greatly to the variety of wood decoration. The development of new finishes possessing exceptional properties has increased the attractiveness and utility of wood products, particularly in the areas of furniture and household woodware.

Every product made of wood represents some need, interest, idea, inspiration, or purpose of some sort. Sometimes perhaps little formal thought is given to the factor of design except in an incidental way. Usually however, design considerations accompany every stage of the development of an idea.

In preliminary sketching, functional qualities usually receive greatest attention. Such fundamental considerations as the following must be included: technical knowledge about properties of particular species of wood; performance characteristics of glues, nails, screws, hardware, and other fasteners; methods of joinery and construction; shapes and dimensions; kinds of finishes; and, of course, the intended service of the product to be developed. Some technical factors are fully as esthetic as they are functional. For example, in determining the particular kind of wood to be used, texture, grain, color, and figure are considered along with fabricating properties and other suitable physical characteristics. Construction is determined mainly on the basis of functional considerations but is greatly influenced oftentimes by esthetic qualities. In the refinement of a design sometimes the method of construction is altered and strength becomes subordinate to beauty or at least is sacrificed to some degree.

Fig. 2-2. Governor Winthrop Desk (Courtesy Ford Motor Co., Industrial Arts Awards)

Fig. 2-3. Candlestand

Thus it can be seen that both esthetic and technical decisions are made at every stage of the development of a product. Oftentimes the application of sound technical thinking produces a most attractive result. Craftsmanship gives emphasis to good design and is a constant factor in taste. A well-fabricated object has a certain attraction of its own.

Woodware

Many objects of utility are made of wood and are classified as *woodware*. For a great many inexpensive woodware products, the requirements of design are quite simple, pertaining mainly to size, shape, function, finish, and cost. Woods are selected on the basis of suitable properties, availability, and cost. The price an object of woodware will bring in the market is a very important consideration and sometimes it is necessary to compromise somewhat in strength and beauty in order to meet a particular price level. Where natural wood beauty is not a factor, opaque finishes are employed and completely obscure blemishes and defects. Use, style, and color are probably the characteristics that concern the great majority of people. The student of woodwork and the amateur craftsman should bear in mind all these realistic considerations when designing projects in woodware.

Furniture Design

In the area of wood furniture design there has been considerable experimentation. Efforts have been made to introduce new and

Fig. 2-5. Danish Occasional Chairs (Courtesy Selig Manufacturing Co.)

Fig. 2-4. Queen Anne Lowboy

Fig. 2-6. Desk or Dining Chairs (Courtesy Selig Manufacturing Co.)

Fig. 2-7. Danish Coffee Table (Courtesy Selig Manufacturing Co., Inc.)

different shapes and styles. Many pieces have been simplified and streamlined by rounding corners and by bending and molding parts. New finishes and fabrics appropriate to the newer shapes have given a genuinely new look to many pieces of furniture. There has been a decided increase in the use of metal in combination with wood. Sheet iron, stainless steel, brass, copper, aluminum, and expanded metal have been used for legs, feet, frames, shelves, and drawer guides. Plastic and glass also have been used in combination with wood.

Most furniture manufactured today is mass-produced. It is made to serve the mode and temper of contemporary living. Generally it is light in weight, compact, and readily cleaned and maintained. Either traditional or modern finishes may be had, according to one's preferences, although the advantages of modern finishes are becoming widely recognized. In upholstered goods, the covering must possess

Fig. 2-8. Danish Corner Table (Courtesy Selig Manufacturing Co., Inc.)

beauty of design, color and texture, as well as serviceability. Latex foam and other new fillers are sought after for their resilience, longer wearing qualities, and their attractive appearance and comfort. Appearance, sometimes called "customer appeal," is a foremost consideration in furniture design.

In planning their furniture projects, students and amateur furniture makers would do well to study the characteristics of good furniture of all periods. They should try to identify the qualities which give a piece character and attractiveness. In so doing they will likely discover that the best in contemporary or traditional furniture is not only suited to its use, but there is harmony and unity in the respective parts as well as in the whole and that its style represents a fashion rather than a fad.

A chair presents an excellent problem in furniture design. The relation of the chair to the human body is most intimate. It must fit the body and provide comfort and rest. A chair must be relatively easy to handle, portable, strong enough to resist complex stresses, and it must be attractive. All chairs must be functional, which means that the user must be able to sit relaxed, in comfort and safety.

The Windsor chair, Fig. 2-10, is an interesting study in wood structure. The back spindles act as an open-work, cantilevered truss with the bow member serving as a tie rod. The sweep of the bow and the arc of the spindles as they come forward on the sides create flanges like those of a channel beam. Finer and longer back spindles, somewhat bowed instead of straight, provide greater support and comfort. Combs and fans contribute additional attractiveness.

A Windsor chair has exceptional stability. The cant of the legs assures this feature. Their angle stiffens the entire base against side sway. Invariably the stretchers are arranged in the form of an "H" with the front part open between the legs. This design provides both horizontal and vertical bracing against the outward diagonal strain of the splayed legs, thus reducing the likelihood of the joints pulling apart. The saddle seat provides formfitting comfort.

Fig. 2-10. Windsor Chair

Fig. 2-9. Dining Table and Chairs (Courtesy Selig Manufacturing Co.)

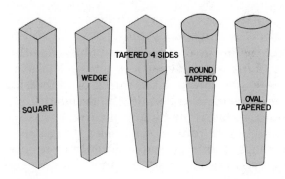

Fig. 2-11. Shaped Legs

SQUARE   WEDGE   TAPERED 4 SIDES   ROUND TAPERED   OVAL TAPERED

Design in Turning

While general principles of design apply to turning, there are unique effects obtained through it. The general profile of a turned design is a combination of basic molds and/or angular lines complementing each other in a unified design. Many spindle turnings are adaptations of the classic shapes found in columns and pedestals. Normally, turnings should be composed of two or three divisions, one of

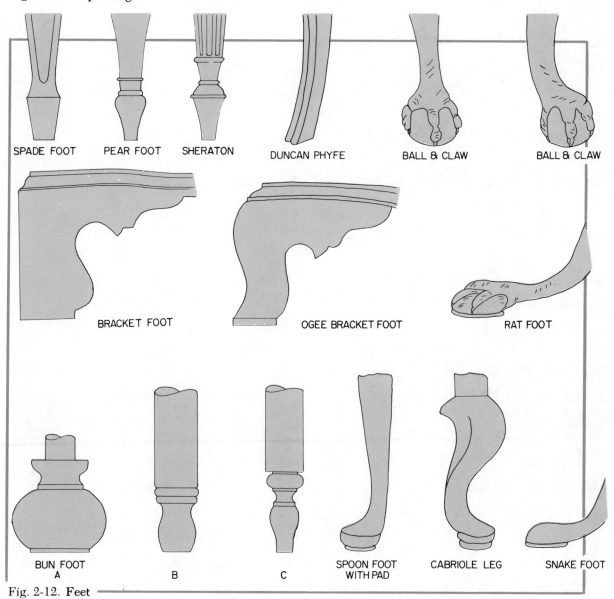

SPADE FOOT   PEAR FOOT   SHERATON   DUNCAN PHYFE   BALL & CLAW   BALL & CLAW

BRACKET FOOT   OGEE BRACKET FOOT   RAT FOOT

BUN FOOT
A   B   C   SPOON FOOT WITH PAD   CABRIOLE LEG   SNAKE FOOT

Fig. 2-12. Feet

which dominates. Each division should be distinct, yet related and contribute to the overall pattern. The flow of curves should be graceful and in keeping with the mass. Long curves should terminate with an abrupt change of direction. Reverse curves should be broken by a square shoulder or bead. Subdivisions usually consist of well-formed beads, flutes, and "V's."

Experienced wood turners sometimes select stock for turning because of its particular grain pattern.

In developing a design for a turning, a profile of half the object is drawn and a mirror placed on edge along the axis which will reflect the image of a completed object. Tilting the mirror or moving it (shifting the axis) creates the effect of increasing or decreasing the diameter and permits the designer to select the most pleasing proportion. Experienced wood turners sometimes design their turnings to bring out the natural beauty of a particular grain pattern and feature this beauty in their turning.

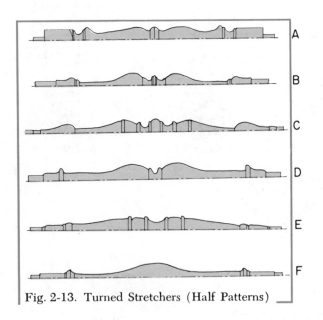

Fig. 2-13. Turned Stretchers (Half Patterns)

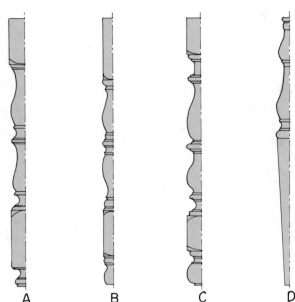

Fig. 2-15. Turned Legs (Half Patterns)

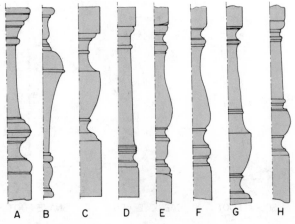

Fig. 2-14. Pedestals (Half Patterns)

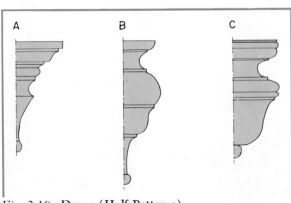

Fig. 2-16. Drops (Half Patterns)

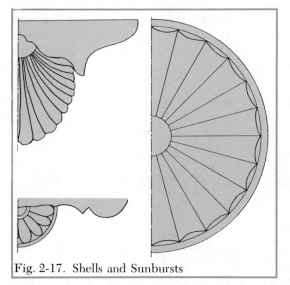

Fig. 2-17. Shells and Sunbursts

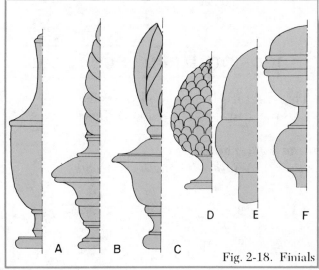

A   B   C   D   E   F

Fig. 2-18. Finials

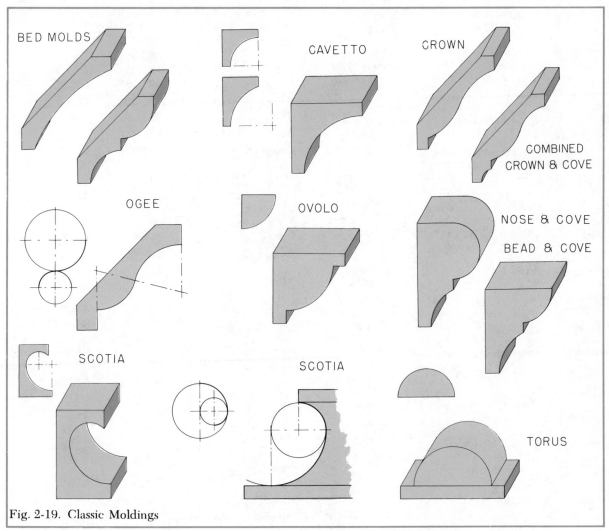

BED MOLDS

CAVETTO

CROWN

COMBINED
CROWN & COVE

OGEE

OVOLO

NOSE & COVE

BEAD & COVE

SCOTIA

SCOTIA

TORUS

Fig. 2-19. Classic Moldings

Dimension Reference Chart

This chart has been compiled to give a suggested range of sizes of common articles.

Home Furnishings

Name	Width	Length	Height
Beds			
Cribs	2'6"	4'10"	22" to mattress
Twin	3'-3'9"	6'10"	"
3/4	3'6"-4'	6'10"	"
Junior	2'9"-3'1"	6'-6'3"	"
Double	4'10"-5'	6'10"	"
Benches, work			30"-34"
Bookcases	7¾"-12"	15"-36"	9"-14" between shelves 18"-84" high
Buffets	1'5"-2'1"	4'-6'6"	42"
Chairs (wood)	seat width 13"-32"	depth 13"19"	15"-18" seat
	arm height 23"-25"	back height 30"-48"	
Chests, Cedar	17"-21"	35"-47"	15"-21"
Chests of drawers	18"-22"	34"-42"	28"-48"
China cabinets	18"-22"	3'-4'	5' and up
Clocks, Grandfather's			6'3"-7'6½"
BASE	16"-18"	8"-9¼"	
WAIST	12"-14½"	7"-7½"	
BONNET	16"-18"	8"-9¼"	
Clocks, Grandmother's			4'4"-5'2"
BASE	12"-13"	6½"-7"	
WAIST	10"	6"	
BONNET	12"-13"	6½"-7"	
Desks	15"-31"	30"-60"	28"-34" to the writing surface

Name	Width	Length	Height
Dry Sinks	19"-20"	38"-46"	37"-40"
Tables			
Bedside	14"-24"	12"-24"	20"-28"
Card	2'6"-3' sq.		28¼"
Coffee	15"-36"	22"-60"	14"-17"
Console rd., sq.	14"-22"	30"-48"	29"-32"
Dining	30"-48"	40"-8'10"	29"-30"
Dressing	15"-22"	36"-50"	29"
End	10"-14"	18"-36"	20"-29"
Harvest	41"-44"	48"-96"	29"-30"
Lamp	16"-28"	16"-30"	22"-29"
Living room	14"-36"	36"-72"	28"
Nest of	12"-20"	14"-24"	18"-29"
Tea, oval, rd., sq.	20"-36"	24"-30"	24"-29"
Telephone	12"-24"	14"-24"	22"-30"
Tilt-top table	16"-30"	20"-36"	26"-30"
TV table	20"-24"	24"-30"	17"-24"
Sewing box	8"-11"	10"-14"	2½"-5"
Sewing cabinets	12"-18"	20"-30"	26"-28"
Footstool	8"-17"	11"-24"	4"-15"
Hall trees			4'-6'
Hutches	19"-20"	46"-75"	69"-77"
Ironing boards	12"-19"	36"-56"	30"-36"
Ironing sleeve	2½"-4¾"	17"-24"	4"
Kitchen stools	8½"-12"		35"
Luggage racks	17"	22"	22"
Magazine racks	7¾"-12"	10"-17"	14"-18"

Name	Width	Length	Height
Shelves for wall	3″-6″	18″-26″	22″-26″
Shoeshine kits	7″-10″	10″-16″	8″-14″
Smoking stands			25″-26″
Stepladders	10″ between steps, width varies with height		
Step stools	12″-14″, 8″ between steps, 9″-24″		
Serving trays	8″-16″	14″-24″	

Name	Width	Length	Height
Packracks	10″ at the top, 16″ at the bottom, 23″ long		
Paddles canoe		4′-5½′	
ping-pong	5¼″ across the blade, 5¼″ handle, 6½″ length of blade, total length is 11¾″.		
Skiis	length approximately 3″ to 6″ more than the height of the skier.		
Skiis, water	the size of the water ski is determined by the weight of the rider and the power towing the skier.		

Sports Equipment

		Length	
Arrows	Men	25″-28″	
	Women	24″-27″	
Bows	Men	5′8″-6′	
	Women	5′2″-5′10″	
Basketball backboards	4′	6′ •	9′ from floor
Baseball bats	2¾″ max. diam.	42″ max.	

The general rule for weight of baseball bats is about 1 oz. to each inch of length.

Softball bats	2⅛″ max. diam.	34″ max.	
Bobsleds, 2 man		7′-11″	10½″
Bobsleds, 4 man		9′	"

Grandfather Clock Case

Topic 2. Glossary of Furniture Terms

This list defines popular forms of feet, legs, spindles, moldings, ornamentation, and structural elements which provide suggestions for designing and identifying designs.

Applique — applied ornaments, such as carvings and turnings, which are fastened to a surface and closely resemble moldings.

Apron — a horizontal member which joins legs and supports the table top or chair rest.

Arrow foot — an arrow-shaped turning at the base of a leg of some styles of Windsor chairs.

Ball and claw — a carved foot common to Chippendale designs representing a bird's claw grasping an egg.

Ball foot — a spherical foot usually quite large in diameter and normally used on chests. (Called in England a *bun foot*.)

Bracket foot — a foot formed of two pieces, equal in size and shape, joined at a 90° mitered angle reinforced with dowels or splines.

Cabriole leg — a leg shaped like the calf of the human leg.

Chest on chest — a chest of drawers divided into two sections by a prominent horizontal molding. The upper chest is slightly smaller in width and depth.

Comb back — a double splatted Windsor chair back, the upper section of which resembles a high comb.

Cornice — a protruding portion of a roof or cabinet top composed of moldings.

Cove — a concave molding.

Crow's nest — a cage-shaped arrangement found on tilt-top tables between pedestal and top which permits table top to be rotated as well as tilted.

Dish top — a table top with a raised rim giving the effect of a large shallow dish.

Drake foot — a three-toed carved foot.

Drop — a turned ornament fastened to the bottom edge of the apron of a lowboy or highboy.

Escutcheon — a brass, bone, or ivory keyhole plate.

Finial — a turned, carved, cast, or pressed ornament used in the break of pediments and at the top of chair posts, highboys, mirrors, and four poster beds. May be one of a number of different shapes.

Fluting — a series of concave grooves or channels extending along the length of flat or turned surfaces.

French foot — a slender, flared-out, modified bracket foot.

Fretwork — the ornamental cutout of interlaced woodwork.

Hood — the semicircular top found on William and Mary cabinet furniture.

Intarsia — pattern of woods of natural but different coloring, inlaid on wood or other materials.

Marquetry — flat, pictorial pattern of veneer woods of natural but different coloring, glued on a core.

Muntin — the molding or division between panes of glass in a door or window.

Pad foot — a pad or base underneath a shaped foot.

Pear foot — a foot turned to resemble the shape of a pear.

Piecrust — the raised, scalloped rim of a table top bearing a resemblance to the thumb print of a piecrust design.

Pigeon holes — open compartments in the cabinet of a desk or secretary.

Pilaster — a flat-back column fastened to a wall or cabinet.

Quarter column — a fourth of a column usually placed into a niche at the corner of a lowboy or the base of a highboy, chest of drawers, or grandfather's clock.

Plinth — the lower square base of a column or pedestal.

Rat foot — a slender ball and claw foot or a splayed leg.

Reeding — a carved ornament composed of a series of convex molds and resembling parallel rows of reeds.

Rule joint — a joint on table leaves in which a "cove" molding on one leaf slides over a "thumb nail" molding on the other leaf.

Saddle seat — a recessed formed seat.

Serpentine — a series of alternate concave and convex curves suggesting the effect of a serpent in motion.

Shield back — a chair back, the outline of which resembles a heart-shaped shield used by Hepplewhite.

Snake foot — a foot shaped like a modified snake head.

Trumpet turning — a turned leg resembling a trumpet and used on William and Mary styled furniture.

Turnip foot — similar to a ball foot with base lip.

Topic 3. Wood, Trees, and Lumber

The Nature of Wood

Wood, the basic substance of trees, is made up of long cells which grow closely together, forming a compact, yet porous, material. It has been referred to as an elastic, plastic honeycomb. The relatively light weight of most wood is explained by the fact that approximately half of its volume is made up of these hollow cells. If wood were dried and crushed into a solid material, it would weigh approximately 1½ times as much as an equal volume of water and consequently would sink. It is because of this hollow cell structure that most woods are buoyant, can take finishing materials, and can hold nails, screws, glue, and other fasteners.

Each year tiny cells containing sap or moisture develop along the circumference of the tree. Rapid growth takes place in the spring of the year, caused by greater amounts of food and moisture and producing a wide, porous layer of wood. This is called "spring" or "early" growth. As the season progresses, layers of darker, heavier, thicker-walled cells develop. The wood thus formed is called "summer" or "late" growth. When the tree is cut, these layers are seen as circles or rings called annual rings, Fig. 3-1. In drying, wood shrinks along these annual rings. Thus, a log shrinks in circumference as it dries, but expands as it absorbs moisture, Fig. 3-2. So powerful is this force that wood may pull itself apart

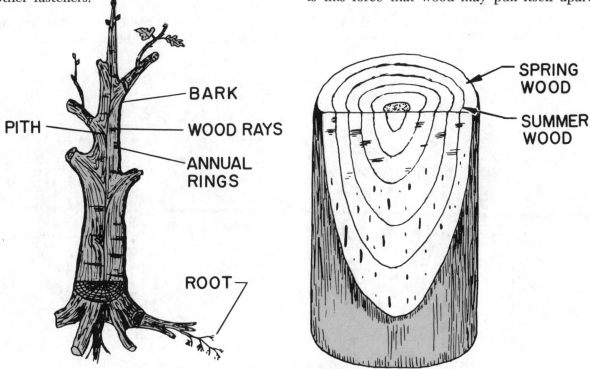

BARK

WOOD RAYS

ANNUAL RINGS

PITH

ROOT

SPRING WOOD

SUMMER WOOD

Fig. 3-1. Structure of a Tree

WARP DUE TO SHRINKAGE

SHRINKAGE IN CIRCUMFERENCE

SHRINKAGE OF QUARTERED LOGS

Fig. 3-2. Warp and Shrinkage

in excessive shrinking or crush itself in excessive swelling. This shrinking or swelling of wood can be reasonably well controlled by observing established cutting and drying procedures. It is interesting to note that moisture accounts for over 50% of the total weight of some woods. Dry wood splits readily at right angles to the annual rings — along the lines (called medullary rays) that radiate from the center. Checking, warping, casehardening,

and honeycombing are all results of adverse drying.

Though most wood is readily recognized as wood, every piece is different from every other due to the fact that it comes from a living plant that differs in species or in growing conditions. Trees belong to botanical families, and lumber from each family has its identifying characteristics. Each separate tree is different from other trees of the same family. Pieces of lumber cut from the same section of a tree will often differ in color, grain, and figure.

Wood is named and classified *hard* or *soft* according to the species of tree from which it is cut. *Hardwoods* come from the *deciduous* or broad-leaved trees and *softwoods* come from the *coniferous* or needle-bearing trees. This classification is a botanical one and does not indicate the degree of hardness of wood. Some of those listed as hardwoods are actually softer than some of those listed as softwoods. The pines, firs, and other evergreens are softwoods, and the maples, oaks, elms, poplars, and other shade and fruit trees are the hardwoods.

It is impossible to identify woods by chemical analysis; they may be identified only by

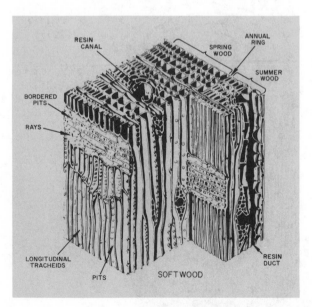

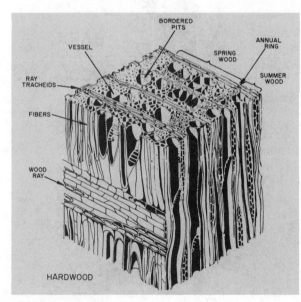

Fig. 3-3. Cellular Structure of Wood Sections (Enlarged section of a ⅟₃₂″ cube.)

physical characteristics such as cell structure and cell pattern, color, grain, figure, and sometimes by odor or taste. Shakes, stains, sap streaks, pitch pockets, knots, cross grain, bird pecks, and other blemishes frequently are present and either improve the quality of the lumber or are considered defects.

Wood does not decay naturally through age, nor will it decay if it is kept constantly dry or continuously submerged in water. The principal conditions affecting the rate of decay are moisture, temperature, and air supply. Damp or wet wood is likely to become a nest for wood ants, termites, and other insects. Such wood is subject to the action of fungi which cause it to become spongy and decomposed (dry rot).

Wood is tested for various types of strength and is rated according to physical, mechanical, and chemical properties. In general, wood is very strong and durable. It can be worked with tools and machines, and it can be compressed, bent, and joined. Wood is also graded in terms of its fabricating properties. Reputable authorities have established data on the degree of success with which nails, screws, glue, paint, and other materials can be applied to specific woods. Data are also available on the insulation and fire-resistant qualities of wood. The commercial users of wood utilize available scientific data, and their selection of lumber is usually based on fitness to purpose. See Table 5, p. 83.

Cells

Wood consists essentially of *lignin* and *cellulose*. The major portion of the complex material that binds the cellulose fibers together is called lignin. Wood is not completely solid. It is composed of tiny, hollow units called cells, Fig. 3-3. Each cell consists of a four-layer wall enclosing a cavity.

Each cell is separated from the next one by a thin layer called "middle lamella." The cellulose of the primary and secondary walls is made up of minute *microfibrils*, formed into a threadlike rectangular cross section. The *fibrils* in the primary wall are arranged in a loose, feltlike mesh. The secondary wall con-

sists of layers of fibrils developed in a spiral fashion at different angles, Fig. 3-4.

The three major types of cells are called fibers, rays, and vessels or pores. A short, thin-walled cell, called *parenchyma*, has the primary function of food storage and distribution. It is the living portion of the sapwood and generally can be seen in the cross-sectional area of hardwoods viewed with a glass

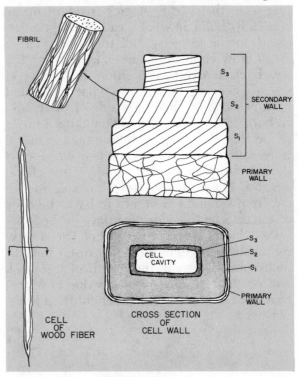

Fig. 3-4. Cell of Wood Fiber

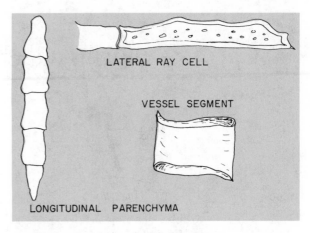

Fig. 3-5. Parenchyma or Food Cells

providing a magnification of ten diameters. (See Fig. 3-5). A *ray* is the longitudinal development of parenchyma.

It is the growth of the fibers and not the growth of the tree that determines the grain of the wood. The texture of wood is determined by the size and quantity of cells.

Reaction wood is a general term applied to trees which grow on a slant. Softwood trees that lean, that is do not grow straight up or vertically, build up what is called *compression wood* on the lower side of the trunk. These fibers grow vertically in an effort to bring the tree back to a vertical position. In hardwood species, leaning trees grow what is termed *tension wood* on the upper side of the trunk. In both cases, reaction wood contains a lesser proportion of lignin-to-cellulose than found in trees with straight trunks. Since wood cells do not shrink lengthwise to any appreciable amount, but shrink in circumference, lumber cut from leaning trees tends to have the ends of the cells on the edge or surface of the stock rather than the end of the piece. The shrinking of these angular fibers will result in a dimensional change in the length of the stock and produce unusual problems due to distortion. This is also true of lumber cut from limbs of trees.

Reaction wood is often slightly heavier and tougher than normal wood, but its crushing strength and bending strength is lower, Fig. 3-5A. The greatest disadvantage of reaction wood is its tendency to produce a woolly or fuzzy surface in machinery and veneer cutting. As a rule, reaction wood does not affect the basic properties of the wood to such an extent that it interferes with the normal use of the material.

For identification purposes, softwoods generally are considered to be *nonporous* woods, as the cells are only detected with a magnification of 75 diameters or more. Hardwoods have one of the following types of porosity:

1. *Ring porous* woods are those woods in which the pores are very large in the spring growth and very small in the summer growth, with an abrupt transition between each, Fig. 3-6.
2. *Semi-ring porous* woods are those woods in which the pores are large in the spring growth and gradually get smaller, until they are very small in the late summer growth, Fig. 3-7.
3. *Diffuse porous* woods are those woods in which the pores are fairly uniform in size and evenly distributed in both the spring and summer growth, Fig. 3-8.

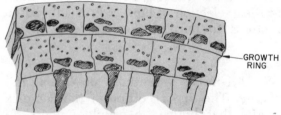

Fig. 3-6. Ring Porous Wood
Spring growth has large vessels: late summer growth has small vessels.

Fig. 3-7. Semi-Ring Porous Wood

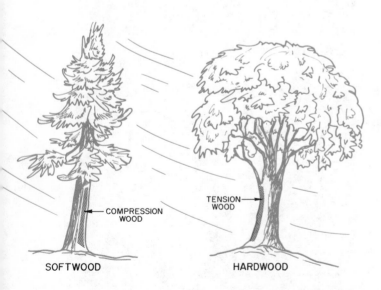

Fig. 3-5A. Reaction Wood of Slanted Tree

The figure of wood is the pattern formed by variations or irregularities of coloring matter, annual rings, rays, cross-grain, wavy grain, knots, burls, or other distortions of the normal growth of the fibers. The method of sawing lumber determines, to a large extent, the appearance of the figure pattern.

Log Measure

To find the number of feet (board measure) in a log of a given size, deduct four inches from its diameter at the small end. Square the remainder. Multiply the product by the length of the log and divide by 16. The result will be the board measure content of the log. Logs over 24′ in length are usually measured at the center for diameter.

Fig. 3-8. Diffuse Porous Wood

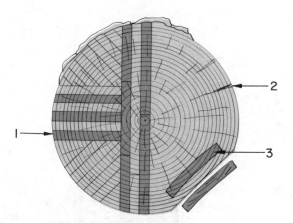

Fig. 3-9. The Making of Lumber
1. Common method of quartering a log for "comb grain" or "rift" boards. This quarter-sawed lumber tends to shrink less and be stiffer than plain or slash grain boards. It is generally used in flooring.
2. Wood is subject to more shrinkage around the circumference of the annual rings than it is in radial thickness. Therefore a log will tend to check and sometimes split open in seasoning.
3. Plain-sawed boards (slash grain) tend to warp opposite to the annual rings.

Sawing Considerations

Trees are cut into logs, usually of eight or more feet depending largely on the relative straightness and ease of handling. The individual logs are squared by slabbing, or the log is first split through the center and squared into a *cant*. In most cases, the cant is then sawed into timbers, planks and boards. Sometimes logs are selected for special purposes and are cut accordingly. Some logs, for example, are sawed radially into clapboards.

In some cases, figure is the determining factor in whether a log is plain or quarter-sawed. In other cases, an effort is made to minimize warping. Slash, radial, and quarter-sawed boards each have their particular qualities.

Lumber is graded for market according to the natural condition of the wood and the method by which it was sawed and milled. Sawyers, in their cutting, take into account the properties of lumber and the probable use to be made of it. Thus each log is cut for maximum quantity, for grain pattern, strength, a minimum of warpage, or some other purpose. (See Fig. 3-9.)

Seasoning of Lumber

When a tree is cut down, the cell cavity is filled with water and the S_2 layer contains all the molecular water it can hold, see Fig. 3-4. The moisture content of the wood may be well over 100% and it is said to be "dead green." The evaporation of this moisture must be controlled if good lumber is to be obtained, as rapid drying causes checking and cracks. To help prevent this rapid drying, freshly cut logs are frequently submerged in water until they are to be cut into lumber dimensions. During this time the green log absorbs additional moisture.

After the log has been cut into lumber, it is either piled horizontally and placed in vertical storage racks (see Air Drying, pp. 21-23) where the water in the cell cavity evaporates. During this process of evaporation, the lumber is dimensionally stable, the only change is in the decrease in moisture content and weight. When the cell cavity is dry and the S_2 layer contains all of the molecular water it can hold, it is said to have reached its *Fiber Saturation Point* (F.S.P.). At this point, the moisture content will be between 25% and 28%, depending on the specie.

As the lumber continues to dry, the molecular water leaves the S_2 layer and the stock will decrease in width, thickness, and weight. Stock which has been *slash sawn* (cut tangent to the annual rings) will shrink in width approximately 8% from the F.S.P. to oven dry. This is due to the fact that the *medullary rays* which radiate out from the center of the tree do not shrink lengthwise, hence there is decreased width shrinkage in quarter sawn lumber, but the shrinkage in thickness is likely to be double that of slash sawn lumber.

Interesting Fact: While the effects of daily temperature changes must be allowed for in metal bridges and other constructions, wood is not subject to these conditions. Temperature changes have no significant effects on wood. In terms of its length, wood is quite stable, even when subject to high humidity. Because of this constancy of length, wood was formerly chosen for the rod in old pendulum clocks of high accuracy.

In the early stages of the drying process, the outside of the lumber dries first and shrinks, resulting in a state of tension on the surface; the center remains wet and does not shrink, resulting in a state of internal compression. As the drying process continues, the center dries and shrinks, changing it to a state of internal tension. The outside, which is already dry, does not shrink, changing it to a state of compression. This condition is called *case hardening*, Fig. 3-10.

Controlled drying conditions (regulation of temperature and humidity) reduce the intensity of these forces. Continued adverse drying conditions may cause these forces to go beyond the elastic limits of the wood fibers, resulting in surface checking and internal collapse (called honeycombing).

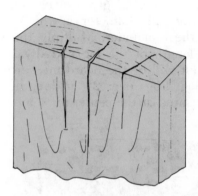

Fig. 3-11. Splits and checks
Open wood cells in end grain dry rapidly. This results in frequent splits and checks. To prevent this, the ends of green lumber are painted or sealed.

Fig. 3-10. Test Samples
Examples of case hardening and reverse case hardening resulting from internal stresses of compression and tension set up by adverse drying conditions.

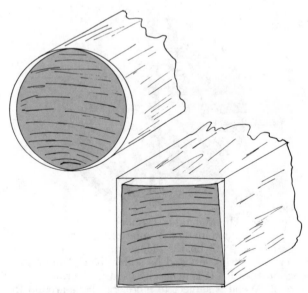

Fig. 3-12. Effects of Cutting Green Wood
If a true square were cut from green wood, it would become a smaller trapezoid when seasoned.

If a cylinder were cut in green wood, it would become an oval when seasoned.

The drying may be done by air seasoning or by the modern, faster, and more expensive kiln-drying process. (Air-dried lumber is better for outside work and kiln-dried for inside.)

Air Drying

Air seasoning reduces moisture content to 12% to 18%, depending upon the climatic conditions. This method consists of piling the lumber outside so that its lengthwise slope is about one inch to the foot. The first layer of boards is supported about twelve inches above the ground. The boards are laid flat with a space of about 1½″ between each edge. Each layer of boards has sticks called *stickers*, about 1½″ x 2″ laid at right angles to the length of

Fig. 3-13. Squaring the Ends of Logs

When the saw completes its cut, it is brought back to a position above the log by the long, beam-like, lever arm which acts as a counterbalance. (Courtesy Simonds Saw & Steel Co.)

Fig. 3-15. Inserted Tooth Edger Saws

Edger saws are used for "edging" or cutting bark from the edges of boards, as well as ripping slabs into desired widths and for breaking down large cants. (Courtesy Simonds Saw & Steel Co.)

Fig. 3-14. Slabbing

Large, circular saw cuts slab off the log, thus providing a flat surface for the gang saw. The saw can also be used to cut logs into boards. (Courtesy Simonds Saw & Steel Co.)

Fig. 3-16. Gang Saw

This machine cuts logs or cants into boards or planks of specified thickness in a single operation. The saw blades oscillate as a unit similar to the blade action of a jig saw. It will take logs up to 20″ in diameter and up to 20′ in length. The rate of feed is from 0 to 40 feet per minute, and it is equipped with 20 saws, each approximately five feet long and making 330 strokes per minute. (Courtesy Simonds Saw and Steel Co.)

the rows. (See Fig. 3-22.) This provides an air space around each board and between layers of boards. Coverings are placed over the tops of the piles for protection from sun and rain. Air drying may also be done in a well-ventilated building. Care must be taken that

Fig. 3-17. Colonial Times Log Saw

This vertical, upright log saw was powered by a water wheel. (Courtesy Old Sturbridge Village, Inc.)

Fig. 3-18. Band Mill Cutting Mahogany Log into Boards

The saw blade is approximately eight inches wide. The upper wheel is partially shown, while the driving wheel is on the floor below. The carriage moves the log into the saw. (Courtesy Palmer & Parker Lumber Co.)

Fig. 3-19. Multiple Overhead Automatic Trimmer

The left end saw cuts one end of every board while the other is cut to standard length as determined by the operator. The saws not selected are lifted out of cutting position by the wheels riding over the face of the lumber. (Courtesy Simonds Saw and Steel Co.)

Fig. 3-20. Battery of Swing Saws

These saws are used to cut long pieces of lumber into specific lengths. A conveyor on the left (not visible) brings the lumber to the operators. In the right foreground is the belt conveyor which carries the cut pieces to stacking, where the various lengths are grouped by size. (Courtesy Heywood-Wakefield Co.)

the piles of green lumber are properly spaced and stuck. This process of drying takes from one to five years. A general rule is to allow a year for each inch of thickness. The longer the period of drying, the more even the moisture content.

Forced Air Drying

Forced air or fan drying is the process of accelerating seasoning or achieving faster and more uniform predrying prior to kiln drying. In this method, fans are used for boosting and making more uniform the air circulation over, under, and around each of the boards, which are stuck and piled in tiers within a building or arranged in parallel rows outside but covered to shed rain and divert the direct rays of the sun. In either case, fans approximately 48″ in diameter are so arranged that the air is controlled at desirable temperatures and is thoroughly circulated. In some cases, automatic humidity controls add to the effectiveness of this method. Some authorities claim that this rapid drying is made possible by the continuous rapid movement of the air film surrounding the surface of the lumber. In still air, this film becomes saturated with moisture from the lumber and acts as an insulator, slowing the rate of evaporation. The quicker air movement hastens the drying process.

Fig. 3-21. Vertical Storage Racks
Mahogany is being air dried prior to being put into kilns. Boards range from 14 to 20 feet in length. (Courtesy Palmer & Parker Lumber Co.)

Temperature is a great factor in the drying of lumber. The greatest use of forced-air drying in the United States is in the South and Southwest. It is most effective when the temperature is 70° F. to 95° F.; below this, it is not economical to use. Within this temperature range, forced-air drying can reduce stock from 40% to 15% moisture content in a matter of weeks.

Kiln Drying

Kiln drying begins with forced-air or fan drying. It differs from air drying in that the process is speeded by control of the temperature and humidity, as well as the circulation of air, in a specially built room or chamber. Partially dried lumber (air dried four to six weeks) is piled on racks (similar to air drying), so that the air may circulate around each piece. These racks are moved into the rooms where the controlled drying process takes place. First the lumber is heated by steam so that all pieces have a uniform temperature and moisture content. Then the heat is gradually decreased, while air is circulated to carry off the excess humidity. (See Fig. 3-23.) Another method consists of passing the racks of lumber through a series of chambers which have regulated temperature and moisture conditions.

Kiln drying reduces the moisture content of lumber to five to eight percent in a period of three to four weeks for one-inch lumber. Thicker dimensions take proportionately longer periods.

Radio-Frequency Dielectric Drying

The use of radio-frequency dielectric heating for drying wood has improved its shear strength, impact resistance, resistance to checking, and surface finish. One manufacturer has dried up to 3,500 board feet of turning squares in twenty-four hours, bringing the moisture content (M.C.) down from 30% to 6%. The same manufacturer has dried 6,000 board feet in twenty-four hours, starting with stock at 20% M. C.

When the electronic disturbance occurs, the innermost molecules begin moving. Because the heat is generated uniformly throughout, the normal problems of case hardening and checking are eliminated. Steam merely continues to push out through the pores until the piece is dry.

With uniform shrinkage and no distortion from internal stresses, dry dimensions for rough (green) blocks can be computed quite accurately. Reducing the necessity for a large allowance for final cuts to dimensions desired produces more usable wood. This reduction in waste is a factor in cost.

This method of drying reduces end checking, eliminates staining, as well as improves the natural color and other physical properties of the wood.

The drying heaters are about 36″ square and stand six feet high. The end opening is 6″ x 12″ and accepts stock up to 5″ x 10″ in cross section. The maximum practical stock length has not been established, but 5′ and 6′ lengths have been dried.

Any wood easily impregnated with preservatives is more tolerant to electronic drying; therefore open-pored woods are ideal. Softwood species are a problem. The drying of wood is a methodical, scientific process.

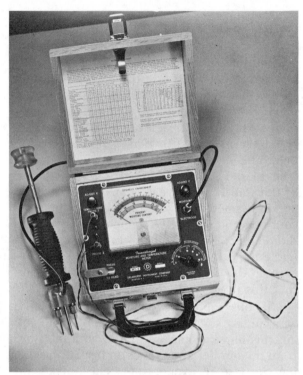

Fig. 3-22A. Battery-Operated Moisture Meter (Courtesy Delmhorst Instrument Co.)

Fig. 3-22. Careful Piling and Sticking of Boards for Gradual Air Drying

Piling sticks are placed close to the end of each board, for it is claimed that checks normally will run only as far as the first stick.

Pile bottoms and covering boards are very carefully arranged to provide adequate air circulation. Efficient piling makes for straight lumber, for the weight of the pile tends to keep lumber from warping during drying. Covering boards prevent spoilage of top layers of lumber from water penetration.

Some piles are so stacked that the rear is lower than the front to facilitate drainage. (Courtesy Northern Hardwoods Assn.)

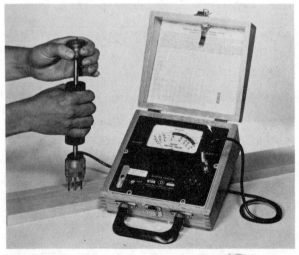

Fig. 3-22B. Driving Prongs into Board (Courtesy Delmhorst Instrument Co.)

Moisture Content of Lumber

The approximate moisture content of lumber can be easily determined. Cut sections from three or four samples or test pieces. The samples should be taken at least two feet from the end and across the width of the board. Each sample should be weighed before and after heating. Maintain the samples at 212° F. until stock ceases to decrease in weight. The loss in weight divided by the dry weight is the percent of moisture content of the lumber.

Battery-operated *moisture meters*, Figs. 3-22A and 3-22B, give reasonably accurate reading as to the amount of moisture in a piece of stock. The electrical resistance of wood depends on the amount of moisture in the wood. The higher the moisture content, the greater the conductivity; hence, the moisture meter is basically an ohmmeter. The two outer prongs of the moisture meter which are driven into the wood determine the moisture content below the surface; the center pin determines the moisture content on the surface; and the needle indicates the average of the two.

Wood is an anisotropic material; that is, it does not have the same properties in each dimension.

Experiments of the Forest Products Laboratories have shown that the shrinkage from the green to the oven-dry condition across the grain for a flat-sawed board is about eight percent, and for a quartersawed board, about four and one-half percent, while the shrinkage parallel to the grain is practically negligible for most species.

The reasons for this are:
1. The ray cells give resistance.
2. The summer wood is harder and more dense than the spring wood. This denser wood shrinks more.
3. The fibril angle is greater on the radial surface.

Equilibrium Moisture Content

Whatever the process used for drying the lumber, it should be conditioned to its place

Part of 9,500 ton consignment of 2,000 large mahogany logs from Ivory Coast of French West Africa, with some individual logs running 27 or 28 feet long and over 6 feet in diameter, weighing as much as 15 tons each. This shipment could provide 75,000,000 square feet of 1/28" veneer. Actually only 25 per cent of the wood will be suitable for veneer, thus 18,000,000 feet of veneer will be cut and the remainder will be manufactured into lumber. (Courtesy Palmer & Parker Lumber Co.)

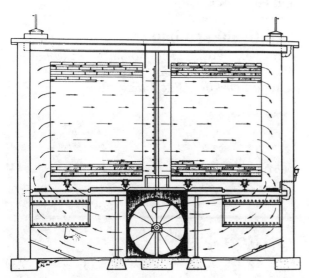

Fig. 3-23. Schematic of Kiln

Lumber to be suitable for furniture must be dried to between five per cent and eight per cent moisture content. The kiln mechanically blows dry air back and forth and around the stuck lumber. The heat and humidity of the air is automatically controlled. (Courtesy Heywood-Wakefield Co.)

of use by further storing. Wood is a hygroscopic material; that is, it takes on and holds moisture from the air. Wood also tends to acclimate itself with its surroundings; that is, if the air surrounding a piece of wood is drier than the wood itself, the wood gives off molecules of water; if the air contains more moisture than the wood, the wood takes on moisture. This is E.M.C. Because of the structure of wood, it takes on and gives off moisture 12 to 15 times faster on the end grain than it does on the side grain.

Wood Stabilization

Recent technical developments enable wood processors to stabilize the dimensions of wood. Polyethylene glycol is an excellent agent for improving dimensional stability of the cellulose in the wood over a wide range of relative humidity conditions. When stock is submerged in this agent, the solution saturates the wood fibers, thus replacing most of the water moisture. This reduces shrinkage which would otherwise occur when water in the cell walls evaporated. The treatment is most effective on green wood, but can be used on dry wood. When used on dry wood, it reduces both swelling and shrinkage.

Either air- or kiln-dried lumber should be stored (stuck for air circulation) for a period of time (three to six months), in the environment in which it is going to be processed so that minimal dimensional change will take place.

This factor of dimensional change by the continual process of wood either giving up or taking on moisture is important in the selection of lumber for a given job. Even after they have been used in a piece of furniture, boards that have been slash or plain sawn will have a tendency to cup and dimensional change will be noticeable. *Quarter sawn boards,* however, *will have less dimensional change and warping will be minimized.* (See Figs. 3-2 and 3-9).

This dimensional change is a continuous process as the humidity of the surrounding atmosphere changes. It cannot be controlled completely, but can be minimized by the structural design of the article being constructed and by the use of sealers, finishes, and laminates.

Additional Reading

Brown, Panshin and Forsaith, *Textbook of Wood Technology,* Vol. I and II.
Woodworking Digest magazine

High Quality Yellow and White Birch Veneer Logs (Courtesy U. S. Forest Service)

Logs Soaking in Log Pond Prior to Sawing (Courtesy Palmer & Parker Lumber Co.)

Topic 4. Lumber Terms, Defects, and Grading

Terms Applied to Lumber

Lumber is the term applied to wood when it is sawed or split into timbers, planks, and boards. It is classified by its degree of manufacture:

1. *Rough lumber* is as it comes from the saw.
2. *Surfaced* or *dressed lumber* has at least one smooth side as it comes from the planer.
3. *Worked lumber* is milled on the molder to a specified edge.
4. *Shop lumber* is usually of the better grades that are intended to be cut up into further manufacture.
5. *Yard lumber* is less than five inches in thickness and includes strips, boards, and framing members (studs, joists, and rafters). Yard lumber is graded by length and the condition of that length.
6. *Dimensioned lumber* is yard lumber which is two to five inches thick.
7. *Structural lumber* is similar to yard lumber but is over five inches in thickness and in width. The grading of structural lumber is based on the strength of the entire piece.
8. *Slab* — a piece cut tangent to the annual rings, running the full length of the log and containing one flat surface.
9. *Timber* — a piece of lumber five inches or larger in its smallest dimension.
10. *Plank* — a wide piece of lumber ranging from one and one-half inches to five inches in thickness.
11. *Board* — a piece of lumber less than 1½″ thick and 4″ or more in width.
12. *Sheet* — a term applied to a piece of veneer, plywood or other manufactured board.
13. *Flitch* — a thick piece of lumber or log which is to be cut into veneer. It may also refer to the pile of veneer cut from one log.

Terms Applied to Shaped Stock

1. *Billet* — a general category of stock cut to rough dimensions for specialized purposes, such as bat billets and turning squares.
2. *Blank* — pre-cut or partially formed stock selected for appropriate grain structure and other properties, used in the making of such items as gun stocks, water skiis, and table tops.
3. *Cant* — a log that has been slabbed, or a longitudinal section taken from a log.
4. *Shook* — a bundle of parts ready for the making of barrels, casks, boxes, etc.
5. *Stave* — prepared strips which, when assembled, form a rounded container such as a pail, tub, or barrel. This term is also used to describe the blanks or billets for bows and skiis.
6. *Square* — a bundle of any, similarly shaped, wood forms sufficient to cover one hundred square feet.
7. *Turning square* — pre-cut dimensioned square forms for turning legs, pedestals, or spindles.
8. *Withe* — ribbon-like strips that are split from ash, willow, or dogwood, producing a tough flexible band.

Surface Characteristics of Lumber

When lumber is sawn, surfaces formerly hidden are exposed. These new surfaces have characteristics which are generally classified as figure and/or defects.

1. *Figure* — the overall appearance of a wood face, including grain, blemishes, and texture (as they are affected by methods of sawing).
2. *Grain* — the direction, arrangement, and appearance of the fiber growth of wood.

It does not include texture. Grain patterns produced by plain or slash sawing and rotary cutting usually appear as wavy lines, commonly referred to as *flame* or *leaf grain*. This effect is the result of cutting the stock tangent to, and severing, the annual rings. *Straight grain* patterns are produced by cutting at right angles to the annual rings. This is called *quarter-sawing*.

3. *Blemish* — discoloration or imperfection caused by foreign matter or injury to the tree in its growth and resulting in an unusual appearance of the wood face when boards are sawn.

4. *Texture* — a description of the surface determined by the size and degree of uniformity of cells, varying from fine to coarse and even to uneven. Softwoods are generally fine textured, while hardwoods vary from fine to coarse, as illustrated by the extremes represented in basswood and oak.

Defects

Defects are *irregularities in wood* such as checks, knots, pitch pockets, holes, shakes, pith, wane, and bird pecks which tend to lower the strength, durability, and utility value of the piece. *Standard defects are as follows:*

1. *Check* — a separation of the wood, a fissure, usually across the annual growth rings, caused by internal stresses in drying.

2. *Knot* — a mass of compact, hard, cross-grained fibers at the starting point of a limb or branch.

3. *Pitch pocket* — internal cavities which contain pitch and/or bark in varying quantities.

4. *Holes* —
   a. Pinworm holes — not over $\frac{1}{16}''$ in diameter.
   b. Spot worm holes — over $\frac{1}{16}''$ in diameter, but not over $\frac{1}{8}''$ in diameter.
   c. Shot worm holes — over $\frac{1}{8}''$ in diameter, but less than $\frac{1}{4}''$ in diameter.
   d. Grub holes — $\frac{1}{4}''$ in diameter or larger.
   e. Rafting pin holes — caused by peavies and cant hooks when rolling logs and turning stock on the saw.

5. *Shake* —
   a. Ring shake — a separation between the annual rings which becomes accentuated in seasoning.
   b. Wind shake — a break across the annual rings produced during growth by excessive bending caused by wind.

6. *Pith* — the small, soft core occurring in the structural center of a log.

7. *Wane* — the natural bevel formed on the edge of a board cut from a log which had not been completely squared.

8. *Bird pecks* — a patch of distorted grain resulting from birds pecking through the growing cells in the tree and sometimes containing a hole or ingrown bark.

While not classed as "Standard Defects," other considerations which affect the suitability of stock for a particular purpose are *crook, bow, wind, or cup.* (See p. 101.)

Standards for Grading Defects

Defects in lumber are graded according to the following standards established by the lumber manufacturers' associations:

1. One knot or hole $1\frac{1}{4}''$ in diameter is a standard defect.

2. When located away from the edges and ends where they cannot be admitted as the equivalent to wane defects, the following shall be considered as defects:
   a. Four pinworm holes or their equivalent is one defect.
   b. Three spot worm holes or their equivalent is one defect.
   c. Two knots or other defects, the diameter of which when added together do not exceed $1\frac{1}{4}''$, is one defect.

3. Not more than two standard defects of the above types can be admitted to the piece and each additional pinworm hole, spot worm hole, knot, or hole $\frac{5}{8}''$ or less shall be considered as one additional standard defect.

4. Defects larger than one standard defect, except wane and split, shall be considered in the following diameter measure:

   a. 2½″ knots or their equivalent shall be two defects.

   b. 3¾″ knots or their equivalent shall be three defects.

   c. 5″ knots or their equivalent shall be four defects.

5. One split equal in length in inches to the surface measure of the piece in feet and averaging not more than 1″ to the foot in length is one defect.

6. Wane or its equivalent in other defects 1″ wide, one-sixth the length of the piece along the edges or its equivalent at one or both ends is one defect.

7. Worm, grub, knot, and rafting pin holes not exceeding 1¼″ is one defect.

Grading of Hardwood Lumber

Hardwood lumber is inspected and graded according to rules and regulations established and published by the *National Hardwood Lumber Association*. For specific grading rules, the Association's publications must be consulted, but the grade to which a particular board is assigned is based on the usable content, exclusive of defects, in relation to the *surface measure* of the board in square feet. This usable content is expressed in the total number of *cutting units* which the board contains. (A cutting unit is 1″ wide and 1′ long, thus the number of cutting units in each clear cutting is determined by multiplying the

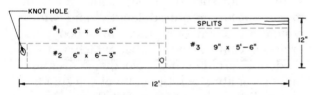

A. First and Second Grades (F.A.S.)

    $6 \times 6.5 = 39$ units
    $6 \times 6 = 36$ units
    $9 \times 5.5 = 49.5$ units
            124.5 units

$$\frac{12 \times 12}{12} = 12 \text{ surface measure}$$

    $12 \times 10 = 120$ units required for F.A.S. hence the piece is F.A.S.

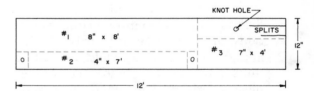

B. Selects F.A.S. Face

    Clear Cutting #1 $8″ \times 8′ = 64$ units
    Clear Cutting #2 $4″ \times 7′ = 28$ units
    Clear Cutting #3 $7″ \times 4′ = 28$ units
               120 total units

Since this face has 120 units, it meets F.A.S. specifications.

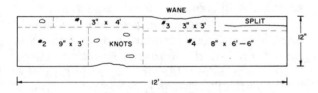

C. No. 1 Common Face

    Clear Cutting #1 $3″ \times 4′ = 12$ units
    Clear Cutting #2 $9″ \times 3′ = 27$ units
    Clear Cutting #3 $3″ \times 3′ = 9$ units
    Clear Cutting #4 $8″ \times 6½′ = 52$ units
               100 total units

Since this face has 100 units, it meets the specifications for #1 Common Face.

D. No. 1 Common

    Cutting #1 $3″ \times 5′ = 15$ units
    Cutting #2 $9″ \times 4′6″ = 40½$ units
    Cutting #3 $3½″ \times 4′ = 14$ units
    Cutting #4 $8″ \times 5′ = 40$ units
               109½ total units

This board meets the requirements for #1 Common.

Fig. 3-24. Grading of Hardwood Lumber

width of the clear stock in inches and fractions by the length of the clear stock in feet and fractions. Repeat for each clear cutting and total the number of cutting units in the board.) The grading rules also specify the maximum or minimum width, length, and number of clear cuttings as well as the cutting units for various grades. The grades are:

1. *First Grade* — pieces in which 91⅔% of the surface measure is clear face material.
2. *Second Grade* — pieces in which 83⅓% of the surface measure is clear face material.
3. First and Second Grades (see Fig. 3-24A) are usually combined into one classification called *F.A.S.* which admits boards that are not less than 6″ wide and 8′ long and requires that the number of cutting units be ten times the surface measure of the piece.
4. *Selects* — face side must be equal to seconds, minimum size of boards 4″ wide and 6′ long, and the yield in cutting units must be ten times the surface measure; reverse side, sound and as good as #1 Common and yield cutting units equal to eight times the surface measure. (See Figs. 3-24B and 3-24C.)
5. *#1 Common* — should be at least 3″ wide and 4′ long and yield cutting units equal to eight times the surface measure. (See Fig. 3-24D.)

Surface measure of board $\dfrac{12 \times 12}{12} = 12'$

For #1 Common, four clear cuttings are required, the minimum size of which is 4″ x 2′ or 3″ x 3′.

The clear face cutting units for #1 Common is eight times the surface measure (12) or 8 × 12 = 96.

6. *#2 Common* — minimum size of clear cuttings 3″ wide and 2′ long and yield cutting units equal to six times the surface measure.
7. *Sound Wormy* — as good as #1 Common or better except that worm holes, bird pecks, stain, and small sound knots are admitted in clear cuttings and the cutting units must equal eight times the surface measure.
8. *#3A Common* — minimum size of clear cuttings 3″ wide and 2′ long, the better face must grade as good as #2 Common, and the reverse must be sound. There is no limit to the number of cuttings of clear stock, but must yield cutting units equal to four times the surface measure.
9. *#3B Common* — minimum size of sound cuttings 1½″ wide and 2′ long and must yield cutting units equal to three times the surface measure.
10. *Below-Grade* — includes all hardwood lumber of poorer quality than #3B Common.

Normally, orders placed for use in school shops do not specify grades below #1 Common to insure required lengths and widths which are commonly used in school shop projects. Conversely, lumber which is to be used for architectural woodwork requires higher quality stock than any of the standard grades listed above. Even F.A.S. permits defects *not acceptable* for architectural woodwork.

Computers are now used in grading hardwood lumber. This method may be faster than grading done exclusively by human minds. It does a better job of getting the utmost in quality lumber from each log. However, grading for color and percentage of heartwood and sapwood still requires *visual inspection*.

The computer grading program was developed for hardwood standard grades of the *National Hardwood Lumber Association*. These grades are adaptable to expression in the mathematical language required for computer programming. The program has been used for F.A.S., Selects, and part of the #1 Common grades.

Information inputs to the computer about each board is a mathematical description of the board and its defects. This is done by graphical location of defects according to a vertical scale divided into ¼″ units along the length and width of each board. A given knot is thus located so many quarter inches from the lower-left corner of the board. The size of the board is similarly designated by lower-left and upper-right corners of a rectangle enclosing it. Irregular defects such as wane and checks are described by a series of such rectangles. The computer system analyzes each piece and reaches a decision as to the optimum placement and sizes of cuttings it will yield.

Scientists are experimenting with a scanning instrument to read the size and location of defects by shooting sound pulses through a log at various angles. Variations are interpreted by the computer which, it is hoped, can make decisions as how to best edge trim, crosscut, and rip the log to get the maximum grade and size of hardwood lumber. If this system works satisfactorily, it is planned in the foreseeable future to experiment with log scanning devices that can give appropriate information to control the head rig of a sawmill for best yield of high quality flitches.

Grading of White Pine Lumber

There is no single procedure for grading soft woods. All soft woods have the same grades, but the standard varies with each particular kind. The rules governing the grading of white pine are as follows:

The best grade is called *#1 & 2 Clear* (B & Better). This grade consists of all the better cuttings of the stock and must be at least 4″ wide. Much of the stock is clear, but a typical piece might have one or two minor blemishes which do not detract from its appearance or high quality.

"*C*" *Select* is the next best grade. It must also be 4″ wide or wider. The characteristics are the same as #1 & 2, but the blemishes are larger and more numerous. Medium stain covering one-third of the face or a lighter stain covering a greater area is permissible when not in combination with other marked defects.

"*D*" *Select* stock must also be 4″ wide or wider. This grade belongs between the higher finish lumber and the common grades. Many pieces have a finish appearance on one side, but the reverse side may show numerous or serious defects. A piece in this grade may have a defect which requires a cut to make it usable in finish work. Medium stain over the entire face is permissible.

Common lumber is distinguished from the finish grades by a general coarseness of appearance, caused by various defects and combinations of defects. Checks in tightened knots in common lumber are not considered a defect unless the opening is so pronounced as to impair its use.

#1 Common grade includes all sound, tight knots, with the size of the knot the determining factor in the grade. Very small pitch pockets, light stains, season checks, or equivalent characteristics are permitted. This grade is of a character that fits it for shelving, cornices, and all uses where best quality and appearance of common lumber are required.

#2 Common grade permits larger and more pronounced defects.

#3 Common takes in a part of the lower cutting of the log and the permissible characteristics are of a more pronounced nature than admitted in #2 common.

#4 Common is much the same as #3 common but defects are more extensive or more pronounced.

#5 Common is the lowest recognized grade and admits all defects provided the piece is of usable quality.

Additional Reading

Department of Agriculture, *Wood Handbook*, pp. 106, 111

National Hardwood Lumber Association, *Rules for the Measurement and Inspection of Hardwood and Cypress Lumber.*

Topic 5. Practices of Lumber Computation

Classification

Methods of computing lumber quantity

Procedure

1. The common unit of measure for lumber is the board foot. This standard unit is 144 cubic inches and represents the volume of a piece of wood 1″ thick, 12″ wide, and 12″ long, or any piece of equivalent volume such as a board 1″ thick by 2″ wide by 72″ long.

   For purposes of computation, any board under 1″ in thickness is figured as being one inch. Commercially, lumber is sawed to standard thicknesses of ⅜″, ½″, ⅝″, and 1″ and surfaced two sides to ¼″, ⅜″, ½″, ¾″ or ¹³⁄₁₆″. Stock sawed to dimension and not surfaced is scaled in price according to thickness.

   When it is necessary to machine a board to thickness in order to fulfill the specifications set by the buyer, the board footage is computed on the thickness of the board before surfacing. The purchaser pays for the board feet contained in the rough stock. Thus it could be claimed that he pays for the waste, as well as for the lumber he gets.

2. When figuring the amount of board feet in soft woods, boards which are less than an even number of inches in width, except 3″ and 5″, are counted as the next higher, even width. Soft woods are sawed to 3″, 4″, 5″, 6″, 8″, 10″ and 12″ in width. A 3″ board is computed as such. A 3½″ board is figured as a 4″ width. A 5¼″ board is figured as 6″ in width.

3. Thickness of hardwood lumber which is between 1″ and 2″ is figured by quarters, between 2″ and 3″ by halves, and thereafter in full inches. In stock 1″ to 2″ thick, a piece which is between the quarters is figured as the next highest quarter. A piece which is between halves in stock 2″ to 3″ thick is figured as the next highest half. For example, 1⅛″ stock is figured as 1¼″ or ⁵⁄₄ (five quarters), 2⅛″ stock is figured as 2½″ or ¹⁰⁄₄ (ten quarters), while 3⅛″ is considered as 4″ or ¹⁶⁄₄ (sixteen quarters).

4. Boards which vary in width are figured at the average width of that board.

5. To figure board feet when all the dimensions are in inches, the following formula should be used:

$$\frac{T'' \times W'' \times L''}{144} = \text{Board Feet}$$

   T − thickness, W − width, L − length

   If the length is in feet use:

$$\frac{T'' \times W'' \times L'}{12} = \text{Board Feet}$$

6. Strip lumber, such as moldings, trim, furring, and grounds, is sold by the lineal foot.

7. Structural lumber is sold by either the board foot or the lineal foot.

8. Cedar lining and manufactured board such as plywood, pressed wood, and wall board are sold by the square foot at a price scaled according to grain pattern.

9. Some building materials, such as clapboards, shingles, and flooring, are sold by the "square," a unit which covers 100 square feet of surface.

Standards and Results

All measurements and figures should be accurate and consistent with recommended methods.

Additional Reading

Topic 157, "Figuring Board Measure by Use of the Essex Scale on a Framing Square"

Topic 6. Ash

(BLACK, BROWN, BLUE, GREEN, RED, WHITE)

Classification

Hardwood

Composition or Description

Ash timber is not ordinarily very large. The wood is comparatively light for its strength, straight grained, and appears similar to plain sawn oak, except that it has no visible medullary rays. The color is pale brown in the heartwood and nearly white in the sapwood. It is an open-grained wood. See Fig. 3-36.

Properties

Ash is commonly used where hardness, strength, and shock-resistance is important. It can be planed with average ease; can be shaped with average ease; high percentage of breakage from bending is low; splitting due to nailing is average; splitting due to use of screws is low; nail and screw holding power is average, glue-holding strength is average.

Uses

Ash is used in over fifty different types of industries. Examples: long tool handles such as shovels, rakes, hoes, and pitch forks; kitchen equipment such as cabinets, tables, and chairs; boxes, barrels, crates, tubs, baskets, upholstered frames, house trim, doors, oars, boat ribs, gun stocks, baseball bats, snowshoes, hockey sticks, tennis racquets, skiis, ski poles, billiard tables, playground equipment, and gymnasium apparatus.

Market Analysis

Shapes

Boards, planks, baseball bat billets, bow staves, ski staves, and withes.

Sizes

Boards 5″ to 12″ in width; 6′, 8′, 10′, 12′, 14′, 16′ lengths; 2″, 2½″, 3″ and 4″ planks; bat billets 2½″ x 2½″ x 36″, 3″ x 3″ x 36″, 3″ x 3″ x 39″; ski stock 1″ x 4″ x 8′, 1¼″ x 4″ x 8′; bow staves 6′ x 1¼″ x 1¼″, 6′ x 1½″ x ¾″.

Grades

Available in all standard hardwood grades.

Sales Units

Board foot, billets, and staves.

Maintenance

The ends of green or air-dried lumber should be painted or sealed by some other method to minimize checking, and stuck to allow air to circulate to aid in even drying and reduce warping. Dry lumber should always be stored in a dry place.

Additional Reading

Brown, Panshin, and Forsaith, *Textbook of Wood Technology*, Vol. I, pp. 606-610

Department of Agriculture, *The Identification of Furniture Woods*, pp. 12, 35, 38, 39

Department of Agriculture, *White Ash*

Department of Commerce, *American Hardwoods and Their Uses*

Southern Hardwood Producers, *The Southern Hardwoods*

Architectural Woodwork Institute, *Guide to Wood Species Selection*

Fig. 3-25. White Ash (from *Yearbook of Agriculture*, 1949)

Topic 7. Balsa

Classification

Botanically a hardwood but physically very soft

Composition or Description

The color of the heartwood is pale brown or slightly tinged with red; the sapwood is nearly white or oatmeal colored, often with a yellowish or pinkish hue. The wood is odorless and tasteless. It possesses a uniform texture, has a sheen when cut, and has a velvety feel.

Properties

Balsa is extremely light in weight and very soft. It is a good insulator from heat and sound, but will not withstand moisture and is subject to sap stains. The strength of balsa is in direct proportion to its weight; hence it is not a strong wood.

Uses

Balsa is used largely for life-saving equipment including life preservers, ring buoys, floats, and rafts. It is used as a core for lightweight plywood. Another important use is in connection with the maintenance of low temperatures for food such as yeast, fresh fruit, and dairy products during transportation. It is very suitable for lining refrigerator trucks. Other uses include cushioning for machinery to prevent vibration, and for sound-deadening in ceilings and in radio loudspeakers. It is used in packing precision instruments, fragile articles, and highly polished furniture. It is used for making fragile furniture to be broken in movie and stage scenes. Large quantities are consumed in the making of models and novelties.

Market Analysis

Shapes

Boards, planks, and sheets.

Sizes

Balsa comes in pieces 1¼″ to 2½″ thick and 3′ to 8′ long.

Sales Units

Board foot, sheets, and blocks.

Maintenance

Store in a dry place.

Topic 8. Basswood

(AMERICAN, WHITE)

Classification

Botanically a hardwood but physically soft

Composition or Description

Basswood lumber is easily recognized by its light weight and figureless appearance. It is a pale, yellowish-brown (often streaked with dark brown), uniformly textured, fine-grained wood. The sapwood is creamy white and blends gradually with the heartwood which has no distinctly defined color. Basswood has a characteristic odor.

Properties

Basswood is a soft, stringy, straight-grained wood. It is easily worked though it does not cut clean nor split easily. It paints well, glues well, and its nail- and screw-holding power is average. It withstands weather and tends to hold its shape.

Uses

Among the more common uses of basswood are drawing boards, picture frames, piano keys, moldings, handles, honeycomb frames, food containers, trunks and luggage, core stock in veneered panels, and in making veneer itself. It is the best excelsior wood known and is also used for pulp wood in certain specialized branches of the paper industry. Because of its soft texture, freedom from warping, and lightness in weight, it is used in patterns and templates.

Market Analysis

Shapes

Boards, planks, plywood veneer, and excelsior.

Sizes

Basswood is available in all regular lengths and widths.

Grades

Available in standard hardwood and plywood grades.

Sales Units

Board foot for boards and planks.
Square foot for plywood sheets.
Pound or bale for excelsior.

Maintenance

It should be stored in a dry place and stuck.

Additional Reading

Brown, Panshin, and Forsaith, *Textbook of Wood Technology*, Vol. I, pp. 593-594
Department of Commerce, *American Hardwoods and Their Uses*, pp. 33-34
Southern Hardwood Producers, *The Southern Hardwoods*, pp. 45-46

Interesting Fact: A very satisfactory substitute for a glue brush may be made by soaking the end of a small strip of basswood for an hour or more. After the wood is saturated, place it on a hard surface and strike it repeatedly with a hammer to break down the fibers.

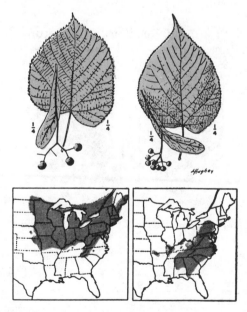

Fig. 3-26. American and White Basswood (from *Yearbook of Agriculture*, 1949)

Topic 9. Beech

Classification

Hardwood

Composition or Description

Beech is a fairly hard, close-grained, even-textured wood with a straight, interlocking grain. The sapwood is white and the heartwood varies from reddish-brown to almost white. Short pencil-like lines run throughout the wood. Quarter-sawed beech shows the medullary rays as flakes running through the wood. See Fig. 3-30.

Properties

Of the American hardwoods, beech ranks first in tensile strength and holding power of nails and screws. Its glue-holding quality is low. It is a moderately stiff, shock-resistant wood which holds its shape well and resists shrinkage when properly dried. It turns well and is not difficult to plane smoothly. It responds to all machine tools with satisfactory results. It stains and finishes well.

Uses

Beech is used for flooring, furniture, handles, boxes, crates, food containers, baskets, woodenware, novelties, toys, shutters, spools, bobbins, shuttles, laundry appliances, musical instruments, piano cases, pipe organs, barrel staves, dowels, veneers, brush backs, and railroad ties.

Market Analysis

Shapes

Boards, planks, plywood, dowels, barrel staves, and withes.

Sizes

Available in all regular lengths, widths, and diameters.

Grades

Available in standard hardwood and plywood grades.

Sales Units

Board foot for boards and planks.
Square foot for plywood sheets.
Dowels available in single pieces or bundles of 50 and 100.

Maintenance

It must be stored in a dry place and stuck.

Additional Reading

Brown, Panshin, and Forsaith, *Textbook of Wood Technology*, Vol. 1, pp. 532-533

Department of Commerce, *American Hardwoods and Their Uses*, pp. 29-30

Southern Hardwood Producers, *The Southern Hardwoods*, pp. 3-5

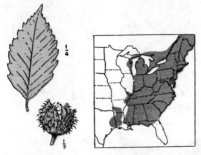

Fig. 3-27. Beech (from *Yearbook of Agriculture*, 1949)

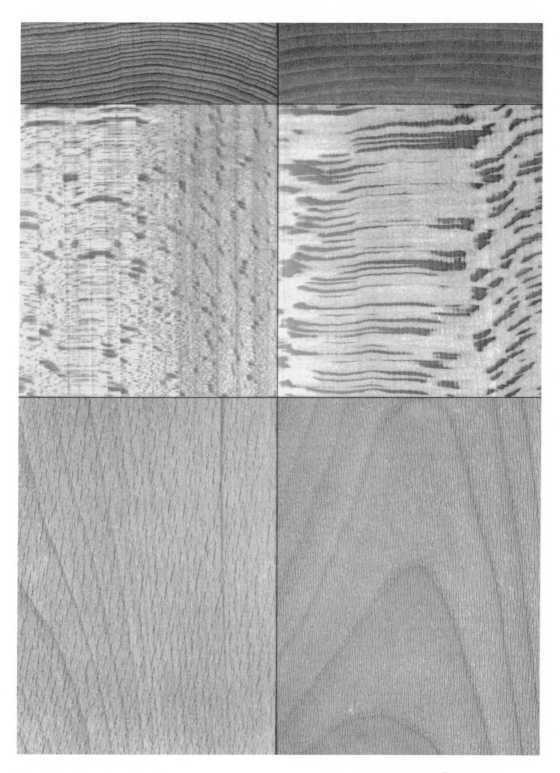

Fig. 3-30. American Beech   Fig. 3-31. American Sycamore

Topic *10.* Birch

(BLACK, GRAY, RED, WHITE, YELLOW)

Classification

Hardwood

Composition or Description

Birch is a beautiful, close-grained, uniformly textured wood. In both yellow and sweet birch, the sapwood is of light color while the heartwood is brown with a reddish tinge. The grain of some birch is highlighted with a curly or wavy figure. Through selected cuttings, a variety of distinctive and attractive grain figures is achieved for veneers.

Properties

Birch is a very strong, hard, heavy, stiff, shock-resistant wood. It is difficult to work but good results can be obtained except in turning. It glues reasonably well but does not possess good nail- and screw-holding properties. Birch has fine finishing characteristics and is popular in natural and blonde finishes. It can also be stained to imitate mahogany, walnut, and maple. It is an excellent wood for finishing with enamels. It is low in comparative shrinkage, but does not weather well. Birch has great bending strength.

Uses

Birch is used for furniture, millwork, interior sash and doors, kitchen cabinets, fixtures, radio and phonograph cabinets, boxes, baskets, crates, cooperage, woodenware, novelties, tops, butcher blocks, dowels, shuttles, spools, bobbins, boot and shoe findings, musical and scientific instruments, agricultural implements, toothpicks, flooring, fuel, and hardwood distillation. Birch is one of the leading hardwoods employed in the manufacture of pulp, wood alcohol, acetate of lime, charcoal, and birch tar oil.

Interesting Fact: The bark of the white birch was used as a covering for windows and as a writing material for letters.

Market Analysis

Shapes

Boards, planks, plywood sheets, veneers, and dowels.

Sizes

Birch is available in all regular lengths and widths.

Grades

Available in standard hardwood and plywood grades.

Sales Units

Board foot for boards and planks.
Square foot for plywood and veneer.
Dowels available in single units or bundles of 50 and 100.

Maintenance

It should be stored in a dry place and stuck to allow air circulation around each piece.

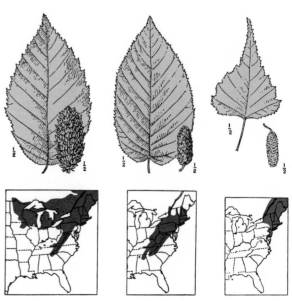

Fig. 3-28. Yellow, Sweet, Gray Birch (from *Yearbook of Agriculture,* 1949)

Additional Reading

Brown, Panshin, and Forsaith, *Textbook of Wood Technology*, Vol. 1, pp. 526-527

Department of Agriculture, *Birch*

Department of Agriculture, *Hardwoods of the South*

Department of Agriculture, *The Identification of Furniture Woods*, pp. 41-43

Department of Commerce, *American Hardwoods and Their Uses*

Architectural Woodwork Institute, *Guide to Wood Species Selection*

Topic *11.* Cedar

(RED, WHITE)

Classification

Softwood

Composition or Description

Red cedar has a light red heartwood with a white sapwood. It is very knotty and possesses a characteristic fragrance caused by resin. Knotty cedar contains more resin, consequently more fragrance. White cedar is pale tan with a lighter sapwood. It is not as fragrant. See Fig. 3-51.

Properties

Cedar is low in stiffness, weak in bending, low in shock-resistance, low in shrinkage, and resists warping and checking. Red cedar has moth-repellant qualities. It is a soft wood which is easily worked with hand tools and may be fastened with ease. It has low tensile strength, glues well, and its nail- and screw-holding ability is good. White cedar is very soft and easily worked. It holds paint well and stays in place well.

Uses

The greatest use for red cedar is in making cedar chests and in lining closets and wardrobes. The resinous oil in cedar helps prevent dry rot and worms, but is corrosive on metal, so polished instruments should not be stored in cedar cabinets. It is also used for fences, fence posts, rustic furniture, and pencils.

White cedar is used for boat planking, canoes, tanks and vats, wood piles, duck decoys, shingles, crating, poles, posts, exterior trim, paneling, and residence gutters.

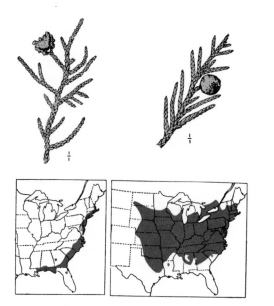

Fig. 3-29. Atlantic White, Eastern Red Cedar (from *Yearbook of Agriculture*, 1949)

Fig. 3-33. Black Walnut   Fig. 3-34. Black Cherry

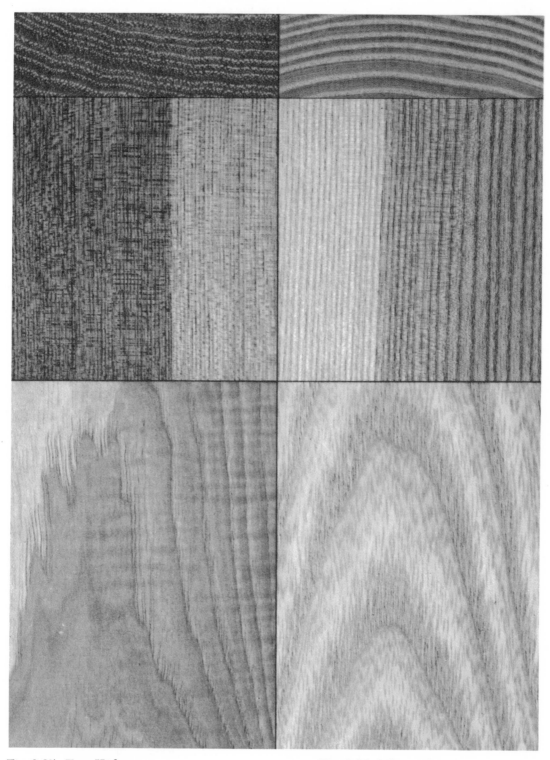

Fig. 3-35. True Hickory   Fig. 3-36. White Ash

Market Analysis

Shapes

Boards, lining, planks, posts, shingles, clapboards, novelty siding, and gutters.

Sizes

Boards 4″ - 8″ wide.
Planks 4″ - 8″ wide.
Lining ⅜″ x 2¼″ in bundles of 40 square feet.
Gutters per running foot.

Grades

There are no official grading rules applied to cedar, but manufacturers separate it into four general classes: #1, #2, #3, and culls.

Sales Units

Board foot, square foot, running foot, and bundles.

Maintenance

Cedar should be stored in a dry place and stuck.

Additional Reading

Department of Agriculture, *Cedar*

Interesting Fact: Well-preserved pieces of cedar have been found which are known to be over 2700 years old.

Topic *12.* Cherry

Classification

Hardwood

Composition or Description

Cherry is a hard, straight, close-grained wood. The heartwood varies in color from light to dark red. The sapwood is narrow and light. See Fig. 3-34.

Properties

Cherry is a very strong, shock-resistant wood. It polishes very smoothly and finishes well. It is not easily worked with hand tools but machines well. Its nail- and screw-holding power is high, and it glues well. It warps and shrinks very little, but will not stand the weather. When finished with oil, it takes on a characteristic cherry color, ranging from reddish tan to reddish brown.

Uses

Cherry is used for furniture, interior trim and paneling, woodware, patterns, toys, novelties, engravers' blocks, scientific instruments, caskets, and gun stocks.

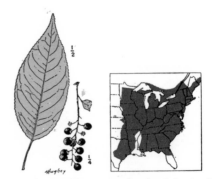

Fig. 3-32. Cherry (from *Yearbook of Agriculture,* 1949)

Market Analysis

Shapes

Boards, planks, plywood and veneer.

Sizes

Boards 6″ to 14″ in width; 8′, 10′, 12′, 14′ and 16′ lengths; 2″, 3″ and 4″ planks.

Grades

Cherry is available in all standard hardwood grades.

Sales Units

Board foot and square foot.

Maintenance

Cherry must be kept in a dry place. The ends should be painted and the lumber stuck.

Additional Reading

Brown, Panshin, and Forsaith, *Textbook of Wood Technology*, Vol. 1, pp. 572-573

Department of Agriculture, *Wood Handbook*, pp. 13-14

Department of Commerce, *American Hardwoods and Their Uses*, pp. 43-44

Southern Hardwood Producers, *The Southern Hardwoods*, p. 45

Architectural Woodwork Institute, *Guide to Wood Species Selection*

Topic *13.* Cypress

Classification

Cypress is a conifer. Botanically it is a softwood, but it sheds its foliage annually like all hardwoods and therefore is graded as a hardwood.

Composition or Description

Cypress is a soft, even-textured, fine-grained, oily wood. The heartwood is reddish, and the sapwood is reddish-white.

Properties

Cypress is often regarded as one of the most durable woods that grows in America. It has moderate strength, a natural resistance to termites, is slow-drying, shrinks considerably in drying, but does not warp nor check and stays in place well. It stands the weather well, holds nails and screws well, and is one of the best woods in paint-holding quality. It is a softwood that is easily worked with hand tools. In recent years "tidewater cypress" has not replenished itself in sufficient quantity to meet the demands of commercial users. Most available cypress, while similar in appearance, does not contain the heartwood of high decay resistance.

Uses

The manufacture of tanks and vats consumes the greatest amount of cypress, followed by shipbuilding and pilings, exterior trim, sash and doors, freight cars, flag poles, bridges, stadium seats, containers for corrosive acids, greenhouse construction, tobacco humidifiers, food processing containers, machinery parts, and agricultural supplies such as incubators, fruit and vegetable boxes, and barrels. It is also used for lawn furniture, kitchen cabinets, and caskets.

Market Analysis

Shapes

Boards, planks, and shooks.

Sizes

Boards 6″ to 12″ in width and 8′, 10′, 12′, 14′ and 16′ lengths; 2″, 2½″, 3″ and 4″ planks; box and barrel shooks.

Fig. 3-39. Sweetgum   Fig. 3-40. Black Tupelo

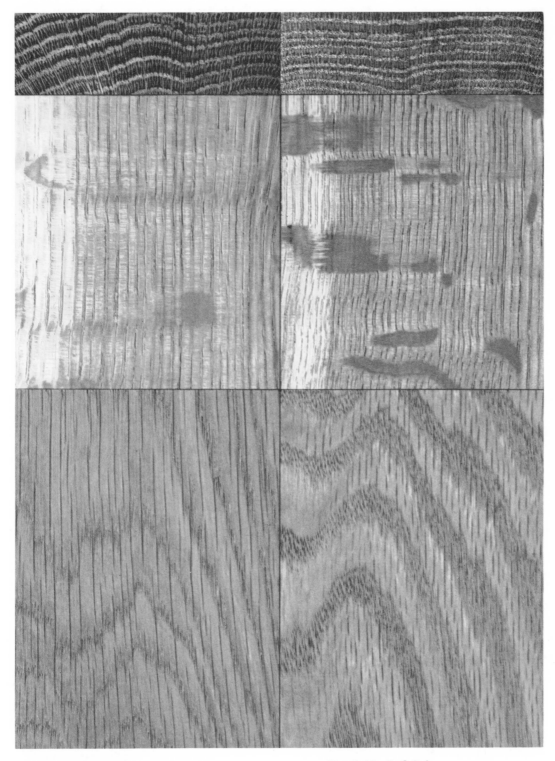

Fig. 3-41. White Oak   Fig. 3-42. Red Oak

Grades

Cypress is graded under three categories: yard lumber, factory lumber, and structural lumber. It is available in all standard hardwood grades as well as a special grade called "pecky cypress" which describes that wood which contains numerous round pits or holes through the wood caused by fungi. This grade is often used for false beams, panels, and interior trim in houses to give a rustic appearance.

Sales Units

Board foot and shook.

Maintenance

Cypress should be stored in a dry place and stuck to provide a circulation of air around each board.

Additional Reading

Brown, Panshin, and Forsaith, *Textbook of Wood Technology*, Vol. 1, pp. 489-491

Department of Agriculture, *Wood Handbook*, pp. 23-24

Department of Commerce, *American Hardwoods and Their Uses*, pp. 8-12

Architectural Woodwork Institute, *Guide to Wood Species Selection*

Interesting Fact: Cypress is an extremely durable wood. The cypress coffin of Tutankhamen (King Tut), the Egyptian King who lived about 1358 BC, is still in good condition. Cypress grave markers in southern states have much more legible inscriptions than marble ones of the same period.

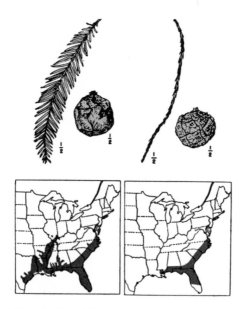

Fig. 3-37. Bald and Pond Cypress (from *Yearbook of Agriculture*, 1949)

Topic *14.* Fir

(WESTERN, LARCH, DOUGLAS, WHITE)

Classification

Softwood

Composition or Description

Fir is a straight, close-grained, moderately dense wood. The sapwood is very narrow and almost oyster-white in color. The heartwood is orange-red.

Properties

Fir is one of the strongest of the softwoods. Its load-bearing capacity is equal to that of many mild steels. White fir ranks with the western pines in stiffness, shock resistance, and bending strength.

Fir is a resinous wood; and though it can be worked readily by machine or hand tools, the resin does clog and dull tools. When dry

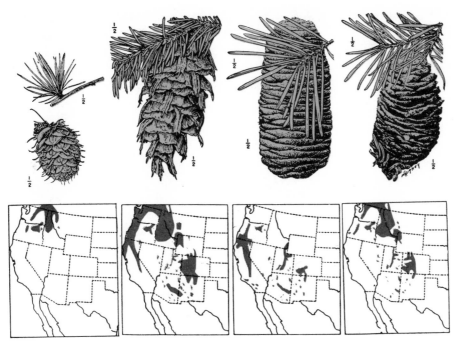

Fig. 3-38. Larch, Douglas, White, Alpine Fir (from *Yearbook of Agriculture*, 1949)

it holds its shape and stays straight, but has a tendency to splinter. There is considerable variation of properties within the firs. In general, they all hold nails, screws, and glue reasonably well. They have good paint retention, but do not cover readily. Of the different kinds, white fir is generally superior.

Uses

Fir is the leading wood in the production of veneer. It is also used in boxes, crates, trunks, pails, barrels, doors, casings, window sash and frames, concrete forms, house roof framing, interior finish, moldings, oars, toys, novelties, woodenware, paint brush and broom handles, shade rollers, dairy supplies, silos, gliders, veneer cores, crossarms, fences, snow fences, pulpwood, stage scenery frames, and timbers.

Market Analysis

Shapes

Boards, planks, plywood, and structural timbers.

Sizes

All standard, millwork, and plywood sizes.

Grades

1. Fir is available in all standard grades.
2. Structural grades are classified according to strength requirements rather than appearance. Strength is based on the amount of straight grain remaining in the cross section.

Sales Units

Board, lineal, and square foot.

Maintenance

Fir should be stuck to allow air to circulate.

Additional Reading

Western Pine Association
  Facts About White Fir
  Facts About Larch and Douglas Fir
  Facts About White Fir

Architectural Woodwork Institute, *Guide to Wood Species Selection*

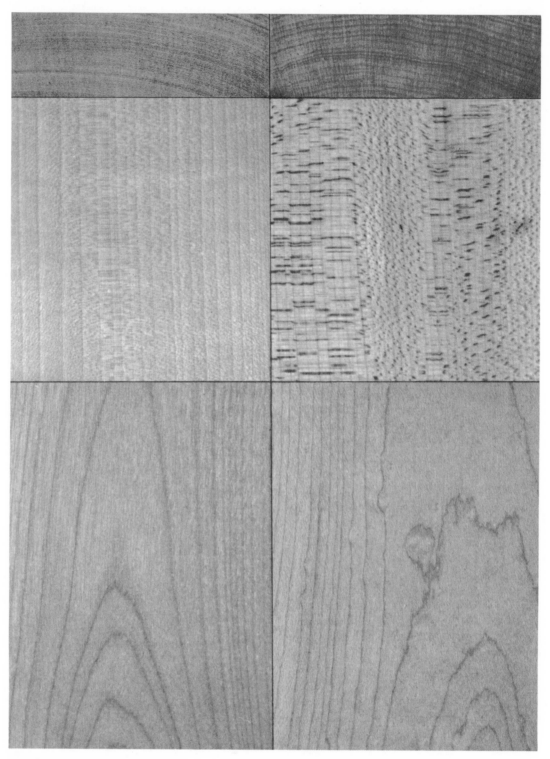

Fig. 3-45. Yellow Birch   Fig. 3-46. Sugar Maple

Fig. 3-47. Limba (Korina)   Fig. 3-48. Tropical American Mahogany

Topic *15.* Gumwood

(RED, OR SWEET, BLACK, TUPELO)

Classification

Hardwood

Composition or Description

Gum is an attractive, uniformly textured wood. The heartwood of red or sweet gum is reddish-brown. The sapwood is pinkish-white. The heartwood of both tupelo and black gum is light brown to gray. The sapwood is very light and almost white. The change in color between the heartwood and sapwood is gradual. See Figs. 3-39 and 3-40.

Properties

Red gum is a medium-hard wood that is easily worked, fastens well, and is a perfect base for paint. Black gum is a medium-hard wood of moderate strength and stiffness, but it has an interlocking grain which makes it difficult to split. This interlocking grain makes a beautiful figure when quarter-sawn, and it is also the reason why black gum is tough and resists wear. Gum has a strong tendency to warp when exposed to moisture. In gluing up wide surfaces, no piece should be wider than four inches, and the pieces should be turned so that the annual rings are opposite on each piece. This reduces warpage.

Uses

The furniture industry is the leading consumer of red gum. It is also used for trim, flooring, doors, cabinets, showcases, tables, chairs, kitchen cabinets, bedroom furniture, picture frames, woodenware, novelties, tobacco boxes, toys, veneer, and musical instruments.

The lower grades are used for shipping containers, boxes, baskets, barrels, and crates.

Tupelo and black gum cannot be separated with certainty once they are mixed. The National Association of Lumber Manufacturers does not recognize any distinction between the two woods. Their uses are the same. They are used for furniture, mauls, pulleys, saddle trees, mallets, toilet seats, rolling pins, plank floors, tobacco boxes, toys, boxes, crates, and dairymen's and poultrymen's supplies.

Market Analysis

Shapes

Boards, planks and veneers.

Sizes

Available in all standard hardwood sizes.

Grades

Standard grades in plain and quarter-sawn. Veneers are graded according to figure. The heartwood is marketed as red gum and the sapwood as sap gum.

Sales Units

Board and square foot.

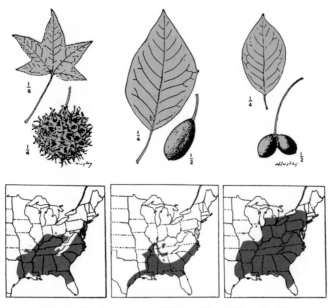

Fig. 3-43. Sweetgum, Water, Black Tupelo (from *Yearbook of Agriculture*, 1949)

Maintenance

Gumwood that has been kiln dried should be dead piled until ready for use; that is, one board on top of another without sticks to separate the layers. If the edge of one board is allowed to lap over the edge of another, it may split or become excessively heavy through moisture absorption due to free passage of air over the surfaces. Ends should be painted.

Additional Reading

Brown, Panshin, and Forsaith, *Textbook of Wood Technology,* Vol. 1, pp. 20

Department of Agriculture, *The Identification of Furniture Woods*, *Gumwood*

Topic *16.* Hemlock

(EASTERN, WESTERN)

Classification

Softwood

Composition or Description

Hemlock is a close-grained, light-colored wood. Eastern hemlock is pale buff in color with a reddish tinge. Western hemlock is brownish-white.

Properties

Eastern hemlock has a medium texture, is moderately light in weight, and is low in strength. It has a tendency to splinter, is subject to ring shake, and is not decay-resistant.

Western hemlock has a uniform, fine-textured grain. It is comparatively free of ring shakes. It is light in weight and fairly strong. It is non-resinous, and its knots are usually tight. Both types are easily worked with hand tools. They nail well and paint well. Eastern hemlock is cut slightly heavier than standard

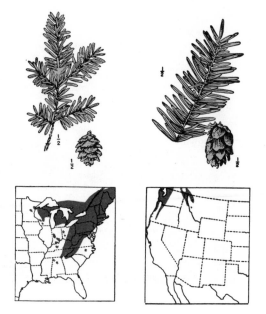

Fig. 3-44. Eastern, Western Hemlock (from *Yearbook of Agriculture,* 1949)

Fig. 3-50. Philippine Mahogany   Fig. 3-51. Eastern Red Cedar

sizes in order to give it strength equal to that of stronger structural woods.

Uses

Eastern hemlock is used largely for framing, sheathing, roofing, and subflooring. Western hemlock is used for the same purposes, plus doors, sash, blinds, ladders, pulp wood, and packing boxes.

Market Analysis

Shapes

Boards, planks, and structural timber.

Sizes

All standard millwork sizes.

Grades

Available in standard softwood grades. It is often mixed and sold with Douglas fir.

Sales Units

Board foot and lineal foot.

Maintenance

Dried in an area protected from the elements and stuck to give proper air ciculation.

Additional Reading

Brown, Panshin, and Forsaith, *Textbook of Wood Technology*, Vol. 1, pp. 476-480

Department of Agriculture, *Eastern Hemlock, Western Hemlock*

Department of Agriculture, *Wood Handbook*, pp. 25-26

Topic *17*. Hickory

Classification

Hardwood

Composition or Description

Hickory is an open-grained, even-textured wood. The heartwood of hickory is reddish brown and the sapwood is whitish. Second growth has more sapwood than heartwood. See Fig. 3-35.

Properties

Hickory surpasses all other woods for strength, toughness, and elasticity. In hardness and shock resistance it outranks all other woods of the United States. It is a heavy wood which is difficult to work with hand tools. Hickory does not nail well, does not stand the weather well, and warps and shrinks excessively. It is the heaviest wood grown in the United States: up to fifty-five pounds per cubic foot when kiln-dried. It will not float in water when green.

Uses

Hickory was widely used for spokes and rims of wheels, single trees, double trees, poles, and shafts. Today it is used for ladder rungs, dowel pins, gymnastic bars, baseball bats, skiis, clothespins, skewers, textile loom fixtures, and wall paneling. It is used for handles, such as hammer, axe, pick, and hatchet. Hickory is one of the best woods for smoking meats.

Market Analysis

Shapes

Boards, planks, billets, staves, and dowels.

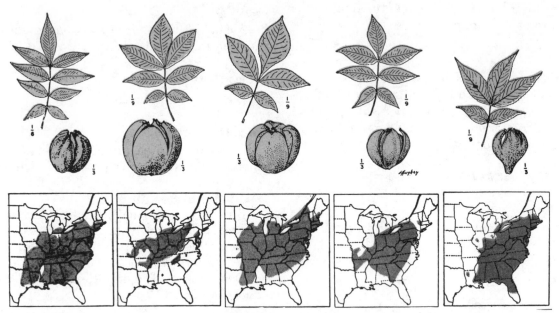

Fig. 3-49. Mockernut, Shellbark, Shagbark, Red, Pignut Hickory (from *Yearbook of Agriculture*, 1949)

Sizes

Boards and planks available in all regular lengths and widths.

Billets — 3″ x 3″.

Staves — standard bow, ski, and barrel sizes.

Grades

All standard hardwood grades.

Sales Units

Board foot for boards and planks.
Unit for billets and staves.
Dowels available in single units or bundles of 50 or 100.

Maintenance

Hickory should be stored in a dry place and stuck to allow circulation of air around each piece.

Additional Reading

Brown, Panshin, and Forsaith, *Textbook of Wood Technology*, Vol. I, pp. 513-516

Department of Agriculture, *Wood Handbook*, p. 16

Department of Commerce, *American Hardwoods and Their Uses*, pp. 38-40

Southern Hardwood Producers, *The Southern Hardwoods*, pp. 21-22

Topic 17A. Limba (Korina)

Classification
Hardwood

Composition or Description
Limba is a uniformly textured, open-pored wood. There is no distinct line between the heartwood and sapwood since this wood is pale yellow with a light green tinge. It often contains gray-brown or black streaks. It has a characteristic odor when freshly sawn and is sometimes referred to as "White Mahogany."

Properties
Limba works well with hand and machine tools. However, the grain has a tendency to lift in planing. It fastens well with screws and glue, but has a tendency to split in nailing. It does not stand the weather well and is apt to stain if not dried rapidly. It shrinks and swells moderately and stays in place well. It turns well and finishes well. These properties are similar to those found in African Mahogany.

Uses
Limba is used for blond home and office furniture, store fixtures, radio, television, and stereo cabinets, and in paneling.

Market Analysis

Shapes
Boards, planks, veneer, and plywood.

Sizes
Limba is available in wider and longer pieces than most other hardwoods.

Grades
Limba is available in all standard hardwood plywood and veneer grades.

Sales Units
Board foot for boards and planks, square foot for plywood and veneer.

Maintenance
Limba should be sealed on the ends to prevent checking and stuck to allow air circulation around each piece.

Additional Reading
Architectural Woodwork Institute, *Guide to Wood Species Selection*

Topic 18. Mahogany

(WEST INDIAN, TROPICAL AMERICAN, AFRICAN)

Classification
Hardwood

Composition or Description
Mahogany ranges in color from light pink to a rich golden brown or amber, although some pieces are a much deeper red or brown. There is no distinct line between the heartwood and the sapwood. It has a medium open grain with a silky texture and is of medium weight. Its figure resembles the general shape of a flame or a leaf when slash sawed, while when quarter sawed it has a decided stripe, frequently with a mottled or flaky effect. Through selective cuttings, a great variety of beautiful grain figures is achieved for veneer. Mahogany contains tannic acid and changes color when exposed to potassium permanganate or bichromate of potash. See Fig. 3-48.

Properties

Mahogany has the reputation of having all the characteristics that make an ideal cabinet wood. It is easily worked with both hand and machine tools; fastens well with nails, screws, and glue; takes finishes well; resists warping; and does not shrink or swell to any great extent when exposed to changing temperature and climatic conditions. It bends well, resists splitting, and is considered a strong wood.

The Forest Products Laboratories made a series of tests including boring, planing, shrinking, warping, shaping, and turning — and on the basis of the results, classified woods into three groups. Mahogany placed in the top group in every test.

Uses

Mahogany is used for home and office furnishings, phonographs, radio and television cabinets, piano cases, and musical instruments. It is used for models and patterns. During World War II, eight hundred million square feet of mahogany veneer was used in the manufacture of aircraft. It was also used for submarine detecting devices. The list of other items in which mahogany holds top preference is virtually endless; it includes turnings, bowls, plates, trays and candle sticks, lamps, ornamental objects, moldings, picture frames, looms, bar fixtures, gaming equipment, sewing machines, trailers, and doors. It is widely used in boat building.

Market Analysis

Shapes

Boards, planks, veneer, plywood, and squares.

Sizes

Mahogany is available in wider and longer pieces than other hardwoods.

Grades

Available in standard hardwood, plywood, and veneer grades.

Sales Units

Board foot for boards and planks.
Square foot for plywood and veneer.
Lineal foot for square stock.

Maintenance

Mahogany should be stored in a dry place and stuck to allow air circulation around each piece.

Additional Reading

Department of Agriculture, *The Identification of Furniture Woods*

Mahogany Association, *The Mahogany Book*

Architectural Woodwork Institute, *Guide to Wood Species Selection*

Fig. 3-52. West Indies Mahogany (from *Yearbook of Agriculture*, 1949)

Topic *19.* Philippine Mahogany

Classification

Hardwood

Philippine mahogany resembles true mahogany somewhat in color and grain, but belongs to a different botanical family and therefore has its own classification.

Composition or Description

Philippine mahogany varies in color from light salmon to dark red. It is open-grained and is similar in weight to true mahogany. When quarter-sawed, a characteristic ribbon grain appears. Special cuttings are highly figured. See Fig. 3-50.

Properties

Philippine mahogany works well with hand and machine tools. It is rather difficult to plane and is apt to tear in turning. It is straight grained, free from knots, resists decay, does not warp excessively, and stands the weather well. "Leading boat builders looking for a wood with strength, elasticity, and the ability to take it at high speeds in sun, wind, and water prefer Philippine mahogany. These experts have seen Philippine mahogany prove itself superior under the exacting test conditions. Lighter in weight, yet less absorbent than many other woods of equal strength, this rugged hardwood is, in short, more seaworthy."[1]

Uses

Philippine mahogany is used for furniture, paneling, trim, patterns, fixtures, cabinets, pews, altars, pulpits, boats, airplanes, and exterior trim on houses.

Market Analysis

Shapes

Boards, planks, plywood sheets, and squares.

Sizes

Philippine mahogany is available in all regular lengths and widths.

Grades

Available in standard hardwood and plywood grades.

Sales Units

Board foot for boards and planks.
Square foot for plywood.
Lineal foot for squares.

Maintenance

Philippine mahogany should be stored in a dry place and stuck to allow air circulation around each piece.

Additional Reading

Department of Agriculture, *The Identification of Furniture Woods*, pp. 49-52

Philippine Mahogany Association, *Philippine Mahogany for the Building and Furniture Industry, Philippine Mahogany for Churches,* and *Philippine Mahogany for American Industry.*

Architectural Woodwork Institute, *Guide to Wood Species Selection*

---

[1] "Philippine Mahogany for American Industry," A. I. A. File #19E

Topic 20. Maple

(SUGAR, BLACK, SILVER, RED, BIGLEAF)

Classification

Hardwood

Composition or Description

Maple is a close-grained wood which is odorless and tasteless, and is of uniform texture. The sapwood is nearly white and the heartwood is light reddish-brown to pale tan. The grain is usually straight, but it is not uncommon to find curly, wavy, or bird's-eye maple. Quarter-sawed maple shows the medullary rays as flakes running through the wood. See Fig. 3-46.

Properties

Maple is heavy, strong, hard, and stiff and has good shock-resisting ability. It wears well, takes a high polish, turns well, and glues well. It has average nail- and screw-holding power. However, tests show that in over 40% of the cases where nails were used in maple, the stock split. The same was true in 30% to 39% of the cases when it was fastened with screws. Maple shrinks moderately in drying and resists warping. It has poor resistance to decay.

Uses

In the manufacture of colonial furniture, maple is in big demand. It is is also used for frames of upholstered furniture, as well as for boxes, crates, butter tubs, trucks, toys, flooring, interior trim, tool handles, wood novelties, woodenware, musical instruments, shuttles, spools, bobbins, athletic goods, tool boxes, shoe lasts, wooden heels, wear strips, wooden bearings, bowling pins, general millwork, and dairy and poultry appliances. The sap of sugar maple is the source of maple syrup.

Market Analysis

Shapes

Boards, planks, dowels, veneer, and plywood.

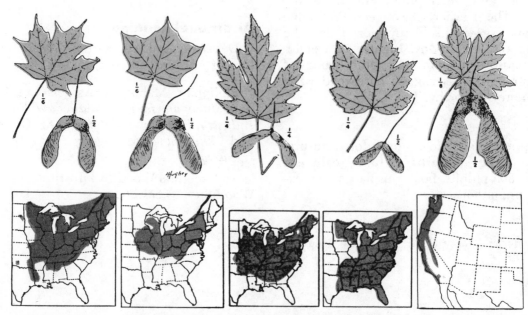

Fig. 3-53. Sugar, Black, Silver, Red, Bigleaf Maple (from *Yearbook of Agriculture*, 1949)

Sizes

Boards and planks available in all regular lengths and widths.

Grades

Available in all standard hardwood, plywood and veneer grades.

Sales Units

Board foot for boards and planks.

Square foot for veneer and plywood.

Dowels available singly or in bundles of 50 or 100.

Maintenance

Maple must be stored in a dry place and stuck.

Additional Reading

Brown, Panshin, and Forsaith, *Textbook of Wood Technology*, Vol. 1, pp. 583-585

Department of Agriculture, *Wood Handbook*, p. 18

Department of Commerce, *American Hardwoods and Their Uses*, pp. 21-23

Architectural Woodwork Institute, *Guide to Wood Species Selection*

Topic 21. Oak

(WHITE, RED)

Classification

Hardwood

Composition or Description

Oak is an open-grained, uneven-textured wood. The heartwood of red oak has a reddish tinge. Its annual rings are usually widely separated, resulting in a coarse-textured wood. The heartwood of white oak is tan and brownish. The annual rings are more compact for a finer textured wood. See Figs. 3-41 and 3-42.

Oak when quarter-sawn shows broad medullary rays or flakes which give its characteristic figure. Oak contains tannic acid, which reacts and causes the color of the wood to change when exposed to chemicals such as ammonia, potassium permanganate, and bicromate of potash.

Properties

Red oak and white oak are of about equal hardness and strength. White oak is more durable and shrinks and swells less. Virgin lumber is softer, more easily worked, and takes a better finish than second growth lumber, but it isn't as strong or tough. White oak is more resistant to decay. Both types plane easily, turn well, and are adapted to many types of finish. Oak has all the strength needed for structural use. It bends well, carves well, has excellent nail- and screw-holding properties. It is stiff, heavy, and has good shock resistance.

Uses

Oak is used for inside finish, furniture, floors, doors, carvings, millwork, boxes, crates, caskets, agricultural implements, handles, truck bodies, railway car construction, and rail crossties. White oak is used in tight cooperage and boats. The bark is an important source of tanning materials.

Interesting Fact: Cork comes from the bark of the cork oak, which grows only along the shores of the Mediterranean. Beginning when the tree is twenty years old, the bark is stripped every nine or ten years without harming the tree.

Market Analysis

Shapes

Boards, planks, flooring, plywood, and veneer.

Sizes

Oak is available in all regular hardwood widths and lengths. Flooring by the square.

Grades

Standard hardwood grades.

Sales Units

Board foot and square foot.

Maintenance

Oak should be stored in a dry place and stuck to allow air to circulate around each piece.

Additional Reading

Brown, Panshin, and Forsaith, *Textbook of Wood Technology*, Vol. 1, pp. 537-548

Department of Agriculture, *Oak*

Department of Agriculture, *Wood Handbook*, pp. 18-20

Architectural Woodwork Institute, *Guide to Wood Species Selection*

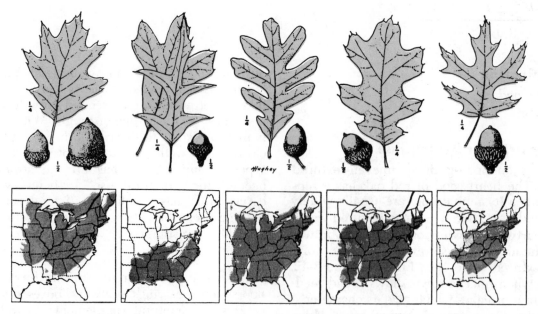

Fig. 3-54. Northern Red, Southern Red, White, Black, Scarlet Oak (from *Yearbook of Agriculture*, 1949)

The Deacon's Masterpiece

Or, The Wonderful "One-Hoss Shay"

So the Deacon inquired of the village folk
Where he could find the strongest oak,
That couldn't be split nor bent nor broke, —
    That was for spokes and floor and sills;
    He sent for lancewood to make the thills;

The crossbars were ash, from the straightest trees,
The panels of white-wood, that cuts like cheese,
But lasts like iron for things like these;
    The hubs of logs from the "Settler's ellum," —
    Last of its timber, — they couldn't sell 'em,

Never an axe had seen their chips,
And the wedges flew from between their lips,
Their blunt ends frizzled like celery-tips;
    Step and prop-iron, bolt and screw,
    Spring, tire, axle, and litchpin too,
    Steel of the finest, bright and blue;

Thoroughbrace bison-skin, thick and wide;
Boot, top, dasher, from tough old hide
Found in the pit when the tanner died.
    That was the way he "put her through."
    "There!" said the Deacon, "naow she'll dew!"
              by — Oliver Wendell Holmes

Topic 22. Eastern Pine

Classification

Softwood

Composition or Description

Eastern pine is a uniform, medium-textured, close-grained wood. The heartwood is light brown, often tinged with red; the sapwood is narrow or medium wide, is yellowish-white. Tight knots are red; loose knots are black.

Properties

Eastern pine stands the weather exceptionally well, has small shrinkage, glues well, nails and screws well, takes paint well, and is soft, strong, and easily worked with hand tools. It resists warping and is moderately light in weight.

Uses

This lumber is probably put to a greater variety of uses than any other wood, with the possible exception of oak. Eastern white pine can be used for sills, studs, subflooring, both interior and exterior finish, flooring, walls, roofs, panels, windows, and sash — in fact, it has been used for everything in house construction. It is also used for furniture, woodenware, caskets, signs, patterns, boxes, crates, and matchsticks.

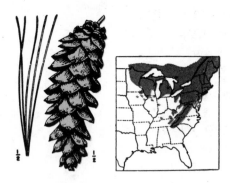

Fig. 3-55. Eastern White Pine (from *Yearbook of Agriculture*, 1949)

Market Analysis

Shapes

Boards, planks, structural timber, and plywood.

Sizes

All standard sizes.

Grades

Available in all standard softwood grades.

Sales Units

Board foot, lineal foot, and square foot.

Maintenance

Lumber should be stuck to allow a passage of air around each piece. Air-dried pine should be painted on the ends.

Additional Reading

Brown, Panshin, and Forsaith, *Textbook of Wood Technology*, Vol. I, pp. 448-450

Department of Agriculture, *Wood Handbook*, p. 27

Yates-American Company, *Short Talks on Wood*

Architectural Woodwork Institute, *Guide to Wood Species Selection*

Topic 23. Ponderosa Pine

Classification

Softwood

Composition or Description

Ponderosa pine is a light yellowish-white wood of straight but uniform grain and medium texture. It possesses the characteristic pine odor, but is generally free of resin and pitch pockets. The sound knots are red.

Properties

Ponderosa pine is easily worked, warps and shrinks very little, and is strong and light. It is weak in bending, low in shock resistance, and moderately stiff. It resists splitting, holds nails and screws well, glues well, and maintains a smooth surface. It has high insulating value, holds paint well, and permits good penetration of preservatives for moisture- and fire-retardatives.

Uses

This uniform wood excels for use in millwork in the manufacturing of sash, doors, screens, window and door frames, moldings, siding, panels, building finish, shelving, boxes, crates, wood novelties, toys, caskets, patterns, turned columns and rails, and many other fixtures and models.

Market Analysis

Shapes

Boards, planks, standard moldings, and veneer.

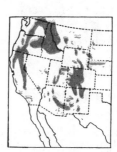

Fig. 3-56. Ponderosa Pine (from *Yearbook of Agriculture*, 1949)

Sizes

All standard sizes up to 18″ wide.

Grades

Available in all standard softwood grades.

Sales Units

Board foot, lineal foot, and square foot.

Maintenance

This lumber is usually dried in a kiln. It should be stored to allow air to circulate around each piece.

Additional Reading

Brown, Panshin, and Forsaith, *Textbook of Wood Technology*, Vol. I, pp. 455-458

Department of Agriculture, *Wood Handbook*, pp. 28-29

Western Pine Association, *Facts About Ponderosa Pine*

Architectural Woodwork Institute, *Guide to Wood Species Selection*

Topic *24.* Yellow Pine or Hard Pine

(LONGLEAF, SHORTLEAF, SLASH, LOBLOLLY)

Classification

Softwood

Composition or Description

1. *Longleaf pine* is heavy, hard and resinous. The heartwood ranges from reddish-yellow to reddish-brown. The sapwood is narrow with no distinct color change. The growth rings are narrow, uniform in width, and very hard.
2. *Shortleaf pine* is not as hard or heavy as longleaf pine. The heartwood is reddish-brown, and the sapwood (which is usually very thick) is whitish-brown.
3. *Loblolly pine* is not as close-grained as the other two species just mentioned, and it is not as hard or as heavy. The heartwood is reddish-brown, and the sapwood is yellowish-white.
4. *Slash pine* is as hard and heavy as longleaf pine. The heartwood is reddish-brown, and the sapwood is yellowish-brown.

Properties

Yellow pine is a strong, tough, hard wood. It fastens well with screws and glue and has good nail-holding ability, but due to the hard, dark summer-growth rings, it is often difficult to drive nails straight in it. It works well with hand and machine tools. It shrinks and swells greatly but stays in place well. It takes all kinds of finish well. Longleaf and slash pine are highly resistant to decay; shortleaf and loblolly pine moderately resistant.

Uses

Yellow pine is used for sills, joists, studs, rafters, subflooring, finished flooring, sheathing, and interior and exterior trim in house construction. It is also used for furniture, paper pulp, crossties, railroad cars, concrete forms, boxes, crates, tanks, vats, bridge and dock construction, fences, duck decoys, agricultural implements, musical instruments, sash, lawn furniture, telephone poles, and excelsior.

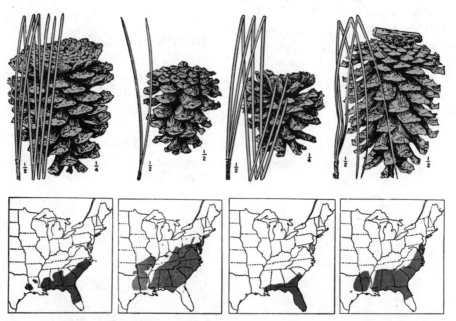

Fig. 3-57. Longleaf, Shortleaf, Slash, Loblolly Pine (from *Yearbook of Agriculture,* 1949)

Market Analysis

Shapes
Boards and planks.

Sizes
Yellow pine is available in all regular lengths and widths.

Grades
Available in all standard softwood grades.

Sales Units
Board foot.

Maintenance
Yellow pine must be stored in a dry place and stuck.

Additional Reading
Brown, Panshin, and Forsaith, *Textbook of Wood Technology*, Vol. I, pp. 452-455

Department of Agriculture, *Wood Handbook*, pp. 29-30

Department of Commerce, *American Southern Pine*

Southern Pine Association, *The Southern Pine Story*

Topic 25. Yellow Poplar
(WHITE WOOD)

Classification
Hardwood

Composition or Description
Yellow poplar is a straight, close-grained, even-textured wood which is light in weight. The heartwood is greenish-yellow, and the sapwood is nearly white. Black, purple, red, green, and blue streaks are sometimes found in the heartwood. This discoloration is due to certain minerals in the soil.

Properties
Yellow poplar is a soft, moderately strong wood which shrinks and swells moderately. It stays in place well, is fairly stiff, but is not decay-resistant. It works well with hand tools, fastens well with nails, screws, and glue, and makes an excellent base for stains, paints, and enamels. It contains no pitch.

Uses
The largest consumers of yellow poplar are the furniture and box industries. It is also used for core wood for veneers, drawer bottoms, paper pulp, siding, balusters, interior trim moldings, sash, doors, boats, billiard tables, musical instruments, toys, novelties,

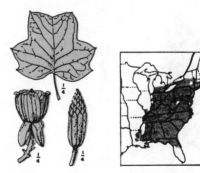

Fig. 3-58. Yellow Poplar (from *Yearbook of Agriculture*, 1949)

stepladders, caskets, fruit and vegetable baskets, farm implements, and ironing boards.

Market Analysis

Shapes

Boards, planks, plywood, and veneer.

Sizes

Boards and planks available in all regular lengths and widths.

Grades

Available in all standard hardwood and plywood grades.

Sales Units

Board foot for boards and planks; square foot for plywood.

Maintenance

White wood should be stored in a dry place and stuck to allow a passage of air around each piece.

Additional Reading

Brown, Panshin, and Forsaith, *Textbook of Wood Technology*, Vol. I, pp. 562-564

Department of Agriculture, *Wood Handbook*, pp. 23-24

Department of Commerce, *American Hardwoods and Their Uses*, pp. 23-26

Southern Hardwood Producers, *The Southern Hardwoods*, pp. 37-39

Architectural Woodwork Institute, *Guide to Wood Species Selection*

Topic 26. Redwood

Classification

Softwood

Composition or Description

The heartwood is dark reddish-brown; the sapwood is narrow and almost white. It is light in weight, close-grained, and moderately strong. Its characteristic grain is not pronounced.

Fig. 3-59. Redwood (from *Yearbook of Agriculture,* 1949)

Properties

Redwood is highly resistant to decay, and since it contains no highly flammable substance such as pitch or resin, it is very resistant to fire. It is easily worked with tools. It has low shrinkage (less than any other American wood) and warps very little. It does not nail as well as some other softwoods. It takes paint, stain, and enamel well. It has excellent insulating properties.

Uses

Redwood is used for interior and exterior trim, shingles, clapboards, siding, doors, structural timbers, fences, silos, sign posts, aqueducts, bridges, storage tanks, vats, lawn furniture, sash, and doors.

Market Analysis

Shapes

Boards, planks, structural timber, shingles, and clapboards.

Sizes

All standard softwood and structural sizes.

Sales Units

Board foot and lineal foot. Bundles of shingles and clapboards.

Maintenance

Lumber should be stuck and stored in a dry place.

Additional Reading

Brown, Panshin, and Forsaith, *Textbook of Wood Technology*, Vol. I, pp. 486-489

Department of Agriculture, *Redwood*

Department of Agriculture, *Wood Handbook*, p. 33

Yates-American Company, *Short Talks on Wood*

Architectural Woodwork Institute, *Guide to Wood Species Selection*

Topic 27. Spruce

(ENGELMAN, SITKA, EASTERN)

Classification

Softwood

Composition or Description

Spruce is a lightweight, soft, close-grained, uniformly textured wood which is odorless and tasteless.

1. *Eastern spruce* is white to light brown, with little difference in sapwood.
2. *Engelman spruce* is pale off-white in color.
3. *Sitka spruce* heartwood is yellowish, varying to a pale brown. The sapwood is cream and light yellow.

Properties

Spruce is a very strong, soft, easily worked wood. It has high nail-holding ability, glues well, holds paint well, and shrinks and warps little when properly seasoned. Sitka spruce has the highest strength and weight ratio of any wood in the world.

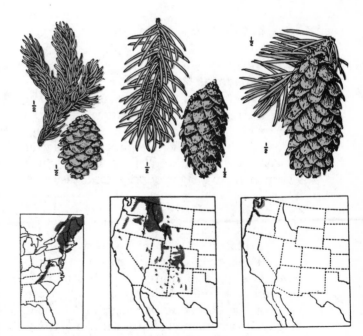

Fig. 3-60. Red Eastern, Engelmann, Sitka Spruce
(from *Yearbook of Agriculture*, 1949)

Uses

Spruce is used for strong, lightweight construction such as ladders, scaffolding, sail masts, and airplanes. The absence of large knots makes it valuable in dimension stock. It is used in siding, moldings, paneling, window frames, turned stock, food containers, pulp wood, canoe paddles, oars, tanks, flooring, box lumber, piano sounding boards, clothes chests, snow fences, and furring strips.

Market Analysis

Shapes

Boards, planks, siding, and dimensional stock.

Sizes

Available in all regular dimensions.

Grades

Spruce is available in all standard lengths, widths, and grades.

Sales Units

Board foot for boards and planks; bundles for siding and flooring.

Maintenance

Spruce should be stored in a dry place. Dimensioned lumber, siding, and flooring usually come in bundles which should be opened for air circulation before use.

Additional Reading

Brown, Panshin, and Forsaith, *Textbook of Wood Technology*, Vol. I, pp. 467-473

Department of Agriculture, *Wood Handbook*, pp. 33-34

Western Pine Association, *Facts About Engleman Spruce*

Topic 27A. Sycamore

Classification
Hardwood

Composition or Description

Sycamore is a close-grained, even, but rather coarse-textured wood. The heartwood is flesh pink to brownish pink and the narrow sapwood is light reddish with a pink cast. Quarter sawn stock shows a small flake figure which is very attractive. It is odorless and tasteless.

Properties

Sycamore has interwoven fibers which make it difficult to split and work with hand tools. It works best with high-speed equipment. It shapes and turns well, has average nail, screw, and glue holding power. It resists warping and shrinking, is tough and light in weight. It is moderately hard, stiff, and strong. It finishes well and is often stained to represent maple.

Uses

Large quantities of sycamore veneer are used by the packing industry for berry, fruit, and vegetable containers. Solid stock is used for furniture, cabinets, laundry appliances, interior trim, paneling, boxes, crates, and shelving, as well as for drawer sides and backs.

Market Analysis
Shapes
Boards, planks, plywood, and veneer.

Size

Because sycamore is a large tree, it is not uncommon to find boards 14″ and wider and lengths 16′ and over. It is also available in 2″, 3″, and 4″ planks.

Grades

Sycamore is available in all standard hardwood lumber grades.

Sales Units

Board foot for boards and planks; square foot for plywood and veneer.

Maintenance

1. Sycamore should be kept in a dry place.
2. The ends should be sealed to prevent end checking.

3. The lumber should be stuck to allow circulation of air around each piece.

Additional Reading

Department of Commerce, *American Hardwoods and Their Uses*

Southern Hardwood Producers, *The Southern Hardwoods*

Topic 28. Black Walnut

Classification

Hardwood

Composition or Description

Black walnut is a heavy wood with a medium, open, straight grain. The heartwood is chocolate brown, and the sapwood ranges from creamy white to gray. See Fig. 3-33.

Properties

Black walnut is strong, hard, and shock-resistant. It shrinks very little in drying and resists warping. It fastens well with nails, screws, and glue, and can be finished to a high polish. It works well with hand tools, can be steam-bent with success, turns and carves well, resists wear and abrasion, and possesses natural beauty of figure and grain. All these qualities make it an ideal cabinet wood.

Uses

Walnut is used for interior finish; home, office, and church furniture; caskets; gun stocks; musical instruments; radio and television cabinets; piano cases; finish in boats, airplanes, and railroad cars; veneers; and airplane propellers. The poorer grades are used for fence posts and railroad ties.

Market Analysis

Shapes

Boards, planks, plywood, and veneers.

Sizes

Boards and planks available in all regular lengths and widths.

Grades

Available in all standard hardwood, plywood, and veneer grades.

Sales Units

Board foot for boards and planks; square foot for plywood and veneer.

Fig. 3-61. Black Walnut (from *Yearbook of Agriculture,* 1949)

Maintenance

Walnut should be stored in a dry place and stuck to allow passage of air around each piece.

Additional Reading

Brown, Panshin, and Forsaith, *Textbook of Wood Technology*, Vol. I, pp. 510-512

Department of Agriculture, *Wood Handbook*, pp. 21-22

Department of Commerce, *American Hardwoods and Their Uses*, pp. 35-38

Walnut Manufacturers Association, *Of Course It's Walnut*

Walnut Manufacturers Association, *Working Wonders With Walnut*

Architectural Woodwork Institute, *Guide to Wood Species Selection*

Topic 29. Black Willow

Classification

Hardwood

Composition or Description

Willow is a very lightweight, interlocked, close-grained wood of uniform texture. The color varies from dark red to purplish-brown and gray. The sapwood is pale tan to nearly white or creamish-yellow.

Properties

Willow is one of the lightest and softest woods that grows on this continent. It is very strong for its weight. It works well with hand and machine tools, fastens well with nails and screws, and is rated number one for perfection in gluing. It finishes well with either stain or paint; resists warping, denting, and splitting; and shrinks and swells moderately.

Uses

Willow is used for paneling, furniture, turnings, veneer, cores, beverage boxes, packing cases, baskets, interior trim, doors, toys, shipbuilding, farm equipment, artificial limbs, and charcoal. It is a widely used school-shop lumber.

Market Analysis

Shapes

Boards, planks, withes, veneers, plywood, and shooks.

Sizes

Boards and planks available in all regular lengths and widths.

Grades

Available in standard hardwood, plywood, and veneer grades.

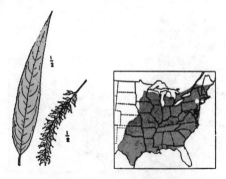

Fig. 3-62. Black Willow (from *Yearbook of Agriculture*, 1949)

Sales Units

Board foot for boards and planks; square foot for plywood and veneer.

Maintenance

Willow should be stored in a dry place and stuck to allow circulation of air around each piece.

Additional Reading

Brown, Panshin, and Forsaith, *Textbook of Wood Technology*, Vol. I, pp. 521-523

Department of Agriculture, *Wood Handbook*, p. 22

Department of Commerce, *American Hardwoods and Their Uses*, p. 46

Southern Hardwood Producers, *The Southern Hardwoods*

Topic *29A.* Manufactured Board

The complete utilization of wood has led to an expanded field of manufactured boards. This has been brought about to meet competition from other materials and to make use of residue in the manufacture of lumber and its products.

Lumber is classified as hardwood, softwood, and manufactured board. Manufactured board, as the name implies, is made of wood, but does not appear in its natural state. There are three common kinds of manufactured board: plywood, hardboard, and particle board.

Plywood is made up of an odd number of veneer sheets glued together face to face with the grain on adjacent pieces running at right angles to each other.

Hardboard (pressed wood) is made from wood chips which have been exploded into fibers under high-pressure steam, then pressed into sheets. The lignin in the fibers hold the material together without additional adhesives, resulting in a reconstituted product. This type panel is called untempered hardboard. Tempered hardboard is impregnated with a special adhesive, then baked to make it harder and more moisture resistant. Some of these sheets are embossed with patterns which resemble tile or grained to resemble Spanish leather.

Particle board (called flakeboard, chipboard, splinterboard, and crumble board in different geographic areas) is manufactured from chips, curls, fibers, flakes, shavings, slivers, strands, wood wool (excelsior) and wafers of wood. The types of raw material generally used in the manufacture of particle board are green logs, veneer cores, cull lumber, slabs and edgings, veneer clippings, pulp chips, shavings from planers, sawdust and plywood sander dust. Vegetable fibers such as bagasse, esparto, and lemon grass are also used. These materials are bonded with either urea formaldehyde or phenolic resin glues, depending upon whether it is for either interior or exterior use, and pressed into sheets and other molded shapes such as chair seats cores for irregular shapes, parts for upholstered furniture, molded table tops, siding for homes, and many other uses.

Particle board is made in presses which exert pressures of up to 3500 PSI at high temperature. All three types of manufactured board are (1) more dimensionally stable than wood in its natural state, (2) have better design possibilities, (3) good rigidity, and (4) good impact strength. In some types of particle board unbalanced construction is not a detriment when the core is made of particle board. This means that one surface can be veneered or finished with plastic laminate without treating the opposite surface in a similar manner.

Topic 30. Plywood

Classification

Manufactured board

Composition or Description

Plywood is made up of an odd number of veneer sheets, glued together face-to-face, with the grain of adjacent pieces running at right angles to each other. See Figs. 3-63A and 3-63B.

Properties

Forest Products Laboratories has found that plywood shrinks less than ½ of 1% in drying from saturation to 6% moisture content. This is substantially less than the shrinkage which occurs in solid woods of the same species under similar conditions. Weight-for-weight, plywood is stronger than steel. Screws and nails can be driven close to the edges without danger of splitting, but it is difficult to glue edge-to-edge unless a spline is used. It resists twisting and buckling. Exterior and marine plywoods are made for exterior use. Plywood is light in weight. It may be bent to slight curves, but fixed shapes are best achieved through the process of gluing up in the desired form.

Uses

Plywood is used for home and office furnishings, toys, sports equipment, kitchen cabinets, drawer bottoms, door panels, wall sheathing, boats, aircraft, boxes, caskets, forms, floors, and radio and television cabinets.

Market Analysis

Shapes

Plywood is available in various sizes of panels.

Sizes

⅛″ thick, 3-ply—36″ x 72″, 84″, 96″
48″ x 96″

³⁄₁₆″ thick, 3-ply—24″ x 72″
30″ x 72″
36″ x 72″, 84″, 96″
48″ x 96″

¼″ thick, 3-ply—24″ x 48″, 60″, 72″, 84″, 96″
30″ x 60″, 72″, 84″, 96″
36″ x 60″, 72″, 84″, 96″
48″ x 60″, 72″, 84″, 96″, 108″, 120″, 144″

⁵⁄₁₆″ thick, 3-ply—30″ x 84″
48″ x 96″, 108″, 120″

⅜″ thick, 3-ply—24″ x 48″, 60″, 72″, 84″, 96″
30″ x 60″, 72″, 84″, 96″
36″ x 60″, 72″, 84″, 96″, 120″
48″ x 60″, 72″, 84″, 96″, 120″, 144″, 168″, 192″

Plywood is also available in 5-ply panels in ½″, ⅝″, ¾″, and 1″ thicknesses, ranging in size from 24″ x 60″ to 60″ x 108″. Seven-ply panels of 1⅛″ and 1³⁄₁₆″ thicknesses are available in 36″ x 84″ and 48″ x 96″ sheets.

Grades

Softwood Plywood (Most common for structural use)

Within each type of plywood there is a variety of grades determined by the grade of veneer (N, A, B, C, and D) used for face and back of panel. See Table 1, *Classification of Species*. Grades are designated by the type of glue and the veneer grade. Plywood is manufactured from thirty different species of varying strength. These species are grouped on the basis of stiffness into five categories designated as Group I, II, etc. The strongest woods appear in Group I.

Structural I and II

Unsanded construction grade made only with exterior glue and designed for applications demanding properties such as high nail bearing, sheer, compression, and tension.

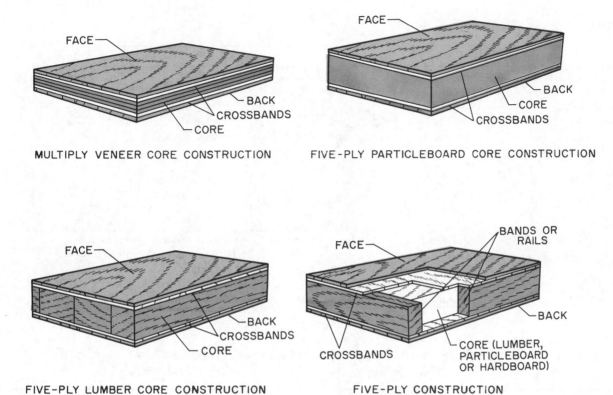

MULTIPLY VENEER CORE CONSTRUCTION

FIVE-PLY PARTICLEBOARD CORE CONSTRUCTION

FIVE-PLY LUMBER CORE CONSTRUCTION

FIVE-PLY CONSTRUCTION
WITH BANDING OR RAILING

Fig. 3-63A. Typical Plywood Constructions (Courtesy Hardwood Plywood Manufacturers' Association)

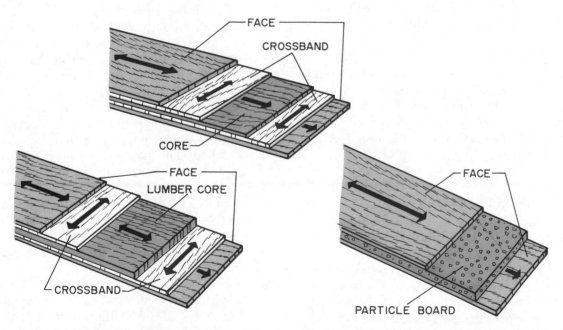

Fig. 3-63B. Typical Plywood Constructions (Courtesy Hardwood Plywood Manufacturers' Association)

Table 1
Classification of Species

Group I	Group II	Group III	Group IV	Group V
Douglas Fir—1°	Cedar	Cedar	Cedar	Fir Balsam
Larch Western	Port Orford	Alaska Yellow	Incense	
Pine—Southern	Douglas Fir—2°°	Pine	Western Red	
Loblolly	Fir	Jack	Fir Subalpine	
Longleaf	California	Lodge Pole	Hemlock Eastern	
Shortleaf	Grand	Ponderosa	Pine	
Slash	Noble	Redwood	Sugar	
	Pacific Silver	Spruce	Eastern White	
	White	Black	Spruce Engleman	
	Western Hemlock	Red		
	Pine	White		
	Ponderosa			
	Red	° Douglas Fir—1 is from Washington, Oregon, California, Idaho, Montana, Wyoming, British Columbia, and Alberta.		
	Western White			
	Sitka Spruce	°° Douglas Fir—2 is from Nevada, Utah, Colorado, Arizona, and New Mexico.		
	Tamarack			

Standard with Exterior Glue

Interior type, C-D sheathing is available with waterproof adhesives the same as those used in exterior type grades. Although these panels will retain their structural strength under most conditions, the presence of D grade veneers in inner plies and backs may result in glue line weakness when subjected to wet or highly humid conditions.

Class I and Class II

Applies only to plyform grade for concrete form applications, it indicates species mix permitted in this grade. Class I is limited to Group I for the faces, and Group I or II for the core. Class II is limited to Group I or II for the faces and the inner plies from any group.

Identification Index Number

Two numbers, separated by a dash, appear in the grade mark on Structural I and II and Exterior C-C. The number on the left indicates spacing in inches for rafters when the panel is used for roof sheathing. The number on the right shows the spacing in inches for floor joists when the panel is to be used for subflooring.

Hardwood Plywood (Most common for cabinet and architectural use.)

Hardwood plywood is graded as to veneer, core, and adhesive. The veneer grades are as follows:

1. *Premium Grade A* — The face veneer shall be of the type of wood specified, and each face of the panel shall be made of tight, smooth surface of the veneer. The veneer must be the outside face of the slice (that side of the sheet that was farthest from the knife as the sheet was being cut) that contains no cutting checks. The veneer should be a smooth, full length cut. When the face consists of more than one piece, it shall be edge matched. The face veneer may contain small burls, occasional pin knots, color streaks or spots, inconspicuous small patches and the usual characteristics inherent in the given specie. *Large knots, worm holes, rough cut veneer, splits, shakes, and decay will NOT be permitted.*

2. *Good Grade A* — The face veneer shall be of the type of wood or density specified and shall be made of tight cut veneers. When the face consists of more

Table 2
Grade-Use Guide for Appearance Grades of Plywood[1]

Interior Type

Use these symbols when you specify plywood	Description and Most Common Uses	Typical Grade-trademarks (2)	Face	Back	Inner Plys	Most Common Thickness (inch) (3)
N-N, N-A, N-B, N-D INT-DFPA	Natural finish cabinet quality. One or both sides, select all heartwood or all sapwood veneer. For furniture having a natural finish, cabinet doors, built-ins. Use N-D for natural finish paneling. Special order items.	N-N·G-1·INT-DFPA·PS 1-66 N-A·G-2·INT-DFPA·PS 1-66	N	N,A, B or D	C or D	1/4 ... 3/4
A-A INT-DFPA	For interior applications where both sides will be on view. Built-ins, cabinets, furniture and partitions. Face is smooth and suitable for painting.	A-A·G-3·INT-DFPA·PS 1-66	A	A	D	1/4 3/8 1/2 5/8 3/4
A-B INT-DFPA	For uses similar to Interior A-A but where the appearance of one side is less important and two smooth solid surfaces are necessary.	A-B·G-4·INT-DFPA·PS 1-66	A	B	D	1/4 3/8 1/2 5/8 3/4
A-D INT-DFPA	For interior uses where the appearance of only one side is important. Paneling, built-ins, shelving, partitions.	A-D GROUP 1 INTERIOR	A	D	D	1/4 3/8 1/2 5/8 3/4
B-B INT-DFPA	Interior utility panel used where two smooth sides are desired. Permits circular plugs. Paintable.	B-B·G-3·INT-DFPA·PS 1-66	B	B	D	1/4 3/8 1/2 5/8 3/4
B-D INT-DFPA	Interior utility panel for use where one smooth side is required. Good for backing, sides of built-ins.	B-D GROUP 3 INTERIOR	B	D	D	1/4 3/8 1/2 5/8 3/4
DECORATIVE PANELS	Rough-sawn, brushed, grooved or striated faces. Good for paneling, interior accent walls, built-ins, counter facing.	DECORATIVE·B-D·G-1·INT-DFPA	C or btr.	D	D	5/16 3/8 5/8
PLYRON INT-DFPA	Hardboard face on both sides. For counter tops, shelving, cabinet doors, flooring. Hardboard faces may be tempered, untempered, smooth or screened.	PLYRON·INT-DFPA			C & D	1/2 5/8 3/4

Exterior Type

Use these symbols when you specify plywood	Description and Most Common Uses	Typical Grade-trademarks (2)	Face	Back	Inner Plys	Most Common Thickness (inch) (3)
A-A EXT-DFPA (4)	For use in exterior applications where the appearance of both sides is important. Fencing, wind screens, outdoor storage units, cabinet work exposed to the weather.	A-A·G-4·EXT-DFPA·PS 1-66	A	A	C	1/4 3/8 1/2 5/8 3/4
A-B EXT-DFPA (4)	For use similar to A-A EXT panels but where the appearance of one side is less important.	A-B·G-1·EXT-DFPA·PS 1-66	A	B	C	1/4 3/8 1/2 5/8 3/4
A-C EXT-DFPA (4)	Exterior use where the appearance of only one side is important. Sidings, soffits, fences, structural uses, privacy screens.	A-C GROUP 2 EXTERIOR	A	C	C	1/4 3/8 1/2 5/8 3/4
B-B EXT-DFPA (4)	An outdoor utility panel with solid paintable faces.	B-B·G-1·EXT-DFPA·PS 1-66	B	B	C	1/4 3/8 1/2 5/8 3/4
B-C EXT-DFPA (4)	An outdoor utility panel for farm service and work buildings.	B-C GROUP 3 EXTERIOR	B	C	C	1/4 3/8 1/2 5/8 3/4
HDO EXT-DFPA (4)	Exterior type High Density Overlay plywood with hard, semi-opaque resin-fiber overlay. Abrasion resistant. Painting not ordinarily required. For concrete forms, cabinets, counter tops.	HDO·A-A·G-1·EXT-DFPA·PS 1-66	A or B	A or B	C plgd	3/8 1/2 5/8 3/4
MDO EXT-DFPA (4)	Exterior type Medium Density Overlay with smooth, opaque, resin-fiber heat-fused to one or both panel faces. Ideal base for paint. Highly recommended for siding and other outdoor applications. Also good for built-ins.	MDO·B-B·G-2·EXT-DFPA·PS 1-66	B	B or C	C (5)	3/8 1/2 5/8 3/4
303 SPECIAL SIDING EXT-DFPA	Grade designation covers proprietary plywood products for exterior siding, fencing, etc., with special surface treatment such as V-groove, channel groove, striated, brushed, rough-sawn.	303 SIDING 16 oc GROUP 4 EXTERIOR	C Plgd. or btr.	C	C	3/8 5/8
T 1-11 EXT-DFPA	Exterior type, sanded or unsanded, shiplapped edges with parallel grooves 1/4" deep, 3/8" wide. Grooves 2" or 4" o.c. Available in 8' and 10' lengths and MD Overlay. For siding and accent paneling.	T-1-11 GROUP 1 EXTERIOR	C or btr.	C	C	5/8
PLYRON EXT-DFPA	Exterior panel surfaced both sides with hardboard for use in exterior applications. Faces are tempered, smooth or screened.	PLYRON·EXT-DFPA			C	1/2 5/8 3/4
MARINE EXT-DFPA	Exterior type plywood made only with Douglas fir or Western larch. Special solid jointed core construction. Subject to special limitations on core gaps and number of face repairs. Ideal for boat hulls. Also available with overlaid faces.	MARINE·A-A·EXT-DFPA·PS 1-66	A or B	A or B	B	3/8 1/2 5/8 3/4

NOTES:

(1) Sanded both sides except where decorative or other surfaces specified.

(2) Available in Group 1, 2, 3 or 4 unless otherwise noted.

(3) Standard 4x8 panel sizes, other sizes available.

(4) Also available in STRUCTURAL I (face, back and inner plys limited to Group 1 species).

(5) Or C plugged.

(Courtesy American Plywood Association)

Table 3
Grade-Use Guide for Engineered Grades of Plywood

	Use these symbols when you specify plywood (1) (2)	Description and Most Common Uses	Typical Grade-trademarks	Face	Back	Inner Plys	Most Common Thickness (inch) (3)						
Interior Type	STANDARD INT-DFPA	Unsanded Interior sheathing grade for sub-flooring, wall sheathing and roof decking.	STANDARD 32/16 INTERIOR DFPA	C	D	D		5/16	3/8	1/2	5/8	3/4	
	STANDARD INT-DFPA (with exterior glue)	Same as STANDARD sheathing but has exterior glue. For construction where unusual moisture conditions may be encountered.	STANDARD 32/16 INTERIOR DFPA EXTERIOR GLUE	C	D	D		5/16	3/8	1/2	5/8	3/4	
	STRUCTURAL I and STRUCTURAL II INT-DFPA	Unsanded structural grades where plywood strength properties are of maximum importance. Structural diaphragms, box beams, gusset plates, stressed-skin panels. Made only with exterior glue. STRUCTURAL I limited to Group 1 species for face, back and inner plys. STRUCTURAL II permits Group 1, 2, or 3 species.	STRUCTURAL I 32/16 INTERIOR DFPA EXTERIOR GLUE	C	D	D		5/16	3/8	1/2	5/8	3/4	
	UNDERLAYMENT INT-DFPA (4)	For underlayment or combination subfloor-underlayment under resilient floor coverings, carpeting. Used in homes, apartments, mobile homes, commercial buildings. Ply beneath face is C or better veneer. Sanded or touch-sanded as specified.	UNDERLAYMENT GROUP 1 INTERIOR DFPA	C Plugged	D	C & D	1/4		3/8	1/2	5/8	3/4	
	C-D PLUGGED INT-DFPA (4)	For utility built-ins, backing for wall and ceiling tile. Not a substitute for Underlayment. Ply beneath face permits D grade veneer. Unsanded or touch-sanded as specified.	C-D PLUGGED GROUP 2 INTERIOR DFPA	C Plugged	D	D		5/16	3/8	1/2	5/8	3/4	
	2-4-1 INT-DFPA (5)	Combination subfloor-underlayment. Quality base for resilient floor coverings, carpeting, wood strip flooring. Use 2-4-1 with exterior glue in areas subject to excessive moisture. Unsanded or touch-sanded as specified.	2-4-1 GROUP 2 INTERIOR DFPA	C Plugged	D	C & D							1-1/8
Exterior Type	C-C EXT-DFPA	Unsanded grade with waterproof bond for subflooring and roof decking, siding on service and farm buildings.	C-C 32/16 EXTERIOR DFPA	C	C	C		5/16	3/8	1/2	5/8	3/4	
	C-C PLUGGED EXT-DFPA (4)	Use as a tile backing where unusual moisture conditions exist. For refrigerated or controlled atmosphere rooms. Also for pallets, fruit pallet bins, reusable cargo containers, tanks and boxcar and truck floors and linings. Sanded or touch-sanded as specified.	C-C PLUGGED GROUP 4 EXTERIOR DFPA	C Plugged	C	C	1/4	5/16	3/8	1/2	5/8	3/4	
	UNDERLAYMENT C-C Plugged EXT-DFPA (4)	For underlayment or combination sub-floor underlayment under resilient floor coverings where excessive moisture conditions may be present; for instance, bathrooms or utility rooms. Sanded or touch-sanded as specified.	UNDERLAYMENT GROUP 3 EXTERIOR DFPA C-C PLUGGED	C Plugged	C	C	1/4		3/8	1/2	5/8	3/4	
	STRUCTURAL I C-C EXT-DFPA	For engineered applications in construction and industry where full Exterior type panels made with all Group 1 woods are required. Unsanded.	STRUCTURAL I C-C 32/16 EXTERIOR DFPA	C	C	C		5/16	3/8	1/2	5/8	3/4	
	B-B PLYFORM CLASS I & II EXT-DFPA	Concrete form grades with high re-use factor. Sanded both sides. Edge-sealed, and mill-oiled unless otherwise specified. Special restrictions on species. Also available in HDO.	B-B PLYFORM CLASS I DFPA EXTERIOR	B	B	C					5/8	3/4	

NOTES:

(1) All Interior grades shown also available with exterior glue.

(2) All grades except Plyform available tongue and grooved in panels 1/2″ and thicker.

(3) Panels are standard 4x8-foot size. Other sizes available.

(4) Available in Group 1, 2, 3 or 4.

(5) Available in Group 1, 2 or 3 only.

Typical Back-stamp   ## Typical Edge-mark

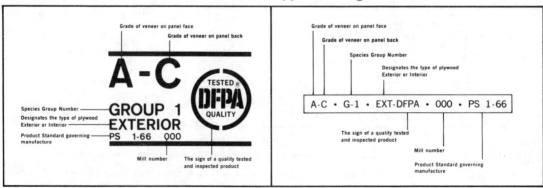

(Courtesy American Plywood Association)

Table 4
Summary of Veneer Grades Used in Plywood

Veneer Grade	Defect Limitations	
N Intended for Natural Finish	Presents smooth surface. Veneer shall be all heartwood or all sapwood free from knots, knotholes, splits, pitch pockets, other open defects, and stain, but may contain pitch streaks averaging not more than 3/8" wide blending with color of wood. If joined, not more than two pieces in 48" width; not more than three pieces in wider panels. Joints parallel to panel edges and well-matched for color and grain. Repairs shall be neatly made, well-matched for color and grain, and limited to a total of six in number in any 4' x 8' sheet.	• Maximum of three "router" patches not exceeding 3/4" x 3-1/2" admitted. No overlapping. • Shims admitted not exceeding 12" in length but may occur only at ends of panel. (Examples of permissible combinations: 3 router patches and 3 shims, 2 router patches and 4 shims, 1 router patch and 5 shims, or 6 shims). Suitable synthetic fillers may be used to fill 1/32" wide checks, splits up to 1/16" x 2", and chipped areas or other openings not exceeding 1/8" x 1/4".
A	Presents smooth surface. Admits—Pitch streaks blending with color of wood and averaging not more than 3/8" in width. —Sapwood. —Discolorations. Veneer shall be free from knots, knotholes, splits, pitch pockets and other open defects. If of more than one piece, veneer shall be well joined. Repairs shall be neatly made, parallel to grain, and limited to 18 in number in any 4' x 8' sheet, excluding shims; proportionate limits on other sizes.	Patches of "boat," "router," and "sled" type only, not exceeding 2-1/4" in width, and may be die-cut if edges are cut clean and sharp. Radius of ends of boat patches shall not exceed 1/8". • Multiple patching limited to 2 patches, neither of which may exceed 7" in length if either is wider than 1". • Shims admitted except over or around patches or as multiple repairs. Suitable synthetic fillers may be used to fill 1/32" wide checks, splits up to 1/16" x 2", and chipped areas or other openings not exceeding 1/8" x 1/4".
B	Presents solid surface. Admits—Knots up to 1" across the grain if both sound and tight. —Pitch streaks averaging not more than 1" in width. —Discolorations. —Slightly rough but not torn grain, minor sanding and patching defects, including sander skips not exceeding 5% of panel area. Veneer shall be free from open defects except for splits not wider than 1/32", vertical holes up to 1/16" in diameter if not exceeding an average of one per square foot in number, and horizontal or surface tunnels up to 1/16" in width and 1" in length not exceeding 12 in num-	ber in a 4' x 8' sheet (proportionately on other sizes). Repairs shall be neatly made and may consist of patches, plugs, synthetic plugs and shims. • Patches may be "boat," "router," and "sled" type not exceeding 3" in width individually when used in multiple repairs or 4" in width when used as single repairs. • Plugs may be "circular," "dog-bone," and "leaf-shaped," not exceeding 3" in width when used in multiple repairs or 4" in width when used as single repairs. • Synthetic plugs shall present a solid, level, hard surface not exceeding above dimensions. Suitable synthetic fillers may be used to fill small splits or openings up to 1/16" x 2", and chipped areas or other openings not exceeding 1/8" x 1/4".
C	Admits—Tight knots up to 1½" across the grain. —Knotholes not larger than 1" across the grain. Also an occasional knothole not more than 1½" measured across the grain, occurring in any section 12" along the grain in which the aggregate width of all knots and knotholes occurring wholly within the section does not exceed 6" in a 48" width, and proportionately for other widths. —Splits ½" by one-half panel length; ⅜" by any panel length if tapering to a point; ¼" maximum where located within 1" of parallel panel edge. —Worm or borer holes up to ⅝" x 1½".	Repairs shall be neatly made and may consist of patches, plugs, and synthetic plugs. Patches ("boat," including die-cut) not exceeding 3" in width individually when used in multiple repairs or 4" in width when used as single repairs. Plugs may be circular, "dog-bone" and leaf-shaped. Synthetic plugs shall present a solid, level, hard surface not exceeding above dimensions.
C (plugged)	Admits—Knotholes, worm or borer holes, and other open defects up to ¼" x ½". —Sound tight knots up to 1½" across the grain. —Splits up to ⅛" wide.	—Ruptured and torn grain. —Pitch pockets if solid and tight. —Plugs, patches and shims.
D	D veneer used only in Interior type plywood and may contain plugs, patches, shims, worm or borer holes. Backs: Admits tight knots not larger than 2½" measured across the grain and knotholes up to 2½" in maximum dimension. An occasional tight knot larger than 2½" but not larger than 3" measured across the grain or knothole larger than 2½" but not larger than 3" maximum dimension, occurring in any section 12" along the grain in which the aggregate width of all knots and knotholes occurring wholly within the section does not exceed 10" in a 48" width and proportionately for other widths. Inner Plys: Knotholes limited as for backs.	All Plys: Pitch pockets not exceeding 2-1/2" measured across the grain. Splits up to 1" except in backs only not more than one exceeding 1/2"; not exceeding 1/4" maximum width where located within 1" of parallel panel edge; splits must taper to a point. White pocket in inner plys and backs, not exceeding three of the following characteristics in any combination in any area 24" wide by 12" long. (a) 6" width heavy white pocket. (b) 12" width light white pocket. (c) One knot or knothole or repair 1-1/2" to 2-1/2", or two knots or knotholes or repairs 1" to 1-1/2".

(Courtesy American Plywood Association)

than one piece, the edges shall be tight and approximately parallel to the length of the panel. The pieces need not be matched for color or grain, *but sharp contrasts between adjacent pieces of veneer with respect to grain, figure, and natural character markings* (such as large knots, worm holes, rough cut veneer, splits, shakes, and decay) *will NOT be permitted.* Face veneer in this grade may contain small burls, pin knots, color streaks, inconspicuous patches and the usual characteristics inherent in the given specie.

3. *Sound Grade 2* — The face veneer shall be free from open defects and the grade provides for a sound, smooth surface. Matching for grain and color is not required. The natural and other characteristics which will be permitted are as follows: sapwood, discolorations and stains, mineral streaks, sound tight knots ¾″ or less in diameter, worm holes which have been filled or patched, and green spots. *Large knot holes, open splits or joints, cross breaks, and joint laps are NOT permitted.*

4. *Utility Grade* — allows sapwood discoloration and stain, mineral streaks, sound tight burls, sound tight knots up to ¾″

in diameter, knot holes up to 1″ in diameter, worm holes, open splits or joints ³⁄₁₆″ wide for one half the length of the panel, shakes, brashness, small area of rough cut veneer, cross breaks 1″ in length, bark pockets, green spots, and lapped joints. *Some decay is allowed in the back and inner plies.*

5. *Backing Grade* — permits all the defects permitted in the other grades but knot holes may be a maximum of 3″, open splits and joints 1″ wide for one-fourth the length of the panel, ½″ wide for one-half the length of the panel, ¼″ for the full length of the panel. *Shakes, brashness, and decay are allowed in small areas of the face, and large areas on the back and inner plies.*

6. *Specialty* or *Custom Grade* — The actual description of this grade will be at the option of the manufacturer, or as agreed upon by the buyer and seller. This grade may include veneer that does not conform to any of the other grades. It may permit more or fewer characteristics and defects, and it may permit different characteristics. Species such as wormy chestnut, birdseye maple, and English brown oak having unusual decorative features are considered as Specialty Grade.

Fig. 3-64. Clipping Machine
This Merritt-Solem cutting machine clips the finished Craveneer into sheets which, when dried, will be 56½ inches wide and 82 inches long. (Courtesy The Lumberman Magazine)

Fig. 3-65. Laminator
Veneer moves between rollers in the laminating machine which applies glued heavy kraft paper to each side of wood making Craveneer. (Courtesy The Lumberman Magazine)

The thickness of veneers generally used in hardwood plywood is as follows: $\frac{1}{50}''$, $\frac{1}{36}''$, $\frac{1}{32}''$, $\frac{1}{28}''$, $\frac{1}{26}''$, $\frac{1}{24}''$, $\frac{1}{20}''$, $\frac{1}{16}''$, $\frac{1}{12}''$, $\frac{1}{10}''$, $\frac{1}{8}''$, $\frac{1}{7}''$, $\frac{1}{6}''$, $\frac{3}{16}''$, and $\frac{1}{4}''$.

Lumber cores unless otherwise specified shall be optional as to specie of lumber, except the specie in a single core must be the same. The maximum width of core strips shall be 2½″ for high density woods, 3″ for medium density woods, and 4″ for low density woods. Under all grades, end grain glued finger joints will be allowed as full length strips.

There are three grades of lumber cores: clear grade with full length strips; sound grade with full length strips; and regular grade.

1. *Clear Grade* — shall be free from knots and other defects that will not properly shape or mold. Wood patches or plugs are not permitted, but wood filler is allowed.
2. *Sound Grade* — wood strips shall be free of defects except that discoloration, small knots, and small open defects, if securely patched or plugged with wood or filler, are permitted.
3. *Regular Grade* — wood strips shall be of sound grade except that random lengths with tightly butted end joints are permitted. In all grades lumber core edges shall be of clear stock with all edges free of defects to permit shaping or molding to a depth of 1½″.

Particle Board and Hardboard Cores

Particle board cores shall be of the type, grade, and class specified and shall be in accordance with the latest commercial standard. Hardboard cores shall be of the type specified and shall be in accordance with the latest commercial standard.

1. *Type I* — fully waterproof bond for severe moisture conditions.
2. *Type II* — water resistant, suitable for most interior applications.
3. *Type III* — will withstand only occasional wetting. Should be used where it will not be subjected to water, dampness, or high humidity.
4. *Technical Type* — fully waterproof for use where severe moisture conditions exist.

Sales Units

Plywood is sold by the square foot.

Interesting Fact: One plywood for structural use is built up of 29 plies, but the record is a 93-ply panel.

Maintenance

Plywood should be stored in a dry place, either vertically or horizontally. It should not be stuck. If stored vertically, it should be supported in a manner that will minimize buckling.

Additional Reading

American Plywood Association, *Guide to Plywood Grades*

Hardwood Plywood Manufacturers' Association:
1. *Where to Buy Hardwood Plywood*
2. *Versatile Hardwood Plywood*
3. *Interim Industry Standard for Hardwood Plywood*

Topic *31.* Hardboard or Pressed Wood

Classification

Manufactured board

Composition or Description

Pressed wood is made from wood chips which are exploded into fibers under high-pressure steam. The fibers are refined, felted, and pressed into heated, hydraulic-bed presses to form sheets. No fillers or artificial adhesives are used. The lignin in the wood itself holds pressed wood together. Tempered pressed wood is made by impregnating the formed sheet with a special tempering compound and then baking. This increases its strength and resistance to abrasion and reduces the rate of moisture absorption. It is darker in color and has more sheen than the untempered pressed wood. Pressed wood varies in color from light brown to dark brown. It is very hard and smooth, and free from all resin and oil.

Properties

Pressed wood is equally strong in all directions, but very brittle. It is moisture-resistant, mold- and fungus-proof, and resists dents, scuffing, abrasion, splitting, splintering, shrinking, or swelling. It can be sawed, shaped, routed, and drilled with hand or power wood- or metalworking tools. It can be punched, die cut, laminated, and bent to simple curves; compound curves cannot be made. It can be painted, enameled, stained, or varnished. Pressed wood can be nailed, screwed, glued, or bolted. Resin, casein, or hide glue are satisfactory adhesives. It cannot be toe-nailed or used for base nailing.

Uses

Pressed wood is used for backings of case goods, food containers, signs, refrigerators, chair seats, toys, trays, house trailers, sink cabinets, card tables, baby carriages, play pens, ironing boards, subflooring for tile and linoleum, exterior finish, templates, jigs, circuit breakers, control switch panels, terminal bars, and interiors of busses, trucks, railroad cars, and airplanes.

Market Analysis

Shapes

Sheets.

Sizes

1. Tempered and untempered are available in $\frac{1}{10}''$, $\frac{1}{8}''$, $\frac{3}{16}''$, $\frac{1}{4}''$ and $\frac{5}{16}''$ thickness in $1' \times 4'$, $1\frac{1}{2}' \times 4'$, $2' \times 4'$, $3' \times 4'$, $4' \times 4'$, $4' \times 6'$, $4' \times 8'$, and $4' \times 12'$.
2. Smooth, two sides tempered and tile marked are made $\frac{1}{8}''$ thick only. Smooth two sides is made in sheets $1' \times 4'$, $1\frac{1}{2}' \times 4'$, $2' \times 4'$, $3' \times 4'$, $4' \times 4'$, $4' \times 6'$, $4' \times 8'$, and $4' \times 12'$. Tile marked is only made in sheets $4' \times 8'$ and $4' \times 12'$.
3. Embossed tempered is made in $\frac{1}{8}''$ sheets $1' \times 4'$, $1\frac{1}{2}' \times 4'$, $2' \times 4'$, $3' \times 4'$, $4' \times 4'$, $4' \times 6'$, $4' \times 8'$, $4' \times 10'$ and $4' \times 12'$.
4. Die stock and Benelex are made in thicknesses from $\frac{1}{4}''$ to $2''$ in sheets $3' \times 4'$, $4' \times 6'$ and $4' \times 12'$.

Grades

1. Untempered — Smooth one side with a screen impression on the opposite side.
2. Tempered — Smooth one side with a screen impression on the opposite side. It is best for exterior use.
3. Smooth two sides — tempered only.
4. Tile marked — Same as tempered, but has lines scored on the surface forming $4'' \times 4''$ squares.
5. Embossed — Same as tempered, with a pattern which resembles Spanish leather.
6. Die stock — Most dense of all types; requires the use of high-speed tools.

7. Benelex — Structural, electrical insulating panel.

8. Cellufoam — Semirigid sheet used for its insulating and acoustical properties. It is light in weight.

9. Perforated hardboard (Pegboard).

Sales Units
Square foot.

Additional Reading
Masonite Corporation, various pamphlets
Columbia Hardwood Company, Seattle, Washington, various pamphlets

Topic 32. Particle Board

(FLAKEBOARD, CHIPBOARD, SPLINTER BOARD, CRUMBLE BOARD)

Classification
Manufactured board

Composition or Description
Particle board is made from resin-bonded wood chips, curls, fibers, flakes, shavings, slivers, strands, wood wool (excelsior) and wood wafers, as well as vegetable fibers such as bagasse (sugar cane), esparto, and lemon grass. The wood fibers are the residue from fir, pine, aspen, hemlock, poplar, gumwood, redwood, cedar, maple, and oak. *The low density woods are preferred.* In some particle board products, hardwood bark may be included up to 5% without detrimentally affecting the properties of the product. The particles are oriented to control dimensional stability. The controlled mechanical distribution of particles assures preferred physical and surface properties. The particles are formed into sheets and other shapes under high pressure (up to 3500 PSI) at a temperature of 325°F. and bonded with resin glue. The pressure is controlled to assure a uniform density product. A small amount of petroleum wax (1%) is placed in particle board (1) to facilitate removal from the press, (2) to help insure dimensional stability, and (3) to make the product more water resistant.

Properties
Particle board has equal strength in all directions of a given cross sectional area, it is not brittle, and resists warping. It works well with hand and machine tools, shapes and finishes well, but should not be run through a surfacer as it chips out. However, it may be run through a bed sander with good results. Particle board has good rigidity, dimensional stability, water resistance, good impact strength, and superior acoustical properties. In high density particle board, unbalanced construction (covering or coating one surface without covering the opposite surface) is not a detriment as it is in solid or veneered construction.

Uses
Particle board is used as a core for veneer, plastic laminates, and solid core doors as well as for tables, desks, bench and counter tops, floors, store fixtures, panels, furniture, cabinets, and underlayments. Molded shapes are available in the form of drawers, boxes, phonograph cabinets, foundation parts for upholstered furniture, chair seats, cores for irregular curves to be veneered, and siding on structures.

Market Analysis

Shapes
Sheets and molded shapes.

Sizes

Thickness	Lengths and Widths				
	2½' x 4'	4' x 8'	4' x 10'	4' x 12'	4' x 18'
¼"		•			
⅜"		•	•	•	•
½"		•			
9/16"		•			
⅝"		•			
11/16"		•			
¾"	•	•	•		
13/16"		•			
1"		•	•	•	
1⅛"		•	•		
1¼"		•	•		
2"		•	•		

Particle Board Standards

There are two types of particle board:

1. *Type I* — board is *urea bonded* and composes 90 to 95% of the particle board produced. It is intended for interior use.
2. *Type II* — is made with a *phenolic resin binder* and is suitable for exterior use and interior use which is subjected to high temperatures.

Each type is made in three grades. *Grades refer to density* (the higher the density, the harder and heavier the panel will be).

1. *Grade A* (High Density) — indicates a density range of 50 pounds per cubic foot and over.
2. *Grade B* (Medium Density) — 37 to 50 pounds per cubic foot.
3. *Grade C* (Low Density) — under 37 pounds per cubic foot.

There are two classes for each grade. *Classes refer to properties which include modulus of rupture, modulus of elasticity, internal bond, expansion, and screw holding power on both the face and edge. Class I has the lower range, but both classes have a higher modulus of rupture and modulus of elasticity in the higher density than in either the medium or low density grades. Panel identification includes (1) type, (2) grade, and (3) class.*

Maintenance

Store flat in a dry place.

Additional Reading

National Particle Board Association, various pamphlets

Table 5
Summary of Properties of Selected Woods

Name	Color	Grain	Weight	Hardness	Workability	Holding Power Nails & Screws	Glue
Ash	pale brown	open	heavy	hard	difficult	average	average
Balsa	pale brown	open	very light	soft	easy	poor	good
Basswood	creamy white	close	light	soft	easy	good	good
Beech	white & reddish brown	close	heavy	hard	difficult	high	poor
Birch	brown	close	heavy	tough	difficult	good	good
Cedar	red	straight, even, close	light	soft	easy	medium	good
Cherry	light to dark red	close	medium	hard	good	high	good
Cypress	reddish	close	medium	soft	good	good	poor
Fir	white to reddish	close	medium	medium	good	reasonably good	average
Gumwood	reddish brown	close	medium heavy	hard	medium	average	average
Hemlock	buff	close	light	medium	easy	good	good
Hickory	reddish brown	open	heavy	hard	difficult	low	poor
Mahogany	red to dark brown	open	medium	medium	easy	good	good
Mahogany, Philippine	pink to dark red	open	medium	medium	medium	good	good
Maple	light brown & tan	close	heavy	hard	medium difficult	average	good
Oak	tan to reddish	open	heavy	hard	difficult	good	average
Pine, Eastern	light brown	close	light	soft	easy	good	good
Pine, Ponderosa	yellowish	close	light	soft	easy	good	good
Pine, Yellow	yellowish & reddish brown	close	heavy	medium	medium	good	good
Poplar	greenish yellow to brown	close	moderately light	soft	good	good	good
Redwood	reddish brown	close	moderately light	soft	good	good	good
Spruce	yellowish to pale brown	close	light	soft	good	good	good
Walnut	chocolate brown	open	heavy	hard	good	good	good
Willow	purplish brown	close	light	soft	good	good	high

An illustration of the selection of wood for its properties in early manufacture:

Excerpt from:

The Song of Hiawatha

by Henry Wadsworth Longfellow

"Give me of your bark, O Birch-Tree!
Of your yellow bark, O Birch-Tree!
Growing by the rushing river,
Tall and stately in the valley!
I a light canoe will build me,
Build a swift Cheemaun for sailing,
That shall float upon the river,
Like a yellow leaf in Autumn,
Like a yellow water-lily!

With his knife the tree he girdled;
Just beneath its lowest branches,
Just above the roots, he cut it,
Till the sap came oozing outward;
Down the trunk from top to bottom,
Sheer he cleft the bark asunder,
With a wooden wedge he raised it,
Stripped it from the trunk unbroken.

"Give me of your boughs, O Cedar!
Of your strong and pliant branches,
My canoe to make more steady,
Make more strong and firm beneath me!"

Down he hewed the boughs of cedar,
Shaped them straightway to a framework,
Like two bows he formed and shaped them,
Like two bended bows together,

"Give me of your roots, O Tamarack!
Of your fibrous roots, O Larch-Tree!
My canoe to bind together,
So to bind the ends together
That the water may not enter,
That the river may not wet me!"

Thus the Birch canoe was builded
In the valley, by the river,
In the bosom of the forest;
And the forest's life was in it,
All its mystery and its magic,
All the lightness of the birch-tree
All the toughness of the cedar,
All the larch's supple sinews;
And it floated on the river,
Like a yellow leaf in Autumn,
Like a yellow water-lily.

Interesting Fact:
"The bark canoe of the Chippeways is, perhaps, the most beautiful and light model of all the water crafts that ever were invented. They are generally made complete with the rind of one birch-tree, and so ingeniously shaped, and sewed together with roots of the tamarack, which they call wattap, that they are water-tight and ride upon the water, as light as a cork."

Topic 33. Tools

Over the centuries men have improvised jigs and devices for making work easier and more efficient. These devices are commonly known as tools. Tools are of many types. Some are quite simple in their design while others are rather complex. Complex tools are generally classified as machines. Many machines are amazingly ingenious creations.

Tools and machines provide increased mechanical advantage, accuracy, efficiency, speed, and sometimes safety in the performance of work. Through the proper selection and use of tools, a person is able to perform processes that he could not perform as well or would be unable to do at all, if he had to rely on only his hands or the use of crude, primitive implements.

Man is continuously refining the design of old tools or inventing new ones in his search for greater efficiency. The application of new materials, along with contemporary design methods, has improved the appearance and the quality of tools as well as their efficiency.

Tools are classified according to their particular function and in terms of the simple machines of science. Thus, in woodworking, there are cutting tools (knives, saws, planes, and chisels) which are *wedges*; driving tools (hammers, spiral screwdriver, and bit brace) which are examples of the *lever, inclined plane,* and *wheel and axle* respectively; and boring tools which are applications of the *wedge, inclined plane,* and *screw.* (See Figs. 4-1, 4-2, 4-3.) Obviously, some tools are a

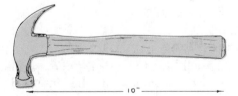

Fig. 4-1. Hammer — a Lever

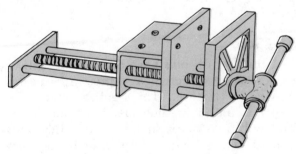

Fig. 4-2. Vise — an Application of the Screw

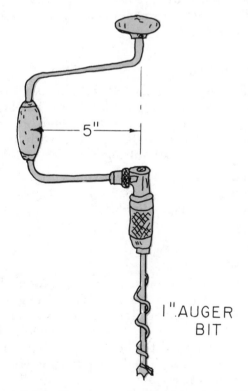

1".AUGER BIT

Fig. 4-3. Bit Brace — an Application of the Wheel and Axle

combination of several of the simple machines. Complicated power tools contain applications of each of the six simple machines of science: the wedge, the lever, the inclined plane, the screw, the wheel and axle, and the pulley.

The name and the functional classification of woodworking tools indicate their use and purpose. Thus a screwdriver is a *driving tool;* a saw is a *cutting tool;* a square is a *testing* and *layout tool.* A knowledge of the particular class of simple machine of science to which a tool belongs should provide some insight into the basic principle by which that tool and its principal parts are operated, for the purpose of achieving mechanical advantage and efficiency.

Students of woodworking classify tools functionally as measuring, layout, and testing tools; cutting, drilling, and boring tools; driving, striking, holding, and clamping tools; and sharpening tools. All but the measuring, layout, and testing tools are examples of the wedge, lever, inclined plane, screw, wheel and axle, and pulley.

The Wedge

All edge and toothed tools such as knives, planes, chisels, gouges, files, saws, hatchets, and the cutting edges of drills and bits are examples of the wedge. Those with teeth contain a series of cutting wedges.

The wedges of woodworking cutting tools separate the wood fibers by processes of shearing, slicing, shredding, scraping, and splitting.

The Lever

Leverage is applied in the operation of a number of hand tools requiring strength or pressure. Sometimes the *fulcrum* is a part of the arm. Sometimes it is an especially designed feature of the tool. Pinch bars, nippers, pliers, vise handles, and hammers are examples of first class levers where the forces pivot about a fixed fulcrum. Scrapers, chisels, planes, and other tools are levers and wedges used in combinations to increase mechanical advantage. The wedge is the cutting part and the handle helps the user to obtain leverage.

When using the hammer to drive nails, it becomes a lever arm of force. The handle length multiplied by the weight of the hammer head times the effort equals the force applied to the nail in the direction of the path of the hammer head.

Using a sixteen-ounce hammer with a ten-inch handle to drive a nail, you strike the nail with 100 pounds force when 10 pounds is applied at the handle end.

Example:

wt. of hammer head $\times$ effort applied at handle $\times$ length of handle = force

$$1 \times 10 \times 10 = 100 \text{ lbs.}$$

When the hammer is used to withdraw nails (first class lever, most common use in tool applications) the fulcrum is located between the effort and the force. Effort times distance to fulcrum *equals* force distance to fulcrum.

Example:

Hammer handle   10″
Claw   1½″
Effort   25 lbs.

$$25 \times 10 = 1\frac{1}{2} \times \text{force F}$$
$$250 = 1\frac{1}{2}\,F$$
$$F = 166 \text{ lbs.}$$

The Inclined Plane

Auger bits, drill bits, twist drills, and spiral screwdrivers are examples of the inclined plane. Mechanical advantage and efficiency are obtained by distributing the resistance or weight in such a way as to effect an indirect, gradual pull or lift as on an incline or spiral.

The Screw

A number of tools have a threaded section or screw by which heavy pressure can be exerted with ease. The application of the screw is found in such clamping and holding tools as clamps, handscrews, vises, and chucks. The screw is a form of inclined plane and is used to facilitate the operation of adjustment mechanisms (adjusting wheel of plane) or to lessen resistance (screw portion of boring tools).

A bench vise is a good example of this simple machine. The handle represents the wheel and the bolt shaft the axle. The thread of the bolt is the inclined plane.

Combining the formulas for wheel and axle and the inclined plane we have: weight of closing jaws (W) × pitch distance traveled in one revolution (P) = effort to turn handle (E) × the distance effort travels in making one turn (circumference of circle vise handle describes — 2πr).

pitch of screw = ¼″ $W \times P = E \times 2\pi r$
effort to turn = 10 lbs.

$$W \times .25 = 10 \times 2 (3.14) \times 8$$
$$W = 2009 \text{ lbs.}$$

In the preceding problem, no allowance was made for friction. The bearing on the screw sets up tremendous friction which reduces the push of closing the jaws and leaves about ten per cent working efficiency. This would give a closing push of 2009 × .10 or 200 lbs. push.

The Wheel and Axle

In some tools great leverage is obtained by the act of twisting, winding, or cranking in such a manner that force is distributed in a circular motion around a fixed point or pivot. Screwdrivers, hand drills, bit braces, and ratchets are examples of the application of the principle of the wheel and axle.

Radius of wheel × effort = radius of axle × wt.

This principle of driving force is used in the turning of the bit brace.

A five-pound push on the crank arm produces a force on the auger cutters of fifty pounds.

Radius of crank × effort = radius of
auger (axle) × force
$$5 \times 5 = .5 \times \text{force}$$
$$\frac{25}{.5} = \text{force}$$
$$50 \text{ lbs.} = \text{force}$$

The Pulley

Belt-driven machines have single and cone pulleys by means of which power is transmitted. The cone pulley also serves to vary the rates of speed.

The pulley attached to the driving force (usually a motor) is called the *driver,* and transmits power by means of a belt to another pulley, called the *driven.* If both pulleys are of the same diameter, the driven will rotate at the same speed as the driver. If the driven is smaller than the driver, it will be rotated at a *higher* speed than the power source (motor); if the driven is larger than the driver it will rotate at a *lower* speed than the driving force (motor).

As the driver pulley rotates one revolution, it causes the belt to advance a distance equal to the circumference of the driver. This may be computed using the formula for the circumference of a circle. Circumference (C) equals pi (π) times the diameter (D) or:

$$C = \pi D$$

Thus a 2″ diameter driver has a circumference of 3.1416 × 2″ or 6.2832″, and will advance the belt 6.2832 inches. Since the belt is responsible for turning the driven pulley, a 6.2832″ advance of the belt will drive the driven pulley 6.2832″ of circumference, thus a 2″ driven pulley will rotate one revolution. ($C = \pi D$ *or* $C = 3.1416 \times 2$) for each revolution of the driver pulley.

To compute speed of pulleys:
Driver   Driven
$$\pi D = \pi D x$$
Example: A 2″ driver driving a 1″ driven would be:

$$\pi 2'' = \pi 1'' x$$
$$3.1416 \times 2'' = 3.1416 \times 1x$$
$$6.2832'' = 3.1416x$$
$$\frac{6.2832''}{3.1416} = x$$

2 = x or two revolutions of the driven for each revolution of the driver

Example: A 2″ driver driving a 4″ driven would be:

$$\pi D = \pi Dx$$
$$\pi 2'' = \pi \times 4x$$
$$3.1416 \times 2'' = 3.1416 \times 4x$$
$$6.2832'' = 12.5664x$$
$$\frac{6.2832''}{12.5664} = x$$

½ = x or ½ revolution of the driven for each revolution of the driver

Combinations of Simple Machines

Many woodworking hand tools are combinations of several of the simple machines of science. One principal part may function as a screw and another as an inclined plane or wheel and axle. The jack plane, for example, contains applications of the wedge, lever, inclined plane, and screw. Power tools and woodworking machines represent the application of a variety of combinations of the simple machines.

Topic 34. Introduction to Measurement and Layout

Linear measure (measure in inches and feet) is the basic system used in woodworking. While measurement in this area may not be as precise as in some other fields, it is imperative that accuracy be practiced. Parts have to fit, joints have to be tight, and individual members must be square, sit flat, or meet other similar demanding requirements.

In furniture making the tolerance may be ¹⁄₃₂″, in patternmaking it may be ¹⁄₆₄″ or closer, while in carpentry and other rough work it may be ¹⁄₁₆″ or even larger. An accomplished woodworker is an accurate worker capable of performing within the tolerance necessary.

Woodworkers are also concerned with such principles as straight, square, and parallel. Many wood products contain parts that are square or rectangular. Boards, planks, cants, and turning squares are all basic geometric forms whose surfaces are relatively straight and approximately perpendicular or parallel.

The principle of parallelism is basic in laying out and cutting stock (or even in turning, boring holes, and other processes). Stock is milled to parallel thickness and cut to parallel widths. It is typical procedure in processing stock to select or prepare a surface that is reasonably flat, prepare an edge that is straight and at right angles, 90° to the surface, and prepare an end that is straight and 90° to both the edge and the surface. Once those working planes are established, measurements and layouts can be made from them and opposite surfaces, edges, and ends can be cut parallel and square. The principle of *parallelism* also applies when shaping irregular and circular cutouts.

In making measurements and layouts, the woodworker starts with a straight surface as a reference for all measurements. Layout tools such as gauges and squares are designed with the principles of both the perpendicular and parallel planes. The *adjacent parts* (blade) of these tools form a right angle (to the handle) and all marks or lines made with them are readily made *perpendicular to the handle* or parallel to the blade. All squares and marking gauges exemplify in their operation standard geometric theorems such as:

1. Two lines are parallel if they lie in the same plane and do not intersect, even if extended.
2. Two lines parallel to a third line are parallel to each other.
3. Two lines perpendicular to a third line are parallel.
4. If a line is perpendicular to one of two parallel lines, it is perpendicular to the other.

It may thus be said that gauges and squares are instruments of mathematics. Certainly their correct application in measuring, marking, layout, and testing are based on the acceptance of the mathematical principles or theorems.

Topic *34A.* Rules

(BENCH RULE, FOLDING RULE, YARDSTICK, EXTENSION RULE, FLEXIBLE STEEL RULE AND
TAPES, HOOK RULE, SHRINK RULE, CALIPER RULE, SPOKE CALIPER RULE, HOOK STAVE
RULE, LUMBERMAN'S BOARD RULE, LOG RULE, FOREST CRUISER'S STICK, SHIP CARPENTER'S
BEVEL RULE)

Classification

Linear measuring instrument

Application

Principle of Operation

Rules are used for duplicating measurements and testing against standard units of measure. Woodworking rules are usually graduated in ¼″, ⅛″, and ¹⁄₁₆″. Accurate measurements are best made by holding the rule on edge so the graduations are next to the work. Because the ends of rules often get worn, it is advisable to make measurements from one of the inch marks to insure accuracy.

Kinds and Uses

1. *Bench rules and folding rules,* Figs. 4-4 and 4-5, are instruments used in layout to measure relatively short distances. They are made of boxwood, maple, brass, or steel, and are available in 1′, 2′, and 3′ lengths.

2. *Steel rules and tapes* are usually made of flexible steel, with nickel chrome, blued, or white face, in lengths from 6′ to 100′, and are used for measuring longer distances. See Fig. 4-6.

3. *Extension rules* are made of boxwood or maple in lengths of 4′ and 8′. They are used for inside measurements, such as door and window openings, or for measuring distances greater than the capacity of a bench rule. See Fig. 4-7.

4. *Caliper rules and hook rules* are made of boxwood, brass bound, 6″ long, and are used to measure outside diameters of cylindrical pieces, Fig. 4-8.

5. *Shrink rules* are made of steel or boxwood and are used by patternmakers. The divisions of a shrink rule are slightly greater than those of standard rules to allow for shrinkage of metals in casting. Thus a ¼″ shrink rule would be 12¼″ long. They are available in 1′ and 2′ lengths with shrinkage allowances of ¹⁄₁₀″, ⅛″, ³⁄₁₆″, and ¼″ to the foot, Fig. 4-9.

6. *Spoke caliper rule* is made of boxwood, brass bound. It is six inches long and is designed to measure the diameter of wood spokes for wheels.

7. *Hook stave rules* are also made of boxwood, brass bound. They are six inches long and are used to measure barrel staves.

8. *Lumberman's board rule* is used to measure footage of lumber. It is made

Fig. 4-4. Boxwood Rule

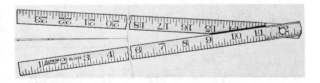

Fig. 4-5. Two-Foot Folding Rules: Wood at Left,
Brass at Right

of hickory and is three feet in length, Fig. 4-12.

9. *The Lumtape* is a pocket-size lumber rule, reading directly in board feet, Fig. 4-13. It is ten feet long, has standard ⅛″ markings, and is calibrated for even and odd lengths up to 16 board feet.

10. *Log rules* are used to determine the lumber footage in a log. They are made of hickory and are available in 3′, 4′, 5′, and 6′ lengths, Fig. 4-14.

11. *Forest cruiser's sticks,* made of maple, 38¾″ long, are used to estimate timber tracts, Fig. 4-15. Height and diameter of trees can be so estimated.

12. *Ship carpenter's bevel rule* is similar to a one-foot bench rule except it has a bevel blade at each end which folds into the rule. As the name implies, it

is used in shipbuilding. It is 12″ long, made of boxwood, with brass, bevel blades.

13. *Folding extension* or *zig-zag* rule is available in 4′, 6′, and 8′ lengths, with locking joints which permit each member to fold either way. Each member is graduated in *inches and sixteenths* on both edges of both sides. Available in three types of joints: (1) concealed; (2) riveted; and (3) springless. Because of the number of joints, its accuracy is limited. It is the most common rule used by carpenters for rough layout.

Principal Parts and Function of Each

1. Hinges on folding rules permit a more compact unit.

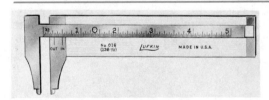

Fig. 4-6. Push-Pull Rule (Courtesy Stanley Tool Co.)

Fig. 4-7. Extension Rule

Fig. 4-8. Slide Caliper Rule

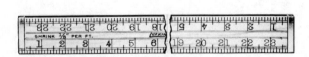

Fig. 4-9. Shrink Rule—⅛″ per Foot

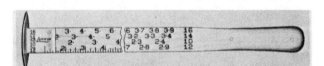

Fig. 4-12. Lumberman's Board Rule

Fig. 4-13. Lumberman's Tape (Courtesy Lumtape Corp.)

Fig. 4-14. Log Rule

2. Tips, made of harder material, prevent wearing of ends which might make rules inaccurate.

3. Hooks on hook rules and caliper rules facilitate measuring of diameters.

4. Cases on steel tapes provide housing.

Fig. 4-15. Forest Cruiser's Stick

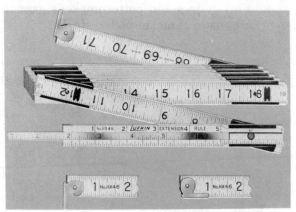

Fig. 4-17. Folding Extension, or Zig-Zag, Rule

Maintenance

Cleaning

Rules should be kept clean from dirt or rust so that divisions and figures can be easily read. It is sometimes necessary to use steel wool and oil to clean metal rules and mild soap and warm water to clean rules made of wood.

Storing

Steel rules should be stored in a dry place to prevent rusting. They should be coated with a film of oil when left unused for long periods of time.

Lubricating

Joints on folding rules should be lubricated with light machine oil.

Market Analysis

Attachments

Some two-foot folding rules have a protractor and level attachment.

Additional Reading

Manufacturers Catalogs

Topic 35. Gauges

(MARKING GAUGE, BUTT GAUGE, PARALLEL GAUGE, MORTISE GAUGE, PATTERNMAKER'S GAUGE)

Classification

Marking and layout tools

Application

Principle of Operation

A wedge-shaped pin marks or scores a line to a set distance from the head.

Kinds and Uses

1. *Marking gauges* are used to make lines parallel to an edge. They are usually 8″ long, Fig. 4-18A and 4-18B.

2. The *butt gauge* is used for laying out hinges. It has two bars, each 2½″ long. One bar has a spur on each end; the other on one end only. An oval spur is attached with a screw to the end of the

bar. This makes possible internal marking. The body holds the bars, and the knurled nut locks the bar, Fig. 4-19.

3. *Mortise gauges* are used for laying out mortises and tenons. They are similar to marking gauges except they have two spurs. Both sides of the mortise can be marked with one stroke. One type of mortise gauge has a bar within a bar; another has a double or split bar with a spur on each, Fig. 4-20.

4. *Parallel gauges or panel gauges* have a longer bar and a larger head. They are used to lay out lines at a greater distance from the working edge than the marking gauge would allow, Fig. 4-21.

5. The *roller marking* or *patternmaker's gauge* is also similar to a marking gauge. It has a spur at one end of the beam and a roller cutter at the other end, Fig. 4-22. This roller cutter scores lines on concave and convex surfaces.

Principal Parts and Function of Each

1. The *head* or *block* of marking gauges, parallel gauges, and mortise gauges is made of either beech, maple, boxwood, or rosewood. The better gauges have brass insets to prevent wear at the bearing surface.

The block or head slides on the beam or bar and may be set at any point by means of a thumbscrew. The block serves as a guide.

2. The *beam* or *bar* of the marking gauge is usually 8″ long and is graduated in inches by sixteenths. It is made of hard wood or steel.

3. The *spur* is a steel pin fastened near the end of the beam. This pin scores a line on the board.

4. Butt gauges and patternmaker's gauges are made of nickel-plated steel.

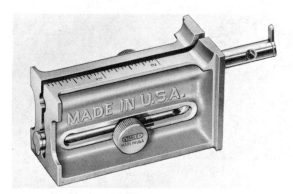

Fig. 4-19. Butt Gauge (Courtesy Stanley Tool Co.)

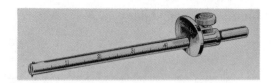

A. Single Spur

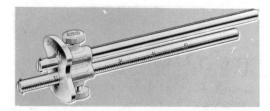

Fig. 4-20. Double Spur Marking and Mortise Gauge

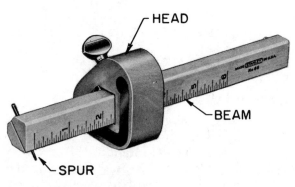

B. Boxwood

Fig. 4-18. Marking Gauges (Courtesy Stanley Tool Co.)

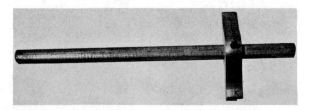

Fig. 4-21. Panel Gauge

Maintenance

Adjusting

Spur may need to be adjusted; it should protrude $\frac{1}{16}''$ to $\frac{1}{8}''$ below the beam.

Shaping of Spur

Spurs may need to be shaped with a mill file. Either a chisel point or a knife point is acceptable.

Note: Defective parts may be replaced.

Market Analysis

Capacity

Determined by length of the bar.

Fig. 4-22. Roller Marking Gauge or Patternmaker's Gauge

Attachments

Inside and outside attachments are fastened to the head of the marking gauge for marking lines on curved edges.

Additional Reading

Manufacturers Catalogs

Fig. 4-24. Marking Line with Rule and Pencil

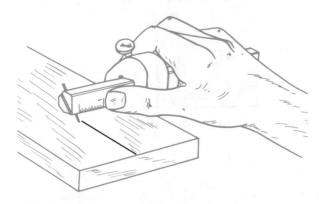

Fig. 4-23. Using the Marking Gauge
The beam of the marking gauge is laid flat on the wood with the pin to the rear. The gauge is then pushed away with the pin in contact with the wood, scoring a line.

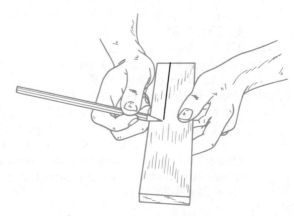

Fig. 4-25. Finger Gauging
This is a fast method but care must be taken for splinters. It is used where a scored line with the marking gauge would mar the face of the work.

Topic 36. Squares

(TRY SQUARE, MITER SQUARE, COMBINATION SQUARE, STEEL SQUARE, FRAMING SQUARE)

Classification

Measuring, layout, and testing tools

Application

Principle of Operation

The right angle of the square is used in testing the squareness (right angle) of adjacent sides of a piece or adjacent parts of an object.

The square is also used as a guide for a pencil or knife when drawing guide lines. The combination square may be used with a pencil to gauge lines parallel to a surface.

Kinds and Uses

Squares are used in testing 45°, 90°, and 180° angles, for laying out straight lines and angles; and for measuring.

1. *Try squares* usually have a 6″ to 10″ blade. There are smaller ones of 3″ and 4″, Fig. 4-26.
2. *Miter square* (see Fig. 4-34).
3. *Combination squares* have 6″, 8″, 10″, and 12″ blades, Fig. 4-29.
4. *Combination set* (see Fig. 4-33).
5. *Steel squares* usually have a 12″ or 24″ blade and an 8″ or 16″ tongue, Fig. 4-35.
6. *Framing squares* usually have a 24″ blade and a 16″ tongue and contain tables to assist in making calculations. (See Fig. 4-38.)

Fig. 4-27. Testing an Edge
Hold the handle tightly against the stock.

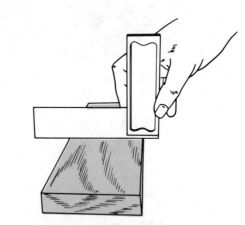

Fig. 4-28. Testing a Flat Surface

Fig. 4-26. Try Square (Courtesy Stanley Tool Co.)

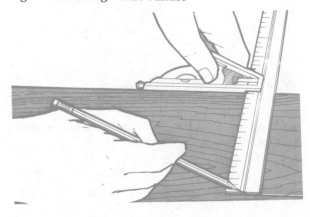

Fig. 4-29. Scribing a Line, Using a Combination Square

Fig. 4-30. Scribing a Line with Try Square and Sloyd Knife

Fig. 4-30A. Utility Knife with Retractable Blade Used for Normal Cutting, Delicate Work, and Scoring (Courtesy Stanley Tool Co.)

Fig. 4-31. Early Forms of Testing and Layout Tools
Note the ingenuity displayed in the dividers — a single bent piece of wood regulated in radius by a turnbuckle. (Courtesy Old Sturbridge Village, Inc.)

Principal Parts and Function of Each

1. The *handle* or *butt* is the shortest part of a try square. It is made of rosewood or cast iron. The shorter member on a steel framing square is called the tongue. On the combination square it is called the squaring head. This head is made of cast iron with the working surfaces machined.

2. The *blade* or *beam* of the try square is the flat steel part which is graduated into sixteenths or eighths of an inch. It is longer than the handle. The blade of a combination square is graduated into eighths, sixteenths, thirty-seconds and sixty-fourths of an inch, and the head slides on the blade. This is called the blade on steel or framing squares.

3. Framing squares are made of either polished, blued, or stainless steel, royal copper, or aluminum. The edges are ground true. There are four tables which often appear on framing squares. They are: (1) rafter or framing tables which are used to determine the length and angle of the common, valley, hip, and jack rafters; (2) the Essex board measure table which lists board measure for standard lengths and widths; (3) the octagon scale for laying out eight-sided figures; and (4) the brace table which shows the length for common braces.

4. There are take-down framing squares, where the tongue can be removed from the body. This makes it easier to store the square in a tool box.

Fig. 4-32. Early Wooden Level with Dial Indicator and Adjustable Wooden Thumbscrews (Courtesy Jason Bushnell, Vernon, Vt.)

Maintenance

When storing tools for an indefinite period, apply a light coating of oil to all metal parts to prevent rust. Care should always be taken not to drop or give rough treatment, which may cause the square to get out of alignment and limit its use. Because of wear of the slide, the combination square may not always remain accurate. Therefore, it is not recommended as a testing tool.

Market Analysis

Capacity

The capacity of a square is determined by the length of the blade.

Attachments

A combination set includes three types of heads: the miter and squaring head, which has a level glass in the head and is used for testing for levelness and laying out miters; the center head, used for finding the center of a cylinder; and the protractor head which is used to determine or lay out any angle from 0° to 360°. See Fig. 4-33. Stops for framing squares (called gauges or clips) are used when laying out stair stringers.

Additional Reading

Stanley Tool Company, *Stanley Framing and Rafter Square*
   Manufacturers Catalogs

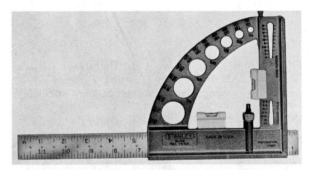

Fig. 4-33A. All Purpose Layout Tool (Courtesy Stanley Tool Co.)

This tool may be used as a level, plumb, square, marking gauge, protractor, depth gauge, beam compass, stud marker, screw gauge, dowel gauge, and nail gauge.

Fig. 4-33. Combination Set (Courtesy L. S. Starrett Co.)

Topic 37. Laying Out and Testing Angles

Classification

Measuring, marking, and checking

Procedure

Angles of 45° and 90°

1. Angles of 90° are layed out and tested with a try square. Angles of 45° and 90° are layed out and tested with the aid of the framing square, miter square, and combination square.
2. A short bevel of 45° may be layed out or tested with the aid of the miter square (Fig. 4-34) or combination square (Fig. 4-29).
3. A larger bevel of 45° may be laid out by using the framing square or by measuring an equal distance on the sides of a 90° angle and connecting with a diagonal as illustrated in Fig. 4-35.

Using the T-Bevel

1. The T-bevel is the most common tool for laying out angles other than 90° such as bevels, chamfers, miters, and various kinds of polygons. The protractor head of the combination set may also be used.
2. Set T-bevel to the required angle. The blade is moved by loosening the clamping screw, and set to the desired angle with the aid of a protractor or a fram-

ing square. (See Table of Angles.) The T-bevel is used in the same manner as the try square, but not as a substitute for it. See Figs. 4-36 and 4-37.

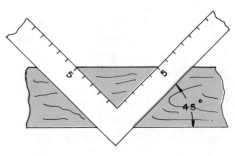

Fig. 4-35. Using Steel Square to Lay Out 45° Angle

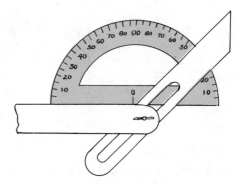

Fig. 4-36. Setting a T-Bevel with a Protractor

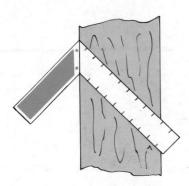

Fig. 4-34. Using Miter Square at 45° Angle

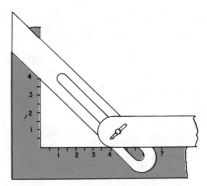

Fig. 4-37. Setting a T-Bevel with Steel Square and Table

3. A wood fence attached to the framing square is a convenient jig used in laying out the above angles, Fig. 4-38.

Table of Angles

The table below indicates the angle which is formed when a line is drawn between given pairs of measurements on the framing square. The T-bevel may be set according to this angle.

The table could be used to lay out the included angles of a given polygon. Half the respective included angles would be used in laying out the miter for the cut.

Table 6
Table of Angles

Polygon No. of Sides	Angle (degree)	Tongue (inches)	Blade (inches)
3	30	12	$20\frac{7}{8}$
5	54	12	$8\frac{25}{32}$
6	60	12	$6\frac{15}{16}$
7	$64\frac{2}{7}$	12	$5\frac{25}{32}$
8	$67\frac{1}{2}$	12	$4\frac{31}{32}$
9	70	12	$4\frac{3}{8}$
10	72	12	$3\frac{7}{8}$

Angle Divider

1. The angle divider may also be used for testing and laying out angles.

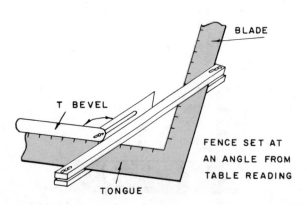

Fig. 4-38. Setting a T-Bevel with Framing Square and Fence

2. This tool has two blades which form the bevels for the miter cut for polygons having 4, 5, 6, 8, 9, and 10 sides. See Figs. 4-40 and 4-33.

Standards and Results

1. The tool must be set at the proper angle.
2. Care must be taken in testing the angle so that the set or adjustment is not changed.

Additional Reading

Stanley Tool Company, *How to Use the Stanley T-Bevel*

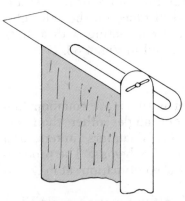

Fig. 4-39. Checking Angle with T-Bevel

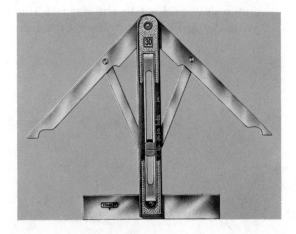

Fig. 4-40. Angle Divider (Courtesy Stanley Tool Co.)

Topic 38. Layout

A. TRANSFERRING OR LAYING OUT IRREGULAR DESIGNS USING PROPORTIONAL SQUARES

Classification

Enlarging and reducing pictures or drawings

Procedure

Most project ideas as pictured in books and magazines are scaled drawings that must be enlarged to full size if a pattern is necessary. If the design is symmetrical (the same on each side of the center line), only half of the design must be drawn full size. See Fig. 4-41.

1. Determine how much larger or smaller the pattern is to be in relation to the original drawing or picture. Keep in mind that the grid squares in the larger figure normally should not exceed 1″.

2. When this scale has been determined, secure a piece of wrapping paper or cardboard large enough to make the full-size pattern.

3. Lay out the vertical and horizontal lines for both figures in accordance with the predetermined scale. It will help if the corresponding lines on both the original and on the enlargement are marked with matching numbers.

4. Carefully duplicate on the full-size grid all of the intersecting lines of the scaled pattern. Indicate the direction of the curved lines at the points of intersection.

5. Sketch the curves as indicated by the directional lines on the grid. Use a French curve to go over the contours to produce a sharp line drawing.

6. This pattern may be transferred onto the material by tracing with carbon paper or by carefully cutting out the profile and tracing around it. If the pattern is to be used frequently, one made of sheet metal will retain its original shape for a longer period of time.

Standards and Results

1. Lines should be sharp and clear-cut.
2. The finished pattern should be in proper proportion to the original drawing.

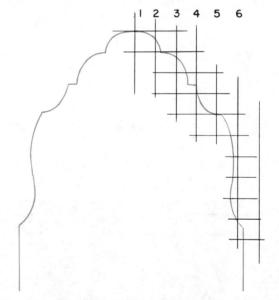

Fig. 4-41. Use of Proportional Squares on Irregular Design

B. OTHER METHODS OF LAYOUT

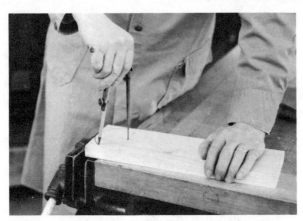

Fig. 4-42. Using Wing Divider to Scribe Circle

Fig. 4-43. Using Wing Divider to Scribe Irregular Shape

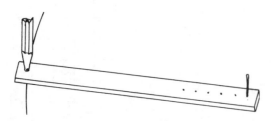

Fig. 4-44. Method of Circle Layout with Trammel Points

Fig. 4-45. Using Two Sticks to Measure Opening

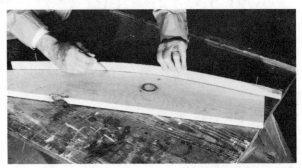

Fig. 4-46. Laying Out Long Curve with Flexible Stick and Two Brads

Fig. 4-47. Snap a Taut Chalk Line Square with the Surface for Straight Lines on Long Boards

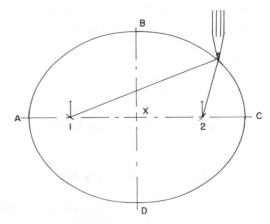

Fig. 4-48. Laying Out an Ellipse — Pin and String Method

Line A-C equals the major axis. Line B-D equals the minor axis. With AX as the radius, scribe arcs B_1 and B_2. Insert pins at points 1, 2 and B. Tie a string to form a loop around the three pins, allowing no slack in the string. Remove pin at B and replace with a sharp pencil. With tension on the string draw a steady line forming the ellipse.

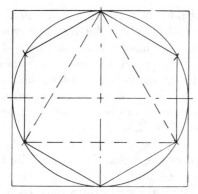

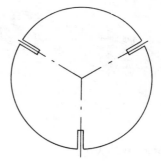

Fig. 4-50. Laying Out 120° Angles for Pedestal Legs

Fig. 4-49. Laying Out a Hexagon or Equilateral Triangle in a Circle

Using the radius of the circle step off six equal parts. To form a hexagon, connect each point to adjacent points with straight lines. To form a triangle, connect alternate points as shown by the dash line.

A simple jig may be made from sheet metal if many pieces must be laid out.

Topic 39. Getting Out Stock

(SELECTING, LAYING OUT, CUTTING APPROPRIATE MATERIAL)

Classification

Selecting, Measuring, Laying Out, and Cutting

Procedure

1. Determine kind of stock, dimensions, and other necessary data from drawing or stock bill.
2. Look in short-piece storage container for the material. Many times, satisfactory material is available there.
3. If you cannot find suitable material in the short-piece container, go to the material storage center. Check kind and grade of stock and check dimensions. Examine stock for warp, defects, or blemishes and determine if they will interfere with the use of that material for your particular job. Select that stock which will result in the least amount of waste. Make proper considerations for color, texture, figure, grain, and other qualities; and be sure each piece is best suited for the purpose it is to serve.

Stock that has a *waney edge* may be usable if the wane is removed. Using a straightedge or a chalk line (Fig. 4-47), mark a line on the surface of the board as close to the wane as possible. With either a rip saw or a band saw, cut on the waste side (wane) of the board. Plane the edge to the line, or joint on a jointer.

Stock that has a *crook* may be straightened in the same manner. See Fig. 4-51.

Stock that has either a *wind* or a *bow* should first be faced; this may be done by either hand planing or using a jointer. If a hand plane is used, it is best to plane the convex surface. If a jointer is used, it is best to face the concave surface. This will give a better bearing surface in both cases. See Figs. 4-52 and 4-53.

On stock that has a *cup*, it may be necessary to rip the piece down the center, square the joint, and then glue to achieve the desired

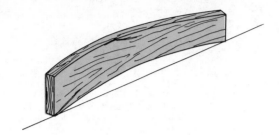

Fig. 4-51. Stock with Crook

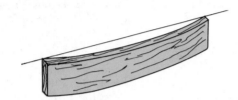

Fig. 4-52. Stock with Bow

Fig. 4-53. Stock with Wind

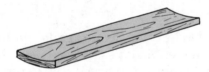

Fig. 4-54. Cupped Stock

width. If narrower pieces are required, rip to rough widths before facing and surfacing. Whether stock has bow, crook or wind, maximum dimensions in *thickness and width* are obtained by cutting in *short lengths*.

Stock that has *end checks* may require cutting off this end, or checks may be ripped out if narrow pieces are required.

Knots may be eliminated by either laying out the pieces between the knots or by ripping the knots out and gluing to get the desired widths. The same procedure may be followed in eliminating grub holes, worm holes or shakes.

4. Lay out stock, keeping in mind all necessary considerations of waste, defects, strength, beauty, etc.

5. Secure instructor's approval before you cut any stock.

6. Properly support stock and avoid overcutting, tearing, bending, or other damaging of stock or equipment.

7. Use proper tools and be certain cut is correct.

8. Store unused material in proper place and in a safe, neat, and appropriate way.

9. Return tools to their proper places.

10. Record on your stock bill all the material you have taken. Be sure all necessary dimensions and specifications are noted.

Topic 40. Theory Underlying the Design and Action of Cutting Tools

In cutting wood the purpose of the cut — whether sawing, planing, boring, shaping, routing, or sanding — is to separate stock along its length, width, or thickness.

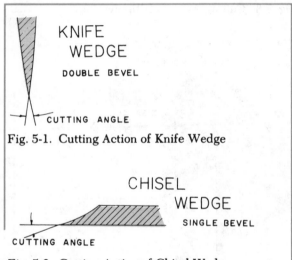

Fig. 5-1. Cutting Action of Knife Wedge

Fig. 5-2. Cutting Action of Chisel Wedge

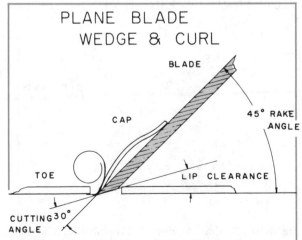

Fig. 5-3. Cutting Action of Plane Blade

1. Every wood cutting tool is a wedge or series of wedges, with a single or double bevel, Fig. 5-1.

Chisels, plane irons, turning tools, gouges, drawknives, spoke shaves, and scrapers are all modified chisels or gouges, with either single or double bevel. (See Figs. 5-2, 5-3, 5-4, 5-5.) Jointer, router, shaper, molding, and thickness planer knives are of this type, Fig. 5-6.

The lips of an auger bit are, in effect, two chisels set up with the blades pointing in opposite directions, Fig. 5-7. When the bit is rotated, the lips cut in a clockwise direction. The twist drill has its cutting edge on an angle, but the effect is the same.

The ripsaw is merely a battery of single-edge chisels, alternately set from left to right, Fig. 5-8.

The crosscut saw is, in effect, a battery of double-bevel skew chisels, alternately set from left to right, Fig. 5-9.

SKEW CHISEL

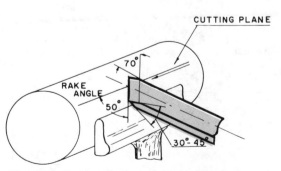

Fig. 5-4. Cutting Action of Skew Chisel

The teeth of all saws — hand or machine operated — can be classified as either of the above or as a combination of the two, Fig. 5-10.

2. In cutting wood by any method, stock is removed through the shearing action of the wedge-shaped cutter or series of

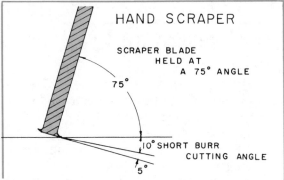

Fig. 5-5. Cutting Action of Hand Scraper

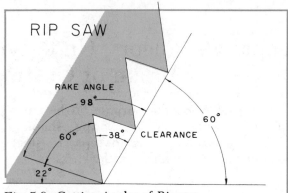

Fig. 5-8. Cutting Angles of Ripsaw

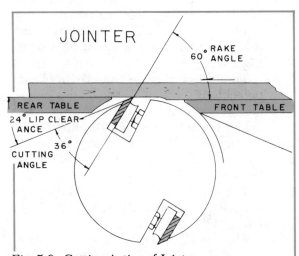

Fig. 5-6. Cutting Action of Jointer

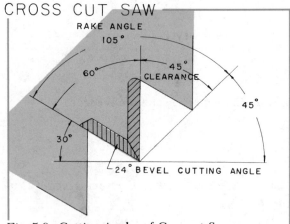

Fig. 5-9. Cutting Angles of Crosscut Saw

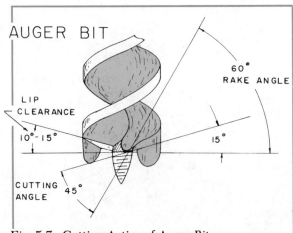

Fig. 5-7. Cutting Action of Auger Bit

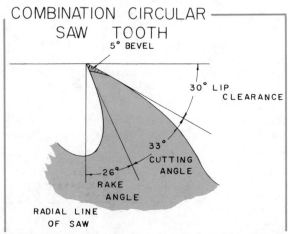

Fig. 5-10. Cutting Angles of Combination Circular Blade

cutters. The wedge or wedges pare the fibers, and the incline of the face of the wedge causes the fibers to curl or to be separated, producing shavings, chips, or dust.

3. The shearing is accomplished by the cuttting edge of the blade (or teeth) being wedged into the stock in a sliding motion and usually to a regulated depth.

4. The wedge or wedges are driven by hand or machine power and engage the stock in a given plane, arc, or angle.

5. The wedge or wedges may be pushed, may revolve or reciprocate in the stock, or the stock may be pushed or revolved against the wedges.

6. The smoothness of the cut is determined largely by the shape of the wedge, the angle at which it is inserted into the stock, the depth of the cut, the moisture content, and the grain pattern. The smoothest cuts usually result in shavings. Under a microscope the finest sawdust appears as minute shavings.

7. The most effective angle of approach of the tool cutting edge to the wood fibers is approximately 30°, and each type of tool is so designed that in use the wedge enters the stock at that approximate angle. At certain angles the wedging action is erratic because the cutting edge of the tool tears and breaks the fibers ahead of the cut.

8. The *lip clearance* is the relief given the cutting edge so that it may enter the material to be cut. Much of the effectiveness of the cutting edge depends on the correct lip clearance angle. If no clearance angle were provided, the cutting edge would be prevented from entering the work. Too great a lip clearance angle weakens the cutting edge. The angle may range from 6° for metal cutting tools to 35° for woodworking tools.

9. The *rake angle* is the angle at which the face of the cutting edge enters the work. This angle partially controls the tightness with which the shavings are curled. A large rake angle requires a great force to drive the tool. Too small a rake angle results in a thin cutting edge. Tools such as the plane, auger bit, and saws are designed by manufacturers for maximum stiffness and most efficient cutting angle.

Topic 41. Safety

The most important factor in safety is the attitude of the worker himself. Modern tools and machines are designed to be relatively safe. It is the method of using them that causes accidents. By developing safe working habits and an awareness of good safety practices, accidents may be avoided. One must recognize the danger in the operation being performed. An appreciation of good craftsmanship will develop a need for proper maintenance of tools. One should never use a broken or dull tool. The adverse method of control in using a broken tool and the extra force needed to operate a dull tool restrict the safe control of the operation.

If one analyzes the situation, there are more safe ways to do a job than unsafe ways. *Don't take chances; become familiar with an operation and follow the correct procedure.*

Personal Safety Rules

1. Clothing — Avoid loose clothing; sleeves should be tight; remove ties, rings, watches, etc.

2. Eye safety — It is good practice to wear safety glasses when doing any cutting or when in proximity to the cutting operation. Many state laws require that safety glasses be worn by all students

when in the vicinity of any cutting operation.
3. Report injuries of any type to instructor
immediately.
4. Never put fasteners or hardware of any
description in the mouth.
5. Avoid throwing tools or any type of material to another person.
6. Keep working area free of excess waste,
such as shavings and pieces of wood.
7. When carrying long stock, secure help
to maintain proper control.
8. Be careful when handling rough stock;
splinters are painful.
9. Lift heavy objects only with judgment.
When doing so, lift with the legs — not
with the back.

Hand Tool Safety Rules

1. Keep fingers away from the edges of
sharp cutting tools. It is good practice to
work away from your body when using
a sharp cutting tool. The work should
be secured in a holding device, so that
both hands are free to control the tool.
2. Protect the cutting edge of sharp tools
when carrying or storing.
3. Do not use dull or broken tools.
4. Be sure that tool handles are in good
condition and securely fastened to the
body of the tool.
5. Store clamped-up stock so that protruding clamps are not dangerous to fellow
workers.
6. Tools with ragged or mushroomed edges
should not be used. Grind such tools to
remove the danger of flying particles of
metal.
7. Observe all special safety considerations
for each tool or operation.

Machine Safety Rules

1. Secure instruction in the use of a machine or permission to operate machine.
2. Make sure all guards and eye shields are
in place.
3. Cleaning and removing chips should be
done only when machine is not running.
Use a brush, bellows, or vacuum.

4. Check all adjustments to make sure the
machine is in proper operating condition.
5. Think through all operations carefully
before starting the machine.
6. Do not talk to others when operating
the machine.
7. Generally, there should be only one person at a machine at one time; however,
when processing large or long pieces,
secure the services of a helper and ex-
plain his duties to him before beginning
the process.
8. Make sure that spectators do not stand
directly in line with revolving cutters or
stock.
9. Make adjustments or repairs when the
machine is inoperative. If oil is spilled
on machine or floor, be sure to remove it
completely.
10. Stand by the machine until it stops.
11. While machine is running, be alert to
sounds which indicate that it is not
operating properly.
12. Be alert for odors which indicate the
machine and/or stock is overheating.
13. Do not touch moving stock or a cutting
tool while it is in motion.
14. Observe all special safety considerations
for each machine.
15. Report all defective electrical outlets
and cords.
16. Examine all stock for physical defects
and foreign objects.

Fire Safety Rules

Wood shavings and finishing materials are
very combustible. The following aspects of
safety and cleanliness in the shop should not
be neglected:
1. Flammable liquids should be stored in
metal containers in a safe place.
2. Rags used in oil or paint should be de-
stroyed or stored in covered metal containers.
3. Sawdust and shavings should be regularly swept up and removed from the
shop.

Topic *42.* Hand Saws

(CROSSCUT, PANEL, BACK, DOVETAIL, MITER BOX, VENEER, STAIRBUILDER'S FLOORING, HALF-BACK, RIP, COMPASS, KEYHOLE, TURNING, COPING, AND CABINET)

Hand saws are divided into two main classes: crosscut saws and ripsaws, but broadly speaking, the term "hand saw" includes all hand-operated, special-purpose saws.

Classification

Reciprocating, toothed cutting tool

Application

Principle of Operation

1. The *crosscut saw* cuts both as a knife and as a chisel. The extreme points on either side of the saw score parallel lines, Fig. 5-11. This action is like two knives cutting parallel lines across the face of the wood.

As the sawing action continues, the cutting edge on the inside of the teeth comes into contact with the wood, shearing it out of the kerf, Fig. 5-13.

When a full bite is taken, the points of each tooth continue to score the outside of the kerf, and the sharpened, beveled sides of the teeth shear and crumble the wood left between the cutters.

At each stroke of the saw the sawdust is carried out of the kerf in the throat or gullet formed between the teeth of the saw.

The teeth of a saw are set alternately to the right and left so that the cut, or *kerf*, is wider than the thickness of the saw blade. This off-setting of the teeth is known as "set." See Fig. 5-12.

Fig. 5-13. Side View of Cutting Action of Crosscut Saw

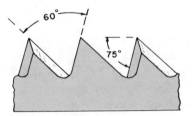

Fig. 5-11. Crosscut Saw Teeth—Side View

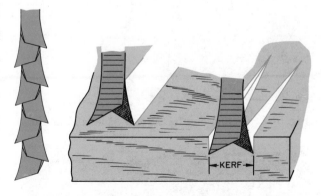

Fig. 5-12. Top View of Crosscut Saw Teeth and Cutting Action

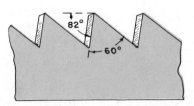

Fig. 5-14. Ripsaw Teeth — Side View

2. The *teeth of a ripsaw* are chisel shaped, Fig. 5-15. These teeth have a straight front and sever the fibers at one place only. They do not score either side of the cut. The front edges of the tooth cut the fibers of the wood, Fig. 5-16. As sawing continues, the fibers on the bottom and sides of the cut give way and the chips are carried out in the teeth gullets, Fig. 5-16.

Kinds and Uses

Saws with Crosscut Teeth

1. The *crosscut saw* is considered an all-purpose saw, but it is especially designed to cut across the grain of the wood or at an angle to the grain. It is used to cut boards to length. A crosscut saw with large teeth is used for rough work; one with fine teeth is used for finish work.

2. A *panel saw* is a short, fine-toothed, crosscut saw used for doing fine work.

3. The *back saw* has fine crosscut teeth with a thin blade and a steel reinforcing bar on the back. It is used for fine cutting or where a straight, even cut is required. One special type is an offset, double-end backsaw.

4. A *dovetail saw* is similar to a back saw, except that it has a thinner blade and a straight handle, Fig. 5-18. It is used for cutting dovetails and doing other fine work.

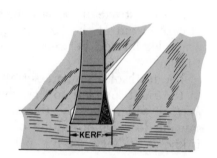

Fig. 5-15. Top View of Ripsaw Teeth and Cutting Action

Fig. 5-16. Side View of Cutting Action of Ripsaw

Fig. 5-17. Keyhole Saw (Courtesy Disston Div., H. K. Porter Co., Inc.)

Fig. 5-18. Dovetail Saw (Courtesy Disston Div., H. K. Porter Co., Inc.)

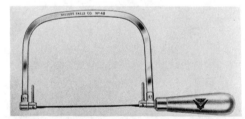

Fig. 5-19. Coping Saw (Courtesy Millers Falls Co.)

Fig. 5-20. Veneer Saw

5. The *miter box saw* is similar to the back saw except it is wider and larger. It is used in a miter box.
6. A *veneer saw* has crosscut teeth on both edges of the saw with a very slight set, Fig. 5-20. It is used for cutting veneer.
7. The *stair builder's saw* has crosscut teeth used for sawing into flat surfaces where it is necessary to cut an even depth.
8. A *flooring saw* is used to eliminate boring or chiseling when sawing into flat surfaces. The blade comes to a point and the bottom edge is curved, Fig. 5-21. Crosscut teeth are filed on both edges.
9. A *half-back saw* combines the action of both the hand saw and the back saw. It gives the advantages of a stiffened cutting edge and the ability to cut entirely through the work.

Saws with Rip Teeth

1. The *ripsaw* is used for cutting along the grain of the wood. In the hands of a skilled workman, a fine ripsaw may be used for cutting across the grain of wet or green lumber.
2. The *compass saw* has rip teeth with a narrow blade so it can cut to a curve.
3. The *keyhole saw* is a fine compass saw, Fig. 5-17.
4. A *turning saw* has a narrow blade with rip teeth held in a frame under tension. It is used for cutting curves.
5. A *coping saw* has a narrow blade with rip teeth, which is held in a steel frame under tension, Fig. 5-19. It is used for cutting along a curve.

Saws with Crosscut and Rip Teeth

1. A *cabinet saw* is similar in size and shape to a back saw except that it has no back. One edge of the blade has crosscut teeth and the other has rip teeth.

Fig. 5-21. Flooring Saw (Courtesy Disston Div., H. K. Porter Co., Inc.)

Principal Parts and Function of Each

1. The handle is shaped to hold and apply pressure on the cutting stroke.
2. The blade is the part in which the teeth are filed.
3. The toe is the end of the blade opposite the handle.
4. The heel is the portion of the blade nearest the handle.
5. The back is the edge of the blade opposite the teeth. Saws are made with straight or skew (curved) back.

   Some blades are taper ground; that is, the blade is made thinner at the back than at the teeth. This allows for a narrower kerf and less set in the teeth.

Maintenance

For good service a saw must have a smooth blade. Rust pits roughen a saw blade causing wood fibers to bind against it. To prevent rust a saw blade should be wiped with oil or wax.

Storing

Saws should be stored in a dry place in such a way as to have the cutting edge away from accidental contact with other objects.

Adjusting

Saws are sharpened by hand or machine filing. It is too difficult a job for the inexperienced person and should be done by an expert. Saws should be filed in terms of the kind of work on which the saw is to be used. Soft, wet woods require more set than hard, dry woods.

Market Analysis

Significant Materials Used

The handles of saws are made of apple wood, beech, or plastic.

The blade is made of high grade tool steel.

Sizes

Hand saw blades are described by a "point" system; that is, the number of full teeth in one inch — plus one.

Usually the number of points is stamped on the heel of the saw. A large number of points indicates a fine saw. A low number of points indicates a coarse saw. A six-point saw would be fairly coarse and would give a rough cut, but would cut rapidly, while a ten-point saw would make a fine cut, but would cut more slowly. Back and miter box saws have 12 to 16 points to the inch.

The length of blades varies from 20″ to 26″ for crosscut and ripsaws, 8″ to 16″ for back saws, and 24″ to 28″ for miter saws.

Additional Reading

Atkins Saw Company, *Saw Sense*

Disston Company, *Disston Saw, Tool, and File Manual*

Manufacturers' catalogs

Topic 43. Sawing a Board With a Hand Saw

Classification

Cutting by scoring and shearing with especially shaped teeth

Procedure

1. Lay out a guide line to follow when hand sawing. Use a rule, straightedge, or marking gauge and a pencil or knife.
2. For sawing, short pieces may be held in a vise or on a bench hook. Longer pieces are usually placed on a saw horse using the knee to help hold the work.

3. Grasp the saw with your right hand, with the thumb and index finger extended along the two sides of the handle, Fig. 5-22. This helps to guide the saw in a straight line.
4. Stand so that your forearm, shoulder, and eye follow the line of the saw blade, Fig. 5-25.
5. In using a saw horse, place your knee on the piece to be cut, Fig. 5-26. Start the cut as close to the line as possible — on the waste side. The line

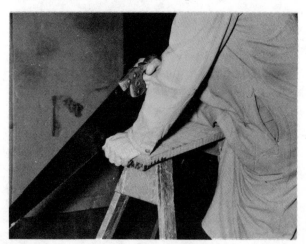

Fig. 5-22. Starting the Cut for Ripping

Fig. 5-23. Angle for Ripping (60°)

should be barely visible after the cut is made. Grasp the edge of the board with the left hand close to the saw so that some part of the thumb will bear against the saw to act as a guide. See Fig. 5-24. Raise the thumb to prevent it from being cut by the saw teeth. Start the saw with two or three light upward strokes; this will engage the teeth. After the starting stroke has been made, take a few short strokes to deepen the groove. Remove the left hand. Take full-length strokes, applying downward pressure with the arm and body. Applying wrist pressure results in a jerky motion and makes it more difficult to follow the line.

6. If you get off the line, take short strokes, using the teeth at the toe of the blade. Twist the handle slightly to bring the saw back to the line, Fig. 5-27.

Fig. 5-26. Note Positions of Right Knee and Left Hand

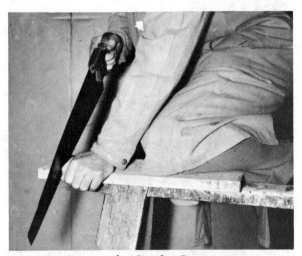

Fig. 5-24. Starting the Cut for Crosscutting

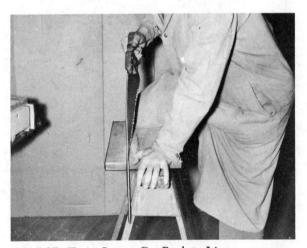

Fig. 5-27. Twist Saw to Get Back to Line

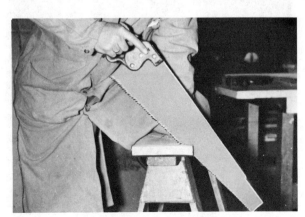

Fig. 5-25. Angle for Crosscutting (45°)

Fig. 5-28. Wedge Spreads Kerf, Prevents Sticking

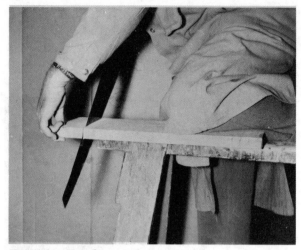

Fig. 5-29. Finishing a Cut

7. The correct angle for the saw in cross-cutting is about 45° with the face of the work, while in ripping about 60° is considered more efficient. See Figs. 5-22, 5-23, 5-24, 5-25.

8. The saw must be guided to cut along the line as well as to cut at right angles with the surface.

9. If the saw binds when ripping, force some type of wedge into the kerf to allow for free action, Fig. 5-28.

10. As the cut nears the end, the operator should hold the piece with his left hand and take short, easy strokes until the

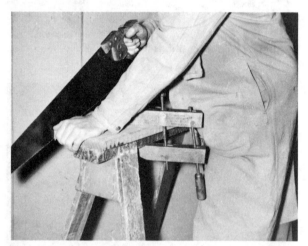

Fig. 5-30. Hand Screw Clamps Work to Saw Horse
Note position of left thumb, which acts as a guide when starting a cut.

Fig. 5-32. Using a Keyhole Saw

Fig. 5-31. Using Bench Hook and Back Saw

Fig. 5-33. Using a Coping Saw

piece is cut free, Fig. 5-29. If the piece is too long to hold conveniently, he should get an assistant or it should be supported.

Standards and Results

1. Saw cuts should be made on the waste side of the line.

2. Unless otherwise specified, the cut should be square with the face of the board.

3. The stock should not be chipped or split at the end of the cut.

Safety Considerations

1. Be careful not to cut your thumb at the start of cut.
2. Be careful not to catch your clothing in the teeth of the saw.
3. Be careful not to cut into the bench.

Topic 44. Miter Box

Classification

Jig for cutting angles

Application

Principle of Operation

The miter box is a jig which guides a fine-toothed crosscut saw in making accurate angle cuts. The saw slides in guides which may be set to certain predetermined angles without the use of any other layout tool. These guides hold the saw in a vertical position at all times. See Fig. 5-34.

Kinds and Uses

The miter box is used for squaring the end of pieces (cutting 90° angle), and for cutting miter joints and polygons. A miter guide may be purchased for use with a hand saw. Wood miter boxes may be purchased or constructed, but they are usually a temporary measure as their accuracy is short-lived.

Principal Parts and Function of Each

1. A specially made carbon steel *miter box saw* is used in the miter box, differing from the conventional back saw only in length and width. It has a heavy, rigid back, which stiffens the blade and rides in the miter box sleeves. Saws are made from 22″ to 30″ long and 4″, 5″, 5½″, 6″, and 6½″ wide.
2. The *frame* holds the board to be cut.
3. *Saw guides* reduce friction and wear and control the angle and depth of cut. They are made of malleable iron or steel and are sometimes bronze-bushed.
4. *Saw guide catches* — lock the saw in a raised position so both hands may be used to adjust work.
5. The cast iron or steel *quadrant* is graduated in degrees and numbered for sawing 3, 4, 5, 6, 8, 12 and 24 sided figures.
6. *Adjustment for width of board* — some miter boxes may be adjusted by pulling

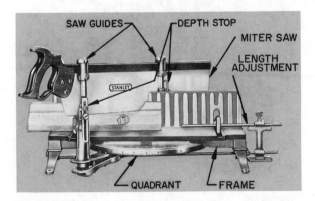

Fig. 5-34. Miter Box (Courtesy Stanley Tool Co.)

the front sleeve forward to permit wider boards to be cut.

7. Some miter boxes are made with a *depth stop* which controls the depth of cut.

8. Some miter boxes are made with a *tie bar* which gives rigidity to the uprights.

Maintenance

1. Bearings in guides should be oiled periodically.
2. All bright parts should be coated with a film of oil or wax to prevent rusting when not to be used over an extended period of time.
3. Saw should be kept sharp.

Market Analysis

Capacity

The capacity is determined by the width and thickness of the board which may be cut, and the angle to which the saw may be moved.

1. *Width* — usually 8″ to 10″ at 90° angle, 5″ to 7″ at 45° angle, 3″ to 4″ at 30° angle.
2. *Thickness* — up to 3″ or up to 4″.
3. *Angle* — some miter boxes cut from 0° through 60° right or left, at intervals of 15°; most miter boxes cut from 0° through 45° right or left, at intervals of 15°; and some miter boxes cut from 0° through 45° right or left, but may be set at any angle within this range.

Attachments

1. The *length gauge* is used to facilitate cutting duplicate lengths.
2. *Stock guides* hold pieces tightly against the back of the frame.
3. The *segment arm* pulls out from the back of frame to permit cutting angles of less than 45°.

Additional Reading

Manufacturers Catalogs

Topic 44A. Motorized Miter Box

Fig. 5-34A. Motorized Miter Box (Courtesy Rockwell Mfg. Co.)

Classification

Rotary cutting tool for cutting angles

Application

Principle of Operation

The rotary cutting saw blade cuts at a predetermined angle of 45° and 90° right or left. It is held in position above the wood and is pivoted downward to make the cut.

Kinds and Uses

The motorized miter box is used to cut angles on stock up to 2½″ thick and 4″ in width in wood, manufactured board, plastics, and lightweight aluminum.

Principal Parts and Function of Each

1. *Motorized head* similar to a portable electric saw drives a 9″ diameter cross-

cut or combination tooth blade at 5000 RPM.

2. *Table* (made of wood) 4″ x 17″ holds the material to be cut.

3. *Base*, made of cast iron, supports table and fence.

4. *Fence*, made of cast iron, holds the wood at proper position for cutting.

5. *Spring-loaded index* adjusts to position for angle cuts.

6. *Index lock* secures mitering arm in position for cut.

7. *Retractable blade guard* made of clear plastic to cover the blade.

Maintenance

1. Saw blades should be kept sharp.

2. Clean sawdust from miter pivot so guide will move easily.

3. Wax bright surfaces. Keep surfaces free of rust and dirt.

Market Analysis

Capacity

Cross cuts 90° 2½″ x 4″
Miter 45° 2½″ x 3⅝″
Miter 45° right or left on edge ⅝″ x 3⅝″

Attachment

Stand for mounting.

Additional Reading

Manufacturers' catalogs

Topic 45. Jig Saw or Scroll Saw

(MAGNETIC, ROCKER ARM, PLUNGER TYPES)

Classification

Power-driven, reciprocating, toothed cutting tool

Application

Principle of Operation

A steel blade, with rip teeth formed on one edge, reciprocates at speeds of about 600, 950, 1325, or 1750 strokes per minute. As the blade moves downward, these teeth cut in the manner of a series of cutting wedges.

Kinds and Uses

The jig saw is used to cut curves. These curves may be completely enclosed or open.

1. The plunger-type jig saw is the most common in school shops. It works on the principle of the wheel and axle. The belt-driven pulley is connected to a cam and pitman mechanism. As the cam rotates, the pitman pushes and pulls the lower chuck up and down. The upper end of the blade may be held in a chuck

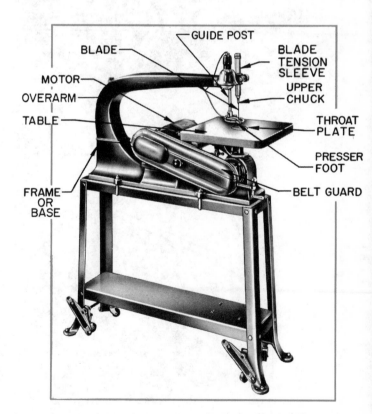

Fig. 5-35. Jig Saw (Courtesy Delta Div., Rockwell Mfg. Co.)

which is attached to the plunger-and-spring tension control. See Fig. 5-35.

2. The magneto-type jig saw is operated by a circuit breaker. In the power stroke an electromagnet pulls down the lower chuck, which holds one end of the blade. When the chuck reaches the lower limit of its stroke, the circuit is broken and a spring in the tension sleeve returns the blade to its upper limit. The cycle is repeated. See Fig. 5-36.

3. The rocker arm type works on the principle of the wheel and axle. The belt-driven pulley is connected to a cam which drives a rocker arm to produce an up-and-down motion.

Jig saws are made in sizes from 12″ to 24″, measured from the blade to the overarm. The most common sizes are 18″ and 24″. The maximum thickness of cut ranges from ¾″ to 4″, depending upon the make.

Principal Parts and Function of Each

1. *Frame* or *base* — iron casting made in two sections bolted together, the upper part of which is the deep throated yoke called the *overarm*, to which the guide-post is fastened and also the *base* which houses the pitman and cam. The frame

Fig. 5-35A. Spring Hold-Down (Courtesy Delta Div., Rockwell Mfg. Co.)

Fig. 5-36. Vibrating Type Jig Saw (Courtesy Dremel Mfg. Co.)

Fig. 5-38. Foot-Powered Vertical Saw — Forerunner of the Jig Saw

Note the wooden spring rod fastened to the ceiling which returns the saw blade to the top of its stroke. (Courtesy Old Sturbridge Village, Inc.)

may be mounted on either a bench or a stand.

2. *Table,* made of cast iron and machined, supports the work being cut and tilts 45° left or right of horizontal.

3. *Tension sleeve,* made of pressed steel, contains the spring to regulate tension on the blade.

4. *Throat plate* — a movable insert in the table, located above the lower chuck, which supports the work close to the blade. It is made of aluminum or wood to prevent damage to the blade if it should run out of line.

5. Upper and lower *chucks,* made of machined steel, hold the blade at the ends. Saber blades, files, and spindle sanders are held in the lower chuck. The upper chuck holds the tension sleeve.

6. Hardened steel *blade guides* prevent blade from twisting when cutting.

7. *Guide post,* made of machined steel, adjusts to the thickness of the stock.

8. *Blades,* made of heat-treated steel, are available from .022″ to ⅜″ wide and from .007″ to .035″ thick, with 5 to 27 teeth per inch.

9. *Hold down* or *presser foot* is fastened to the bottom of the guide post; it rests on the stock and prevents it from moving up and down with the saw.

10. *Cam* and *pitman* convert rotary motion into reciprocating motion.

11. *Plunger* acts as a blower to keep the sawdust away from the saw.

12. *Motor,* ⅓ H.P., 1725 r.p.m., sealed bearings, capacitor type, provides the power.

13. *Cone pulleys* or *variable speed mechanism* regulate the speed.

14. *Belt guard* covers belt and pulleys as a protective device.

Maintenance

1. Oil level should be maintained in driving mechanism.

2. Motor should be periodically oiled unless equipped with sealed bearings.

3. Release tension on blade when not in use.

4. Whenever the jig saw is left unused for a long period of time, all machined parts should be coated with a thin coat of oil to prevent rusting.

Market Analysis

Capacity

The capacity of a jig saw is determined by the distance between the overarm and the blade, called throat capacity, and the thickness of cut allowed by the guide post.

Attachments

1. Lamp to provide better light on the work.

Additional Reading

Delta Manufacturing Company, *Getting the Most Out of Your Band Saw and Scroll Saw*

Manufacturers Catalogs

Fig. 5-39. Treadle-Operated Jig Saw

Topic 46. Using the Jig Saw

Classification

Cutting by shredding and shearing with a rapidly reciprocating toothed blade

Procedure

For General Operation

1. Select the blade appropriate to the particular kind of work.

   There are two types of blades. The jeweler's blade, which is held in the upper and lower chucks, is used for fine work. The saber blade, which is held only in the lower chuck, is used for heavier work.

   Jig saw blades have rip teeth and vary in length, thickness, and number of teeth per inch. The finer the cut to be made, the more teeth per inch and the finer the thickness of the blade. Blades vary from 7 teeth to the inch (for soft woods) to 32 teeth to the inch (for cutting metals and other hard materials). See Table 7, page 120. Blades with about 15 teeth per inch may be used for all purposes.
2. Insert the blade in the upper and lower chucks with the teeth pointing toward the table.
3. Adjust tension on the upper chuck to keep the blade taut.
4. Adjust the blade guide.
5. Determine proper speed. The number of cutting strokes per minute can be regulated by changing the belt on the cone pulleys. Speeds range between 600 and 1750 r.p.m. At low speeds, it is easy to follow the guide line, but a rough cut is produced. Much finer work can be done at high speeds.
6. Adjust the hold-down presser foot so that the spring tension holds the work on the table.
7. Before starting the machine, turn the drive shaft one revolution by hand to check all adjustments.

8. Start machine and feed the work forward evenly. Apply downward pressure to prevent the work from jumping with the saw blade. Always examine stock before cutting to make certain it is free of nails, grit, and other foreign material. When making a turn, maintain the forward motion of cutting, Fig. 5-40.

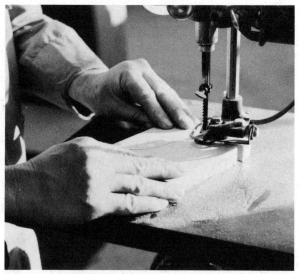

Fig. 5-40. Cutting Outside Curves—Note Position of Hands

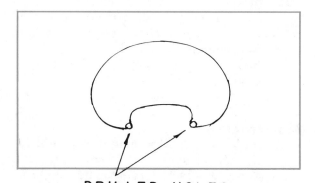

DRILLED HOLES

Fig. 5-41. Location of Drilled Holes for Cutting Inside Curves

Cutting Inside Work

1. Small holes are drilled in the waste stock at points of abrupt change of direction of the curves, Fig. 5-41.
2. Insert the saw blade through one of the drilled holes and secure it in place in the chucks.
3. Follow steps 3-8 as in regular outside cutting.
4. Raise presser foot and remove blade from upper chuck to free the work.

Cutting With a Saber Blade, Filing, or Sanding

1. The saber blade is a stiff blade held in the lower chuck. The upper chuck and guide are removed to give unlimited space for the work.
2. Machine sanding and filing are done by replacing the saber blade with a jeweler's file or sanding strip.

Standards and Results

1. Saw cuts should be smooth and at the desired angle with the surface.
2. Saw cuts should be on the waste side of the line. The line should be barely visible on the stock after cutting.
3. Saw cuts should follow the curve of the line and not be jagged.
4. The work should not be forced into the saw. This might cause the blade to bend and break.
5. The saw selected should cut smoothly for the particular kind of work.

Safety Considerations

1. Belt guards should be in place.
2. Make all adjustments before starting the machine.
3. Use the presser foot to apply pressure on the work.
4. Keep fingers out of saw line.

Additional Reading

Delta Manufacturing Company, *Getting the Most Out of Your Band Saw and Scroll Saw*

Fig. 5-41A. Saber Blade in Lower Chuck (Courtesy Delta Div., Rockwell Mfg. Co.)

Table 7
Jig Saw—Blade and Speed Selection

Material to be cut	Speed	Thickness to be cut							
		Up to 1/16	1/16-1/8	1/16-1/4	1/16-1/2	1/8-1/4	1/8-1/2	1/8-2	1/4-2
		Number of teeth on blade							
Hardwood	1000-1750	20	16	16		15	15	15	10
Softwood	1750	20	18			15	15	10	skip tooth 7
Pressed Wood, Plywood,etc.	1300-1750	20	18	18		15	15	10	10
Veneer	1300-1750	20							
Inlays	650- 900	20	18						
Paper	1300-1750	32	20			15	15 skip	15 tooth	15
Bakelite Plastics	650- 900	20	18	16		15	14	14	
Laminated Plastics, Micarta, Fibertex	650- 900					15	15	15	skip tooth 7-10
Mica	900-1300	30	20	20	20	20	20		
Hard Leather	900-1300	30	20	12		12			
Hard Rubber	650- 900	20	16	15	15	14	14		skip tooth 7
Felt	650- 900	32	20			15	15	15	15
Brake Lining	650- 900		20	20	20	20	20		
Asbestos	900-1300	32	20	20	20	15 skip	20 tooth		
Ivory	650- 900	20	18	16	15	14	14		7
Bone	650- 900					15	15	15	15
Pearl	900-1300	30	20	12					
Aluminum, Brass	650- 900	20-32	20	20	20	15	15		
Copper	650- 900	32	20	20	20	15	15		
Pewter, Lead	650- 900	32	20	20	20	15	15		
Sheet Iron, Mild Steel	650	32	20	20		15			

Table 8
Saber Blades for Portable Saws

No.	Length	Teeth Per 1"	Thickness	Shank Width	Use
S-7	3½"	7	.050	.250	Fast ripping woods, plywood to 2½"
S-10	3½"	10	.050	.250	Medium cuts woods, plywood to 2½"
S-F	3"	10	.040	.250	Finish cuts woods, plywood to 2½"
SHD	6"	7	.050	.250	Fast ripping woods, up to 4"
S-14	3½"	14	.050	.250	Heavy metals over ⅜" thick
S-24	3"	24	.040	.250	Metals ⅛" to ⅝" thick
S-32	3"	32	.040	.250	Metals 1/16" to ⅜" thick

Courtesy of Patterson Brothers, a Subsidiary of Frank Paxton Lumber Company, Clifton, New Jersey.

Topic 47. Portable Electric Saber Saw (Bayonet Saw)

Classification
Power-driven, reciprocating cutting tool.

Application

Principle of Operation
The portable electric saber saw is driven by a high-speed electric motor and has a mechanism for changing rotary to reciprocating motion.

Kinds and Uses
1. The heavy-duty, all-purpose saw is a type designed for construction work. It holds a saber blade from 3″ to 12″ in length and cuts flush to a vertical or horizontal surface.
2. Saber saws are designed to cut scrolls and patterns in wood and other workable materials. They are rated according to amperes under load, the heavy-duty having the higher number. The saws have a tilting base for cutting at an angle.

   The saber saw was originally designed to cut wood, but it has become a very versatile tool with variable-speed adjustments and with blades designed for use on metal, plastic laminates, and composition materials. With some blades, a cut can be started in the center of stock without a pilot hole being drilled.

   One manufacturer's saw has an orbital cutting stroke, which relieves the tension and friction on the return stroke.

   Other saws position the blade on a forward angle, so that the return stroke is not in contact with the work. Each method is designed to reduce heating of blade and to insure longer life.

Principal Parts and Function of Each
1. Housing, made of aluminum, is designed for easy holding and for guiding the cutting action.
2. Motor is the driving power unit.
3. Pitman or cam unit changes rotary motion to reciprocating motion.
4. Chuck, made of hardened steel, holds blade. Some chucks can be adjusted to four positions.
5. Handle.
   a. "D" handle, mounted on the all-purpose, heavy-duty saw, provides means of carrying the tool and guiding the saw in the cutting action. Generally it

Fig. 5-42. Two Styles of Portable Electric Saber Saws (Courtesy Millers Falls Co. and Stanley Tool Co.)

121

is made of aluminum and is part of the housing.

b. Handles for regular saber saws are designed as part of the aluminum housing or extend above the motor housing. Some are made of plastic.

c. An extra side handle or knob on some machines is made of plastic.

6. Trigger or toggle switch, for starting control, is designed into the handle for easy access.

Maintenance

1. Chuck should be cleaned of sawdust.
2. Conductor cords should be handled carefully to prevent wear or cable breaks.

Market Analysis

Capacity

The length of blade the machine will accommodate determines the maximum depth of cut.

All-purpose saws accommodate blades 2¼″ to 12″ long, length of stroke ⅜″ to ¾″, speeds 800 to 2400 strokes per minute.

Saber saws accommodate 2¼″ to 2¾″ long, length of stroke ⁷/₁₆″ to ⅝″, speeds 3000 to 4500 strokes per minute.

Attachments

Guides for ripping, crosscutting and miter cutting.

Topic 48. Circular Saw — Table Type

Classification

Power-driven rotary cutting tool with toothed, circular blade

Application

Principle of Operation

A square or circular saw blade revolves at an arbor speed of approximately 3450 r.p.m. (The rim speed of a saw should be approximately 9000 f.p.m.) The saw cuts on the principle of a continuous set of cutting wedges, Fig. 5-10.

Kinds and Uses

The circular saw is used to cut stock to length and width and to cut rabbets, grooves, dadoes, and tenons. (See "Use of Circular Saw.") There are two basic types: the *variety saw* which has one arbor and one saw blade and the *universal saw* which has two arbors and two saw blades. See Fig. 5-43.

1. Tenoning attachment is used to cut tenons without the use of dado heads.
2. Length gauges or stop rods are attached to the miter gauge and are used when cutting several pieces to the same length.

3. Clearance block is attached to the rip fence and is used when several pieces are to be cut to the same length. (Fig. 5-49)
4. Stop block attached to miter gauge when several pieces are to be cut to same length, Fig. 5-50.

Several jigs may be made up as a control in performing certain operations.

Circular saws are made to accommodate saw blades of 6″, 7″, 8″, 10″, 12″, and 14″ diameters. Larger sizes are not usually found in school shops. The saw table size increases with the diameter of the saw blade.

Principal Parts and Function of Each

1. *Base* supports the table.
2. *Table,* made of cast iron or pressed steel, supports the miter gauge, rip fence, attachments, and stock to be cut.
3. *Miter gauge,* made of cast iron or aluminum, used as a guide for crosscutting stock.
4. *Rip fence,* made of cast iron or pressed steel, used as a guide for ripping stock.

5. *Tilting wheel,* made of cast iron, used to tilt the saw blade.
6. *Hand wheel* is turned to regulate height of saw.
7. *Saw blade* cuts the stock. Saw blade should be made of high-grade steel.

Some saw blades have carbide-tipped teeth; these are much more expensive but stay sharp longer.
8. *Arbor,* a round shaft to which the saw blade is fastened, is made of high-grade steel.

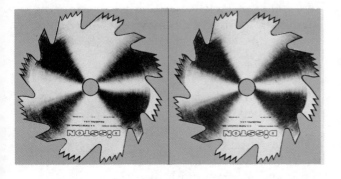

Fig. 5-44A. Dado Head Saws (Courtesy Disston Div., H. K. Porter Co., Inc.)

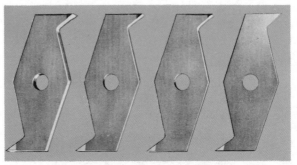

Fig. 5-44B. Dado Head Chippers (Courtesy Disston Div., H. K. Porter Co., Inc.)

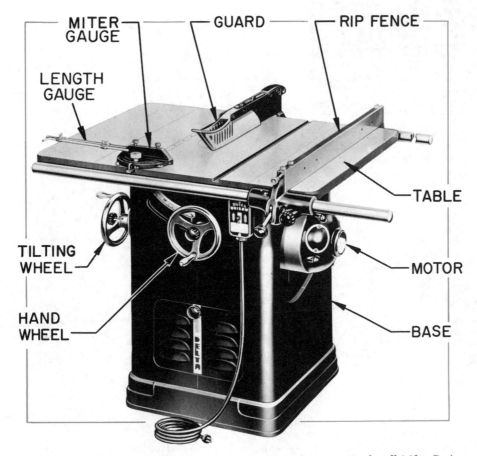

Fig. 5-43. Tilting Arbor Table Saw (Courtesy Delta Div., Rockwell Mfg. Co.)

9. *Guards,* made of plastic, cast iron, or aluminum, protect the operator from injury from the saw blade.
10. *Splitter,* made of sheet steel, keeps stock from binding against the saw while cut is being made.
11. *Motor* provides the power (1 H.P. and up).

Maintenance

1. Circular saw blades should be kept sharp and set. Sharpening should be done by an experienced person. This includes jointing, sharpening, setting, and gumming.

   Mechanical parts of some circular saws require periodic greasing; others have sealed bearings.

CAUTION: If a pin is used to hold arbor or saw blade in locked position when changing blades, be certain to remove the pin before starting the saw.

2. Check alignment of miter gauge and/or fence.
3. Whenever a saw is left unused for an extended period of time, all machined parts should be coated with a film of oil or paraffin wax.
4. Sawdust should be blown from motor and machine with blower or bellows.

Fig. 5-45. Cut-in-Half Saw
Saws of this type are used in gang saw set-ups to permit removal of individual saws without disturbing any of the other saws on the arbor. (Courtesy Simonds Saw & Steel Co.)

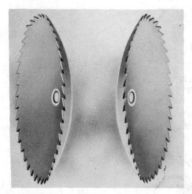

Fig. 5-46. Concave Saws
Concave saws are used in cooperage plants for cutting round barrel heads, also used for cutting out veneer patches and plywood. (Courtesy Simonds Saw & Steel Co.)

Market Analysis

Capacity

A seven-inch saw blade will make a maximum cut of 2″ above the table; an eight-inch, 2¼″ above the table; a ten-inch, 2¾″; and a twelve-inch, 3¼″.

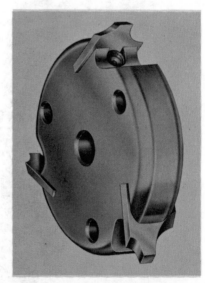

Fig. 5-47. Molding Head for Circular Saw (Courtesy Delta Div., Rockwell Mfg. Co.)

Capacity for width of ripping depends upon the extent of travel of the rip fence.

Attachments (Accessories)

Dado heads, tenoning attachment, molding head, length gauge, stop block, sanding disk, and throat plate for dado and molding heads.

Additional Reading

Manufacturers' catalogs

Topic 48A. Selecting Blades for the Circular Saw

Classification

Rotary edge cutting tool

Circular saws are specified according to the type and number of teeth, gauge thickness of the blade, arbor hole size, and the grade of steel from which they are made.

Clearance (or kerf) for the saw blade is obtained by the use of spring set teeth, swage teeth, carbide tip teeth, and hollow ground blade.

In selecting a saw blade, one must consider that the more teeth in contact with the wood, the more power is required to drive the saw or keep the saw running at its proper RPM. Theoretically, a saw blade extending above the surface of the board will tend to hold the board down on the table and give less feed resistance. However, the more the blade sur-

Fig. 5-47B. Rip Teeth on a Circular Saw (Courtesy Simonds Saw and Steel Co.)

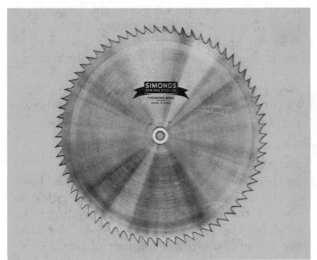

Fig. 5-47A. Crosscut Teeth on a Circular Saw (Courtesy Simonds Saw and Steel Co.)

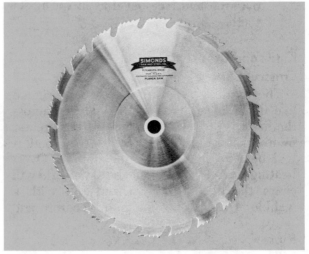

Fig. 5-47C. Planer or Combination Saw with Crosscut and Rip Teeth (Courtesy Simonds Saw and Steel Co.)

face is exposed, the greater the danger to the operator. Thus, the safety rule of ⅛″ to ¼″ projection above the board is required when the saw blade is not covered by a guard.

Procedure

1. In making the *spring set,* the tip of each tooth is bent either right or left in alternate fashion. *The set is no more than twice the thickness of the blade.* More set is used for coarse wood than on finished wood. The more teeth on a blade, the finer the cut.

   Spring set teeth are most common and are found on crosscut saws (sometimes called cutoff saws), ripsaws, and combination saws.

2. *Swage teeth* are obtained by upsetting (or swaging) the tips of all teeth to increase their width. This type of set is used on large diameter production ripsaws, and as a backup seat for cemented carbide tip blades. The teeth of the safe edge or easy cut saws also have swage teeth (chippers).

3. The *hollow ground blade* (planer blade) has a taper, making the blade thicker at the rim than towards the center. These saws are used in smooth surfacing and have teeth sharpened on alternate top and face-bevel as in spring-set teeth.

Kinds and Uses
Crosscut Saws

The crosscut (or cutoff) saw is designed like the hand crosscut saw for cutting across the grain, Fig. 5-47A. Because of the greater number of teeth in contact with the wood, it will heat up fast if used for ripping. Overheating the teeth or rim of the saw blade will cause the blade to warp and run with a wabble. This will not make an accurate cut.

Ripsaw

The ripsaw is designed to cut along the length of the grain, or with the grain, as used in cutting boards to width. The chisel shaped

teeth remove series of chips to make the cut, Fig. 5-47B.

Combination Blades
Combination Rip and Crosscut Blade

This saw is a combination of a crosscut tooth and a rip tooth. The tooth angle, top bevel and front bevel allow this saw to cut (1) across the grain, (2) at a miter to the grain, and (3) with the grain (rip). It is a fast-cutting saw, producing a rough cut.

Hollow Ground Combination Blade

This saw is sometimes called a *planer blade.* It is used in finish work on crosscutting, mitering, and ripping. The name (planer) comes from the smooth surface it produces. The disadvantage of this particular saw is the small clearance from the hollow ground design. The saw blade must be allowed to project above the surface of the stock so that the minimum blade contact in the cut is obtained to prevent overheating.   See Fig. 5-47C.

Carbide Tipped Blades

Carbide tip blades are made for both crosscutting and ripping (and in a combination type). The initial cost of a carbide tipped blade is more expensive than a standard steel blade, but stays sharp up to ten times longer and therefore costs less. The most common style found in smaller sizes is either the swage-tooth rip or the swage-tooth, safe-edge blade. Large sizes for production purposes are found in all tooth shapes. The carbide tip may be resharpened by special machines, or the tips may be replaced. Carbide tip saws are used on hardboard, laminates, and other materials where a regular saw would become dull quickly.

Easy Cut Blade or Safe Edge Blade

This is a *controlled-cut* saw blade. The back of the swaged tooth acts as a stop guide to control the amount of feed and reduces the tendency of kickback of the stock. Because the blade has a fewer number of teeth, it requires less power to run and it is quiet in operation.

Molding Head and Cutters

There are many styles of molding heads designed for use on the circular saw. Each has a set of matched knives with a profile cutting edge to form various molded shapes. The replaceable blades are held in place in the molding head by a self-aligning safety lock. The blades are changed easily and quickly.

The rip fence of the saw table must have a cutout or an attached wood face over the cutter head position to clear the cutters when they project above the table to the highest point. The saw table throat plate must be replaced by a plate with a slot wide enough to accommodate the width of the cutter knives, Fig. 5-47.

Dado Blade Set

The dado blade set consists of two hollow ground ⅛″ combination saws and a series of inside chippers of ¹⁄₁₆″, ⅛″, and ¼″ widths. See Figs. 5-44A and 5-44B. The dado blade set is used to cut grooves (dado and rabbets) from ⅛″ to 1″ in width in any grain direction.

On table and radial arm saws, a single combination saw blade will cut a groove ⅛″ wide. Two saws cut a groove ¼″ wide. Series of chippers in combination can be used so that grooves increment of ¹⁄₁₆″ can be cut up to 1″.

In placing the outside saws in position, arrange them so the raker tooth is opposite the cutting teeth of the other blade. Chipper teeth should be in line with the gullets of the saw raker tooth in an even pattern around the perimeter of the saw blade.

Table 9
Blades for the Circular Saw

Diameter Inches	Crosscut Saws		Ripsaws		Combination Ripsaw and Crosscut Saws		Easy Cut Saws Carbide Tip	
	Gauge	No. of Teeth	Gauge	No. of Teeth	Gauge	No. of Teeth	Gauge	No. of Teeth
6	18	100	18	36	18	44	14	8
7	18	110	18	36	18	44	14	8
8	18	100	18	36	18	44	14	8
9	16	100	16	36	16	44	14	8
10	16	100	16	36	16	44	13	8
12	14	100	14	36	14	44	13	12
14	14	100	14	36	14	44	12	12
16	14	100	14	36	13	44	12	12
18	13	100	13	36	12	44		
20	13	80	13	36				
22	12	70	12	36				
24	11	70	11	36				
26	10	70						
28	10	70						
30	10	70	10	36				

Topic 49. Using the Circular Saw

In the accompanying photographs, the floating guard has been removed in the interests of clearer illustration.

Classification

Cutting by scoring, shearing, shredding, and chipping with toothed, circular blade

Procedure

Examine stock to determine whether it contains nails, grit, etc. If any of these are present the stock should not be cut on the circular saw because they will dull the saw blade and cause injury.

Stock to be cut on the circular saw should have a straight edge and a flat surface. (See Topic 39, Getting Out Stock.) The flat surface should be down (against the table). The straight edge should be held against the miter gauge when crosscutting and against the ripping fence when ripping. If it is necessary to cut cupped stock, the concave face should be down.

Crosscutting or Squaring an End

1. Use either a crosscut or combination blade, and adjust the height of the saw blade so that it is about ⅛" above the stock to be cut.
2. Set the miter gauge at right angles with the saw blade. Usually a graduated scale will indicate this 90° position or it may be checked with a framing square.
3. Use the saw guard and splitter. The rip fence must be moved clear of the work to prevent binding and "kick-backs."
4. One edge of the work to be cut must be straight. Keep the straight edge against the face of the miter gauge and move the stock to cutting position. Hold the stock firmly against the face of the miter gauge. Start the machine and allow it to reach full speed. Make a test cut by nicking the stock. Make any necessary minor adjustment of the stock; then holding the stock firmly against the miter gauge with both hands, feed steadily through the saw, Fig. 5-48.
5. Remove the work (clear of the saw) before returning the guide to the starting position.

Cutting to Length With Stop Block Fastened to Rip Fence

1. When many pieces of the same length are to be cut, a clearance stop may be used for measuring. Location of the stop

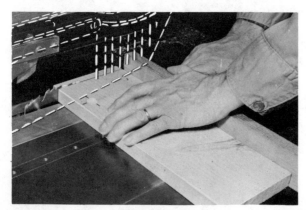

Fig. 5-48. Crosscutting on Circular Saw

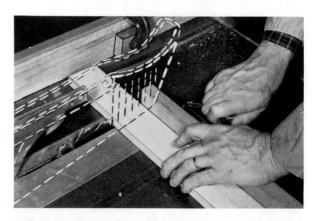

Fig. 5-49. Crosscutting Using Clearance Block and Rip Fence

is determined by the length and width of the work to be cut.

2. For short pieces, fasten a stop block to the rip fence near the front edge of the table with a clamp. The length of the piece to be cut is measured from this block to a tooth on the saw set toward the fence, Fig. 5-49.

3. Secure the rip fence to the table at the correct cutting position.

4. With the work to be cut held against the miter gauge, slide the work along the table until the square end strikes the block. Hold the stock firmly in place and feed into saw, thus cutting to length. Repeat this process for all pieces.

Cutting to Length With Stop Block Fastened to Miter Gauge

1. Fasten a straight, flat piece of stock (called a wood fence piece) to the face of the miter gauge so that it just clears the saw on one end and extends a convenient length (slightly longer than the pieces to be cut) on the other end, Fig. 5-50.

2. The length of the stock to be cut is measured from a tooth set to the left of the saw. Mark the length on the face of the wood fence piece. A stop block with a square edge is fastened at this point with nails, screws, or a lightweight clamp, whichever is suitable.

3. The rip fence must be removed from the table.

4. Square one end of the work; then hold this end against the stop block, while the piece is cut to length. Repeat until all pieces have been cut.

5. Some miter gauges are equipped with a length gauge or stop rod for measuring lengths, but when a wood fence piece is used for extending the working face of the guide, the rod is not convenient to use.

Cutting a Miter or Angle Between 30° and 90°

1. The miter gauge may be set to cut angles between 30° and 90°. The work to be cut is held against the miter gauge, which is set at the required angle, and

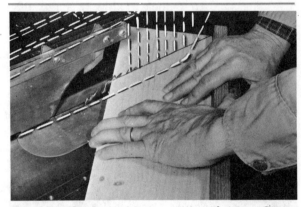

Fig. 5-51. Cutting a Miter at 45° with Miter Gauge

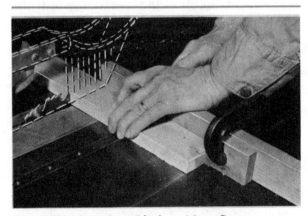

Fig. 5-50. Using Stop Block on Miter Gauge

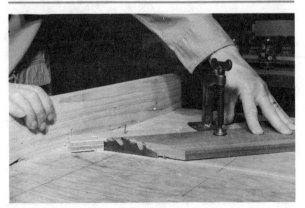

Fig. 5-52. Cutting a Miter at 45° using Sliding Table

the cut is made as in crosscutting. See Fig. 5-51.

2. A stop block fastened to the miter gauge may be used in cutting pieces to length as described above.

3. It is very important that the work be held securely against the miter gauge to insure a straight cut.

4. A smooth cut will be obtained if the angle points to the front of the table so that the cut is made with the grain. The long edge of the work will also be against the gauge.

5. When cutting miters on wide stock, tilt the saw or table to the desired angle and proceed as in square crosscutting.

6. When cutting compound angles, set the miter gauge to the desired angle of the face of the stock, and set the blade or table to the desired angle of the thickness of the stock, Table 6, page 98. Feed the stock into the saw as described above.

Ripping or Cutting to Width

1. A rip or combination saw is adjusted to ⅛″ above the thickness of the stock to

be cut. Some workers prefer to have the saw blade at its full height for ripping, but this practice is not recommended here because of safety reasons.

2. Use the saw guard and splitter.

3. One edge of the stock to be cut must be straight. This edge is held against the rip fence. A board with a "wind" or uneven edge should not be cut.

4. Set the rip fence to the required distance to the right of the saw. This may be gauged by the scale on the saw table and checked with a rule by measuring between a tooth set to the right and the rip fence.

5. Stand to one side of the saw (usually left). Start the saw running, and with the straight edge of the board held against the fence, push the board with an even, firm motion to make the required cut.

6. If the cut is made close to the rip fence, use a "push stick" to move the board. Do not reach over the blade to remove the pieces. The section of board between the fence and the saw should always be pushed clear of the saw.

7. Long boards should be supported by a stand of the same height as the saw table.

8. A device used to keep the board firmly against the fence is called a "feather strip" (a piece of hardwood with a series of saw kerfs). The spring action of the fingers pushes the board against the fence, but allows it to be moved in the cutting direction, Figs. 5-53 and 5-55.

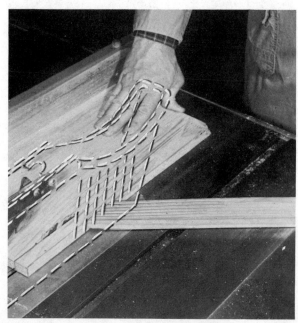

Fig. 5-53. Using Feather Strip in Ripping

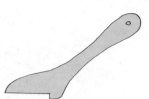

Fig. 5-54. Push Stick

Fig. 5-55. Feather Strip

Resawing on the Circular Saw

1. Set the saw blade ⅛″ to ¼″ higher than half the width of the stock to be cut. The saw should not be set to cut deeper than two inches for each cut. Boards wider than four inches should be cut in four steps.

2. Adjust the feather strip to hold the stock firmly against the rip fence.

3. Start the saw and make a cut along one edge, Fig. 5-56.

4. Turn the stock end-for-end and make the second cut. Make sure the face side is always against the fence.

5. If the stock is more than twice as wide as the saw will cut, the remaining portion may be cut with a band saw or hand rip saw.

Cutting a Taper

1. An adjustable jig may be made as a handy attachment for cutting tapers on the circular saw, Fig. 5-57.

2. The straight edge of the jig is held against the rip fence, and the piece to be cut is held against the notch of the jig. The jig and the board are pushed past the saw as a unit, making the cut at the desired angle or taper. See Figs. 5-58, 5-59, and 5-60.

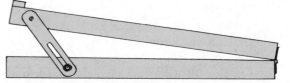

Fig. 5-57. Adjustable Tapering Jig

Fig. 5-58. Using Adjustable Tapering Jig

Fig. 5-59. Fixed Tapering Jig for Cutting Leg Tapers

Fig. 5-56. Resawing on Circular Saw—Note Feather Strip

Fig. 5-60. Using Fixed Tapering Jig

Cutting a Bevel or Chamfer

1. On most saws, the saw may be tilted so that an angle cut between 45° and 90° may be made.
2. On the tilting arbor saw, the work may be cut with the fence on either side of the blade.
3. If the angle to be cut is less than 45°, the saw should be adjusted to the supplement of the angle. The trial cut should be checked for the desired angle; for example, 30° - 60°.

Cutting Grooves, Rabbets, or Dadoes

1. Grooves or rabbets may be cut by making a series of closely spaced cuts, but a dado head attachment will do the job

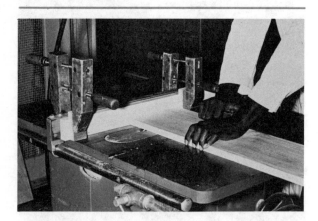

Fig. 5-61. Cutting Stop Dadoes

Fig. 5-62. Finished Stop Dado

much faster. A dado consists of two saws similar to combination saws (having both crosscut and rip teeth) and a series of chippers which act as waste cleaners, between the saws. These saws may be set to cut grooves from ⅛″ to 1″ on most popular saws. See Figs. 5-44A and 5-44B. The throat plate must be replaced either with one supplied with the machine or one made from hard wood.
2. The grooves are cut as in crosscutting or ripping. The guards and splitter cannot be used.
3. A rabbet may also be made by cuts made at right angles — on the adjacent edge and face of the stock. See Fig. 12-30.

Cutting Stop Grooves and Dadoes

1. Cuts which do not run to the end of the board may be started by lowering the work over the saw, Figs. 5-61 and 62.
2. This calls for two stop blocks on a board fastened to the rip fence to limit the travel or cutting length.
3. Hold the board in contact with the fence with one end down on the table and against the stop block nearest the operator. Slowly lower the board over the saw until it rests flat on the table. Proceed to push the board the length of the cut until it strikes the opposite stop block. Raise the end nearest the operator until it clears the saw, being careful to maintain contact with the rip fence until the board is clear of the blade.

Standards and Results

1. All stock should be cut to dimensions. No test marks should show on the finished piece.
2. Cuts should be square or to the determined angle.
3. Grooves and rabbets should be even in depth and width and parallel with edge of board.

4. All stop cuts should run to the length marks.

5. Work should not show saw burns.

Safety Considerations

1. Use all guards, except when blade is covered by the work.

2. Keep blades sharp and set for clean cuts.

3. Cupped boards should rest on the table with the concave side down.

4. Do not force saw to stall. A sharp blade running at full speed will do better work.

5. Stand to one side when starting and using the saw to prevent being struck if stock is kicked back.

6. The blade should not project more than ⅛″ above the work.

7. Let waste pieces fall off table or stop saw to remove. Never reach over or near the blade while it is running.

8. Always use a guide to cut by; never saw freehand.

9. Use a stand as an aid in handling long boards.

10. When cutting to length, use stop blocks for clearance, never the rip fence.

11. Always make adjustments with the machine stopped.

12. (Especially for beginners.) Plan your work before starting machine.

13. Never talk to operator when machine is running.

14. Narrow boards (2″ and under) should not be pushed through with the fingers. Always use a push stick. Do not permit cut stock to remain between blade and fence.

15. The operator should have firm footing. There are nonskid preparations available.

16. No person should be in direct line with a saw blade.

17. Lower the saw blade beneath the table when the cutting operation is completed.

18. Wear an eye-protective device when using the circular saw.

Additional Reading

Delta Manufacturing Company, *Getting the Most Out of Your Circular Saw and Jointer*

Fig. 5-63. Power-Fed Circular Saw

The stock is fed into the saw by the operator until it is gripped by the caterpillar type chain which is below the table. This feeds the stock into the saw. The pressure rolls above hold the stock securely to the table and in contact with the feed chain. The "take-off man," usually a beginner or unskilled worker, removes the cut stock from the table and stacks it on the truck. (Courtesy Mattison Machine Works)

Topic 50. Circular Saw Operator

Classification

Trade and Industrial Application

The table saw of the type used in the school is used similarly in trade and industry. Circular saws are of a variety of types and sizes. In the majority of industries, the crosscut saw and ripsaw are separate, single-purpose machines; but double-arbor saws are sometimes used for both crosscutting and ripping. Among the specialized variations of the table saw are cut-off saws, trimmers, straight-line ripsaws, matching saws, edgers, and saw mills.

Swing saws, radial saws, and portable saws have extensive usage in lumber yards, mills, and construction work.

The saw blades are also of a great variety of types. Each type has been especially designed to serve a specific function.

The saw operator, for the most part, is a semiskilled workman.

Topic 51. Radial Arm Saw

Classification

Power-driven rotary cutting tool with toothed, circular blade

Application

The radial arm saw is a refinement of the overhead swing saw. The saw arbor and motor unit are mounted in a pivoting yoke which rides in a track on a radial arm. The radial arm is adjustable for height and radius angle. Combining the adjustments of the yoke and the radius arm makes it possible to swing the saw unit so that any angle may be set for plain or compound angle cutting.

Principle of Operation

Circular cutters revolve at an arbor speed of between 3450 and 3600 r.p.m. The saw cuts on the principle of a continuous set of cutting wedges.

Kinds and Uses

The radial arm saw is used to cut stock to length and width and to cut grooves, dadoes, and tenons. With necessary attachments to do other specific jobs, the machine becomes a power shop. See Fig. 5-64.

Sizes of radial arm saws are made to accommodate blades 8″, 9″, 10″, 12″, 14″, 16″, 18″, and 20″ in diameter. These are the common sizes found in shops doing cabinet work. Industry uses models up to 44″ in diameter.

Principal Parts and Function of Each

1. *Base,* made of pressed metal, supports the table and column.
2. Hollow steel *column* supports the cantilever arm.
3. *Column lock* fastens column at height.
4. *Arm locks* fasten arm in position.
5. Cast steel *yoke* holds motor and rides in arm track.
6. *Yoke lock* fastens yoke in position on arm.
7. Two *swivel locks* secure yoke in positions between vertical and horizontal for cutting miters and bevels.
8. *Motor* drives saw and other attachments.
9. *Saw guards,* made of cast iron, cover saw and protect worker, also direct sawdust away from the cut.
10. *Anti-kickback lever* keeps work from being thrown back in the ripping operation.

11. *Crank* raises or lowers the cantilever arm to operating position.
12. *Table*, made of wood, supports the stock. It has an insert or guide strip for crosscutting and ripping.

Maintenance

1. All cutters should be kept sharp, in true shape, and in balance.
2. Worn table tops and table guides may be replaced to form a true edge.
3. Most machines have sealed bearings and ball bearing guides for the traverse.
4. All machined parts should be coated with a thin film of oil to protect them from rust.

Market Analysis

Capacity

Capacity for width of ripping depends upon length of arm and width of table.

Table 10
Radial Arm Saw Cuts

Blade Size	Depth of Cut	Length of Crosscut
8″	2″	11¾″
9″	2½″	12″ - 15″
10″	3″	12″ - 16″
12″	3″ - 3½″	14¾″
14″	4½″	20″ - 24″
16″	4″ - 5″	19″ - 31″
18″	6″	depends on length of arm
20″	7″	depends on length of arm

Attachments (Accessories)

Dado heads, molding heads, shaper cutters, rotary planes, router, drill chuck, saber saw, wood lathe, belt sander, disc sander, and grinder.

Additional Reading

Manufacturers Catalogs

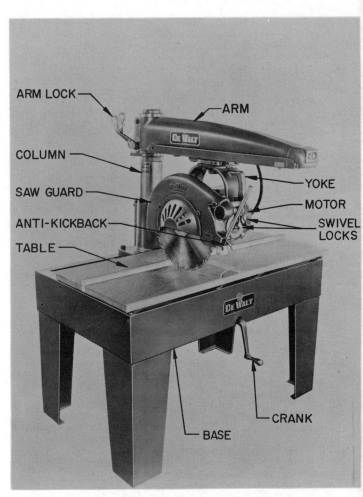

Fig. 5-64. Radial Arm Saw (Courtesy DeWalt Div., American Machine & Foundry Co.)

Topic 52. Using the Radial Arm Saw

Classification

Cutting by scoring, shearing, shredding and chipping with toothed, circular blade

Procedure

Crosscutting (90°)

1. The radial arm must be at right angles to the back guide strip on the saw table. The miter scale will register "zero." Check by making trial cut and test with steel square.
2. To make a through cut, the saw blade must be set to cut slightly below the surface of the wooden saw table, Fig. 5-65.
3. Mark the position at which the stock is to be cut, then place the piece against the insert or guide strip.
4. Adjust the saw guard so that it will be near the location of the cut to be made and does not obstruct the vision of the operator.

5. Raise the kick-back device so that it clears the face of the work.
6. Set the saw to the rear against the stop, making sure that it is not in contact with any wood.
7. Start the machine and allow it to reach maximum speed.
8. Hold the stock firmly against the guide strip with one hand and grasp the handle of the motor yoke with the other hand. Draw the blade forward, making the cut, Fig. 5-65A.
9. After cut has been made, return the saw to the starting position and shut off the motor.
10. To cut several duplicate pieces, clamp a stop to the guide strip at the desired position and proceed as above, holding the squared end of each piece against the stop. Never put one piece of stock on top of another as it will kick over the fence.
11. Because of the direction of rotation of the saw blade, the saw pulls itself into the work and in some cases must be held back. This is especially true when the saw is dull, when cutting hardwood, or when cutting planks.

Fig. 5-65. Crosscutting (Courtesy DeWalt Div., American Machine & Foundry Co.)

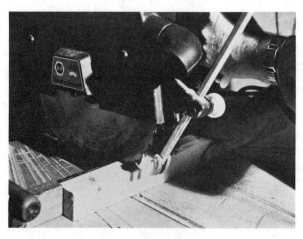

Fig. 5-65A. Crosscutting Using Stop Block to Cut Duplicate Pieces

Cutting Miters

1. Release the arm lock and motor latch. Swing the arm to the desired angle, Fig. 5-66.
2. With the saw in the back position, lower the column until the saw will cut completely through the stock.
3. Adjust the saw guard so that it clears the work and does not obstruct the operator's vision.
4. Check the setup by cutting a scrap piece of stock.
5. If the cut is satisfactory, follow the procedure outlined for crosscutting.

Cutting Bevels

1. Raise the column sufficiently for the blade to clear the saw table when tilted.
2. Release the bevel latch and bevel clamp lever and tilt the motor to the desired angle and relock in this position.
3. Start the saw and lower the column until the saw blade comes in contact with the table. Stop the motor.
4. Adjust the saw guard so that it clears the work and does not obstruct the operator's vision.
5. Check the setup by cutting a scrap piece of stock.
6. If the cut is satisfactory, proceed as in crosscutting.

Ripping

1. The radial arm must be at right angles to the guide strip, and the miter scale on the column must register "zero." Lock in this position.
2. Raise the column until the saw blade clears the table. Draw the saw to the front of the radial arm and lock.
3. Rotate the motor yoke 90° so that the saw blade is parallel with the guide strip. Lock in position.
4. Move the motor assembly to the desired width of cut and lock in position.
5. Adjust the safety guard on the infeed end until it clears the surface of the stock being cut, Fig. 5-67.

Fig. 5-66. Miter Cut (Courtesy Delta Div., Rockwell Mfg. Co.)

Fig. 5-67. Right Hand Ripping (Courtesy Delta Div., Rockwell Mfg. Co.)

6. Lower the kick-back fingers until they rest lightly on the surface of the stock. Lock in this position. See Fig. 5-67.
7. Start the motor and slide the stock on the table with the straight edge in contact with the guide strip. Slowly feed the stock against the rotation of the saw. As the cut nears the end of the board, use a push stick and do not pass the arm beyond the blade.

Bevel Ripping

1. Set the machine for normal ripping.
2. Raise the column, release the bevel clamp, and rotate the motor on the yoke to the desired angle; then relock the clamp.
3. Move the motor assembly to the desired width and lock in position.
4. Lower the column until the saw blade touches the table.
5. Adjust the guard so that it clears the work and lock it in position.
6. Place the stock in position for ripping, start the motor, and slide the stock along the table, keeping it in contact with the guide strip.
7. Feed the stock slowly into the blade. As the cut nears the end of the board, use a push stick and do not pass the arm beyond the blade.

Cutting Dadoes

1. Remove the saw blade and replace with a dado head of the desired width.
2. With the elevating crank, lower the dado head to the desired depth.
3. Lower the saw guard to about one inch above the cut; this will not obstruct the vision of the operator Fig. 5-69.

4. Place a scrap piece of stock against the guide strip, start the motor, and make a test cut.
5. Make any necessary adjustment.
6. Place the stock against the guide strip and in the correct location to cut the dado.
7. Start the motor, grasp the yoke, and slowly feed the dado head into the work. After the cut has been made,

Fig. 5-69. Dado Cutting (Courtesy Delta Div., Rockwell Mfg. Co.)

Fig. 5-68. Cutting Compound Angle (Courtesy Delta Div., Rockwell Mfg. Co.)

Fig. 5-70. Cutting Grooves (Courtesy Delta Div., Rockwell Mfg. Co.)

return to the original position and shut off the motor. Wider dadoes may be made by repositioning the work and taking additional cuts.

8. Angular dadoes may be made by releasing the arm lock and yoke swivel latch, turning the motor to the desired angle, and relocking in position.

9. Rabbets are cut in this same manner.

Cutting Grooves

1. Remove the saw blade and replace with dado heads of the desired width.

2. Release the yoke clamp and swing the motor parallel to the guide strip; relock.

3. Move the motor assembly on the arm to the desired location and lock in position.

4. Lower the column to make the desired depth of cut. Lock in position.

5. Adjust the guard so that it clears the work, and lock in position, Fig. 5-70.

6. Test cut on a scrap piece of wood.

7. Place the stock against the guide strip and slowly feed into the dado head. Keep your hands clear of the dado heads. As the cut nears the end of the board, use a push stick.

Shaping

A molding head with various shapes and sizes of cutters is available as an attachment for some types of radial arm saws.

1. Insert desired cutters in cutter head and lock in position.

2. Remove the saw blade and replace with the cutter head. Lock in position.

3. Release the bevel clamp and bevel latch. Rotate the motor 90° to a position vertical to the table, and lock in this position, Fig. 5-70A.

4. Adjust the column height to the desired position and lock.

5. Release the rip lock and adjust for depth of cut; lock in position.

6. Start the motor and make a trial cut on scrap stock by moving the piece along the guide strip. Stop the motor. Make any adjustments necessary.

7. Slowly feed the stock into the cutters. Keep hands at least four inches away from the cutters.

Routing

Routing attachments are available for some radial arm saws.

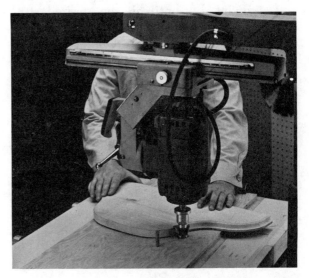

Fig. 5-70A. Using the Shaping Attachment on the Radial Arm Saw (Courtesy Rockwell Mfg. Co.)

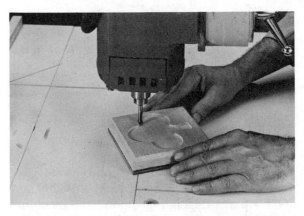

Fig. 5-70B. Routing with the Radial Arm Saw (Courtesy Rockwell Mfg. Co.)

1. Remove the saw guard.
2. Release the bevel clamp and bevel latch. Rotate the motor 90° to a position vertical to the table.
3. Select the desired router bit and secure it to the motor arbor with a chuck adapter.
4. Start the motor, place the stock on the saw table under the cutter, and lower the bit to the desired depth by turning the elevating crank. Lock the motor in this position.
5. Slowly move the work against the revolving bit until all the desired stock has been removed. See Fig. 5-70B.
6. If the stock is not free when the routing is completed, shut off the motor, raise the bit, and remove the work from the table.

Standards and Results

1. Saw cuts should be made on the waste side of the line.
2. Saw cuts should be at the desired angle.
3. Dadoes and rabbets should be of the desired size and in the proper location.
4. Molding cuts should be smooth.
5. Dadoes, grooves, and rabbets should be of an even depth.

Safety Considerations

1. Keep your hands out of the line of the cutters.
2. Guards should be in proper position and locked in place.
3. All adjustments should be made before starting the machine.
4. All adjustments should be locked before starting the machine.
5. Use a push stick when ripping, cutting grooves and cutting rabbets. In ripping, feed the work against the cutting edge. Do not push the board past the saw without using a push stick.
6. Do not reach over the path of the saw when moving stock into position unless the saw is stopped.
7. Saw should not cut more than $\frac{1}{16}''$ into the table.
8. Allow saw to obtain maximum speed before making cuts.
9. In all crosscutting, be sure to return the saw to the starting position.
10. Wear an eye-protective device when using the radial arm saw.

Additional Reading

Manufacturer's booklet of instruction and film

Topic 53. Portable Electric Saw

Classification

Power-driven rotary cutting tool with toothed, circular blade

Application

Principle of Operation

A circular blade (usually combination) revolves at an arbor speed of between 3200 and 4600 r.p.m., depending upon the machine. The saw cuts on the principle of a continuous set of cutting wedges.

Kinds and Uses

The portable electric saw is a handy piece of equipment for construction work. It is used to cut stock to length and width and to make angular cuts such as on roof rafters and stair jacks.

Saws are classified according to blade size. They are available in 6″, 7″, 8″, and 9″ models. See Figs. 5-71, 5-71A, and 5-72.

Safety in Using Portable Electric Saw

1. When the portable electric saw is used, the saw guard should be adjusted so the

blade projects only ⅛″-¼″ below the thickness of the board to be cut.

2. A portable electric saw should not be used without a saw guard in place.
3. Cutting short pieces is dangerous.
4. If the guard catches when making diagonal cuts, stop the saw before freeing the guard.
5. Be sure to keep the electric cord out of the path of the saw.

Principal Parts and Function of Each

1. *Sole plate, shoe,* or *base,* made of aluminum, supports the saw and is adjustable

with the motor housing, to control the depth of cut and the angle of the blade.

2. *Base, housing, guards,* and *handles* are usually made of aluminum, and are designed and balanced so the tool can be easily handled in the cutting position.

3. *Motor* and *gears* provide the power.

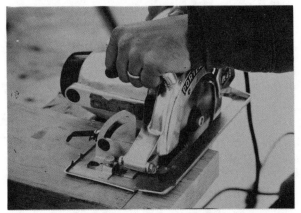
Fig. 5-72. Cutting Off with Portable Electric Saw (Courtesy Porter-Cable Machine Co.)

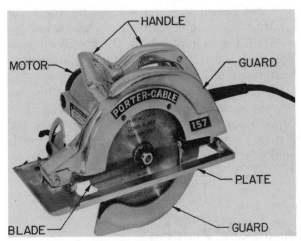
Fig. 5-71. Portable Electric Saw (Courtesy Porter-Cable Machine Co.)

Fig. 5-71A. A Portable Electric Saw with Reversible Motor and Two Bases for Right Hand or Left Hand Cutting (Courtesy Stanley Tool Co.)

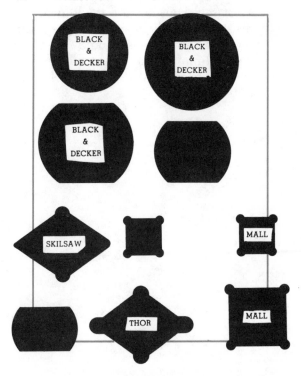
Fig. 5-73. Shapes of Arbor Holes of Portable Electric Saws (Courtesy Simonds Saw & Steel Co.)

4. *Handle* provides method of controlling operation of saw.
5. *Front knob* on some saws provides for two-hand control.
6. *Trigger switch* is built into the handle for quick control of cutting action.
7. *Upper saw guard* covers the portion of the blade that is above the sole plate.
8. *Lower saw guard* is retractable so that the saw is covered when not cutting into a piece of stock. Removal of this guard or tying it back is a very dangerous practice.
9. *Saw blade,* made of high-grade steel, cuts the stock. Saw blades must be selected so that the arbor hole will match the arbor seat, Fig. 5-73. Inserts are available to convert to various shapes.

Maintenance

1. Circular saw blades should be kept sharp and set.
2. The gear reduction unit should be checked periodically for lubrication.
3. Most saw housings are made of a rust-resistant metal; however, steel parts such as saw blades should be coated with oil film or wax or stored in proper containers to prevent rusting when not in use.

Market Analysis

Capacity

A six-inch saw will cut to a depth of 1⅞"
A seven-inch saw will cut to a depth of 2½"
An eight-inch saw will cut to a depth of 2¾"
A nine-inch saw will cut to a depth of 3¼"

Any width or length cut may be made free-hand by following a line or guiding the side of the saw base against a straightedge.

Attachments

Special-purpose blades may be used for cutting many materials other than wood.

A rip fence may be attached and adjusted for cutting up to 12" widths on some materials.

An adjustable saw track is available for some machines or one can be made. This equipment makes it possible to cut true and square and to cut bevels and bevel miters. It makes the use of the portable saw similar to that of the radial arm saw.

Additional Reading

Manufacturers booklets of instruction.

Topic 54. Band Saw

Classification

Power-driven, endless, toothed-band cutting tool

Application

Principle of Operation

An endless, flexible steel belt with rip teeth filed on one edge moves at a speed ranging from 3,000 to 5,000 feet per minute (600 to 1,200 wheel r.p.m.) cutting on the principle of a continuous set of cutting wedges.

Kinds and Uses

The band saw is used to cut curves and for resawing. See Fig. 5-74. Where a circular saw is not available, the band saw may be used for crosscutting and ripping. It is available in the following wheel sizes: 12″, 14″, 16″, 18″, 24″, 30″, 36″, and 40″. Large size machines are not usually found in school shops. The table size increases with the size of the wheels; 14″ machines have a table 14″ x 14″. Blade widths of ⅛″, 3/16″, ¼″, ⅜″, ½″, ⅝″ and ¾″ are available.

The motor is usually a ½ H.P., 1725 r.p.m., 60 cycle, either single or three phase.

Principal Parts and Function of Each

1. *Wheels,* usually two, although there are some three-wheel band saws, are made of cast iron, aluminum, or pressed steel. Outer rims of wheels are covered with a rubber band called a tire. The saw blade runs on these rubber tires which serve to protect the teeth, act as a cushion for the saw blade, and prevent it from slipping.
2. The machined cast iron *table* supports the work being cut. Large band saws have two tables; the one to the right is larger and can be tilted 45° to the right and about 10° to the left. The left table is stationary. Smaller band saws have one table which usually tilts 45° to the right and 10° to the left.

The table through which the saw blade runs has a slot through which the blade is inserted. This table is kept in alignment by means of a *table aligning pin.*
3. *Throat plate,* usually made of aluminum, prevents unnecessary damage to the blade if breakage occurs or saw runs off track.
4. *Guide blocks,* made of hardened steel, are positioned above and below the table. They prevent the blade from being twisted during the cutting operation.
5. *Thrust wheels,* made of pressed steel or cast iron, prevent blade from being pushed off the wheels and serve as an indicator for tracking of saw.
6. The *tension mechanism* is made of spring steel and is used to put proper tension on blade. Some saws have a tension indicator, which gives proper tension for each size blade.

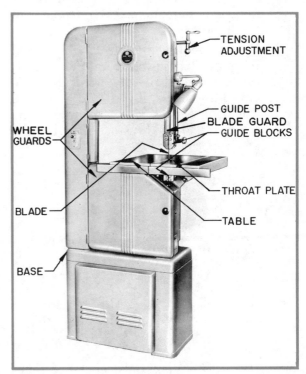

Fig. 5-74. 16″ Band Saw (Courtesy Walker-Turner Div., Rockwell Mfg. Co.)

7. *Tracking mechanism* is an adjustment which pivots the upper wheel, so that the saw blade tracks in the middle of the wheels.

8. *Blades* are made of high-carbon, chromium steel and have rip teeth.

9. *Wheel guards* (made of pressed steel or sheet metal) cover the wheels, protecting the operator.

10. Adjustable *guide post* is made of steel and may be moved up or down to accommodate different thicknesses of work.

11. Cast iron *frame or yoke* serves as a mounting for the two wheels.

12. *Base or stand* made of cast iron, pressed steel, or wood, supports the machine.

13. *Motor* provides the power.

Maintenance

1. Band saw blades should be kept sharp. Sharpening should be done by someone skilled in this line.

2. The saw should be maintained at the proper tension and tracking in the center of the wheels.

3. Upper and lower guide blocks should be properly adjusted so that two-thirds of the width of the saw blade runs between the blocks, Fig. 5-74A.

4. The blade should be $\frac{1}{64}''$ away from the upper and lower thrust wheels when the saw is not cutting.

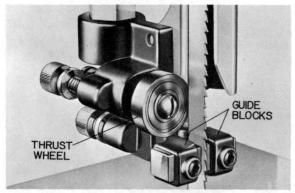

Fig. 5-74A. Detail of Upper Guide Blocks and Thrust Wheel (Courtesy Delta Div., Rockwell Mfg. Co.)

5. Broken saw blades can be brazed. This should be done by experienced persons.

6. Some band saws require periodic greasing while others have sealed bearings.

7. Whenever a band saw is to be left idle for a long period, machined parts should be coated with a thin film of oil and the tension released on the blade.

8. Sawdust should be blown from motor and machine.

9. Throat plate should be replaced when worn, to provide proper clearance.

Market Analysis

Capacity

A twelve-inch band saw usually has an adjustable guide post opening of $4\frac{1}{2}''$; a fourteen-inch has an opening of $6\frac{1}{4}''$. However, stock thicker than three inches is rarely cut on this size machine. (When resawing, the guide post opening may be raised to maximum, although the actual amount of stock cut will be approximately three inches.)

Attachments

1. Miter gauge — used for square, miter, and compound angle crosscutting.

2. Fence — used for straight ripping.

3. Sand belts — used in place of saw blade for sanding edges of curved stock.

4. Template guide pins and pivot pins — used for cutting circles.

Additional Reading

Delta Manufacturing Company, *Getting the Most Out of Your Band Saw and Scroll Saw*

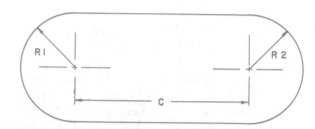

Fig. 5-75. Determining Length of Band Saw Blade

Topic 54A. Band Saw Blades

Band saw blades can be purchased in welded lengths for a specific machine, or in coil of 100' and 250' lengths.

To determine the blade length:
1. Measure the radius of the band wheels. See R_1 and R_2 in Fig. 5-75.
2. Adjust the upper wheel to the halfway takeup position. Measure the center distance between the two wheels. See C in Fig. 5-75.
3. Use formula $(R1 \times 3.1416) + (R2 \times 3.1416) + (2 \times C)$ = band length.

Band saws have two types of teeth:
1. The regular standard rip shaped tooth, Fig. 5-75A.
2. Raker tooth used on the saber and skip tooth blades, Fig. 5-75B. Blades designed for wood cutting are generally set for both crosscutting and ripping.

Regular Rip Tooth Blade

This is an all-hard blade designed as a long lasting saw. It may be resharpened for longer usage. It has a rake angle of 8° to 10° with round gullets, designed for all types of cutting and alternate set.

Fig. 5-75A. Standard Tooth Shape for Rip Band Saws

Fig. 5-75B. Raker Tooth for Rip Band Saws

Table 11
Regular Rip Tooth Blade Size

Width	Gauge	Teeth/in
1/8″	25	6
3/16″	21	3-4
	22	4-5-6
	25	5-6
1/4″	21	2-3-4-5
	22	4-5-6
	25	5-6
5/16″	21	3
3/8″	20	2
	21	2-3-4-5
	22	4-5
	25	5-6
1/2″	20	2-3
	21	2-3-4-5
	22	3-4-5
	25	5-6
3/4″	19	2
	25	4-5
1″	19-22	2-3-4-5

Skip Tooth Blade

The skip tooth (raker shaped) blade generally has a hardened cutting edge and it is designed to be thrown away when the cutting edge finally becomes dull. The large gullet gives extra capacity for the chips, permitting fast cutting.

Table 12
Skip Tooth Blade Size

Width	Gauge	Teeth/in
3/16″	23	4
1/4″	23	4-6
3/8″	23	3-4
1/2″	23	3-4
3/4″	21	3
1″	20	2-3

Saber Tooth or Hook Tooth Blade

This blade has similar design as the skip tooth blade, but the face of the tooth has a 10° hook or rake angle. The tooth edge is flame-hardened and is designed as a throw-away blade. The angle of the tooth with chip-breaker design permits fast feed and prevents soft, gummy materials from sticking in the gullets.

Table 13

Saber Tooth or Hook Tooth Blade Size

Width	Gauge	Teeth/in
¼″	23	4-6
⅜″	23	3-4-6
½″	23	2-3-4-6
¾″	21	2-3-6
1″	20	2-3-6

Topic 55. Using the Band Saw

Classification

Cutting by shearing and shredding with an endless, toothed blade

Procedure

Cutting Curves

1. Determine the width of the saw blade necessary to cut the curve.

Table 14

Saw Blade Width for Cutting Curves

Width of Saw Blade	Minimum Diameter of Circle
⅛″	1″
3/16″	1½″
¼″	2″
⅜″	2½″
½″	3″
⅝″	3½″

NOTE: The saw must be sharp and properly set to make cuts of the diameter given.

Outside curves of less than a one-inch diameter should be made using relief cuts or should be cut on a jig saw. Inside curves of less than 1 inch should be drilled or bored.

2. Make sure all outlines to be cut are clearly marked. When several pieces are to be cut, they may be fastened together with brads or with a wedge in a saw cut in the waste stock. Check the stock for grit and nails.

3. Adjust the saw guide to give about ¼″ clearance above the thickness of the stock.

4. Stand slightly to the left of the center of the table, Fig. 5-76. Start the machine and apply even, forward pressure with the right hand. Guide the stock with the left hand, Fig. 5-77.

5. To cut a sharper curve than the width of the blade will permit, make relief cuts in the waste stock, Fig. 5-78. Relief cuts should not touch the line.

Backing the blade out of the cut is not recommended. The work should be planned so that on each cut you can saw out, Fig. 5-79. Backtracking has a tendency to run the blade away from the guide.

Resawing

Thin stock may be resawed from thicker boards or planks. It is sometimes advisable to start the cuts on the circular saw.

1. The work to be resawed must have one side and an adjacent edge straight and square.

2. Select the widest saw blade for the machine.
3. A rip fence or wooden guide is secured to the table — the distance from the fence to the blade should be the desired thickness of the resawed piece. See Fig. 5-80.
4. Set upper saw guide for clearance of work.
5. A line along the edge to be cut will aid in guiding the work.
6. Hold the stock against the fence and guide it steadily past the saw.

Ripping or Crosscutting

1. Ripping or crosscutting may be done on the band saw when a circular saw is not available.
2. It is important to use a sharp saw and proper guides. A dull saw will have a tendency to follow the grain.

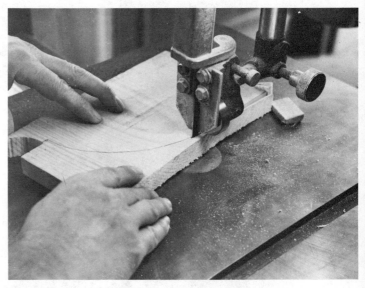

Fig. 5-77. Cutting to a Line
  Left hand pushes stock while right hand serves as a pivot.

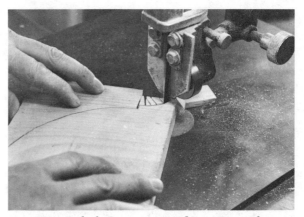

Fig. 5-78. Relief Cuts Are Made to Saw Along a Sharp Curve

Fig. 5-76. Proper Position and Stance at Band Saw

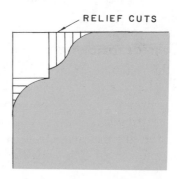

RELIEF CUTS

Fig. 5-79. Plan of Relief Cuts

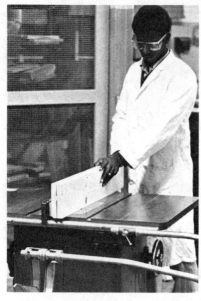  

A. Cuts made from each edge on the circular saw in preparation for finish cutting on the band saw.

B. Completing the cut on the band saw.

C. Two pieces cut — the result of resawing. Note the symmetry of the matching pieces.

Fig. 5-80. Resawing

Standards and Results

1. All saw cuts should be on the waste side of the line.
2. When cutting more than one piece fastened together, the nail holes should not appear in the finished piece.
3. Band saws cut rapidly, but should not be forced so that the edges of cut are burned.

Safety Considerations

1. Use the machine only when all guards are in place.
2. Adjust upper guide for clearance. Too high a setting leaves the saw unguarded.
3. Keep the hands away from a moving blade and out of line with the rotation of the saw.

4. Small chips which lodge in the guide blocks may jam the blade. Stop the saw and remove them.
5. Check blade guide adjustments.
6. Do not backtrack. Always cut the saw clear.
7. All observers should stand clear of the working area.
8. Do not cut cylindrical stock on the band saw.
9. Stop saw and investigate any unusual noise.

Additional Reading

Delta Manufacturing Company, *Getting the Most Out of Your Band Saw and Scroll Saw*

Topic 56. Replacing a Band Saw Blade

1. Remove upper and lower wheel guards, throat plate, and table aligning pin.
2. Release the tension on the blade by lowering the upper wheel.
3. Remove the saw blade by slipping it off the wheels and out of the table slot.
4. Coil the blade which was removed.
   a. With the blade almost touching your body, grasp it at arm's length in front of your body, with the back of the blade resting in the palm of each hand, teeth pointing up.
   b. Twist the wrists up and in, and bring them together. This will automatically form three loops.
   c. Place loose loop flat on bench top and release the hands. The blade is coiled.
5. Select proper blade for the job to be done. (See "Cutting Curves" under Topic 55, "Using the Band Saw.")
6. If necessary, clean the tires by turning the wheel against a piece of 100 grit sandpaper.
7. Grasp blade so that teeth are pointing toward you and down. If the teeth point up, the blade is inside-out and must be reversed.
8. Insert the blade in the slot in the table and into position on the upper and lower wheels.

9. Make sure blade is between upper and lower guide blocks.
10. Apply tension by raising the upper wheel. (Most modern band saws are equipped with a gauge for checking tension of various widths of blades. If this is lacking, the tension may be checked by gently plucking the blade.)
11. When changing blades, back off the upper and lower thrust wheels and guide blocks.
12. Rotate the upper wheel by hand and note whether the blade is tracking.
13. If the blade is running toward the back or front of the wheel, adjust the tracking mechanism until the blade tracks in the center of the wheel.
14. Adjust the guide blocks so they are behind the set of the teeth and close to the blade, but not close enough to cause friction. One-half to two-thirds the width of the blade should run between them.
15. Position the thrust wheels behind the blade, so that they are free when the saw is not cutting, but make contact when the saw is cutting.
16. Replace the upper and lower guards, throat plate and table aligning pin.

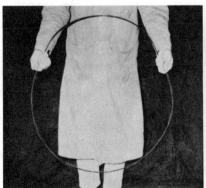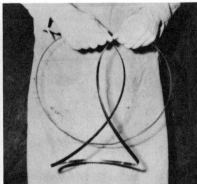

Fig. 5-80A. Steps in Coiling a Band Saw Blade

Topic 57. Band Saw Operator

Fig. 5-81. Workman Trimming Chair Back on a Large Industrial Band Saw (Courtesy Heywood-Wakefield Co.)

Classification

Trade and Industrial Applications

The band saw has numerous industrial applications in the general woodworking shop, small cabinet shop, sample maker's shop, and pattern shop. Practically all woodworkers need a reasonable degree of skill in operating the band saw.

In larger factories and cabinet shops, the band saw operator is a machine attendant who cuts shapes to a template. The use of templates°and jigs° reduces the amount of special skill needed by such an operator. Some bandsaw men are skilled in resawing.

In the manufacturing of lumber the band mill operator or sawyer controls the cutting of the logs into lumber forms such as cants, timbers, planks, and boards.

°*Template*—a profile shape used to make duplicate parts or to match test profiles. Templates are usually made of cardboard, metal, or thin wood when used to trace a profile or test a profile. When a template is used to guide the direction of movement of the work or the cutting tool, thicker material should be used.
°*Jig*—a device to aid in setting up (positioning or securing) work to do a particular operation accurately and more efficiently.

Topic 58. Occupations in the Furniture Industry

Most of the furniture manufactured in the United States is done by the mass production method where the majority of workers are semiskilled. Only a short training period is required of these workers, whose jobs are usually limited to a single operation or the tending of a machine.

The making of furniture is divided into three basic areas — wood processing, assembling, and finishing. In each division, work is speeded along on specialty machines. Cutting and shaping of parts are done on special saws and shapers. Jigs and fixtures on as-

sembly machines make them highly efficient for mass production. Finishing is also speeded by the use of machines, although certain operations like shading, wiping, and rubbing are still performed by hand.

The largest occupational group in furniture making operate either manual or **automatic** machines such as cut-off saws, hand shapers, belt sanders, and boring machines. Beginning workers in these shops are usually assigned as helpers and then are advanced to other jobs as they acquire adequate skill and demonstrate their ability to follow directions, to get along with fellow workers, to take responsibility, and to show initiative.

Many of the occupations in furniture making or the woodworking industry have their counterpart in the jobs and operations performed in the school shop. At one end of the scale are jobs which are almost exactly the same in school and industry and at the other extreme are those which are the same in principle only.

The following woodworking occupations are samples of those which can be experienced in actuality or in principle in the school shop:

Band saw, scroll saw, and jigsaw operators
Boring machine operator
Assembly man
Furniture repairer
Table saw operator
Cut-off man
Dado operator
Glue man
Jointer operator
Layout man
Setup man
Sander operator
Shaper operator (single spindle)
Single surfacer operator
Woodturner

Topic 59. Hand Planes

(Smooth Plane, Jack Plane, Junior Jack Plane, Fore Plane, Jointer Plane, Block Plane)

Classification

Edge cutting tool

Application

Principle of Operation

All hand planes work on the principle of the cutting wedge, Fig. 5-3.

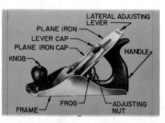

Fig. 6-1. Smooth Plane (Courtesy Stanley Tool Co.)

Kinds and Uses

1. *Smooth planes* are used for smoothing and finishing work, Fig. 6-1. They are 7″, 8″, 9″, or 10″ long with cutters which are 1⅝″, 1¾″, 2″, or 2⅜″ wide, respectively. The cutter is set at an angle of 45° with the bevel facing down.

2. *Jack planes* are used to true edges but are commonly used as all-purpose planes, Fig. 6-2. They are 14″ and 15″ long with cutters which are 2⅜″ wide. A smaller version of a jack plane, called a junior jack plane, has been designed for use by junior high school industrial arts students as it is easier to manipulate. This plane is 11½″ long with a cutter which is 1¾″ wide.

Fig. 6-2. Jack Plane (Courtesy Stanley Tool Co.)

3. *Fore planes* are used for planing large surfaces and edges, Fig. 6-3. They are 18″ long and have a 2⅜″ cutter.

Fig. 6-3. Fore Plane (Courtesy Stanley Tool Co.)

4. *Jointer planes* are used to plane large surfaces and to joint edges on long pieces. Like all members of the plane family except the block plane, the cutter is set at an angle of 45° with the bevel facing down. They are 22″ and 24″ long and have a 2⅜″ or 2⅝″ cutter.

Fig. 6-4. Block Plane (Courtesy Stanley Tool Co.)

5. *Block planes* are used for planing end grain, Fig. 6-4. They differ from the preceding planes in that the cutter is set at an angle of 20° with the bevel facing up, and it does not have a cap iron. The lever cap is shaped to fit the hand, serving as a handle. They are 6″ or 7″ long, with cutters which are 1⅜″ or 1⅝″ wide, respectively.

Principal Parts and Function of Each

1. The *frame* is the body of the plane and determines its size. It is usually made of a casting of gray iron or aluminum, sometimes of pressed steel. The bottom of the frame is called the sole and may be smooth or corrugated.

2. The *frog,* made of cast iron, provides the angle to which the plane iron is held and positions it at the rear of the mouth.

3. The *lateral adjusting lever,* made of pressed steel, is used to adjust the plane iron for an even thickness of shaving.

4. The *adjusting nut,* made of plastic or brass, is used to increase or decrease depth of cut or thickness of shaving.

5. The *plane iron* or cutter, made of the finest tool steel which is tempered and hardened, and sharpened to a bevel, does the cutting.

6. The *plane iron cap,* made of steel, is shaped to give stiffness to the cutting edge and prevent chattering. It breaks the back of the shaving, causing it to curl, and prevents splintering or digging into the surface. It is attached to the plane iron with a *cap screw.*

Fig. 6-6. Jointer Gauge (Courtesy Stanley Tool Co.)

7. The *cast iron lever cap* holds the plane iron securely in place and prevents chatter.

8. *Knobs* and *handles* are made of either plastic, cast aluminum, or rosewood. They are the means by which pressure is applied and direction controlled.

Maintenance

1. Planes should be cleaned of all shavings before being returned to the tool cabinet. This is best done with a brush.

2. Keep screws tight in handle, knob, and frog.

3. Replacement parts are available from most manufacturers.

4. For sharpening, see Topic 69, "Grinding Edge Tools" and Topic 71, "Whetting or Honing a Cutting Tool."

5. Planes should be stored in a dry place. The blade should not protrude below the base surface. When planes are not to be used for a long period of time, all metal parts should be covered with a film of oil.

Market Analysis

Capacity

The only capacity for planes is width and depth of cut. The width of cut is determined by the width of blade, 1⅜″ to 2⅜″. The operator may vary the thickness of cut, according to the kind and condition of stock and the job to be done.

Attachments

The jointer gauge may be used on any plane except the block plane, but it is more practical on a fore plane or a jointer plane. It is used as a guide in planing any bevel from 30° to 90° and as an aid in jointing an edge, Fig. 6-6.

Additional Reading

Stanley Tool Company, *Stanley Tool Guide,* pp. 21-23

Topic 60. Special Purpose Planes

(Router Plane, Rabbet Plane, Cabinetmaker's Rabbet Plane, Bull Nose Rabbet Plane, Bench Rabbet, Duplex Rabbet Plane, Skew Cutter Rabbet Plane, Side Rabbet Plane, Edge Trimming Block Plane, Double End Block Plane, Dado Plane, Plow Plane, Combination Plane, Tongue and Groove Plane, Model Maker's Plane, Scraper Plane, Circular Plane, Core Box Plane, Fiberboard Plane, Scrub Plane)

Classification

Edge cutting tools

Application

Principle of Operation

All types of planes cut on the principle of the cutting wedge.

Kinds and Uses

1. The *router plane* has two knobs, a depth gauge, and an adjustment for cutter depth, Fig. 6-7. Router planes are equipped with three cutters — ¼" and ½" square cutters and a "V" cutter. It is used for surfacing the bottom of grooves, dadoes, and recesses parallel with the surface of the stock.

Fig. 6-7. Router Plane (Courtesy Stanley Tool Co.)

Fig. 6-8. Rabbet Plane (Courtesy Stanley Tool Co.)

2. The *rabbet plane* has no knob, and the handle is part of the plane, Fig. 6-8. The plane iron is the full width of the base. It is fitted with a spur and detachable depth gauge, and is 8" long with 1", 1¼", or 1½" plane irons. It is used to plane a rabbet.

3. The *cabinetmaker's rabbet plane* is made in two pieces to permit increase or decrease in throat opening, Fig. 6-9. It has an adjusting screw and cap, and is available in 5½" and 6" lengths with ¾" and 1" cutters. It is used for fine work.

4. The *bull nose rabbet plane* is similar to a cabinetmaker's rabbet plane except it is shorter and the plane iron seat is close to the front end of the plane, Fig. 6-10. It is 4" long with a 1" plane iron. It is used for working into corners or other restricted places.

5. The *bench rabbet plane* is exactly like a smooth plane except the frame is cut out and the plane iron is full width, Fig. 6-11. It is available 9" and 13" in length and with a 2⅛" plane iron. It is used to cut a rabbet.

Fig. 6-9. Cabinet Maker's Rabbet Plane (Courtesy Stanley Tool Co.)

Fig. 6-10. Bull Nose Plane (Courtesy Stanley Tool Co.)

6. The *duplex rabbet plane* is similar to a rabbet plane, but it has two seats for the plane iron — one for regular work and one for bull nose work, Fig. 6-12. It is equipped with an adjustable fence for making parallel cuts, and is 8¼″ long with a 1½″ plane iron.

7. The *skew cutter rabbet plane* is similar to a rabbet plane, but the plane is wider and the plane iron is set on an angle to take a shearing cut. The plane is 8½″ long with a 1⅞″ plane iron. It is used to cut rabbets on cross grain stock. The spur scores the stock ahead of the blade to prevent chipping.

8. The *side rabbet plane* has a 5½″ body with two ½″ cutters held by clamps and thumbscrews, Fig. 6-13. It is used to increase the width of dadoes, rabbets, and grooves.

9. The *edge trimming block plane* is similar to a side rabbet plane. It has a body, cap iron, and screw, Fig. 6-14. The plane is 6″ long with a 1¹⁄₁₆″ plane iron held at an angle on its side. It is used in trimming and squaring the edge of end rabbets.

10. *Double-end block planes* serve a double purpose. One end is used to do common end-grain planing, while the other is used for working in corners. It is 8″ long with a 1⅝″ cutter.

11. The *dado plane* is similar to the skew cutter rabbet plane. The plane iron is set on an angle, and it has an adjustable spur on each edge of the frame which scores a path for the blade. It is also equipped with a depth gauge. It is 8″ long with ½″ and ¾″ cutters and is used to cut dadoes. The spurs score the sides of the cut, and the skew cutter removes the waste material.

12. The *plow plane* is similar to a dado plane, but the plane iron is set square, Fig. 6-15. It has spurs and a depth gauge, as well as an adjustable fence, and is 9½″ long with cutters ⅛″, ⁵⁄₃₂″, ³⁄₁₆″, ⁷⁄₃₁″, ¼″, ⁵⁄₁₆″, and ⅜″ wide. It is used to cut grooves. A depth gauge and fence are used for accurate work.

13. *Combination planes* are used for cutting various shapes of moldings, Fig. 6-16. They are 9¼″ long.

14. The *tongue and groove* (matching) *plane* has a handle on each end so that

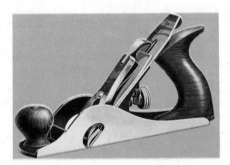

Fig. 6-11. Bench Rabbet (Courtesy Stanley Tool Co.)

Fig. 6-12. Duplex Rabbet Plane (Courtesy Stanley Tool Co.)

Fig. 6-13. Side Rabbet Plane (Courtesy Stanley Tool Co.)

Fig. 6-14. Edge Trimming Block Plane (Courtesy Stanley Tool Co.)

Fig. 6-15. Plow Plane (Courtesy Stanley Tool Co.)

it can be pushed either way, Fig. 6-17. The frog is designed so that the cutter can be set for either direction. The plane iron is 9″ long equipped with two ¼″ plane irons, one to cut the tongue and one to cut the groove.

Fig. 6-16. Combination Plane (Courtesy Stanley Tool Co.)

Fig. 6-17. Tongue and Groove Plane (Courtesy Stanley Tool Co.)

Fig. 6-18. Model Maker's   Fig. 6-19. Scraper Plane
Planes (Cour-
tesy Stanley
Tool Co.)

15. The *model maker's plane* has a curved bottom. It has a curved handle similar to a cabinet scraper handle and has no knob. It is 3½″ to 5″ long with cutters 1¼″ to 1⅜″, Fig. 6-18. It is used in constructing models such as boats and airplanes.

16. The *scraper plane* has two handles which project from the sides of the frame, Fig. 6-19. The frog pivots so that it may be set at any angle from 15° to 90°. This plane has a 2⅞″ blade sharpened with a burr on the end, and is used for final preparation of the surface prior to sanding.

17. The *circular plane* differs from the smooth plane in that it has no knob or handle, but the frame is shaped at each end to fit the hand, Fig. 6-20. The bottom is made of flexible steel and it is fastened on a pivot at each end to the frame. The bottom curvature of the plane is changed from concave to convex by means of a threaded shaft. It is 10″ long with a 1¾″ cutter. It is used for concave or convex surfaces and may be adjusted by means of an internally threaded wheel for varying curves.

18. The *core box plane* is 10″ long with a ⅞″ cutter and it is used to rough out concave surfaces such as cores, Fig. 6-21. The frame is shaped like a square trough.

19. The *fiberboard plane* is similar to a smooth plane except that the plane iron is parallel to the sides of the plane. It also has an adjustable fence. It is 10″

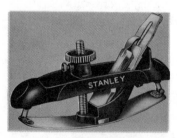

Fig. 6-20. Circular Plane (Courtesy Stanley Tool Co.)

Fig. 6-21. Core Box Plane

long and has shaped plane irons for trimming and grooving.

20. The *scrub plane* is similar to a smooth plane, but it is narrower and has no plane iron cap, adjusting nut, or lateral adjusting lever, Fig. 6-22. It has a 1¼″ plane iron that has a rounded, beveled

Fig. 6-22. Scrub Plane (Courtesy Stanley Tool Co.)

Fig. 6-23. Stanley Plane Type Surforms, Used as a Substitute for a Plane for Rough Shaping (Courtesy Stanley Tool Co.)

Fig. 6-24. Workman Using a Side Handle Wooden Scrub Plane of 1737

For extra heavy work, a second workman pulled forward on a rope which was attached to the dowel pin at the front of the plane. (Courtesy, Old Sturbridge Village, Inc.)

end. The plane is 9½″ long. It is used for roughing down thick stock to dimension.

Principal Parts and Function of Each

1. For a description of common parts, see section on the plane family.
2. *Plane irons* on all planes are made from high grade tool steel, tempered and hardened.

Fig. 6-25. Old-Time Six-Foot Jointer Plane

This was commonly used as a two-man jointer plane, but when used by one man the plane was secured in an inverted position and the stock moved over the blade.

3. *Fence* on special purpose planes is made of machined cast iron.
4. *Spurs* are made of steel that is tempered and hardened.
5. *Depth gauges* are made of steel.
6. *Circular planes* have a flexible steel bottom, adjustable to conform to contour of the curve to be cut.

Fig. 6-26. Two-Man Molding Plane

Maintenance

See the section on "Maintenance" in Topic 59.

Market Analysis

Capacity

The only capacity for planes is the width and thickness of shaving that may be cut. Some types of planes are equipped with an adjustable fence which limits the width of cut. The plane iron may be adjusted to vary the thickness of shaving according to the kind and condition of stock and the job to be done.

Attachments

Specially shaped plane irons for moldings are available for combination planes.

Additional Reading

Manufacturers Catalogs

Topic *61.* Squaring a Board (Hand Process)

Squaring a board means planing and/or cutting stock to dimension with adjacent surfaces at right angles.

Classification

Laying out, cutting, and testing surfaces

Procedure

Planing a Face True and Smooth

1. Select the better of the two faces and examine the board for twist by placing

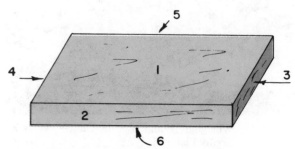

Fig. 6-29. Numbered Surfaces of Board
1 & 6 – Faces
2 & 5 – Edges
3 & 4 – Ends

a straightedge across corners or by sighting across corners. Mark the high corners, if any, and check by turning the board over on the bench and rocking it on the high corners.

2. Determine the direction of the grain on the edge and on the face of the board. Draw an arrow in the direction of the grain as shown in Fig. 6-30.

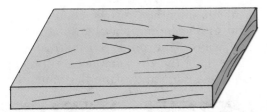

Fig. 6-30. Direction of Grain

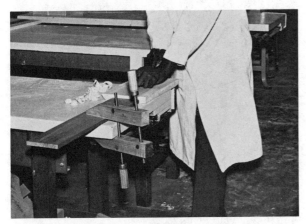

Fig. 6-31. One Method of Holding Board

3. Clamp the board end-to-end between the vise dog and a bench stop, being sure that the waste stock used for a bench stop is thinner than the piece being squared, as shown in Fig. 6-31. Never clamp a board edge-to-edge, for the pressure so applied would compress it and cause it to cup. If it were to be planed flat in this position, the board would very likely be curved when the pressure was released.

4. Set the plane to cut a fine shaving. If in testing the board you found high corners, remove enough material there first to flatten the board. Plane enough to clean the entire surface. Always be sure to plane in the direction of the grain. Remember — when starting to plane, apply pressure on the knob end of the plane. When the entire plane is on the board, bear down equally on both the knob and handle, and as the plane begins to pass off the board, relieve the pressure on the knob.

5. Test this surface frequently with the straightedge of the plane or with the try square, holding it lengthwise, crosswise, and diagonally at several points, Fig. 6-33, always looking toward the light. Where light shows under the straightedge, the surface is low. Further planing is necessary where the straight-

Fig. 6-32. Planing Working Face

Fig. 6-33. Testing Face for Flatness

edge touches the wood. Be careful, as one thin shaving is frequently sufficient.

6. Mark this surface or face so you will recognize it later. It is called the *working face*.

Planing an Edge True With the Face

1. Select the better of the two edges and test the edge for squareness with the working face. Mark any high points where material will be removed first.
2. Fasten the board securely in the vise, with this edge parallel to the bench top.
3. Grasp the handle as in planing a surface. Place the thumb of the left hand on the front of the body of the plane just behind the knob. With fingers sliding against the face of the board, keep the plane parallel with the board. This will aid in holding the plane steady. See Fig. 6-34.
4. Take full length strokes and hold the plane level so that any high spots will be removed first. Keep in mind that you should press down on the knob at the beginning of each stroke and the handle at the end of each stroke. You should finish with a full-width shaving.
5. Hold the board in the left hand and sight down the edge carefully to see that you are keeping the edge straight. To test squareness of edge with working face, hold the handle of the try square snugly against the working face, with the blade on the edge of the board as shown in Fig. 6-35. Where light shows under the blade, the edge is low. Further planing is necessary where the blade touches the wood. This should be done carefully, because one thin shaving may be all you need to remove. Work for a full-width shaving the full length of the board, and you will have little difficulty in getting a true edge.
6. Mark this edge so you will recognize it later. It is called the *working edge*. The working face and working edge may be marked "1" and "2" respectively.

Cutting or Planing an End True With the Face and Edge

1. If the end grain is not going to be shown on the outside of the project, the end may be squared by cutting in the miter box. A cut should be made about ¼″ from the end of the board to prevent the saw from tearing the edge.
2. If the end grain is to show, it will be best prepared by planing. This will give a much smoother surface than sawing. End grain planing may be done in several ways. The preferred method is to plane half the distance across the end from one edge and plane the remaining

Fig. 6-34. Planing an Edge

Fig. 6-35. Testing Edge for Squareness with Face

Fig. 6-36. Planing End Grain — Note Angle of Plane

Fig. 6-37. Planing from Opposite Edge to Center

Fig. 6-38. Testing an End for Squareness with Face

half from the opposite edge. This is done to prevent chipping of corners. Figs. 6-36 and 6-37 show this method.

3. Hold the plane as in edge planing, but at an angle with the side of the board as shown in Fig. 6-36. This gives a shearing cut across the wood fibers.

4. Test with the try square from the face and from the edge, Figs. 6-38, 6-39, carefully planing any high places that you find.

5. Mark this end so you will recognize it later. It is called the *working end*.

Cutting to Length

1. Measure the desired length from the working end and mark across the stock with a sharp pencil or knife. If the end grain is not to be shown on the outside, the end may be cut square by using a miter box. Cut just outside the line.

2. Stock to be planed must be cut at least $\frac{1}{16}''$ longer than the required finished length of the board. Secure the stock either in a vise or on a bench hook and cut off the waste stock with a fine cross-cut saw.

3. To plane the end smooth and square, work to the line in the same manner as you planed the working end, testing it carefully from the working face and working edge with the try square.

Planing to Width

1. Set a marking gauge to the desired width. Check with a rule, measuring the width from the spur of the gauge to the head. Mark the desired width on both faces of the stock, being careful to keep the head of the marking gauge against the working edge while gauging — as shown in Fig. 6-40. Be sure to push the gauge away from you. If the board is more than 3″ or 4″ wide, a panel gauge should be used.

A combination square may also be used. The blade is allowed to project from the head the required width of the board. With the head of the square held firmly against the working edge, hold a pencil against the end of the blade while you push the square along the length of the board.

For a very wide board, measure the width with a ruler at two points, one near each end. Then draw a knife along a straightedge aligned with these two points.

2. Fasten the stock in the vise and plane to the middle of the gauge or knife line.

3. Test from the working face with the try square as in Fig. 6-35. If you have been careful in planing to the middle of the gauge line, this edge should test true.

Planing to Thickness

1. Gauge the desired thickness with the marking gauge, on both edges of the stock, being careful to keep the head of the gauge against the working face while marking. Connect these gauged lines on the ends with a pencil and straightedge; this will give a guide line to which to plane.

2. Clamp the stock on the bench against the stop and plane to the middle of the gauge line.

3. Test this surface with a straightedge. If you have been careful in planing to the gauge line, this surface should be reasonably flat and square.

Standards and Results

1. Each planed surface should be reasonably flat, smooth, square with adjacent surfaces, and of correct dimensions.

2. There should be no chipped edges.

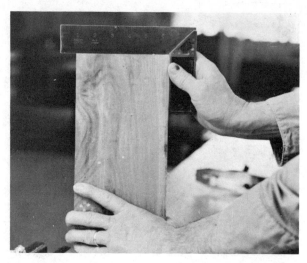

Fig. 6-39. Testing an End for Squareness with Edge

Fig. 6-40. Using Marking Gauge

Safety Considerations

1. Stock should be adequately secured, and adjustments to plane or saw should be made with due caution.

2. There is practically no danger if the person sawing or planing uses the tool properly and keeps his mind on what he is doing.

Topic 62. Spoke Shave

Classification

Edge cutting tool

Application

Principle of Operation

The spoke shave works on the principle of a controlled cutting wedge, similar to the plane.

Kinds and Uses

1. Spoke shaves are made with flat, convex, and hollow faces.
2. The spoke shave is usually pushed in cutting or shaping a curved surface. The flat-face type is used to cut a flat (see Fig. 6-41) while the convex face is used to cut concave edges. The hollow face is used for rounding edges, Fig. 6-42. rounding edges.
3. Spoke shaves are made with cutters 1¾″ and 2¼″ wide with frames of 9″ and 10″, respectively.

Principal Parts and Function of Each

1. The *frame,* made of cast iron or wood, consists of a short face, either round or flat, and two handles. The short face facilitates the following of contours.
2. The *blade,* made of fine carbon steel, is shaped to a beveled cutting edge, like a plane iron.

3. The *cutter cap,* made of cast iron, holds the blade in position.
4. The steel *cap screw* locks the cutter cap and blade in the frame.
5. The steel *adjusting screws* regulate the cutting depth and serve as a lateral adjustment of the cutter blade. Only the more expensive types have this adjustment.

Maintenance

Sharpening — the cutting edge is sharpened like a plane iron to a 25° - 30° angle, then whet on an oil stone to 30° - 35°.

Market Analysis

Capacity

Determined by width of blade.

Additional Reading

Manufacturers Catalogs

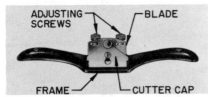

Fig. 6-41. Spoke Shave (Courtesy Stanley Tool Co.)

Fig. 6-42. Hollow Face Spoke Shave in Use

Topic 63. Drawknife or Drawing Knife

Classification

Edge cutting tool

Application

Principle of Operation

The drawknife works similar to a chisel, utilizing the principle of a wedge. See Fig. 6-43.

Kinds and Uses

The drawknife is used for removing large amounts of stock rapidly and for rough shaping molded work. It is often used to remove corners from billets prior to spindle turning on the lathe. The tool is held in both hands, with the bevel edge down and at a slight angle to the work. It is then firmly drawn toward the worker to remove a thin chip from the wood. The wood always should be worked in the direction of the grain.

Principal Parts and Function of Each

1. The long, chisel-shaped, hollow-ground *cutting blade* is 8″ to 10″ long, 1⅜″ wide, made of high-grade tool steel.

2. *Handles,* made of wood, are attached to each end of knife forming a U-shaped tool.

Attachments

Chamfering attachments.

Maintenance

Storing

Drawknives can be suspended over two hooks horizontally on the tool panel. The cutting edge should be protected with a wood or leather sheath.

Sharpening

The cutting edge is hollow ground on the grinding wheel to an angle of 25° - 30°, then whet on the oil stone to 30° - 35°, similar to the plane iron.

Additional Reading

Manufacturers Catalogs

Topic 69, "Grinding Edge Tools"

Topic 71, "Whetting or Honing a Cutting Tool"

Fig. 6-43. Drawknife

Topic 64. Scrapers — Hand, Cabinet, Hook

Fig. 6-44. Hand Scraper Blade (Courtesy Disston Div., H. K. Porter Co., Inc.)

Fig. 6-45. Cabinet Scraper (Courtesy Stanley Tool Co.)

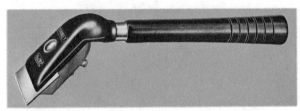

Fig. 6-46. Cabinet Scraper (Courtesy Stanley Tool Co.)

Fig. 6-47. Burnisher (Courtesy Stanley Tool Co.)

Fig. 6-48. Hook Scraper (Courtesy Red Devil Tools)

Classification

Edge cutting tool

Application

Principle of Operation

Scrapers work on the principle of a sharp wedge, in this case a fine burr, cutting a very light shaving. See Fig. 5-5. A dull scraper produces a dust, rather than a shaving.

Kinds and Uses

Scrapers are used to remove paint and varnish and to smooth wood surfaces. They are usually used in the final preparation of the surface prior to sanding. All scraping must be done before sanding as abrasive grit left in the pores or on the surface of the wood will dull the edge of a scraper.

1. The *hand scraper* has an alloy steel blade (Fig. 6-44) with the edges sharpened to a right angle, then turned with a burnisher (rolled to a burr) to form a cutting edge. They are 2½″ or 3″ wide and 5″ or 6″ long.
2. The *cabinet scraper* has an alloy steel blade, similar to a hand scraper, but sharpened to a bevel of 45°, then turned with a burnisher, Fig. 6-51B. The cabinet scraper has a 2¼″ blade and 11½″ frame. The frame is constructed of malleable iron and holds the scraper blade at an angle of about 75°.
3. The hooked-shape blade of the *hook scraper* is designed for rough, heavy work such as scraping floors and painted and varnished surfaces, Figs. 6-48, 6-49, 6-50. The handle, made of hard wood, holds the blade firmly in position. Blades are 1½″, 2″, 2½″, and 3″ wide, with handles 5″, 7½″, 8¾″, and 12″ long.
4. Scraper plane. (See Fig. 6-19.)

Principal Parts and Function of Each

1. *Scraper blades* are made of the finest carbon steel.

2. Cabinet scrapers have a cast iron or malleable iron *frame*.

3. Hook scrapers are held in a metal or hard wood *frame*.

Maintenance

Sharpening

1. Hand scrapers and cabinet scrapers are sharpened as described in Topic 65. When too worn, they are replaced.

2. Hook scrapers are sharpened by draw filing the cutting edge.

Storing

1. Blades of cabinet scrapers should be retracted when stored.

2. Store so the cutting edges will not be damaged.

Additional Reading

Manufacturers Catalogs

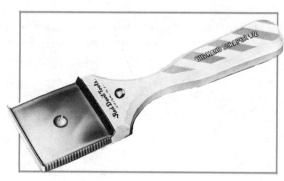

Fig. 6-49. Hook Scraper (Courtesy Red Devil Tools)

Fig. 6-50. Hook Scraper (Courtesy Red Devil Tools)

Topic 65. Sharpening Hand Scrapers and Cabinet Scrapers

Classification

Forming a cutting wedge by shaping, whetting, and burnishing.

Procedure

Hand Scraper

1. File off the remaining burr by holding the scraper flat with one hand and making a few strokes with a mill file on each face.

2. Place the blade in a vertical position in the vise and drawfile the edge straight, holding the file horizontally and at a right angle with the side of the blade.

3. Whet the edge and two adjoining faces of the blade on the medium oil stone, taking full-length strokes, Fig. 6-51. Hold the blade at a right angle to the stone and the faces flat against the stone.

4. Place the blade back in the vise and turn each edge with a burnisher. Start by holding the burnisher in a horizontal position. With a downward pressure, move the burnisher along the edge, rolling the edge on both sides of the blade. Tilt the burnisher slightly until the last stroke is 5° to the horizontal. See Fig. 6-51A.

Cabinet Scraper

1. Remove the blade from the frame.
2. Using a mill file, file off the old burr.
3. Place the blade in a vise and drawfile a new edge at an angle of about 45°.
4. Remove from vise and then whet the blade using a medium oil stone. Remove any new burr formed in filing and whetting.
5. Place the blade back in the vise and, with a burnisher, turn the edge to an angle of about 75°. (NOTE: Check procedure for sharpening hand scraper.) See Fig. 6-51B.

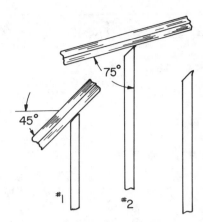

Fig. 6-51B. Burnishing Cabinet Scraper

6. Place the blade in the frame with bevel toward front and slide it in from the base. Place the blade and frame on a flat surface and tighten the clamp thumb screws.
7. Adjust for depth of cut by turning the adjustment thumbscrew. If the scraper does not cut a shaving, the burr may have been turned too much. This may be corrected by turning the burr back somewhat by drawing the point of the burnisher directly under the edge of the burr. A dull blade may be touched up this way.
8. The cutting edge of the blade should form a slight arc to prevent the corners from scoring the surface.

Standards and Results

1. Scrapers should cut a shaving, rather than scrape dust.
2. Blades should not leave scratches or ridges caused by chatter.
3. Scraper blades should take an even cut.

Safety Considerations

1. Observe all precautions in the use of hand tools.
2. Be careful in filing or burnishing to avoid cutting hands.

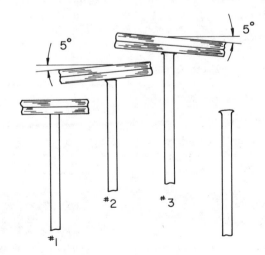

Fig. 6-51. Stoning a Scraper Edge (Courtesy Behr-Manning Co.)

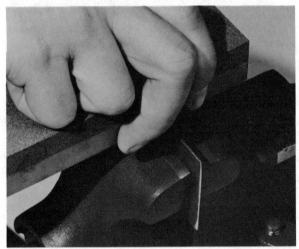

Fig. 6-51A. Burnishing Hand Scraper

Additional Reading

Manufacturers' Catalogs

Topic 66. Chisels, Gouges, and Carving Tools

Classification

Edge cutting tools

Application

Principle of Operation

Edge cutting tools work on the principle of the cutting wedge in a shearing and forcing action. See Fig. 5-2.

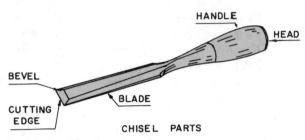

Fig. 6-52. Chisel Nomenclature

Kinds and Uses

Chisels and gouges are used in chipping, paring, trimming, mortising, and carving. They are divided into two groups according to the method of attaching the handle — socket handle or tang handle.

A gouge is a chisel with a curved, shaped blade. There are three degrees of sweep: full, regular, and flat.

1. *Firmer chisel* has a thick blade and it is used for general work, Fig. 6-53.
2. *Paring chisel* has a thin, beveled blade and is used for fine work, Fig. 6-54. The handle usually has a tang set.
3. *Framing chisel* has a heavy blade used in framing construction and shipbuilding. A ferrule replaces the leather cap on the handle to resist splitting of handle under heavy blows, Fig. 6-55.
4. *Butt chisel* has a shorter blade which helps in the control of the tool in fine work and awkward positions, Figs. 6-56, 6-57. It is used for cutting gains when setting hinges.
5. *Mortise chisel* is used in cutting the mortise. It has a thicker blade to allow its use as a lever when making deep cuts.
6. *Inside gouge* has a bevel ground on the inside of the blade, Fig. 6-62, and it is used for hollowing out concave surfaces.
7. *Outside gouge* has the bevel ground on the outside of the blade, Fig. 6-63, and it is used for cutting grooves.

Fig. 6-53. Firmer Chisel (Courtesy Buck Brothers)

Fig. 6-54. Paring Chisel (Courtesy Buck Brothers)

Fig. 6-55. Framing Chisel (Courtesy Greenlee Tool Co.)

Fig. 6-56. Short Tang Butt Chisel (Courtesy Buck Brothers)

Fig. 6-57. Socket Butt Chisel (Courtesy Buck Brothers)

Fig. 6-58. Long Handle Tang Paring Chisel (Courtesy Buck Brothers)

Fig. 6-59. Socket Butt Chisel (Courtesy Greenlee Tool Co.)

Fig. 6-60. Tang Butt Chisel (Courtesy Greenlee Tool Co.)

Fig. 6-61. Socket Framing Chisel (Courtesy Greenlee Tool Co.)

Fig. 6-62. Inside Bevel Gouge (Courtesy Buck Brothers)

Fig. 6-63. Outside Bevel Gouge (Courtesy Buck Brothers)

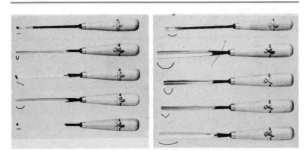

Fig. 6-64. Carving Tools (Courtesy Buck Brothers)

Fig. 6-65. Socket Slick (Courtesy Greenlee Tool Co.)

Fig. 6-66. Glazier's Chisel (Courtesy Greenlee Tool Co.)

Fig. 6-67. Offset Chisel (Courtesy Buck Brothers)

8. An *offset shank chisel*, or *gouge* with an offset handle, aids in working close to the surface being cut, Fig. 6-68.
9. *Carving tools* are chisels and gouges with variously shaped cutting edges for making angular or curved cuts. Some of these are: straight chisel, skew chisel, offset shank chisel, parting tool, straight gouge, and veining tool. See Fig. 6-64.
10. *Socket slick* is a special purpose chisel used in heavy construction work, Fig. 6-65.
11. *Glazier's chisel* is used in setting glass — for removing old putty, setting glazier's points, and reputtying, Fig. 6-66.

Principal Parts and Function of Each

1. The carbon tool steel *blade* is the body of tool. Some blades have chamfered sides. (See Fig. 6-60.)
2. *Bevel* on blade forms the cutting wedge.
3. *Tang* or tapered end fits into the handle.
4. *Socket* is the conical shaped end into which the handle is forced.
5. *Handles* are a means of holding the blade to guide and force the cutting action. They are made of plastic or hardwood, such as maple or hickory.
6. *Leather tip, steel* or *ferrule cap,* on the handle reduces the possibilities of splitting when struck by the mallet.

Maintenance

1. Wipe with a light oil or kerosene to remove rust, pitch, or any other foreign substance.
2. The blade or cutting edge should be re-shaped when nicked, broken, or when bevel is too short. The chisel is ground to an angle of 25° to 30°, then whet on a fine oilstone to a razor edge, Figs. 6-87 and 6-88. Gouges and carving tools are dressed with a slip stone, Fig. 6-91.
3. Damaged handles on tang and socket chisels may be replaced.
4. Chisels should be individually stored in a rack or case to prevent dulling the

keen edge and to insure safety. When left unused for a long period of time, the steel should be coated with a film of oil or wax to prevent rusting.

Market Analysis

Capacity

1. Chisels are commonly made in widths of blades from ⅛″ to 2″ and from 3″ to 6″ in length. The handle is not included in the length.

2. Gouges range from ⅛″ to 2″ in width.

3. Carving tools are sold in sets of 4 to 8 tools.

Additional Reading

Topic 69, "Grinding Edge Tools on the Emery Wheel"

Topic 71, "Whetting or Honing a Cutting Tool"

Fig. 6-68. Offset Gouge (Courtesy Buck Brothers)

Topic 67. Using Chisels, Gouges, and Carving Tools

Classification

Cutting and shaping by wedging and paring

Procedure

A chisel is a necessary tool in shaping and joining. It must be kept sharp and used with caution. To obtain a smooth cut, always work in the direction of the grain. The work must also be held securely, either in a vise or clamped to a sturdy surface, so that both hands may be used to control the cutting action of the tool.

Paring Horizontal Surfaces with a Chisel

Paring is making a fine cut or trimming to a finish line.

1. The chisel is generally held with the bevel up and the back of the chisel parallel to the surface to be cut.
2. Grasp the handle of the chisel in the right hand, with the left hand against the stock. Hold the chisel so that its direction and depth of cut may be guided.
3. Using one hand as a pivot, force the chisel from side to side in a shearing motion, Fig. 6-69.

Cutting End Grain or Shoulders With a Chisel

1. Secure the stock in the bench, protecting the bench top with a bench hook or scrap piece of stock.
2. Hold the chisel with the bevel out from the finish line and in a vertical position.
3. Assume a position so that you can sight the direction of cut.
4. With the left hand guiding the chisel, apply pressure with the right hand, Fig. 6-70. Usually the palm of the right hand is held over the end of the chisel handle.

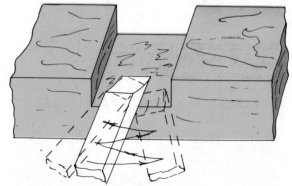

Fig. 6-69. Technique of Paring Bottom of Cross-Lap Joint

5. Cut with only a portion of the width of the chisel—use the remainder as a guide for maintaining a straight line or edge.
6. For deep cuts, use a mallet to strike the handle, Fig. 6-71.

Removing Surplus Stock When Cutting a Mortise or Gain (See Topic 106)

1. Select a socket-type chisel of proper width for the cut.
2. Hold the blade of the chisel in the left hand with the bevel toward the waste side so that the cut may be controlled.
3. Use a mallet to strike the chisel. Make a series of close cuts into the waste material, Fig. 6-71.
4. Remove these chips with a shearing cut, as in horizontal trimming.
5. Continue the process until the surplus stock has been removed.

Trimming to a Curved Surface

1. Convex surfaces are trimmed in the same manner as horizontal trimming, with the bevel side of the chisel up, Fig. 6-72.
2. Concave surfaces are trimmed with the bevel of the chisel down. It is important in both of these operations that the cutting be done with the grain. See Fig. 6-73.

Using a Gouge

1. A gouge is used like a chisel when making a curved surface. A gouge with an inside bevel is used to shape the edge of curved stock. A gouge with the outside bevel (most common) is used for making grooves and fluting.
2. Select a gouge of the proper width and shape.

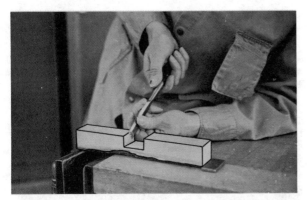

Fig. 6-70. Paring Shoulders of Cross-Lap Joint

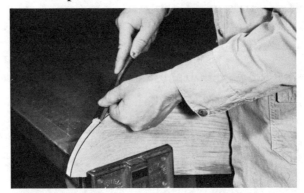

Fig. 6-72. Rounding an Edge with a Chisel

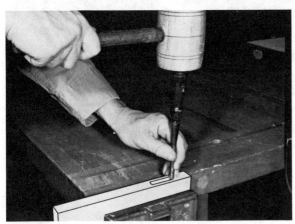

Fig. 6-71. Cutting a Mortise

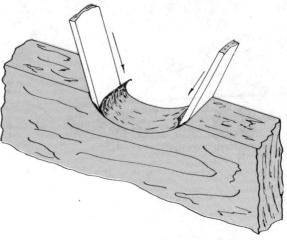

Fig. 6-73. Making a Concave Cut with a Chisel

3. Hold the gouge in one hand so that it may be guided as pressure is applied with the other hand, Fig. 6-74.
4. Use a mallet to strike the gouge when making heavy cuts or for roughing out.
5. Always finish with a light cut made with the grain.

Using Carving Tools

1. Use extreme care when doing fine, intricate work with carving tools.
2. Hold the tool in a similar manner as when using the chisel and gouge. In carving, control is of special importance.
3. Use very light, even cuts to remove material. Never try to remove all the material in one cut.
4. Work from the profile of the pattern to the deepest recess.

Standards and Results

1. All trimming should be done to a line.
2. All cuts should be smooth and true.

Safety Considerations

1. Secure stock firmly.

2. Always keep both hands behind the cutting edge of the tool.
3. Always work the tool away from the body.
4. Keep tools sharp.
5. Protect bench top from cuts.
6. See Topic on Safety.

Additional Reading

Western Pine Association, *Woodcarving for Pleasure*

Manufacturers Catalogs

Fig. 6-74A. Wood Mauls
These wooden mauls are examples of early mallets made of burls and cross-grained tree sections. (Courtesy Old Sturbridge Village, Inc.)

Fig. 6-74. Using a Gouge

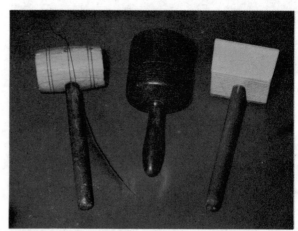

Fig. 6-74B. Types of Mallets

Carved wooden eagle and shield (right) were made by gluing up two-inch stock, cutting to shape on the band saw, and carving with gouge and chisel. Details were cut with various tools.

(Both carvings are courtesy of Vincent G. Mack, who was a student at Fitchburg State College at the time these pieces were carved.)

The cross-bow at the right is a modern version of this ancient weapon. The stock is sculptured of wood by using the band saw, gouges, rasps and files.

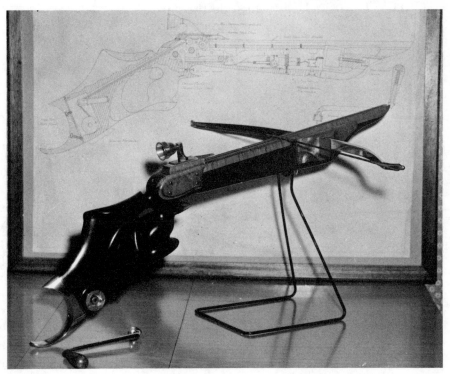

Topic 68. Grinder — Bench, Floor Models

Classification

Power driven abrading tool for shaping metal

Application

Principle of Operation

The grinder works on the principle of a large number of cutting wedges revolving at a speed of from 400 to 3600 r.p.m., Fig. 6-75.

Kinds and Uses

Grinders are used for shaping the cutting edges of tools. The type most often found in school shops is called a dry grinder, but there are also wet grinders and vapor grinders. Standard wheel shapes that may be attached to bench and floor models are: straight, straight tapered, cylindrical, cup, flaring cup, dish, and saucer.

Principal Parts and Function of Each

1. The *abrasive wheels,* which do the cutting, are made of silicon carbide and aluminum oxide. They are graded alphabetically according to size of grain. For sharpening woodworking tools, the recommended hardness is "N," the recommended coarseness is 46 to 60 grit.
2. The ⅓ to 1 H.P. *motor* provides the power.
3. The tool steel *spindle or arbor* drives the wheel.
4. The cast iron *tables* or *tool rest* provide an adjustable bearing surface for materials or tools to be ground.

Table 15
Standard Grinding Wheel Markings

Standard grinding wheel markings accepted by the Grinding Wheel Manufacturers Association are in six parts, designated by letter and number. Example — **B60M5VE**					
B	60	M	5	V	E
Type of Abrasive	Grain Size	Grade	Structure	Bond	Manufacturers Number
Abrasive letters — A Aluminum oxide, regular B Aluminum oxide, refined AB Combination of above C Silicon carbide, regular CD Silicon carbide, refined D Corundum E Emery F Garnet					
Grain Size — number of mesh openings in the grading screen per inch. #8 coarse to #500 very fine.					
Grade — Letters A-Z, soft to hard.					
Structure — 1-15, Most dense to most open.					
Bond — V — Vitrified S — Silicate E — Shellac or elastic R — Rubber B — Resinoid O — Oxychloride					
Manufacturers number — used as a reference for sales purposes.					

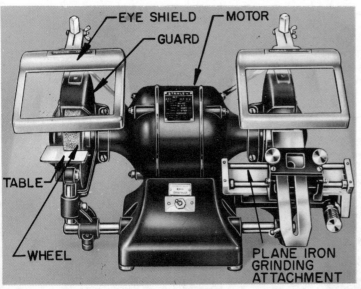

Fig. 6-75. Bench Grinder (Courtesy Stanley Tool Co.)

5. The cast iron or pressed steel *guards* protect the operator from injury.

6. The plastic or safety glass *eye shields* protect the operator's eyes from particles that are torn loose from the abrasive wheel or stock.

7. The *stand* (on floor models) supports the grinder.

8. Some grinders have a *reservoir* to hold water in which to cool the work being ground.

Fig. 6-75A. Grinding Wheel Dresser

Fig. 6-75B. Dressing a Grinding Wheel

Maintenance

1. Grinding wheels should be kept dressed. This is a process of removing the dull or clogged grit from the surface of the wheel by the use of a grinding wheel dresser. (See Figs. 6-75A and 6-75B.)

2. Grinder bearings, unless sealed, should be periodically lubricated.

Market Analysis

Capacity

The capacity is determined by the size and kind of grinding wheel which may be installed and the throat clearance between the tool rest and arbor support.

Attachments

1. The drill grinding attachment is used to sharpen twist drills.

2. The plane iron grinding attachment is used to hold the plane iron at the desired angle for grinding. (Fig. 6-75.)

3. The wire brush is used for removing rust, paint, or other foreign material from metal.

4. The dust collector is a separate unit attached to the grinder to collect the dust which results from grinding.

5. Lights provide better light on the work while grinding.

6. Buffing and polishing wheels are used in finishing processes.

Additional Reading

Grinding Wheel Manufacturers Association, *Use, Care, and Protection of Abrasive Wheels*
Norton Company, *A Handbook on Abrasives and Grinding Wheels*

Topic 69. Grinding Edge Tools

Classification

Shaping by abrasion

Procedure

Grinding is a process of reshaping the cutting edge of a tool. An abrasive wheel or stone is used to give the proper wedge-shaped edge while an oilstone is used to hone to a keen edge. A medium-grain wheel is used for rough shaping and a fine wheel for the tool dressing.

1. Chisels, plane irons, gouges, spoke shaves, and drawknives have a single-bevel, wedge-shaped cutting edge, the angle of which is between 20° and 30°, depending on the hardness of the material to be cut. A 20-degree bevel will produce a fine cutting edge for soft materials but the tool will not hold the edge when used on the harder woods.

2. Adjust the tool rest slightly below the center of the wheel for straight-on grinding and above center for bevel grinding.

3. First dress the cutting edge square with the sides of the tool by feeding the tool straight onto the grinding wheel, Figs. 6-76, 6-78. This is also done to remove nicks. Work the tool across the the face of the wheel with a light pressure which results in a fine cut.

4. Adjust the tool rest so that the angle of contact of wheel and tool is about 30°,

Figs. 6-77 and 6-79. To grind the bevel, work the tool across the face of the wheel. Keep the edge being sharpened square with the side of the tool. Apply only enough pressure to make a light cutting action. Too much pressure

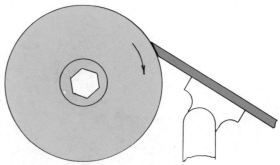

Fig. 6-77. Bevel Grinding

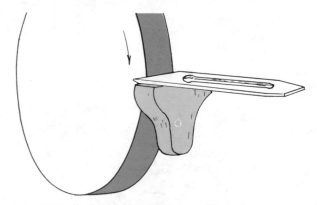

Fig. 6-78. Squaring an Edge on a Plane Iron

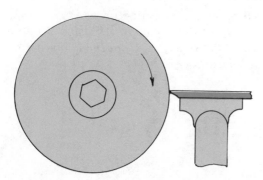

Fig. 6-76. Center Grinding

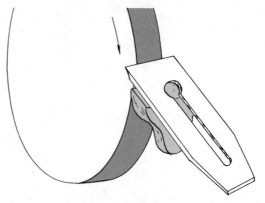

Fig. 6-79. Grinding a Bevel on a Plane Iron

causes overheating. Frequently dip the tip of the tool in water to cool it. Face grinding produces a slightly hollow bevel that allows for honing several times before regrinding is necessary.

Standards and Results

1. The cutting edge should be square.
2. The hollow bevel should be ground to a fine edge at about a 30° angle.
3. Sides of the bevel should be of equal length.
4. The tool should show no evidence of overheating.

Safety Considerations

1. Eye shields must be in proper position and goggles should be worn.

2. Guards and tables should be no more than ¼″ away from the wheel.
3. Tool being ground should be held firmly.
4. Clogged and out-of-true wheels should be dressed. (See Fig. 6-75B.)
5. Badly worn wheels should be replaced.
6. Avoid jamming tool.
7. Always use the face of the wheel.
8. Replacement wheels should be those recommended for use at the speed of the machine.
9. Stand to one side of rotation of wheel when starting grinder.

Additional Reading

Delta Manufacturing Company, *Getting the Most Out of Your Abrasive Tools*
Norton Company, *How to Sharpen*

Topic 70. Oilstone

Classification
Abrasive material graded and formed to a shape for sharpening or dressing

Application

Principle of Operation
The hard crystal edges on the face of the oilstone act as wedges or teeth which shear off the rough or high spots of a carbon steel surface to a smooth finish, Fig. 6-80.

Fig. 6-80. Crystolon Combination Oilstone (Courtesy Behr-Manning Co.)

Fig. 6-81. Slip Stone (Courtesy Behr-Manning Co.)

Fig. 6-82. Gouge Slip Stone (Courtesy Behr-Manning Co.)

Fig. 6-83. Carving Tool Slip Stones (Courtesy Behr-Manning Co.)

Kinds and Uses
1. Oilstones are used to produce a fine cutting edge. They are usually rectangular in shape. They are also available in single bevel, double bevel, conical and wedge shapes. Stones of cylindrical shape are used for machine knife sharpening.

2. There are three major natural stones:

   The *Arkansas stone* is quarried in Arkansas River areas. It is white in color, has a close texture, and produces a fine sharpened edge. It is also used in sharpening surgical instruments.

   Washita stone is a whitish gray color, varying in degree of hardness, not as fine as Arkansas.

   Turkey stone is bluish-brown, sometimes streaked with white. The quality of this stone varies, and a poor one will wear unevenly.

3. Artificial stones are usually made with one fine face and one coarser face.

   India stone is a light brown, flat, durable cutting stone made of aluminum oxide.

   Crystolon and *Carborundum* are fast-cutting stones made of silicon carbide.

   Carborundum files are used for general work — in touching up after use of a steel file or to take the place of a steel file on case-hardened stock.

4. The sizes of stones vary with the type of stone and the type of work to be done.

Oil and sharpening stones are made in various rectangular sizes ranging from 4″ x 1¾″ x ⅝″ to 8″ x 2″ x 1″, Fig. 6-80.

Fig. 6-84. Carborundum File (Courtesy Behr-Manning Co.)

Fig. 6-85. India Files (Courtesy Behr-Manning Co.)

Slip stones are made in sizes of 4″ to 4½″ in length, ⁷⁄₁₆″ to ½″ back edge and ¹⁄₁₆″ to ³⁄₁₆″ front edge, Fig. 6-81.

Machine knife stones are round in shape and are from 2″ to 4″ in diameter and up to 1½″ thick for the combination coarse and fine grits.

Carborundum files are shaped like a steel file with a fixed handle. They are 14″ long.

Auger bit stones are triangular in shape, with one end larger than the other. They are generally available only in one size: 4″ long x ½″ — ⁵⁄₁₆″ wide x ¼″ — ¹⁄₁₆″ thick.

Principal Parts and Function of Each

Artificial stones are usually made with one fine face and one coarse face. The coarse face is used to remove material reasonably fast, but it does not give a keen edge. The fine face is used to produce a keen cutting edge.

Maintenance

1. A hardwood or metal frame should be used for protection against breakage and for ease in handling.
2. A stone may become worn from constant use. The surface may be renewed or trued by rubbing the face on a flat piece of steel or granite, the surface of which is coated with ground emery and kerosene or sand and water. A hard, coarse abrasive or a rust-pitted steel plate may also be used.
3. A glazed stone may be reconditioned by heating in a medium warm (250° F.) oven. The stone should not come in direct contact with a flame.

Market Analysis

Attachments

Hardwood or iron box mounting for protecting and holding securely when whetting.

Additional Reading

Norton Company, *How to Sharpen*

Topic 71. Whetting or Honing a Cutting Tool

Classification

Sharpening by abrading

Procedure

Sharpening Wedge-Shaped Tools

Whetting is the process of sharpening to a fine edge. It is done to remove the wire edge after grinding or to restore a sharp edge. See Fig. 6-86. Usually a combination oilstone is used, which includes a coarse face for rough, rapid cutting and a fine face for dressing a sharp edge.

1. Select a coarse or fine stone, depending upon the condition of the tool edge. Coarse stones cut rapidly but do not produce a fine edge. Fine stones produce a keen edge but should be used only after the tool has been sharpened on a medium stone. A good general-purpose stone is the medium grade. (NOTE: When changing to a fine-grade stone, wipe the tool with cotton waste to remove coarse grits which might scratch the finer stone.)

2. Secure the oilstone on the bench so that it is level. Apply a few drops of thin machine oil to the surface. The purpose of this oil is to float away the particles of metal being cut from the tool, preventing them from becoming embedded in the surface of the oilstone.

3. Hold the tool diagonally across the face width of the stone. The bevel of the tool should form an angle between 30° and 35°. The harder the material — on which the tool is to be used — the greater the angle. See Fig. 6-87.

4. Move the tool back and forth along the stone. Take long, straight strokes, holding the tool at a constant angle. Avoid rocking the tool, as this action produces a rounded edge. For double-beveled tools, whet each bevel equally.

5. Use the entire face of the stone and occasionally turn it end-for-end to insure even wear. The face of the stone should be kept perfectly flat.

6. After the bright edge on single-edge tools has disappeared, place the tool

Fig. 6-86. Magnified (20 Times) Section of Cutting Edge
Top: Dull   *Center*: Sharpened on Coarse Stone   *Bottom*: After Final Stoning on Hard, Fine Stone

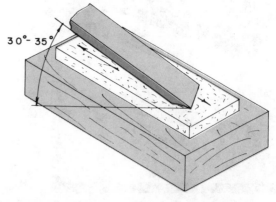

Fig. 6-87. Whetting a Chisel (Bevel Side Down)

with the surface opposite the bevel flat on the stone, and remove the burr with several sidewise strokes, Fig. 6-88.

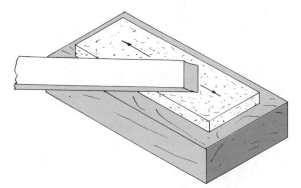

Fig. 6-88. Whetting a Chisel (Bevel Side Up)

Fig. 6-89. Comparison of Kitchen Knife and Chisel

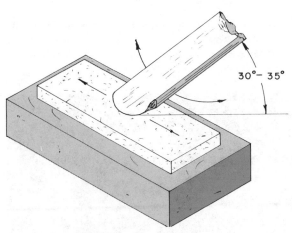

Fig. 6-90. Whetting a Gouge

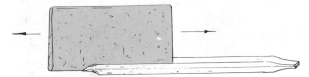

Fig. 6-91. Use of Slip Stone to Sharpen Gouge

7. Some craftsmen test for sharpness by drawing the edge lightly across the back of the thumb nail. If it catches or scores a mark on the nail, it is considered sharp.

8. The use of a leather strap after whetting will produce a keener edge. A piece of leather secured to the oil stone holder cover will serve this purpose. Hold the cutting edge flat on the strap and draw the tool away. Several strokes will remove any fine wire edge.

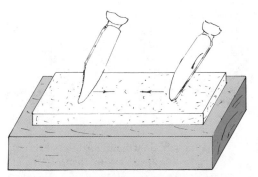

Fig. 6-92. Blade Movement When Sharpening Pocket Knife

Fig. 6-93. Beginning to Sharpen a Knife

Fig. 6-94. Sharpening Second Side

Special Techniques

1. The *drawknife* is sharpened by holding the tool securely in a convenient position. The edge is then whet by holding the oilstone at the proper angle while rubbing it back and forth over the entire length of the blade. See Fig. 6-98.

2. The *turning and outside beveled gouges* are sharpened by following the established curve of the respective tool. Hold

Fig. 6-95. Comparison of Sharpening Angles of Razor, Pocket Knife, and Carving Knife

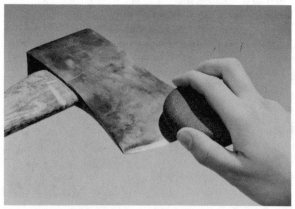

Fig. 6-96. Sharpening an Axe (Courtesy Behr-Manning Co.)

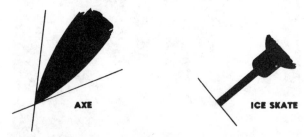

Fig. 6-97. Comparison of Sharpening Angles of Axe and Ice Skate Blade

the tool as before at the proper angle, but instead of the back and forth movement produce a rocking motion rolling the tool from side to side as it is moved over the stone. To remove the wire edge, use a slip stone that fits the contour of the tool. Care must be taken not to produce a bevel on the inside of the tool. See Figs. 6-90, 6-91.

3. To sharpen *Sloyd or pocket knives*, use a medium or fine stone. Hold the blade diagonally with the width of the stone. With the back of the blade raised very slightly, rub the blade back and forth with long, even strokes and pressure. A straight stroke cuts better than a rolling circular motion. Turn the blade over to sharpen the edge on both sides. See Fig. 6-92, 6-93, 6-94.

4. Wipe all oil from the stone when through whetting.

Safety Considerations

1. Keep both hands on the tool.
2. Care must be taken to avoid cuts when testing the sharpness of the cutting edge.
3. Secure the stone to the bench.
4. Care must be taken to avoid cuts when sharpening a tool with a slipstone held in the hand.

Fig. 6-98. Sharpening

Standards and Results

1. No nicks or burrs should appear on the blade.

2. The bevel should be 30° to 35° and form the proper cutting angle with the sides of the tool.

3. On single-edge tools the surface opposite the bevel should be flat.

Additional Reading

Behr-Manning Company, *How to Sharpen*
Delta Manufacturing Company, *Getting the Most Out of Your Abrasive Tools*

Machine Cutting to Basic Form

Topic 72. Jointer

Classification

Power driven rotary cutting edge tool

Application

Principle of Operation

A round cutter head with 2, 3, or 4 knives (generally 3) revolves at a speed of approximately 4000 r.p.m., and the knives cut on the principle of a continuous set of cutting wedges, each cutting a small arc (see page 105), Fig. 7-1A. Also see Fig. 5-6.

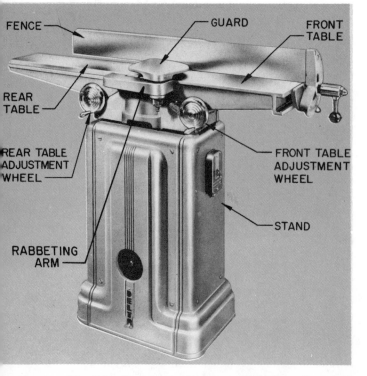

Fig. 7-1. 6″ Jointer (Courtesy Delta Div., Rockwell Mfg. Co.)

Kinds and Uses

The jointer is used for planing faces and edges straight and smooth, cutting rabbets, planing tapers, chamfers, and bevels, and for specialty cuts. Jointers are made in 4″, 6″, 8″, 10″, 12″, 14″ and 16″ blade and table widths. The wider jointers usually have longer tables. Some brands are available with extra long tables.

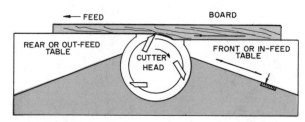

Fig. 7-1A. Cross Section of Jointer

Principal Parts and Function of Each

1. *Adjustable front* or *in-feed table*, made of machined cast iron, supports stock as it is fed into knives. The height of the table regulates the depth of the cut. Some jointers have an extension of the front table called a *rabbeting arm* used to support the stock when cutting rabbets.

2. *Rear* or *outfeed table*, also made of machined cast iron, is usually fixed at the height of the knives, though it is adjustable. It is used to support the stock after it has been cut.

3. *Front table adjustment wheel*, made of cast iron, is used to raise and lower front table to adjust depth of cut.

4. *Rear table adjustment wheel*, made of cast iron, is used to raise and lower rear table.

5. The *fence*, made of machined cast iron, is used as a guide to support stock at correct angle.
6. The *guard*, made of cast iron or aluminum, covers knives and protects the operator.
7. The steel *cutter head* is the unit into which the knives are inserted and locked in position.
8. The high-speed steel *knives* do the cutting.
9. The *motor* supplies the power. The motor on 4″ and 6″ machines is usually ½ H.P., on 8″ and 10″, one H.P., 1700 to 2500 RPM.
10. On other than direct drive machines, a rubber fiber composition *belt* transmits the power.
11. The *stand* supports the machine. It may be made of cast iron, pressed steel, or wood.

Maintenance

Adjusting

Jointers may vibrate out of adjustment from continuous use. The rear or outfeed table should be the same height as the cutting edge of the knives when they are at the highest point (except for specialty cuts). See Topic 73 on "Setting Jointer Knives."

Sharpening

Honing

Knives may be honed with an oilstone while they are still in the cutter head. Select an oilstone with a fine, flat face. Place it on the in-feed table so that it is at right angle to the cutter head and with paper between the table and stone to prevent scratching the table, hold the cutter head so that the blade will be slightly off top center (highest point). Place the stone so the uncovered section is beyond the cutting edge. Move the stone along the length of the blade to remove burrs and produce a sharp edge. Count the number of strokes so each blade is treated alike. When the new bevel caused by honing exceeds $\frac{1}{32}$″,

the knives should be reground. This operation should be done only by an experienced person.

Jointing

When the knives are too dull to be honed quickly and sufficient time is not available to have them reground, they may be jointed. This is done by lowering the out-feed table slightly below the knives ($\frac{1}{64}$″) when the knives are at the highest point. The in-feed table is raised to the level of the out-feed table. Check the level positions with a straightedge with the knives off center. Wrap a piece of paper around each end of a medium oilstone to prevent scratching the tables. Place the stone at a right angle across the knives with one end resting on the in-feed table and the other end on the out-feed table. Start the machine and slowly move the stone from one end of the blades to the other. Stop the machine and examine the blades for sharpness. This should be done in an emergency only and by an experienced person.

Oiling

1. Some jointers are equipped with sealed bearings while others require greasing periodically.
2. Whenever a jointer is to be left idle for a long period of time, all machined parts should be coated with a thin film of oil.

Market Analysis

Capacity

The capacity of the jointer is determined by the length of knives (width of table), the length of the table, and the depth of cut.

Attachments

Some jointers have a grinder attachment which allows knives to be sharpened without removing them from the cutter head.

Additional Reading

Delta Manufacturing Company, *Getting the Most Out of Your Circular Saw and Jointer*

Topic 73. Setting Knives and Aligning Rear Jointer Table

Classification

Adjustment of tables for true cut

Procedure

Setting Jointer Knives

1. Remove the guard and the fence to expose the cutter head.
2. Remove the dull knives from the cutter head by loosening the blade clamp (gib) bolts with a wrench.
3. Wrap a cloth around a screwdriver blade; then clean the cavity in the cutter head in which the blade and blade clamp are located. If pitch or gum is in the cavity, use a solvent to loosen it.
4. Place one sharp blade and the blade clamp in position. The bevel of the blade should face the rear table.
5. Hold the blade in position by tightening the blade; clamp bolts finger-tight.
6. Adjust the blade so that it is as high as the rear table when the blade is at its highest point. (This should not exceed $\frac{3}{16}''$ above the cutter head.) The blade may be adjusted by placing a strong horseshoe magnet or a block of previously-jointed hard wood on the rear table. Raise the blade until it comes in contact with the magnet or the wood. Check to make sure the full length of the blade is even with the rear table.
7. Tighten the blade clamp bolts with a wrench.
8. Repeat Steps 3 through 7 for each of the remaining knives.
9. Recheck each blade to see that it is as high as the rear table when the knife is at its highest point.
10. Recheck to see that each knife clamp bolt is *tight*.
11. Replace the guard and the fence.
12. A trial run should produce a smooth, even cut.

Aligning Rear Jointer Table

The outfeed or rear table on the jointer must be adjusted so that it is level with the cutting edge at the highest point. If this is not done accurately the resultant cut will not be true.

1. Turn the cutter head so that one of the blades is at its highest point.
2. Unlock the outfeed table and lower the table so that it is below the height of the cutter blade.
3. Place a hardwood straightedge on the table so that one end rests on the table and the other end rests on the edge of the cutter blade.
4. Raise the table slowly until the straightedge rests evenly on the table and the edge of the cutter. Move the straightedge on the table back and forth over the cutter. This movement should cause the cutter head to make a slight motion of rotation. It should not raise the straightedge, or move the cutter head excessively.
5. Lock the outfeed table in position and recheck alignment on both sides of the table as well as the center. Do this for each of the blades.
6. Replace all guards.
7. Set the infeed table for a light cut.
8. Start the jointer and make a cut several inches into the face of the flat board.
9. The cut should slide onto the rear outfeed table without hitting the table or showing any light between the table and the surface of the board that has just been cut.

Safety Considerations

1. Disconnect power supply before making adjustments or removing guards.
2. Check that blades are even with the rear table and securely fastened in the cutter head.

3. Tighten all adjustments before using.
4. Replace all guards.
5. Make only light cuts on the face of stock.

Additional Reading

Delta Manufacturing Company, *Getting the Most Out of Your Circular Saw and Jointer*

Topic 74. Smoothing a Surface on the Jointer

Classification

Removing stock by shearing with rotating edge cutters

Procedure

Planing an Edge

CAUTION: **A board less than 12″ in length should not be surfaced on this machine. Be sure the stock is free of nails, grit, paint, and other foreign materials.**

1. Adjust the fence so that it is at the desired angle to the table, Fig. 7-2.
2. Set the front infeed table for a light cut. It is better to make several light cuts than one heavy cut, to reduce possibility of kick-backs and chipping of stock.
3. Be certain all guards are in position.
4. Start the machine, standing to one side. Hold the trued face of the board against the fence with the grain pointing down and to the rear; push the edge of the board over the cutter in a slow, even motion, Fig. 7-3. The speed at which the work is fed over the cutter head will determine the spacing between the cuts (seen as machine marks on the surface). Be sure that enough downward pressure is applied to keep the board flush on the table.

Fig. 7-2. Testing Fence for Squareness

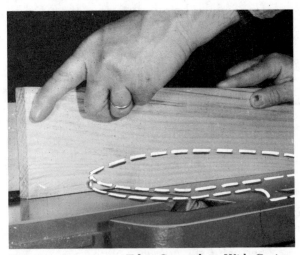

Fig. 7-3. Jointing an Edge Correctly — With Grain

5. If the stock has high spots or an uneven edge, it will need to be passed over the cutters several times to remove the high spots and true the edge.

Planing a Surface

1. The length of the jointer knives will determine the width of the board that may be planed. Jointers are made with knives from 4″ to 16″ in length. (This is the common statement of jointer size.)

2. The width and hardness of the board will determine the depth of cut. Generally, the maximum cut should not exceed ⅟₁₆″.

3. Lay the board on the infeed table with the grain pointing toward the infeed table and away from the knives. With downward pressure, push the board forward over the cutters, Fig. 7-4. Always use a push shoe, Fig. 7-5. When the stock has been passed partially over the cutter, transfer one hand to the stock on the outfeed table and apply downward and forward pressure, continuing the cut. Cupped stock should have the concave face down.

4. Stock that has high places or an uneven surface will need to be passed over the cutter several times to true the surface.

5. Warped or twisted pieces should be held in one position and kept from rocking while being run over the cutter. This is especially important on the first few cuts until a flat surface has been made.

6. Care should be taken to distribute hold-down pressure evenly across the width of the board.

Squaring Stock on the Jointer

1. Check the position of the fence so that it is square with the table.

2. Plane the better face first. The grain should point down to the rear of the table to get a good, smooth cut.

3. Hold this true face against the fence, and joint the adjacent edge.

4. Joint to width. If very much stock is to be removed, cut first on the circular saw leaving ⅟₁₆″ for one full finish cut on the jointer.

5. With one of the previously jointed edges against the fence, joint the remaining surface.

Cutting a Rabbet

1. The depth of the rabbet that may be cut on any particular make of jointer is limited to the travel and bearing surface of the rabbeting arm. Most smaller machines will cut a rabbet the width of the knives and to a depth of ½″.

2. Set the fence to the width of the rabbet. This is measured from the outside edge of the cutters.

3. The cutter guard must be removed on most machines to allow the board to pass by the end of the cutter head.

4. On shallow rabbets lower the infeed table so the depth of the cut may be

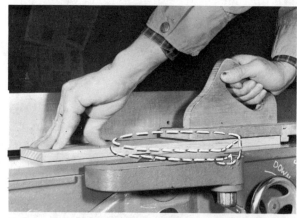

Fig. 7-4. Jointing a Face — Note Use of Push Shoe

Fig. 7-5. Push Shoe

made in one operation. If the rabbet is both wide and deep, it is advisable to make several cuts.

Cutting a Bevel or Chamfer

1. Most fences may be tilted to angles between 30° and 90°. The angle may be measured by the protractor on the locking mechanism or by measuring with a protractor head of a square or a T-bevel.
2. After the desired angle has been obtained, proceed as in regular jointing, Fig. 7-6.
3. Stop-chamfering may be done by lowering both the infeed and outfeed tables to the depth of the chamfer. Clamp stop blocks to the fence to limit the length of cut. With one end of the stock against the infeed block, slowly lower the work over the revolving cutters to the required depth and then push forward till the outfeed stop block is reached. Then lift the work free of the cutters. It is better to take several light cuts when making a heavy chamfer. This will necessitate changing both tables.

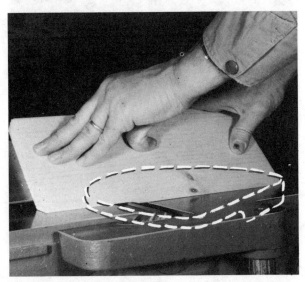

Fig. 7-6. Cutting a Bevel

Cutting Tapers

1. Tapers may be cut on the jointer by lowering the front table and starting the cut with the stock resting on the rear table. However, it is advisable to cut the taper on the circular saw and smooth the surfaces on the jointer in the same manner as jointing an edge, Fig. 7-7.

Standards and Results

1. Light, even cuts will produce a smoother surface than a heavy cut.
2. All surfaces should be smooth with the planer cutter marks very small.
3. Always plane with the grain.

Safety Considerations

1. Never run your hands directly over the cutter head when planing the face of stock.
2. Always keep the hands above the surface of the board.
3. Use a push block on short lengths.
4. Boards less than 12″ should not be planed.
5. Stand to one side while operating machine.

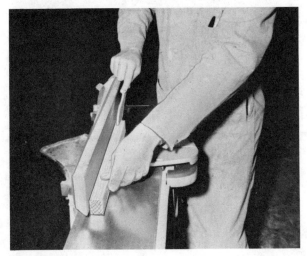

Fig. 7-7. Cutting a Taper

6. Always have guard over the knives when jointer is running.
7. Be sure stock is free of nails, grit, paint, loose knots, and other foreign materials.
8. Never make cuts greater than ⅟₁₆″ when jointing or facing stock.
9. Depth of cut to be made should be adjusted before machine is started.
10. Set-ups for specialty cuts such as bevels, chamfers, stop-chamfers, and tapers should be checked by instructor before cuts are made.

Additional Reading

Delta Manufacturing Company, *Getting the Most Out of Your Circular Saw and Jointer*

Fig. 7-7A. Close-Up of Cutting a Taper

Topic *74A.* Uniplane

Classification

Power driven rotary edge cutting tool

Application

Principle of Operation

The *uniplane* is a round disk shaped cutterhead with eight quick-change highspeed cutting bits. It revolves at speeds of 4000 RPM around a stationary faceplate. The eight cutting bits act as a series of continuous set of cutting wedges making 32,000 cuts per minute.

The eight cutting bits are divided into two sets; (1) one for scoring and (2) the other for shearing. The blades are set alternately (scoring, shearing, scoring, shearing, etc.) in the cutter head. The first cutting bit entering the wood surface scores the depth of cut and the second follows shearing out of the chip. This allows the cut to be made with or across the grain without splintering.

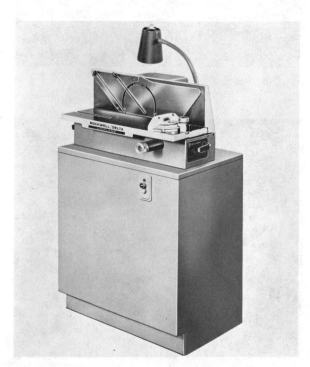

Fig. 7-7B. Uniplane (Courtesy Delta Div., Rockwell Mfg. Co.)

Kinds and Uses

The uniplane is used for planing faces and edges straight and smooth, and to cut bevels, chamfers, and tapers.

Principal Parts and Function of Each

1. *Table* made of cast iron tilts to an angle of 45° for cutting chamfers and bevels. A slot is provided for the miter gauge guide.
2. *Table trunnions* support the table for tilting.
3. *Infeed fence* made of cast iron is adjustable for depth of cut.
4. *Cutters* of high speed steel in a set of eight, four for shearing and four for scoring.
5. *Faceplate*, made of cast iron, supports the wood being cut.
6. *Outfeed fence*, made of cast iron, supports the wood as it is fed through the machine. Also supports arbor arm for cutterhead.
7. *Cutterhead* is dynamically balanced cast iron and contains eight cutting tools.
8. *Base*, made of cast iron, supports trunnion guides for table pivot.
9. *Stand* houses motor and belt drive.

10. *Belt guard* covers driving pulleys and belt.
11. *Micro set control* is graduated in 64ths of an inch to adjust depth of cut.
12. *See-through plastic guard* covers the cutting head in operation.

Maintenance
Adjusting Cutter Bits

Cutter bits are set with a guide to project from the surface of the stationary faceplate to either .003" or .005".

Sharpening Cutter Bits

Cutter bits are sharpened by shaping on a grinder and then honing to a keen edge on an oilstone. The original shape must be maintained.

Preventing Rust

Finished surfaces should be protected from rust with either paste wax or oil.

Market Analysis
Capacity

The uniplane will surface to 6" in width and ⅛" depth.

Additional Reading

Rockwell Delta catalog

Topic 75. Single Surface Planer

Classification

Power-driven rotating edge-cutting tool

Application

Principle of Operation

Three full-width knives are set equidistant along the circumference of the cutter head which revolves at speeds ranging from 3600 to 7200 r.p.m. The knives cut on the principle of a continuous set of cutting wedges. On some surfacers, the rate of feed may be varied, so that generally speaking, the slower speed of feed results in more cuts per inch, producing fewer machine marks (see page 105), Fig.

7-8A. On most surfacers, the stock is passed under the cutter head.

Kinds and Uses

1. Surfacers are used to plane stock to uniform thickness with surfaces parallel.
2. Single surfacers plane one face at a time. Small surfacers will plane stock up to 4" thick and 12" wide, while larger sizes will plane stock up to 8" thick and 50" wide.
3. Double surfacers plane two surfaces at a time. Small double surfacers will plane stock up to 7" thick and 30" wide. Larger machines handle stock up to 14" thick and 40" wide.

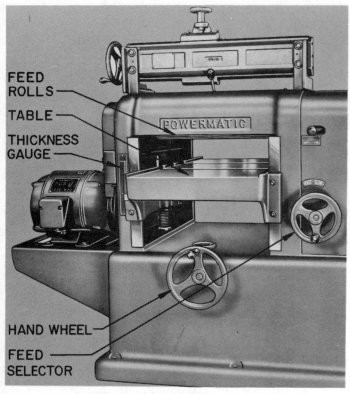

FEED ROLLS
TABLE
THICKNESS GAUGE
HAND WHEEL
FEED SELECTOR

Fig. 7-8. Surfacer (Courtesy Powermatic Machine Co.)

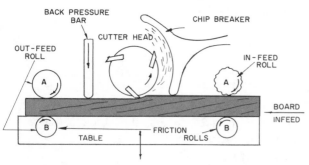

BACK PRESSURE BAR
CHIP BREAKER
CUTTER HEAD
OUT-FEED ROLL
IN-FEED ROLL
A
A
BOARD INFEED
B
B
FRICTION ROLLS
TABLE

TABLE RAISES AND LOWERS FOR DEPTH OF CUT

Fig. 7-8A. Cross Section of Single Surfacer

Principal Parts and Function of Each

1. The cast iron or machined steel *table* is a flat bed which supports the stock as it passes under the knives. The amount of stock removed is determined by the difference between the thickness of the stock and the opening between the knives and the table. The cut is made parallel to the bed.

2. The *feed rolls*, made of machined steel, feed the stock into the machine. The upper infeed roll is usually sectional and corrugated to provide better traction on narrow stock or pieces of uneven thickness.

3. The *chip breaker*, made of steel or cast iron, breaks the shavings and deflects them away from the in-feeding stock. It prevents splintering and helps to hold the stock against the table.

4. The *cutter head*, made of alloy steel, holds the knives (usually three knives).

5. *Knives* of high-speed, oil-hardened steel do the cutting.

6. Back *pressure bar*, made of cast iron or steel, holds the stock firmly to the bed after the cut has been taken and the stock is reduced in thickness. It keeps stock from chattering.

7. *Outfeed* or *delivery rolls*, made of machined steel, carry the stock out of the machine.

8. *Hand wheel*, made of cast iron, raises and lowers the table to regulate the amount of cut for desired thickness of stock.

9. The *motor* size varies with the size of the machine (3 H.P. for 12″, up to 15 H.P. for 36″). The larger surfacers have two motors, one for the cutter head and one for the feed and delivery rolls.

10. *Feed selector* increases or decreases the rate of feed (15 to 45 feet per minute).

11. *Thickness gauge* indicates approximately what the thickness will be if stock is run through on that setting.

Maintenance

1. Follow the manufacturer's recommendations for adjusting rolls, chip breaker, and back pressure bar.

2. Sharpening should be done by an experienced person.

3. Surfacers should be periodically greased. See manufacturer's specifications for S.A.E. number of grease to use.

4. Feed rolls, chip breaker, and back pressure bar should be kept free of pitch.

Market Analysis

Capacity

Small surfacers will plane stock up to 4″ thick and 12″ wide. Larger ones will plane stock up to 8″ thick and 50″ wide.

Attachments

1. Grinding attachments by which the knives are ground without removing them from the cutter head.

2. Honing attachments to hone knives in the head.

Topic 76. Using the Single Surface Planer

Classification

Reducing stock to uniform thickness by passing it through an adjustable opening and under a revolving cutter head

Procedure

For accurate work on single-surface planers, one side of the stock to be planed must first be faced on the jointer, then run through the surfacer with the face side down, until parallel thickness is established.

Stock less than twelve inches in length or ¼″ in thickness should not be run through the surface planer. The stock should be clean and free of all foreign material such as grit, paint, and other finishes.

1. Set the table to the desired opening. In planing soft woods or narrow boards a heavier cut may be taken than on hard woods or wide stock. One-sixteenth of an inch is a recommended maximum amount to be taken in one cut. Check thickness along the board and set the table in accordance with the thickest section. On most surfacers one complete revolution of the hand wheel in a clockwise direction will raise the bed ¹⁄₁₆″.

2. Check the grain of the stock. Try to determine direction and feed the stock so that the cut will be made with the grain.

3. Feed the stock in at right angles to the cutter head.

4. Run the stock through as many times as necessary to reduce to the desired thickness. Once parallel thickness has been established, successive cuts should be taken off alternate faces. In doing this, stock must be turned end for end so that planing will always be with the grain.

5. Boards should not be allowed to drop on the floor. Long boards should be supported at each end.

6. In planing squares, two adjacent faces are first planed straight and square

Fig. 7-9. Surfacing a Board

(jointed). The two remaining faces are then planed parallel to these squared faces.

7. Stock to be used in carpentry work, or that which is impractical to surface on the jointer to get one true face, should be placed on the surfacer table so that the concave surface is face down. Only a light cut should be taken on alternate faces.

8. Stock of ¼″ in thickness should be placed on top of another board and run through the planer.

Standards and Results

1. Stock should be smooth, free from chips, excessive cutter marks, and wind.
2. Long pieces should be free of chip impressions.

Safety Considerations

1. Stand to one side of the stock when feeding or receiving.
2. Keep hands away from feed rolls.
3. Locate stopping mechanism before starting machine. If stock gets stuck, shut off machine; and when machine has completely stopped, lower the table and remove the board.
4. Loose knots should be removed before the board is run through the surfacer.
5. When surfacing wet stock, lubricate the table with kerosene or wax.
6. Crossgrained stock should never be fed through the surfacer.
7. Stock shorter than the distance between the feed and delivery rolls (usually 12″) should not be surfaced. Stock less than ¼″ in thickness is apt to break, if not supported by a backer board.

Topic 77. Squaring a Board by Machine Process

Classification

Cutting to dimension with adjacent sides at right angles; removing warp (which includes wind or twist, cup, crook, and bow, see page 101.)

Procedure

Lumber for cabinet work is usually purchased rough, then planed to specific thickness. Full length boards with warp must be handled in small sections if these distortions are to be removed. Passing a board with distortions through the thickness planer will not correct these conditions. See Figs. 7-10, 7-11, 7-12.

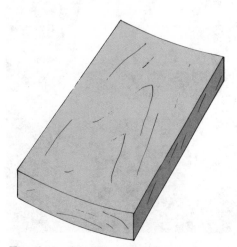

Fig. 7-10. "Cup" in a Board

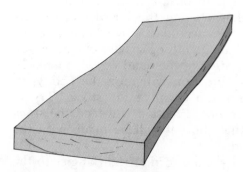

Fig. 7-11. "Wind" or "Twist" in a Board

Getting Out Stock

1. Determine the rough length (desired finish size plus 1″) of the pieces of stock required. Be sure that the sections to be surfaced are longer than 12″, the minimum for safe work on the jointer or surfacer.

2. Crosscut to rough length. Use the radial arm saw, portable circular saw, table saw, or hand crosscut saw.

3. Rip to rough width. Allow about ½″ more than the finished dimension. Note that if there is cup in the board, the dish is placed face down on the table saw, Fig. 7-13. This operation will cut out some of the warp. If a board has excessive cup, it is advisable to rip the board to several equal sections, surface to dimensions, then glue up to needed width. A band saw may also be used to rip to rough width by following a pencil line.

Jointing One Face

1. Use jointer if it is wide enough; if not, joint by hand plane.

2. Plane one side flat and straight. The cup side is the one to straighten, Fig. 7-14.

NOTE: On warped stock, the use of the thickness planer alone for this operation only planes to the original warp. The pressure rolls flatten the board while the cutters do the work. As the board passes the rolls and the pressure is relieved, the board springs back to its original shape. On the jointer where the pressure is controlled by hand one side can be cut perfectly flat.

Jointing One Edge

1. Hold the face that has just been planed against the jointer fence and plane an edge square and straight.

Surfacing to Thickness

1. With the finished face down on the table, the board is passed through the thickness planer until the desired thickness is obtained, Fig. 7-15.

2. If a thickness planer is not available, use a marking gauge to scribe the desired thickness around the perimeter of the board. Then surface on the jointer as close to the scribed line as possible. Finish by hand planing.

Ripping to Finished Width

1. Set the rip fence on the circular saw to the proper dimension, allowing $\frac{1}{16}$″ for finished jointing.

2. With the jointed edge against the rip fence, pass the board through the saw.

Jointing to Finished Width

1. With one face against the fence, joint the second edge to the finished width.

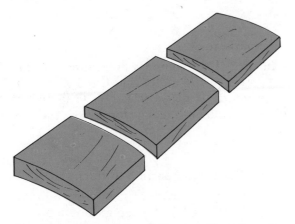

Fig. 7-12. Warped Board Cut into Short Lengths

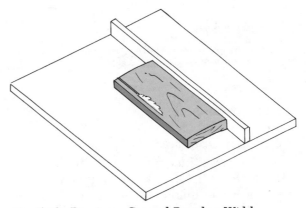

Fig. 7-13. Ripping a Cupped Board to Width

Cutting to Finished Length

1. Square one end of the board on the circular saw. Keep the jointed edge against the miter gauge.
2. Layout and square a line at the finished length. If several pieces are to be cut to the same length, a length gauge or stop blocks should be used with the cross cut fence to insure identical pieces.
3. Cut to finished length. Use the same jointed edge next to the cross cut fence as was used in squaring the first end.

Standards and Results

1. All distortion should be removed from the board. It should test square on all surfaces.
2. All surfaces should be smooth and to the correct dimensions.

3. There should be no chipped edges or excessive planer marks made by the rotary cutters (see page 105).

Safety Considerations

1. All safety practices in the operations of each machine should be observed.
2. Get instructor's approval before proceeding with any operations.

Additional Reading

Topic 49, "Using the Circular Saw"
Topic 55, "Using the Band Saw"
Topic 56, "Using the Band Saw"
Topic 74, "Smoothing a Surface on the Jointer"
Topic 76, "Using the Surface Planer"

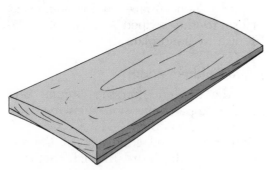

Fig. 7-14. Facing the Cupped Side

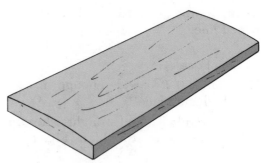

Fig. 7-15. Surfacing the Convex Side to Thickness

Topic 78. Portable Hand Router

Classification

Power driven rotary shaping tool

Application

Principle of Operation

In the router, bits revolve at a spindle speed of 5,000 to 27,000 r.p.m., shaping on the principle of a continuous set of cutting wedges, Fig. 7-16.

Kinds and Sizes

The size of the router is determined by the horsepower of the motor and the diameter of the cutter shaft. The router is used to cut moldings, rout, cut gains for inlay, and cut dovetails.

Principal Parts and Function of Each

1. The *motor* provides the power and may be from ¾ to 3 H.P., depending upon the size of the router.

2. The *base*, made of machined cast aluminum, is adjusted to determine the depth of cut.

3. *Straight* and *circular guide,* made of cast aluminum, acts as a fence for routing out or shaping parallel to a straight or curved edge.

4. The bits made of tempered, high-carbon tool steel, shape the stock, Fig. 7-17.

5. The rosewood or plastic knobs serve to hold and guide the router.

Maintenance

1. Router bits should be kept sharp. Sharpening should be done by an experienced person.

2. Some routers require periodic oiling; others have sealed bearings.

Market Analysis

Capacity

The capacity of a router is determined by the size of the bit which may be used, in terms of its diameter and depth.

Attachments

1. Dovetail attachment including finger template which is used to cut dovetails on case or box work, Fig. 7-18.

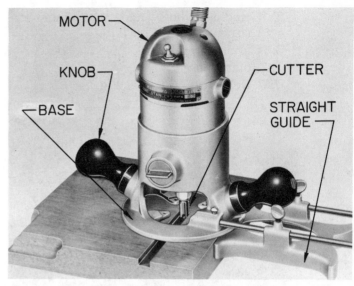

Fig. 7-16. Hand Router (Courtesy Stanley Tool Co.)

Fig. 7-16A. Late Model Router (Courtesy Stanley Tool Co.)

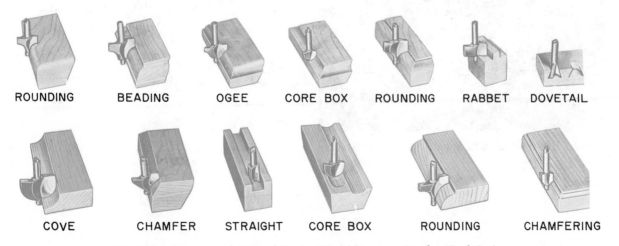

ROUNDING   BEADING   OGEE   CORE BOX   ROUNDING   RABBET   DOVETAIL

COVE   CHAMFER   STRAIGHT   CORE BOX   ROUNDING   CHAMFERING

Fig. 7-17. Shapes and Uses of Router Bits (Courtesy Stanley Tool Co.)

2. Grinding wheels and attachment for sharpening bits, Fig. 7-19.
3. Carving attachment.
4. Rotary files.
5. Circle cutting device, Fig. 7-20.

6. Fluting and beading attachment, Fig. 7-26.

Additional Reading

Stanley Tool Company, *Using Your Router*

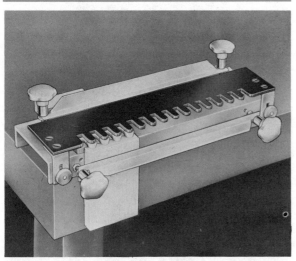

Fig. 7-18. Setup of Finger Template for Dovetailing (Courtesy Stanley Tool Co.)

Fig. 7-20. Circle Cutting Device (Courtesy Stanley Tool Co.)

Fig. 7-19. Grinding Attachment (Courtesy Stanley Tool Co.)

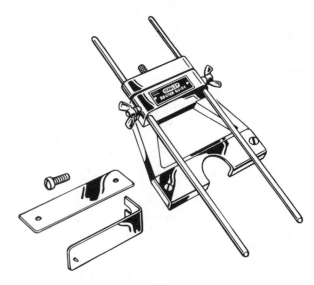

Fig. 7-20A. Straight Gauge for Routing (Courtesy Stanley Tool Co.)

Topic 79. Using a Portable Hand Router

Classification

Shaping, molding, and recessing with a rotary cutter

Procedure

The hand router may be used for cutting gains for inlay lines and insets, cutting rabbets, cutting gains for hinges, (Fig. 7-25), reading and fluting on turnings, (Fig. 7-26), cutting moldings, and cutting dovetails. (For the use of the router to cut gains for inlay lines and insets see Topic 139, "Applying Inlay and Insets.")

Cutting a Rabbet or a Dado

1. Select a straight router bit (Fig. 7-17) of the proper size, and secure it in the chuck (Fig. 7-21).
2. Adjust the base to give the desired depth of cut.
3. Adjust the straight guide to give the desired width of cut, Figs. 7-21, 7-22.
4. The stock to be rabbeted should be fastened securely to a bench.
5. Start the motor and slowly move the router over the stock, making sure that the base is held flat against the stock and the gauge is tight against the edge.

6. Rabbets wider than the diameter of the bit may be made by moving the gauge and taking two cuts. (Dadoes and grooves are cut as above with bits of the same size as the width of the groove or dado.)

Cutting Gains for Hinges

A special bit is available for cutting gains for hinges.

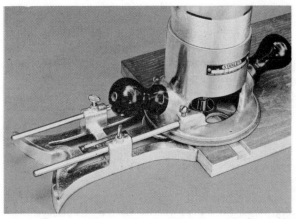

Fig. 7-22. Using Straight Gauge to Cut a Dado (Courtesy Stanley Tool Co.)

Fig. 7-23. Straight Edge forms Guide — Edge Block Prevents Splitting (Courtesy Stanley Tool Co.)

Fig. 7-21. Using Straight Gauge to Cut a Rabbet (Courtesy Stanley Tool Co.)

A special metal template is designed for this type of work. It is adjustable for two or three hinges and for any standard size door.

1. Follow the manfacturer's specifications in setting up this template, Fig. 7-25.
2. Set the base of the router to give the desired depth of cut.
3. In following the template keep the base tight against the template plate.
4. Remove the material within the area of the hinge.
5. When square-cornered hinges are used it will be necessary to cut the corners out with a chisel.

Fluting and Beading

The attachment for beading and fluting consists of a cast iron motor holder that is mounted on a wooden sub-base, Fig. 7-26. The router is mounted in the holder and is adjusted for height. Most beading and fluting is done on stock that has been turned in a lathe.

1. Clamp a board to the ways of the lathe. This provides a base for the attachment.
2. Select the desired bit and collar. The collar size determines the depth of the cut.
3. Lay out the length of flute or bead to be cut on the spindle.
4. Mount the stock between the lathe centers.

Fig. 7-24. New Type Router Gauge (Courtesy Stanley Tool Co.)

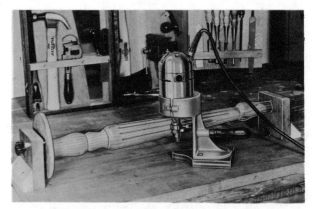

Fig. 7-26. Fluting and Beading Set-Up (Courtesy Stanley Tool Co.)

Fig. 7-25. Cutting Gains for Hinges (Courtesy Stanley Tool Co.)

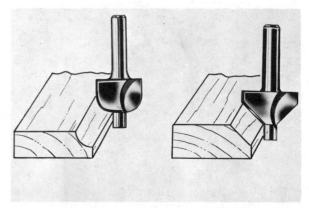

Fig. 7-26A. Molding a Cove or a Chamfer with Router Bits (Courtesy Stanley Tool Co.)

5. With the index head, Fig. 11-18B, lock the spindle so that the stock cannot turn.

6. Start the motor of the router. Make the cut by moving the router along the spindle with the collar in contact with the work at all times.

7. Release the index head, turn the spindle the desired amount and relock. Proceed as in step 6 until proper number of flutes or beads have been cut.

Molding

1. Select the desired bit. Some bits are provided with a pilot to limit the depth of the cut, Fig. 7-27.

2. Lock the bit in the router and adjust the base to the desired height.

3. If the bit has no pilot on it, the straight or circular gauge must be attached and adjusted to give proper depth of cut.

4. Start the machine and move it slowly along the edge of the stock. Make sure that the base is held flat against the surface of the stock being molded and that either the pilot or the straight and circular gauge is in contact with the edge at all times. (See Fig. 7-27.)

5. Care must be taken to prevent too much pressure against the edge when a bit with a pilot is used as this will cause burning. Burning may also occur if the cutter is dull or the router is not moved rapidly enough.

Dovetailing

To cut dovetails with a router requires a dovetail jig, guide template, and dovetail bit.

1. Attach the guide tip to the base of the router.

2. Insert the dovetail bit in the chuck.

3. Adjust the base so that the bit extends the correct depth. (See manufacturer's specifications as furnished with attachment.)

4. Mount the fixture on a bench. This may be done with screws or clamps. The

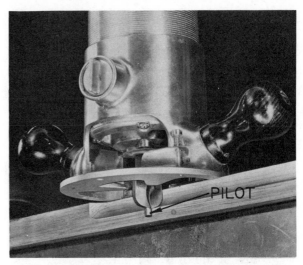

Fig. 7-27. Pilot Tip Molding Bit (Courtesy Stanley Tool Co.)

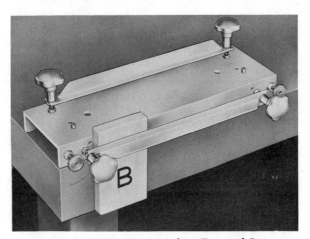

Fig. 7-28. First Piece Mounted in Dovetail Jig (Courtesy Stanley Tool Co.)

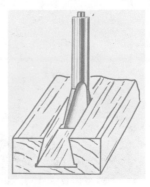

Fig. 7-28A. Dovetailing Bit for Router (Courtesy Stanley Tool Co.)

base should project slightly beyond the front edge.

The following instructions refer to parts of a drawer, since this is the most common dovetailing application. It is good practice to secure scrap stock of the same dimensions as the drawer parts, and make the set-up using this scrap stock for testing.

5. Clamp the board which is to be one side of the drawer, *B* in Fig. 7-28, with the inside surface facing the operator and in contact with the locating pin so that it protrudes above the surface of the base a distance equal to the thickness of the drawer front.

6. Place the drawer front with inside surface up and in contact with the locating pin and the full width of drawer side and clamp to the top surface of the base, Fig. 7-29.

7. Fasten the template to the base making certain that it is flat on the inside of the drawer front, Fig. 7-30.

8. Cut the dovetail by holding the router with the base against the template and with the guide template following the fingers of the template, Fig. 7-31.

9. After the cut has been made, fit the two pieces together. If the fit is too loose, lower the bit slightly, or if the fit is too tight, raise the bit slightly in relationship

to the base. When the fit is satisfactory, the drawer pieces may be cut. See Fig. 7-32.

10. The foregoing instructions apply to the making of any blind dovetail when using a dovetailing attachment.

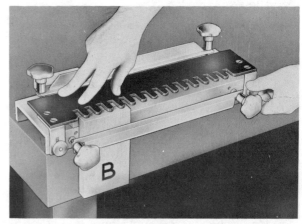

Fig. 7-30. Placing Finger Template in Position (Courtesy Stanley Tool Co.)

Fig. 7-31. Cutting the Dovetail (Courtesy Stanley Tool Co.)

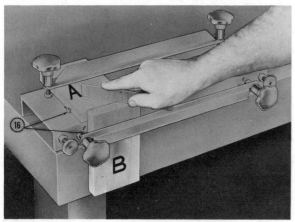

Fig. 7-29. Mounting Second Piece in Dovetail Jig (Courtesy Stanley Tool Co.)

Fig. 7-32. Assembled Dovetail Joints

Standards and Results

1. Rabbets should be parallel to an edge or end and of equal depth.
2. Stock should not be chipped at the end of dadoes, grooves, or rabbets.
3. Hinges should fit snugly in gains.
4. Surface of leaf hinge should be flush with surrounding area.
5. Flutes and beads should be equally spaced and of equal width and depth.
6. No burned marks should show on flutes, beads, or moldings.

7. Dovetail joints should fit snugly and the bottom edges should be even after assembly.

Safety Considerations

1. Safety goggles should be worn in using the router.
2. Keep your fingers and clothing away from the revolving cutters.
3. Be sure the bit is held tightly in the chuck.

Additional Reading

Manufacturers Catalogs

Topic 80. The Shaper

Classification

Power driven rotary cutting tool

Application

Principle of Operation

Standard sets of cutters, revolving at a spindle speed of 5,000 to 12,000 r.p.m., cut shapes on the principle of a continuous set of cutting wedges.

Kinds and Uses

The shaper is used to cut moldings, to make grooves and rabbets, and to smooth curved edges.

Shapers are sized according to the diameter of spindle and the size of table. Most shapers used in school shops are equipped with a 5/16" to 3/4" spindle with a table size of 20" x 28", Fig. 7-33.

Principal Parts and Function of Each

1. The *base or frame*, made of pressed steel, cast iron, or wood, supports the motor and table.
2. The *table*, made of machined cast iron, supports the fence and stock to be shaped.
3. The adjustable *fence*, made of cast iron with maple facing, is used as a guide when shaping.
4. The *spindle*, made of machined, high-grade steel, is a round drive shaft to which the cutters are attached.
5. The *cutters*, made of alloy steel, shape the stock.
6. The *mechanism to raise and lower the spindle* or table is made of machined cast iron.
7. The *guard* is made of pressed steel or hard rubber and protects the operator from injury.
8. The *motor* for a shaper suitable for school shops should be reversible, of 1 to 1½ H.P., 60 cycle, 3450 r.p.m.
9. *Miter gauge* is made of either cast iron or cast aluminum, and is used as a guide in shaping end grain.
10. The *taper pin and collar* is made of machined steel, and is used as a guide for circular and irregular shapes where a fence cannot be used. (See Figs. 7-37, 7-38, 7-39.)

Maintenance

1. Shaper cutters should be kept sharp. Sharpening should be done by an experienced person.
2. Some shapers require periodic greasing; others have sealed bearings.
3. Whenever a shaper is to be left for a long period of time, all machined parts should be coated with a film of oil to prevent rusting.

Market Analysis

Capacity

The capacity of a shaper is determined by the maximum size (diameter) and height of cutter which the machine will accommodate.

Attachments

1. Sliding shaper jig (miter gauge) which is used as a guide in cutting moldings on end grain.
2. Spring hold-downs help to hold work firmly against the fence and table.

3. Safety ring guard protects the operator from the knives and also presses the work against the table when neither a fence nor a miter gauge can be used.

Additional Reading

Manufacturers Catalogs

Fig. 7-33A. Automatic Multiple Spindle Shaper (Courtesy C. O. Porter Machinery Co.)

Fig. 7-33B. Automatic Multiple Spindle Router (Courtesy C. O. Porter Machinery Co.)

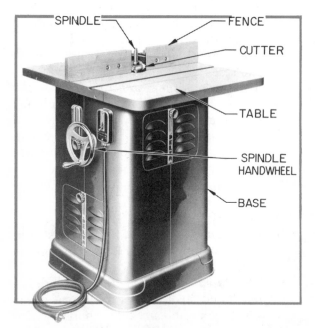

Fig. 7-33. Floor Model Shaper (Courtesy Delta Div., Rockwell Mfg. Co.)

Topic *81.* Cutting Moldings, Molding an Edge, Making Special Cuts for Joining Edges with a Shaper

Classification

Shaping to a profile with edge cutter

Procedure

There are four methods used in shaper operations:

1. Straight stock is run against a fence.
2. Curved stock is shaped by using collars and a pin.
3. Stock is fastened to a template. (This procedure is used when a number of duplicate parts is desired.)
4. A miter gauge is used.

Shaping Straight Stock with the Use of a Fence

1. Select the proper cutter and lock in place on the spindle. A collar may be placed above, below, or both above and below the cutter. See Fig. 7-35.
2. Adjust the cutter or the table to the desired height. Lock after adjustment is made.

3. Adjust the fence so that the cut will be of the desired depth. Lock in position.
4. Single spindle shapers are equipped with reversible motors. A check should be made to see that the motor is turning opposite to the direction of the feed.
5. Make a trial run on scrap stock before cutting finished piece.

Shaping Curved Stock with the Use of a Collar and Pin

1. Select the desired cutter and the proper size collar and lock in place on the spindle. (The diameter of the collar determines the depth of cut that the cutter will make.) Collars may be placed above or below the cutter or both above and below.
2. Adjust the spindle or table until the cutter is at the desired height.
3. If the cutter is set up to turn in a clockwise direction, the pin should be in-

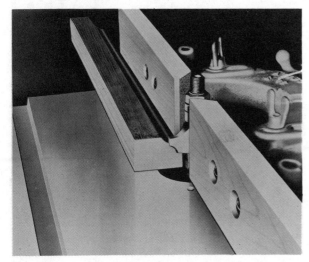

Fig. 7-34. Molding an Edge (Courtesy Delta Div., Rockwell Mfg. Co.)

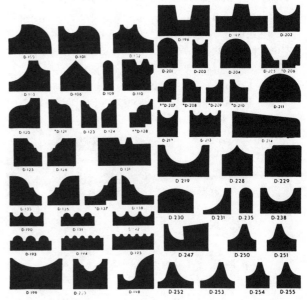

Fig. 7-35. Profiles of Shaper Cutters (Courtesy Delta Div., Rockwell Mfg. Co.)

serted in the hole on the left-hand side of the spindle. If it is to turn in a counter-clockwise direction, the pin should be inserted in the hole on the right-hand side. The pin should always be on the in-feed side of the table. See Figs. 7-37, 7-38, 7-39.

4. A check should be made to see that the motor is turning opposite to the direction of feed.

5. Test cut on scrap stock. Take a scrap piece of wood of the same thickness as that to be cut and place it against the pin.

   Feed stock into the cutter by gradually pivoting it until it is in contact with the collar.

6. Check the cut on the scrap stock. If satisfactory, make the cut on the good stock.

7. Feed the stock for the entire length of cut, making certain that the stock is in contact with the collar at all times. The feed should be continuous. A stop will cause a surface burn. *Keep your hands well away from the cutters.* (Fig. 7-36, 7-38, and 7-39.)

Shaping Stock with the Use of a Template

This method is very similar to the process of using a collar and pin. The difference is that the template is run against the collar rather than the stock itself.

1. Prepare a template which is either slightly smaller or slightly larger but of the same outline as the piece to be

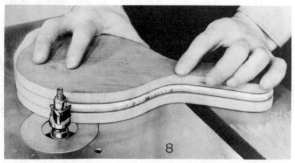

Fig. 7-36. Shaping, Using Template and Collar
(Courtesy Delta Div., Rockwell Mfg. Co.)

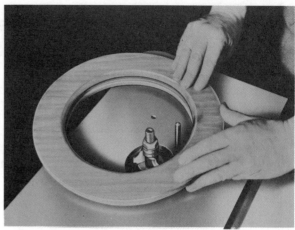

Fig. 7-37. Circular Shaping, Using Collar and Pin
(Courtesy Delta Div., Rockwell Mfg. Co.)

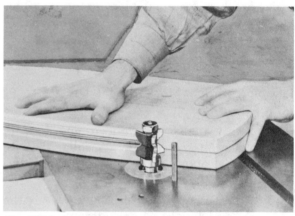

Fig. 7-38. Shaping Top and Bottom Edges, Using Template, Collar, and Pin
(Courtesy Delta Div., Rockwell Mfg. Co.)

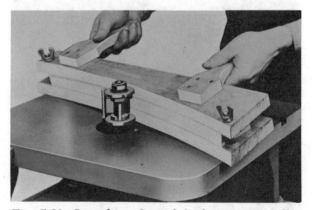

Fig. 7-39. Smoothing Curved Surface, Using Collar Above Cutter, Collar Below Cutter, Two Templates, and Pin
(Courtesy Delta Div., Rockwell Mfg. Co.)

Fig. 7-40. Double Spindle Shaper

Round, oval, irregular, bent, ogee, and numerous other shapes can be made on the shaper. Thousands of identical parts can be accurately duplicated on this machine. The knives of the shaper in this illustration operate at the terrific speed of 7200 r.p.m. The use of a frequency changer doubles the usual speed of driving motors. The faster the knives turn, the better the edge of the cut. (Courtesy Heywood-Wakefield Co.)

Fig. 7-41. Early Form of Hand Seat Saddler Used in Shaping Seats of Windsor Chairs (Courtesy Old Sturbridge Village, Inc.)

shaped. The size is determined by the size collar, size cutter, and depth of cut to be made.

2. Fasten the piece to be shaped to the template so that the overhang is the same all around. Pieces may be held in position by pins or clamps.
3. Follow the same procedure as that described for shaping with a pin and collar.

Shaping End Grain with the Use of a Miter Gauge and a Hold-Down Attachment

1. Select the proper cutter and lock in place on the spindle.
2. Adjust the fence to obtain the desired depth of cut.
3. Adjust the height of cutter or table to the desired position.
4. Make a trial run on scrap stock before final shaping of finished stock.
5. Place stock against miter gauge and secure with the hold-down attachment.

Fig. 7-42. Seat Saddler and Scooper

The stack of seat blanks feeds automatically into the cutter knives. When this picture was taken, the machine was set up for a simple scooping operation; a different arrangement of the knives would produce the saddling effect in addition to the scooping. (Courtesy Heywood-Wakefield Co.)

Fig. 7-43. The Sticker

A sticker is a four-sided molder which takes a rough piece of stock and planes it on all four sides simultaneously. To visualize the mechanism, one would have to imagine a long series of knives rotating from four directions toward a center. The finished cut may be square or molded. (Courtesy, Heywood-Wakefield Co.)

Standards and Results

1. Cuts should be free from chips.
2. Cuts should be the desired shape and depth.
3. Cuts should be uniform.

Safety Considerations

1. Always feed stock into cutter.
2. Keep your hands away from the cutter.
3. Make certain that the shaper is secured so that it will not move during operation.

Fig. 7-44. High Speed Molder

A precision automatic machine, the molder is used for making all sizes of quarter- and half-rounds, small bead moldings, venetian blind slats, as well as heavier moldings. The model illustrated here has a trackless chain feed bed. Sets of knives shaped to desired profile are arranged in each cutter head (2, 3, or 4) to plane or mold multiple surfaces in one feeding. (Courtesy Mattison Machine Works)

4. Make certain the floor area is clear of debris and the surface is not slippery.
5. Make certain spindle nut is tight.
6. Check all attachments and safety devices.
7. Never make cuts on stock less than 10″ in length.
8. Wear safety glasses when using the shaper.
9. The shaper generally is considered to be one of the most dangerous machines in a school shop.

Topic *82.* Wood File and Rasp

Classification

Serrated cutting tool

Application

Principle of Operation

The teeth of a file or rasp cut on the principle of the cutting wedge. The teeth are cut diagonally across the face of the file which permits a shearing cut. See Fig. 8-1.

Kinds and Uses

1. Both the rasp and file should be used only where space and shapes do not allow the use of sharp-edged tools. The various shapes of files are used to file corresponding curves and cuts in wood.
2. The file is used for a smoother cutting, Fig. 8-2.
3. The rasp is used for roughing off surfaces, Fig. 8-3.
4. An open-mesh serrated tool, consisting of a frame and a replaceable blade, may be used as a substitute for a file or rasp. (See Fig. 8-4.)
5. Files and rasps are described by length and shape as well as by *cut*, which refers to the coarseness and shape of the teeth.
6. Wood files are made in the following shapes: half round, cabinet, round, flat, pillar, square, crossing, pippin, knife, slitting, cant, and three square. See Fig. 8-6. The length of a file is measured

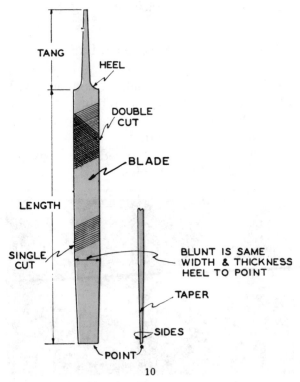

Fig. 8-1. Nomenclature of Files (Courtesy Simonds Saw & Steel Co.)

Fig. 8-2. Wood File (Courtesy Simonds Saw & Steel Co.)

Fig. 8-3. Half Round Rasp (Courtesy Simonds Saw & Steel Co.)

Fig. 8-4. Round Serrated-Tooth Type File — Surform (Courtesy Stanley Tool Co.)

from the shoulder of the tang to the tip of the blade. Files range in size from 4″ to 18″.

7. Files are made in the following degrees of coarseness: coarse, bastard, second cut, and smooth.

Fig. 8-5. Files, *Left to Right:* Single Cut, Double Cut, Rasp, and Vixen (Courtesy Nicholson File Co.)

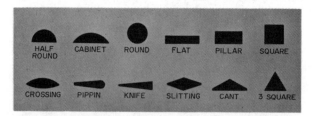

Fig. 8-6. Cross Section of Shapes of Files (Courtesy Nicholson File Co.)

Fig. 8-7. Half Round Files With and Without Handle

Fig. 8-8. Shoemakers' Rasp (Courtesy Nicholson File Co.)

8. Files are also made with two shapes of teeth — single cut and double cut. The single cut has parallel lines of teeth running diagonally across the file face. The double cut has a double series of teeth, crossing each other at an oblique angle. Single-cut files have a series of chisel edges, while double-cut files have staggered cutting points. Some files are made without teeth on the edge. These are called safety-edge files.

9. Wood rasps are made in two shapes: flat and half-round. They are made in four degrees of coarseness: rough, bastard, second cut, and smooth. They are made from 6″ to 16″ in length.

10. The surform (a tool which is often used instead of a rasp for quick removal of material) has a replaceable blade of hardened, tempered Sheffield steel with razor sharp non-clogging teeth designed for shaving wood and plastics. It is available in flat, plane type; flat, half round and round file types, and as an attachment for an electric drill, Fig. 8-4.

Principal Parts and Function of Each

Files and rasps are made of high grade steel. File handles (which do not come with files) are made of maple or birch.

1. The blade is the part on which the teeth are formed.

2. The tang is the tapered end on which the handle is attached.

Fig. 8-9. Cleaning File with File Card (Courtesy Nicholson File Co.)

Maintenance

Cleaning

Files and rasps should be cleaned with a file card after use, Fig. 8-9. When files and rasps are used on woods containing a great amount of pitch, it is wise to first cover the teeth with chalk dust to prevent particles from clogging the spaces between the teeth.

Storing

Files and rasps should be stored so that they do not come in contact with other files hard surfaces, or moisture.

Market Analysis

Attachments

The handle is used in holding the file for control of cut, Fig. 8-7. (Some handles are driven on, while other handles have screw threads in them and cut threads on the tang as the handle is turned on.)

Additional Reading

Disston Company, *Disston Saw, Tool, and File Manual*
Nicholson File Company, *File Filosophy*
Simonds Saw and Steel Company, *File Facts*

Interesting Fact: There are more than 3,000 types of files. They are classified according to length, shape, and spacing of teeth.

Topic 83. Shaping with a File or Rasp

Classification

Removing stock by shearing and shredding with a series of wedges

Procedure

1. The size and shape of the file to be used is determined by the surface of the work (half-round, flat, square, etc.). NOTE: The rasp is used for quick removal of stock when roughing to a line. Finishing cuts usually follow this operation.
2. Secure the work so that it is on a line with the height of the worker's elbow.
3. Grasp the handle of the file in the right hand with the index finger extending on top. The point of the file is held with the thumb and first two fingers of the left hand with the thumb on top. (Hand positions are reversed for left-handers.)
4. The file cuts on the forward stroke so pressure is released on the back stroke.

5. Filing end-grain or curved surfaces is done with a forward, sweeping motion diagonally across the grain to avoid cut-

Fig. 8-10. Filing a Convex Curve

Fig. 8-11. Filing End Grain

Fig. 8-12. Filing a Concave Surface

ting grooves, flat spots or hollow places, Figs. 8-10, 8-11.

When filing a concave surface, the file must be held at right angles with the work, Fig. 8-12.

To file a flat or convex surface, the file may be pointed in the direction of the surface.

6. When the file serrations become clogged, clean with a wire brush called a file card. If the file is to be used on resinous wood, fill serrations with chalk dust. A solvent may be used to clean the file.

Standards and Results

1. The file cut should be clean and smooth.
2. The filed surface should be according to specified shape and dimension.
3. There should be no file marks showing.

Safety Considerations

1. Use a file with a handle to avoid hand injury.
2. Clamp work securely for filing.
3. Allow sufficient clearance for full stroke without injury to hand, work surfaces, benches, or holding devices.

Additional Reading

Disston Company, *Disston Saw, Tool, and File Manual*

Nicholson File Company, *File Filosophy*

Stanley Tool Company, *How to Work With Tools and Wood*

Sanding is the process of using an abrasive to remove material from a surface. The cutting action is derived from the many sharp grains of abrasive material which act as tiny cutting wedges.

Topic 84. Coated Abrasives

Classification

Natural or manufactured abrading materials adhered to flexible backing

Composition or Description

Abrasive Used

1. *Flint quartz* is a natural mineral generally of yellowish cast.

2. *Garnet* is a natural mineral of reddish brown color.

3. *Silicon carbide* is manufactured from silicon (sand) and carbon fused together in an electric furnace. Its color is steel gray to black.

4. *Aluminum oxide* is manufactured from bauxite, carbon, and iron filings fused together in an electric furnace. Its color is light brown.

Backing Used

There are five general classes of backing used for abrasives, namely: paper, cloth, fiber, plastics, and a combination of paper and cloth. Paper backing is used on almost all hand sanding jobs; the others are used on machine sanders because of their strength, pliability, and the ease with which they conform to curved surfaces.

Grit cloth, a plastic screen coated with an adhesive and covered with silicon carbide or aluminum oxide, is a newer backing material.

Adhesive Used

Coated abrasives have two adhesive layers which bond the abrasive to the backing. The first is called the *bond coat* and the second the *size coat*. There are five types of adhesives used: animal glue, glue and filler, resin over glue, resin over resin and waterproof glue.

1. *Animal glue* — Animal hide glue, used both for bond coat and size coat.

2. *Glue and filler* — Animal hide glue to which a fine, inert filler has been added to produce a bond that is both durable and strong.

3. *Resin over glue* — A combination of hide glue for the bond coat and a synthetic resin for the size coat, making a bond that is highly resistant to heat.

4. *Resin over resin* — A synthetic resin glue, used for both the bond and size coat. This bond is resistant to both heat and moisture.

5. *Waterproof glue* — A synthetic resin glue for bonding and sizing. Used on a waterproof backing, permitting the use of water or other liquid lubricants in sanding.

Properties

1. Flint quartz lacks the hardness or durability of other abrasives, and the cutting action is short-lived.

2. Garnet is a fairly hard, tough mineral, making it an ideal abrasive for woodworking.

3. Silicon carbide is extremely hard and sharp. It is second to the diamond for

hardness, but it is a brittle material. This brittleness limits its usefulness in machine sanding.

4. Aluminum oxide is not quite as hard and the crystals are not as sharp as silicon carbide, but it is tough. These properties enable it to stand up under the most severe working conditions, making it an ideal material for sanding belts.

Uses

Coated abrasives in woodworking are used for hand and machine sanding, removing stock, cleaning, and polishing. Resinous woods or stock coated with paint or varnish are apt to clog the paper before it is worn. For this reason flint quartz, the cheapest form of coated abrasive, is recommended for such surfaces since there would be greater waste in the more expensive coated abrasives.

Market Analysis

Shapes

Sandpaper is available in sheets, belts, tapes, disks, rolls, and cylinders.

Sizes

Sheets are available in 9″ x 11″ and 4½″ x 5½″; belts from 2″ to 12″ wide; cylinders 1½″ to 3½″ in diameter; tapes 1″ and 1½″ wide; disks from 3″ to 14″ in diameter; and belts for bandsaws 1″ wide and 93½″ long.

Grades

1. *Open coat,* about 50% to 70% of the surface is covered with abrasive, providing greater flexibility and keeping the paper from clogging up with pitch, paint, or similar materials before the cutting edges of the grit have worn down.
   Closed coat — the abrasive grains cover the surface of the backing. This type gives longer service where the material does not clog.
2. *Cabinet paper* is used for sanding out machine marks and preparing the surface for finish. Grit ranges from 20 (very coarse) to 150 (fine).

3. *Finishing paper* is used for sanding just prior to the application of a finish and for sanding between coats. Grit ranges from 80 (medium) to 600 (very fine).

4. *Self-cleaning cloth* is used in belt sanders for removing glue from surfaces. This type of abrasive cloth has soap between the grains to prevent the grit from clogging.

5. *Self-cleaning paper* is a nonclogging paper which is coated with stearate and silicon carbide. Stearate is a salt of stearic acid, which comes from solids of animal fats (beef and lamb; also in milk and some vegetable fats). It is white in color, but when applied to silicon carbide paper, it gives the paper a grayish color.

Sales Units

1. Sheets of coated abrasive may be purchased in any quantity. The most economical way is in packages of 50 or 100. Handy assorted packages come with 12 quarter sheets to the package.
2. Belts, disks, and cylinders may be purchased in any number in sizes to fit standard machines.
3. Tape comes in 100-foot rolls.
4. The coarser the abrasive, the more expensive it is.

Maintenance

1. Extreme dryness makes the bonding adhesive brittle, while dampness softens the adhesive. Either condition will affect the grain-holding properties of the adhesive, shortening its life.
2. For best results in tearing sandpaper, fold both ways and tear over a square edge or use a special jig for tearing and cutting.
3. Paper clogged with wood dust may be cleaned with a stiff brush or by slapping it over a piece of stock, grit side up.

Additional Reading

Behr-Manning Company, *Sandpaper—Why and How*

Behr-Manning Company, *A Lecture Course in Coated Abrasives*

Table 16
Approximate Comparison of Grit Numbers

Uses		Silicon Carbide	Aluminum Oxide	Garnet	Flint	Grit No.
Hand or Light Machine Sanding		11/0	12/0			
		10/0	10/0		Extra Fine	400
	Finish	9/0	9/0			320
	Sanding	8/0	8/0	8/0		280
	Between	7/0	7/0	7/0		240
	Coats	6/0	6/0	6/0		220
		5/0	5/0	5/0	Fine	180
	Preparation	4/0	4/0	4/0		150
	for	3/0	3/0	3/0	Medium	120
	Finish	2/0	2/0	2/0		100
		0	0	0	Coarse	80
		½	½	½		60
Machine Sanding	Belt	1	1	1		50
	Sanding	1½	1½	1½		40
		2	2	2	Extra Coarse	36
	New	2½	2½	2½		30
	Floors	3	3	3		24
		3¼	3¼			22
	Machine	3½	3½	3½		20
	Sanding	3¾	3¾			18
	Old	4	4			16
	Floors to					
	Remove	4¼	4¼			14
	Finish	4½	4½			12

(Since April 1966, the grit numbers in the last column are used for all abrasives. The "ought" numbers are included for comparison only.)

Topic 85. Sanders—Spindle, Belt, Disk

Classification
Power driven abrading tool (rotary or reciprocating)

Application
Principle of Operation

1. A spindle sander has a rubber-coated spindle to which is fitted the coated abrasive sleeve. The spindle simultaneously rotates and oscillates up and down, Fig. 9-2.

2. In a belt sander, a cloth-coated abrasive belt revolves on one driver and one idler pulley while passing over a flat table on which stock is placed for sanding, Figs. 9-3, 9-4.

3. In a disk sander, a coated abrasive disk is attached to a metal disk which revolves in a clockwise direction, Fig. 9-1.

Kinds and Uses

1. Belt sanders are used to sand flat surfaces. Belt widths range from 4″ to 8″ and lengths from 4′ to 26′.
2. Disk sanders are used to sand straight and convex curves on edge. The diameters of disks range from 8½″ to 18″.
3. Spindle sanders are used to sand concave curves on edge. Sleeve diameters range from ¾″ to 3″ and lengths from 6″ to 9″.

NOTE: Portable belt sanders of various types and reciprocating orbital sanders are treated as a separate topic.

Spindle Sander —
Principal Parts and Function of Each

1. The *base* (made of either cast iron, pressed steel, or wood) supports the motor, table, spindle, and oscillating mechanism.
2. The *motor* (⅓ H.P., 2500 r.p.m.) provides the power.

3. The *table*, made of cast iron, machined, supports the work.
4. The *spindle*, made of machined steel, transmits the motion.
5. The *oscillating mechanism*, made of hardened steel, moves the spindle up and down as it rotates.
6. The *rubber spindle* is covered with a coated abrasive sleeve.

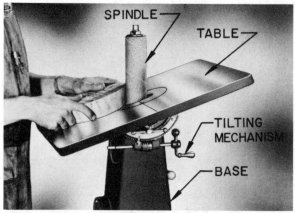

Fig. 9-2. Spindle Sander (Courtesy Boice-Crane Co.)

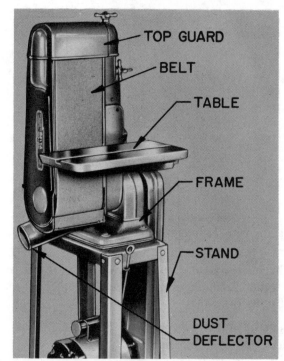

Fig. 9-3. Floor Model Belt Sander (Courtesy Delta Div., Rockwell Mfg. Co.)

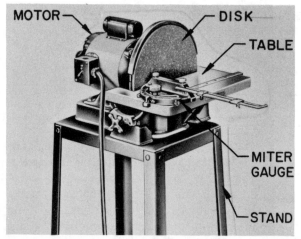

Fig. 9-1. Disk Sander (Courtesy Delta Div., Rockwell Mfg. Co.)

Belt Sander (Floor Model) — (See Fig. 9-4)
Principal Parts and Function of Each

1. *Stand* (made of cast iron, pressed steel, or wood) supports the motor, bed, and table.
2. The *bed* or *table*, made of machined cast steel, supports the work when the sander is in a horizontal position.
3. The *frame*, made of cast iron, supports the drums and table.
4. *Drums* (made of pressed steel covered with rubber) — one transmits the power; the other is adjustable to track and to keep tension on the belt.
5. The *dust deflector*, made of pressed steel or aluminum, deflects sanding dust.
6. *Adjustable table* supports the work when the sander is in a vertical position. It tilts 45° away from the belt and 30° toward the belt.
7. *Belt and pulley guards*, made of pressed steel, protect the operator.
8. The *motor* (½ or ¾ H.P., 1725 to 3450 RPM) provides the power. Horizontal belt sanders require more power than floor model belt sanders.
9. The *fence*, made of cast iron, guides the work to be sanded.

Disk Sander — (See Fig. 9-1)
Principal Parts and Function of Each

1. The *stand* (made of pressed steel, cast iron, or wood) supports the motor, table, and disk.
2. The *table*, made of machined cast iron, supports the work and tilts 45° away from and 20° toward the disk.
3. The *motor* (½ or ¾ H.P., 1725 r.p.m.) provides the power.
4. The *disk*, made of machined cast iron or aluminum, serves as a face plate to which the abrasive is fastened.

Maintenance

1. All moving parts should be kept oiled unless equipped with sealed bearings.

Fig. 9-4. Horizontal Belt Sander (Courtesy Boice-Crane Co.)

2. Whenever sanders are left unused for a long period of time, machined parts should be coated with a thin film of oil to prevent rusting.
3. When abrasive belts, disks, or cylinders become worn, torn or clogged, they should be replaced.

Market Analysis
Capacity

The capacity is limited mainly by the area of contact with the abrasive surface.

Attachments

1. Dust collector serves to minimize dust as a hazard to health, machinery and work.
2. Miter gauge is used as a guide for doing accurate work on the belt and disk sanders.

Topic 86. Portable Sanders—Belt, Disk, Finish

Classification

Power driven abrading tool (incline or rotary)

Application

Principle of Operation

There are three basic types of portable sanding machines, each designed to meet an exact need.

1. On the *belt sander,* a coated abrasive belt is run over a pad guided by an idler and driving drum.
2. On the *disk sander,* a coated abrasive disk rotates on a motor spindle.
3. On *finish sanders,* a coated abrasive strip fitted over a pressure pad is powered in an orbital or inline oscillating motion.

Kinds and Uses

The *belt sander* is used to do flush or regular sanding. Various grit belts are available in width and length to fit a specific make of machine. Sizes of belts range in width from 2″ to 4″ and in lengths from 21″ to 24″.

The *disk sander* is used in rough sanding for fast removal of stock and where a scratch-free surface is not a requisite. A pad may be fitted over the disk, enabling it to be used in a polishing operation.

Finish sanders are named according to their sanding motion.

A. *Orbital motion sander,* used in finish sanding, has a fast, circular pattern. It performs the hand-sanding operation on flat surfaces by its rapid action.
B. The *inline sander's* cutting action is back and forth in a straight line. This is ideal for the final sanding of wood surfaces. It leaves no sanding marks on the surface as produced by the orbital sander.

Principal Parts and Function of Each

Belt Sander

1. *Housing* is an aluminum die-casting designed for efficient handling and non-tiring use.
2. *Universal motor* provides power.
3. *Driving mechanisms* of various makers connect the motor to the driving drum by direct gear, rubber timing belt, spur gear, or chain worm gear drive.
4. *Driving drum,* made of aluminum, is covered by a rubber tire on which belt rides.
5. *Tracking* or *idler drum* is made of aluminum.
6. *Tracking mechanism* controls alignment of tracking drum so that belt rides within proper path.
7. *Tension device,* a spring unit, automatically maintains the correct belt tension by positioning the idler drum.

Fig. 9-5. Orbital Sander (Courtesy Porter-Cable Machine Co.)

Fig. 9-6. In-Line Oscillating Portable Sander (Courtesy Detroit Surfacing Machine Co.)

Fig. 9-7. Portable Belt Sander (Courtesy Black & Decker Mfg. Co.)

8. *Striker bar,* made of hardened steel, prevents the belt from riding against the housing.

9. *Sanding shoe* is positioned in line with the rim of the pulleys and covered by a pad and spring-steel wear strip. It maintains even pressure on the belt in the sanding operation.

10. *Vacuum system,* (on dustless models) collects the sanding dust. It helps prevent belt clogging, for longer belt life and smoother sanding.

11. *Handles,* made of plastic, are designed for positive control in any position.

12. *Trigger switch* is built into handle for on-off control.

Disk Sander

1. *Housing,* an aluminum or magnesium die-casting, is designed for efficient handling.

2. *Universal motor* provides the power.

3. *Driving unit,* most small disk sanders have the disk mounted directly on the motor shaft. In some others, a reduction unit provides high torque. Some disk sanders have the disk at right angles to the motor shaft. This requires a straight gear reduction. Others have the disk mounted on a shaft parallel to the shaft of the motor. This type has less height to the unit, but requires an angle driving unit containing bevel gears.

4. *Backing disk* is made of steel and has a surface pad on which the abrasive disc rotates.

5. *Disk retaining nut* fastens to the center of the disc used to hold the abrasive disk in place.

6. *Handles* are of two types. One type is designed into the housing and the other is made of plastic and attached to the housing. An auxiliary handle fits on the side for easy control.

7. *Trigger switch* is built into the handle for on-off control.

Finish Sanders

1. *Housing,* a die-casting of aluminum, is designed for easy handling in sanding operation.

2. *Universal motor* provides the power.

3. *Driving mechanism* provides either in-line or orbital motion for sanding.

4. *Sanding pad,* a felt or rubber backup pad, distributes even pressure on the abrasive paper.

5. *Pad clamps,* made of spring steel, secure the abrasive paper in place.

6. *Handles* are designed into the housing for easy control in the sanding operation. Some makes have an extra knob made of plastic, which attaches to the front or side of the housing for further control.

7. *Trigger switch* is built into the handle for control of the on-off position.

Maintenance

1. All worn or torn sanding papers should be replaced.

2. Most bearings are of the self-lubricating type, but the level of the oil reservoir on belt sanders must be maintained.

3. Pressure pad must be kept in working condition, in order to sand efficiently.

4. Care should be used in handling the conductor cord, to avoid cable breaks.

Market Analysis

Capacity

The sanding area of portable sanders is controlled by the amount and shape of sanding surface of the machine.

Belt sanders are made for 21″ belts in 2½″, 3″, and 4″ widths; for 24″ belts in 3″ and 4″ widths.

Disk sanders are made for disks measuring (in diameter) 3″, 6″, 7″, and 9″.

Finish sanders are made for sheet sizes 3″ x 8″, 3⅝″ x 9″, 3⅔″ x 9″, and 4½″ x 11″.

Safety Considerations

1. All portable equipment should be operated in a dry place.

2. Avoid placing moist hands on the machine housing.

3. All machines should be grounded by the third wire.

4. Secure material to be sanded.

Topic 87. Using Sanders — Spindle, Belt, Disk

Classification

Removing stock by shearing and shredding

Procedure

Sanders should not be used to remove large amounts of material unless facilities for complete dust control exist.

Using Spindle Sander to Sand Inside and Concave Curves

1. Place the work on the table.
2. Hold the work securely and move it into contact with the revolving spindle. Guide the work to sand the contour of the edge, Fig. 9-8. The oscillating motion tends to prevent grooves in the edge being sanded, and the wear on the abrasive is distributed over the surface. Stopping the movement of the stock at any point causes the edge to hollow-out at the point of contact.
3. Sand until all the waste stock is removed. Because of the speed at which machine sanders revolve (1800 r.p.m.), coarser abrasives may be used and still produce a smoother surface than hand sanding would produce with the same degree of coarseness.
4. If a drill press or lathe is used as a spindle sander, adjust the belt to the proper speed. The spindle sander attachment for the shaper is not recommended because of the high speed at which the spindle travels. This often causes burning of the stock.

Using Disk Sander to Sand Convex and Small Surfaces

1. Place the work on the table.
2. Move the work into contact with the sanding disk.
3. Slowly move the work along until all waste stock has been removed. Keep in mind that sanders are mainly to smooth surfaces and edges and not to remove large quantities of stock.
4. Resinous woods should be sanded close to the center of the disk where the peripheral speed is not so great. This will minimize clogging and heating.
5. A lathe may be converted to a disk sander by cementing a coated abrasive disk to the face-plate and building a table up to the height of the center of the disk.
6. There is also a disk or spinner attachment for electric hand drills. Care must be taken in the use of the latter as they are harder to control and are apt to leave circular scratches on a surface.

Using Belt Sander to Sand Flat Surfaces

1. To sand a flat surface the belt sander should be placed in a horizontal position with the table in a vertical position, see Fig. 9-8A.

Fig. 9-8. Using Spindle Sander

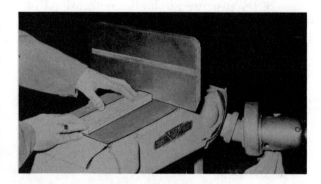

Fig. 9-8A. Using Belt Sander to Sand a Flat Surface

2. Start the machine and hold the stock flat against the moving belt. Care must be taken to keep an even pressure all over the surface. Examine the work often to see that not too much material is being removed in any one section.

Fig. 9-9. Automatic Stroke Sander

Machines such as this are used for sanding large flat surfaces, such as tops, panels, and doors. The two basic functions of stroke machines are (1) the high-speed removal of stock on pieces that have not been previously drum sanded, and (2) the preparation of drum-sanded surfaces for final finishing.

There are three basic stroke sanders in use; the handblock type, the lever arm (or semi-automatic) type, and the automatic type. In the handblock type the operator uses a block as a support for bringing the belt in contact with the work. In the lever arm type the sanding pad or shoe is mounted on a horizontal track with a limited amount of vertical action. The operator controls the pressure and pad movement with a hand lever and he can do spot sanding as well as full length sanding. The automatic type consists of a lever-controlled sanding shoe, mounted on a ball bearing carriage which travels on a horizontal bar and is actuated hydraulically. A feature of this control is that the speed of the stroke does not vary. The operator simply has to control the pad pressure with the lever.

There are single and double belt sanders. In the double belt unit each abrasive belt is driven independently by a reversible motor which accommodates direction of sanding and minimizes grain-raising tendencies in some woods. (Courtesy Mattison Machine Works)

Using Belt Sander to Sand Straight or Curved Edges

1. The belt sander must be placed in a vertical position with the table in a horizontal position, Fig. 9-3.
2. Hold the work firmly against the table and gradually bring the stock against the belt.
3. Slowly move the work along until all waste stock has been removed.

Using Portable Belt Sander to Sand Flat Surfaces

1. Secure the work to be sanded to the bench top.
2. Select the proper grade abrasive belt for the sanding job, see Table 16, page 215.
3. Start the machine and slowly move it back and forth over the surface, keeping the belt always running with the direction of the grain. It is better to start at the end and work in the direction opposite to the rotation of the sanding belt. This will pick up the sanding dust and the surface just sanded may be inspected as the work progresses without stopping the machine.

Fig. 9-10. Sanding Table Tops with a Compressed Air In-Line Sander (Courtesy Heywood-Wakefield Co.)

4. Care must be taken never to hold the machine in one place or to tilt the machine while it is in contact with the surface. This causes deep sanding marks in the surface.

5. Care must be taken in the control of the machine not to cut the electric cord or the dust bag.

Standards and Results

1. Surfaces and edges should be sanded smooth.

2. Finished work should be to the predetermined size and shape, and free of burned marks caused by too great pressure or clogged, worn abrasive.

3. Surfaces should be free of cross-grain scratches.

Safety Considerations

1. Keep your hands away from all moving parts.

2. Belt sanders should be properly tracked to keep belt on the rolls.

3. In using the disk sander, sand on the downward rotation.

4. Do not use torn belts.

5. Care should be exercised in sanding splintered stock.

6. Safety glasses should be worn.

7. Be sure switch is off and belt has stopped running before setting a portable belt sander on the bench.

8. Use portable machines only in dry areas, with dry hands, and when machines are grounded.

Fig. 9-12. Drum Sanding

Planers and other high-speed machines beat the fibers down and produce a glazed surface. These fibers have to be roughed or softened a bit before stain will take evenly. Sanding, regardless of the type of sander used, will accomplish this.

Drum sanders are usually used for irregularly shaped parts. Usually two grades of sandpaper (coarse and fine) are on a single horizontal drum, permitting rough and finished sanding in one operation. (Courtesy Heywood-Wakefield Co.)

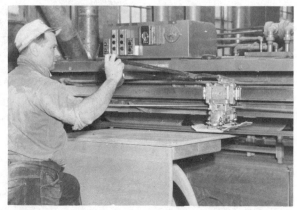

Fig. 9-11. Sanding Table Tops with Automatic Belt Sander (Courtesy Heywood-Wakefield Co.)

Fig. 9-13. Sanding Bowls on a Belt Sander (Courtesy Baribeau & Son)

Topic 88. Selecting the Proper Tool to Cut a Hole

The type of tool and cutter to be selected to make a hole depends on the diameter and shape of the hole to be made and the method by which the cutter will be driven.

There are two basic types of boring tools. In one type, the bit has side spurs which cut the wood fibers on the perimeter of the hole and the cutting lips clean out the center of the hole. This type is best used on face or side grain. In the other type, the cutting lips shear off the ends of the wood fibers as it cuts the hole, thus the twist bit is best suited for boring into end grain. This type of bit will cut a rough hole in face or side grain.

Driving tools for a hand operation include "Yankee" push drill, hand drill (Fig. 10-40), and bit brace (Fig. 10-3). Machine designed cutters are driven by the portable electric drill (Topic 95) and the drill press (Topics 96 and 97).

Fig. 10-1. Brad Awl (Courtesy Stanley Tool Co.)

Table 17
Selecting Cutting Tools for Holes

	Hole Size	Cutting Tool*
HAND OPERATION	1/32″ - 1/8″	Brad or Finish Nail
	1/16″ - 11/64″	Straight shank drill points
	1/16″ - 1/4″	Twist drills or twist bits
	3/16″ - 2″	Auger, Forstner, Machine Auger, or Dowel bits
	5/8″ - 3″	Expansive bits
MACHINE DRIVEN	1/16″ - 1/2″	Twist drill, Machine or Multi spurs
	3/8″ - 1″	Power bore or Forstner bits
	3/8″ - 1½″	Spade bit
	1¾″ - 2⅛″	Lock bit sets
	Pilot Hole by Screw Size	
	1/8″ - 1/4″	Screw mates
	1″ - 5½″	Fly cutter
	3/4″ - 7″	Hole saw

*Many of these cutting tools are illustrated in Section Ten, pages 223-249.

Topic 89. Bit Brace

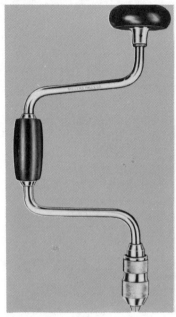

Fig. 10-2. Plain Bit Brace (Courtesy Millers Falls Co.)

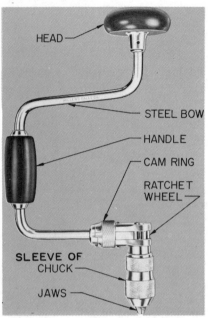

HEAD

STEEL BOW

HANDLE

CAM RING

RATCHET WHEEL

SLEEVE OF CHUCK

JAWS

Fig. 10-3. Open Ratchet Bit Brace (Courtesy Millers Falls Co.)

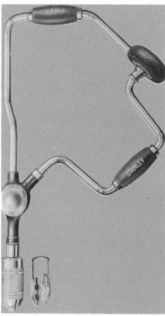

Fig. 10-4. Corner Brace (Courtesy Stanley Tool Co.)

Classification

Rotary driving tool

Application

Principle of Operation

1. The bit brace uses the principle of the wheel and axle in creating its driving force. The pressure on the swing of the bow is in direct proportion to the force applied to the cutters of the auger bit. (Refer to Topic 33, "Tools," and the discussion of the wheel and axle.)

2. This tool is so constructed that downward pressure may be applied on the boring tool while a constant revolving motion directs the cutting action.

Kinds and Uses

The bit brace or bit stock is used for holding and driving all kinds of boring tools with squared tapered tangs, screw driver bits, dowel pointers, and countersinks.

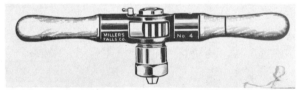

Fig. 10-5. Ratchet Auger Handle (Courtesy Millers Falls Co.)

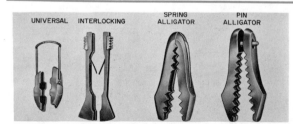

UNIVERSAL   INTERLOCKING   SPRING ALLIGATOR   PIN ALLIGATOR

Fig. 10-6. Types of Jaws on Bit Braces (Courtesy Stanley Tool Co.)

Fig. 10-7. Bit Extension (Courtesy Stanley Tool Co.)

1. Braces are made in three types: (a) the plain brace, (b) the ratchet brace, and (c) the corner brace. See Figs. 10-2, 10-3, 10-4.

2. The concealed type of ratchet has a sleeve which seals the ratchet mechanism and lubricant and also prevents foreign materials from entering.

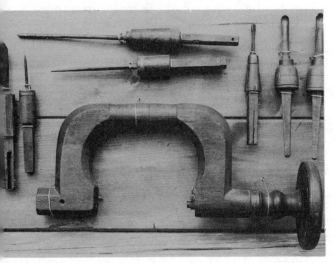

Fig. 10-8. Early Bit Brace, Wooden

One step in the development of the modern bit brace was this bit stock and chuck made entirely of wood. The bit is secured in its own individual chuck, which in turn is held in the bit brace by means of a wooden thumb screw. Note that the handle does not turn, but the head does. (Courtesy Old Sturbridge Village, Inc.)

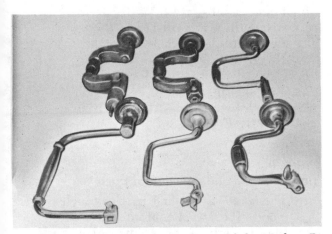

Fig. 10-8A Steps in the Evolution of the Modern Bit Brace

3. The open ratchet isn't as strong as the concealed or box ratchet, nor is it as easily worked.

4. The box ratchet is stronger than either of the other types.

5. Universal jaws are used for round shank and tapered tang bits and drills.

6. Interlocking jaws fit square taper tang bits and drills.

7. Alligator jaws may be used with regular-size, taper tang and medium-size, round shank drills.

8. Bit braces are made from 6″ to 16″ sweep.

Principal Parts and Function of Each

1. The *head*, made of cocobolo, aluminum, or plastic, is fastened to the bow and turns freely on ball bearings. It is a control for direction and pressure.

2. The *steel bow* forms the outer rim of the wheel and axle. It carries the power from the operator's hand to the chuck. This bow shape permits controlled or continuous operation. The larger the bow, the greater the mechanical advantage. (See pp. 87-88.)

3. The *handle*, made of cocobolo, aluminum, or plastic, is fastened to the bow but turns freely on it. It is on the handle that the force is applied to turn the brace.

4. The hardened steel jaws of the *chuck* are held in position by the use of a screw and wedge. Tightening the *sleeve* of the chuck forces the jaws to close. The chuck rotates on ball bearings at the bow joint. (See Fig. 10-3.)

5. Turning the cam ring to the right (clockwise) engages a pawl with the *ratchet wheel*. This causes the bit to turn with the brace in a clockwise direction, but permits the bow to be turned in the opposite direction while the bit is stationary in the wood. Thus, a hole may be bored in a place where the full swing of the bow is not possible.

Maintenance

Cleaning

Rust on the bow or chuck should be removed with an abrasive (steel wool or emery cloth) and oiled with machine oil.

Replacing Parts

Jaws wear out from continued use and may be replaced by unscrewing the shell of the chuck. New heads and bows are also available, but proper care will make replacement of these unnecessary.

Storing

Bit braces should be stored in boxes made for that purpose or hung up securely.

Oiling

The bearings between the head and the bow, and between the ratchet and the chuck should be oiled regularly. When the brace is put away for a long period of time, all the metal parts should be covered with oil.

Market Analysis

Capacity

1. The sweep (or swing) is the diameter of the swing of the handle. It ranges from 6″ to 16″.
2. The chuck capacities range from 0 to ½″.

Attachments

Bit extensions allow the user to bore through walls or floors, Fig. 10-7.

Additional Reading

Stanley Tool Company, *Stanley Tool Guide*

Topic 90. Wood Bits

(AUGER, FORSTNER, PLUG, COUNTERSINK, EXPANSIVE, SCREW-MATE)

Classification

Boring tool (rotating edge tool)

Application

Principle of Operation

All bits work on the principle of the wedge and the inclined plane, Fig. 5-7.

Kinds and Uses

1. Bits are used for boring round holes in wood.
2. Auger bits are made with three types of twists and three types of screws. The coarser the twist and screw, the faster the cutting action and the rougher the cut. The auger with the fine screw and twist is recommended for hard, close-grained woods. The three types of twist are: (a) single, (b) double, and (c) solid center.
3. The three types of screws are coarse, medium, and fine.
4. Auger bit — #3 to #32 (³⁄₁₆″ to 2″ by sixteenths), Fig. 10-9.
5. Dowel bit — #3 to #16 (³⁄₁₆″ to 1″ by sixteenths), Fig. 10-12.
6. Forstner bit — #4 to #16 (¼″ to 1″ by sixteenths), Fig. 10-13.
7. Plug cutter — ⅜″ to 1″ by eighths, Fig. 10-14.
8. Expansive bit cuts holes ⅝″ to 3″ in diameter, Fig. 10-20.
9. Wood twist bits — ¹⁄₁₆″ to 1″ by sixteenths, Fig. 10-23.

Auger Bit —
Principal Parts and Function of Each

1. The *screw* is the first part to touch the wood. It draws the bit into the wood on the principle of the inclined plane. See Figs. 10-9, 10-10, 10-11.

2. The *spurs* or *nibs* score the edge of the hole on the principle of the wedge.
3. The *lips* cut the material from within the scored circle also on the principle of the wedge.
4. The *twist* carries the wood chips to the surface on the principle of the inclined plane.
5. The *shank* is the connection between the twist and the tang.
6. The *tang* is the square tapered part which is locked within the chuck and causes the bit to turn when the bow is revolved. The number on the tang of the bit indicates the size in sixteenths of an inch.

Dowel Bit —
Principal Parts and Function of Each

The dowel bit is similar to the auger, but shorter in length and with a finer twist, Fig. 10-12.

Forstner Bit —
Principal Parts and Function of Each

1. The sharpened circular *steel ring* scribes the circumference of the hole on the principle of the wedge. See Fig. 10-13.
2. The two *lips* cut the wood within the circle on the principle of the wedge and then carry the shavings up the inclined plane out of the hole. Forstner bits ⅜″ and smaller have only one cutting lip.
3. The *shank* connects the cutter and tang.

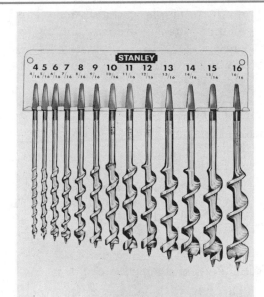

Fig. 10-11. Solid Center Auger Bits (Courtesy Stanley Tool Co.)

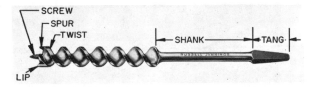

Fig. 10-9. Auger Bit (Courtesy Stanley Tool Co.)

Fig. 10-12. Dowel Bit (Courtesy Stanley Tool Co.)

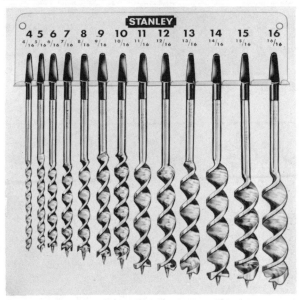

Fig. 10-10. Double Twist Auger Bits (Courtesy Stanley Tool Co.)

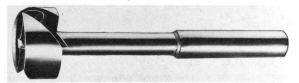

Fig. 10-13. Forstner Bit (Courtesy Conn. Valley Mfg. Co.)

Fig. 10-14. Plug Cutter Bit (Courtesy Greenlee Tool Co.)

Fig. 10-16. Side and End Views of Rose Machine Countersink (Courtesy Millers Falls Co.)

4. The *tang* is the round or squared, tapered end which is locked in the chuck. The number stamped on the tang indicates the size in sixteenths of an inch.

Plug Cutter —
Principal Parts and Function of Each

1. The *cutter disk* scores and cuts a ring on the principle of the wedge. The remaining disk is used as a plug to fill holes, Fig. 10-14.
2. Connecting parts are similar to the auger bit.

Countersink Bit —
Principal Parts and Function of Each

1. Single, double, and rose type bits are available.
2. A cone-shaped *cutter* widens a hole on the principle of the wedge. See Figs. 10-16, 10-17, 10-18.

Expansive Bit —
Principal Parts and Function of Each

1. This type is sometimes called *expansion bit*.
2. The expansive bit has two adjustable *cutters* that may be set at different positions to cut holes ranging from ⅝" to 3". This bit works on the same principle as the auger bit, Fig. 10-20. Some bits have a screw adjustment that regulates the diameter of the hole to be cut.

Machine Bit —
Principal Parts and Function of Each

This bit is similar to the auger but does not have the screw point which is not needed because of the speed and the pressure applied in the machine, Fig. 10-21.

Fig. 10-17. Rose Countersink with Square Tang (Courtesy Stanley Tool Co.)

Fig. 10-18. Machine Rose Countersink (Courtesy Stanley Tool Co.)

Fig. 10-19. Dowel Pointer (Courtesy Stanley Tool Co.)

Fig. 10-20. Expansive Bit (Courtesy Stanley Tool Co.)

Fig. 10-21. Machine Bit (Courtesy Greenlee Tool Co.)

Fig. 10-22. Multi-Spur Machine Bit (Courtesy Greenlee Tool Co.

Multi-Spur Bit
Principal Parts and Functions of Each

This bit consists of saw teeth cut into the rim, a single cutter, and a spur center, Fig. 10-22.

Screw-Mate —
Principal Parts and Function of Each

This is a combination drill and countersink. It makes the pilot, clearance, and countersunk hole for the length and wire size of a given screw, Fig. 10-25. A counterbore makes a hole to sink the head of the screw below the surface and also makes a clearance, pilot, and countersunk hole for the length and size of a given screw, Fig. 10-26.

Fig. 10-23. Wood Twist Bits (Courtesy Butterfield Division, Union Twist Drill Co.)

Fig. 10-24. Spade Bit (Courtesy Irwin Auger Bit Co.)

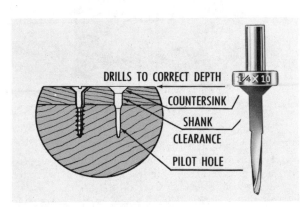

Fig. 10-25. Screw-Mate Countersink (Courtesy Stanley Tool Co.)

Maintenance

Bits should be stored in a canvas roll, container, or mounted on a board individually

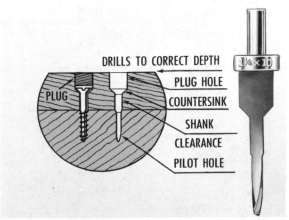

Fig. 10-26. Screw-Mate Counterbore (Courtesy Stanley Tool Co.)

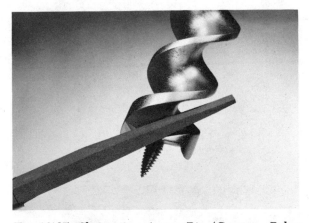

Fig. 10-27. Sharpening Auger Bit (Courtesy Behr-Manning Co.)

Fig. 10-28. Sharpening Rose Countersink (Courtesy Behr-Manning Co.)

so that the cutting edges will not be damaged. Bits get dull from use and may be sharpened by filing the inside of the spurs and the top side of the lips, Fig. 10-27. This should not be attempted by beginners. When bits are left for a long period of time, they should be oiled to prevent rusting.

Market Analysis (Attachments)

Bit gauge for controlling depth of hole, Figs. 10-29, 10-30.

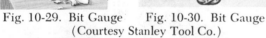

Fig. 10-29. Bit Gauge   Fig. 10-30. Bit Gauge
(Courtesy Stanley Tool Co.)

Fig. 10-31. Fiddle Bow Drill

This fiddle bow drill was used about 1790 and is reputed to have been originally a Revolutionary War sword. The bow holds taut a cord which is looped around a spool. The movement of the bow causes the spool to revolve, driving the bit. (Courtesy Historical Society, Harvard, Mass.)

Additional Reading

Manufacturers Catalogs
Charts and pamphlets

Fig. 10-32. Wooden Spiral Hand Drill

This is the forerunner of the modern spiral hand drill. Note the carved spiral thread. The driving barrel, shown at the bottom of the spindle, was run up and down to cause the drill to turn. (Courtesy Old Sturbridge Village, Inc.)

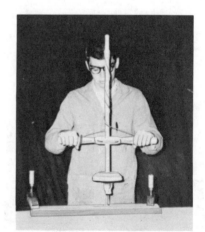

Fig. 10-32A. Pump Drill

Twisting the spindle causes the rawhide thong to form a helix along the spindle. Downward pressure on the crossarm exerts pressure on the thong, causing the spindle to rotate. The flywheel at the base provides sufficient momentum to rewind the thong on the spindle as pressure on the crossbar is released.

Topic 91. Boring a Hole with Bit and Brace

Classification

Driving a boring tool to score and remove stock

Procedure

1. A hole should be cut so that the sides are square with the surface or at a prescribed angle.
2. The center of the hole is located on the surface with intersecting lines. It is good practice to make a mark with an awl at the center point.

Through Boring

1. Select the proper size auger bit for the hole and secure it in the jaws of the bit brace. (See Topic 90, "Auger Bit" and Topic 89, "Bit Brace" for their uses and names of parts.)
2. Secure the stock so that the surface will be at right angles to the natural boring position in order that the hole may be cut perpendicular to the surface. The same principle applies when boring at an angle to the surface. A control must be established to maintain accuracy at any angle.

3. Place the point of the screw at the intersection of the lines. Hold the head of the bit brace so that the auger bit is at the desired angle with the surface of the work. With the left hand, turn the swing of the brace in a clockwise rotation. Apply pressure to the head as you swing the handle.
4. When the bit has started to cut, check to see that the hole is being cut at the desired angle. This may be done by sighting from two directions (not opposite) or by holding a try square or a T bevel (depending on the angle) on the surface close to the bit. See Figs. 10-33, 10-34.
5. Continue to bore the hole until the point of the screw comes through the opposite side. Remove the bit by reversing two turns of the swing, then turning in

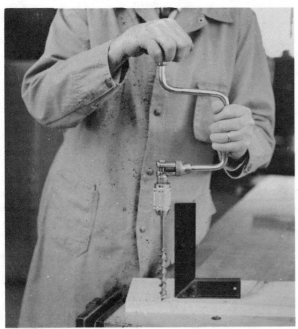

Fig. 10-33. Using Try Square to Check Squareness

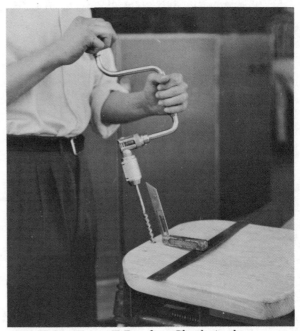

Fig. 10-34. Using T-Bevel to Check Angle

a clockwise direction but pulling up on the head as you turn. To reverse the motion when withdrawing the bit would leave the cuttings in the hole.

6. Turn the board so that the hole may be completed from the opposite side. This method will avoid breaking or splitting the wood at the edges of the hold. (See Fig. 10-35A.)

7. Another method of preventing breaking through the back surface is to clamp the work over a piece of scrap material and bore into the scrap piece. Care must be taken not to go too deeply into the second piece. (See Fig. 10-35B.)

Stop Boring

1. Stop boring is boring a hole that has predetermined depth.

2. The safest method is to use some type of depth gauge attached to the bit, Figs. 10-29, 10-30, and 10-36. There are two types, one of which is the manufactured adjustable bit gauge which clamps to the auger bit. The other type is made in the shop. It consists of a piece of wood through which a hole has been bored to fit over the bit. The wood is cut to length so the bit extends through the hole enough to bore to the required depth. (The depth of the hole is determined by the amount the bit extends below the gauge to the cutting lips.)

CAUTION: **When using either type of bit stop, care must be taken not to mar the surface of the work. When a series of holes of roughly the same depth are to be bored, count the number of turns to make one hole and repeat the process.**

Using Jigs

1. Jigs are used to aid in locating and boring straight holes, Figs. 10-37, 10-38, 10-38A.)

2. When boring through a long piece, it is advisable to bore half way from either side.

3. An extension may be added for increased depth.

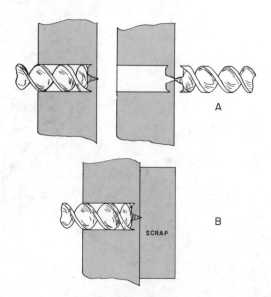

Fig. 10-35. Boring Through — Two Ways to Prevent Splitting Out

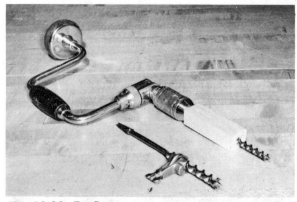

Fig. 10-36. Bit Stops

Fig. 10-37. Homemade Dowel Jig

Counterboring

1. Counterboring is done to recess screw heads. In practice, it is making a smaller hole within a larger hole, Fig 10-39.
2. The larger hole must always be cut first. Care should be taken that the size of the bit selected matches the size of the plug.
3. A plug which fits the larger hole covers the screw head.

Countersinking

1. A countersink cuts a tapered hole. The taper matches the bevel on the underside of screw head. (See Figs. 10-17, 10-25.)

2. It should be cut so that the diameter of the countersunk hole at the surface equals the outside diameter of the screw head.

Standards and Results

1. All holes should have clean-cut edges and sides.
2. The sides should be at the proper angle to the surface.
3. Holes should be located properly.
4. Care should be taken not to mar benches and holding devices.

Safety Considerations

1. Be certain stock is secured properly.
2. Avoid excessive pressure.

Additional Reading

Stanley Tool Company, *How to Work With Tools and Wood*

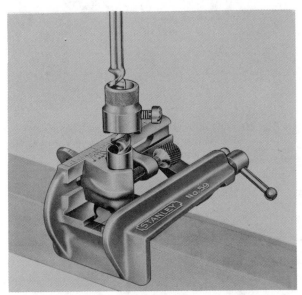

Fig. 10-38. Dowel Jig (Courtesy Stanley Tool Co.)

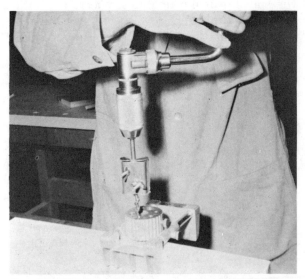

Fig. 10-38B. Doweling Jig

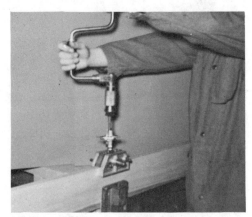

Fig. 10-38A. Self-Centering Doweling Jig

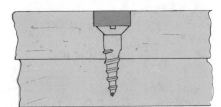

Fig. 10-39. Plugged, Counterbored Hole

Topic 92. Hand Drill and Breast Drill

Classification

Rotary driving tool

The hand drill and breast drill are used in driving a twist drill in drilling small holes.

Application

Principle of Operation

The hand drill works on the principle of the wheel and axle and the inclined plane. Each tooth of the gear is one of a series of inclined planes that combine their mechanical advantage to increase speed and turning power. This speed ratio is in direct proportion to the number of teeth on the pinion gear to that on the speed gear. On the ¼" hand drill the speed ratio is generally 4 or 5 to 1. On the ⅜" and ½" breast drill there are two pinion gears, one in contact near the center of the axle of the speed gear for an almost one to one ratio for larger drills and slow speed, and the second gear for the high speed ratio for small drills. (See Figs. 10-40 and 10-43.)

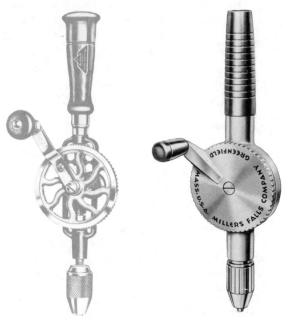

Fig. 10-41. Open Gear   Fig. 10-42. Enclosed
Hand Drill   Hand Drill
(Courtesy Millers Falls Co.)

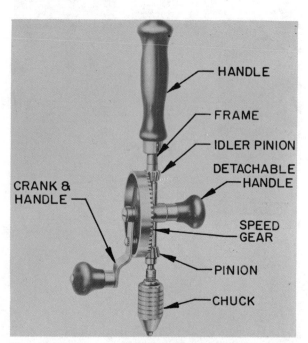

Fig. 10-40. Nomenclature of Hand Drill (Courtesy Stanley Tool Co.)

Fig. 10-43. Breast Drill (Courtesy Millers Falls Co.)

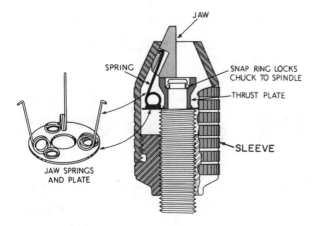

Fig. 10-44. Nomenclature of Chuck (Courtesy Stanley Tool Co.)

Kinds and Uses

The size depends on the chuck diameter opening. These are usually three sizes: ¼″, ⅜″, and ½″.

Principal Parts and Function of Each

1. *Handles,* usually made of wood or plastic, facilitate control of force and direction of drilling.
2. The metal *breastplate* is used to apply pressure in place of the handle.
3. *Frame* is cast or drop-forged to a shape designed for holding attachments.
4. The *speed gear* provides mechanical advantage to increase speed and turning power. There are several style wheels for the speed gear. Some have open spokes (Fig. 10-41) while others have a disk wheel (Figs. 10-42 and 10-43).
5. The *crank* and *handle* attached to speed gear forms the outer diameter of the wheel and axle to provide leverage.

6. The *pinion gear* is attached to the opposite end of the spindle chuck. It meshes with the speed gear.
7. The *idler pinion gear* (Fig. 10-40), same size and number of teeth as the pinion gear, is located on the upper section of the frame and meshes with the speed gear opposite the pinion gear. Its function is to balance the thrust of force applied to the hand wheel speed gear, and is usually found only on better quality hand drills.
8. The hard, carbon-steel *chuck* holds the drill. It has three jaws and is tightened by a clockwise turning of the sleeve (which uses the inclined plane of the jaws as a wedge), locking the jaws around the drill, Fig. 10-44. The three jaws will always center a drill that is properly gripped. Some breast drills have two-jaw chucks.
9. Some breast drills have a *level* in the frame.

Maintenance

The hand drill requires periodic oiling and checking. Screws that fasten the crank arm and breast plate should be kept tight.

Market Analysis

Capacity

There are three sizes of hand drills with chucks of 0-¼″ for light work, 0-⅜″ for medium work and 0-½″ for heavy work.

Additional Reading

Manufacturers Catalogs

Topic 93. Twist Drill

Classification

A spiral-fluted tool with the tip ground to two cutting wedges, used in making round holes in wood and other materials

Application

Principle of Operation

As the drill is turned and pressure is applied, the cutting lips of the drill remove the material on the principle of the wedge. The material is removed from the hole by the flutes on the principle of the inclined plane.

Kinds and Uses

Drills are used for making round holes in wood, metal, plastics, and other materials. They are made of carbon steel for general use and of high-speed steel or with carbide tips for drilling hard materials.

1. Three different numbering systems are used to designate the size of drills:
    a. Numbered 1 - 80 (1 = .2280″ in diameter; 80 = .0135″ in diameter).
    b. Alphabetical, letters from A to Z (A = .234″ in diameter; Z = .413″ in diameter).
    c. Fractions — $\frac{1}{32}$″ to $\frac{1}{2}$″ by 64ths.
2. There are three types of shanks: round, tapered, and tang. The size and type of material of which the drill is made are stamped on the shank.

Principal Parts and Function of Each

1. *Cutting lips* to cut the material.
2. *Flute* to carry the material out of the hole and allow lubrication of the cutting edge. No lubrication is necessary when drilling wood.
3. *Shank* is so shaped that the chuck can grip the drill securely.

Fig. 10-46.   Straight Shank Drill (Courtesy Union Twist Drill Co.)

Maintenance

Storing

Drills should be kept in graduated stands to prevent damage to the cutting edges and for easy selection. They should be oiled to prevent rusting.

Sharpening

The process of sharpening a drill is really a shaping process performed on a grinding wheel. The cutting lips should form an angle of 118° for general use. The clearance angle should be from 12° to 15°. Sharpening should not be attempted by beginners without instruction.

Market Analysis

Capacity

Drills are made from $\frac{1}{32}$″ to 2″.

Attachments

Depth gauge for drilling to predetermined depth.

Costs

Drills may be purchased singly, in sets of sixteen from $\frac{1}{32}$″ to $\frac{1}{2}$″ by 32nds, and in sets of eight from $\frac{1}{16}$″ to $\frac{9}{32}$″ by 32nds. High speed drills cost much more than carbon steel drills.

Topic 94. Drilling a Hole

Classification

Driving an edged cutting tool in a circular motion

Procedure

Holes less than ¼″ are usually drilled with a twist drill driven with a hand, breast, portable electric drill, or drill press.

1. Locate the center of the hole with intersecting lines. Score the exact center with a center punch or awl, depending upon the hardness of the material.
2. Select and secure the drill bit in the chuck. (See Topic 92, "Hand Drill and Breast Drill".)

Fig. 10-47. Drilling a Hole with Hand Drill

3. Place the drill on the center point and position the hand drill so the hole will be drilled at the desired angle to the work surface.
4. Apply light pressure to the handle while the crank is turned in a clockwise direction, Fig. 10-47. One revolution of the crank will revolve the drill four or five times.
5. Check to see that the drill is square with the work and continue to drill until the desired depth has been reached. If the hole is to go completely through the board, let up on the pressure when nearing the bottom to relieve breaking through.
6. To remove the drill, continue to revolve the drill in the same direction while pulling up on the handle. To reverse direction of rotation of the crank will sometimes open the jaws of chuck.
7. If a drill tends to wander from the starting point, the drill may be tipped slightly until the center is reached. The drill is then set at right angles with the surface and the hole continued.

Standards and Results

1. Holes should have clean-cut surfaces and sides.
2. The hole should be started on the exact center point and at desired angle with the surface.
3. Care should be taken not to drill into the bench top.

Safety Considerations

This is a simple operation, and if care and judgment are used, there should be no difficulties.

Topic 95. Portable Electric Drill

Classification
Motorized rotary driving tool

Application

Principle of Operation
The portable electric drill operates from a small, high-speed electric motor with a gear-reduction driving unit.

Kinds and Uses
Electric drills are designed with a pistol-shaped housing for holding drill shanks up to ⅜″ diameter, and with a "D"-shaped handle for heavy-duty work, up to ½″ diameter. The electric drill is used to drive all types of rotary cutting tools, for cabinet and construction work. There are many attachments that use the drill motor as the driving unit for sanding, polishing and grinding, as well as special attachments for circular and jigsaws.

Principal Parts and Functions of Each
1. *Housing*, made of aluminum or plastic, is designed for holding, guiding, and applying pressure to the twist drill.
2. *Motor* is a rotary power unit.
3. *Gear reduction unit* reduces speed of the motor to high-torque driving force. See Table 18.

Fig. 10-48. Portable Electric Drill (Courtesy Stanley Tool Co.)

4. *Chuck* is a 3-jaw, nonslip, gripping unit made of hard-carbon steel. It works on the principle of the inclined plane, wedging the jaws on the drill shank.
5. *Handle*, made of aluminum depending upon size of drill, is designed to give maximum holding power. Pistol grip is part of housing design. "D" handle is used on large (over ½″) drills. A side handle, made of plastic or solid rod, is used to guide drill and to overcome torque.
6. *Trigger switch*, starting control of the drill, is designed into handle for on-off control.
7. Some drills have a *variable speed unit* incorporated in the trigger switch unit to give speeds from 0-2250 r.p.m.

Maintenance
Jaws should be cleaned and oiled for care-free operation. Conductor cords should be handled so as not to cause wear or breaks in the cable.

Portable electric drills should be stored and used in a dry place.

Market Analysis

Capacity
The maximum opening of the chuck is the determining factor indicating the size of the electric drill. Electric drills of the following sizes operate in the speed ranges shown.

Table 18
Electric Drill Sizes and Speeds

¼″ — speeds to 2000 - 2450 - 5000 r.p.m.
⁵⁄₁₆″ — speeds to 1000
⅜″ — speeds to 750 - 1000
½″ — speeds to 450 - 750
⅝″ — speeds to 300
¾″ — speeds to 250
1″ — speeds to 200 (This drill has a #3 taper sleeve for drills up to 1″ diameter.)

Attachments

10-volt rechargeable power pack, making a portable power supply. This special drill can be operated on 10-12-volt batteries or 115-volt a.c.

Attachments are available for use with the drill, for disk and orbital sanders; grinding, buffing and polishing; jig, saber, and circular saws; plane units; lathe units; and hedge trimmers.

A chuck to increase the capacity of a drill from ¼″ to ½″. A friction clutch may be added for driving screws.

A flexible unit to drill in close quarters and at angles.

Additional Reading

Manufacturers catalogs.

Topic 96. Drill Press — Floor and Bench Models

Classification

Power driven rotary driving tool

Application

Principle of Operation

The drill press provides the rotary power for driving drills, bits, plug cutters, and many auxiliary attachments such as mortise chisels, grinding wheels, and shaper cutters. The vertical power is applied through the feed wheel or lever (wheel and axle) to a pinion gear which engages a rack on the quill (inclined plane). The speed of the drill press may vary from 300 to 7000 r.p.m. Speed is controlled by shifting the drive belt on a set of cone pulleys which operate on the principle of the wheel and axle. See Figs. 10-48 and 10-49, A and B. Some drills have a variable speed unit to regulate speed.

Kinds and Uses

The drill press is used for rotating cutting bits and drills and controlling the depth and angle of holes. When used in connection with various attachments, it substitutes as a sander, planer, shaper, router, and mortiser.

Table size: 10″ x 10″, 10″ x 14″, 11″ x 16″.

School shops usually have single-spindle drill presses. Industrial drills often have multiple spindles, Fig. 10-59.

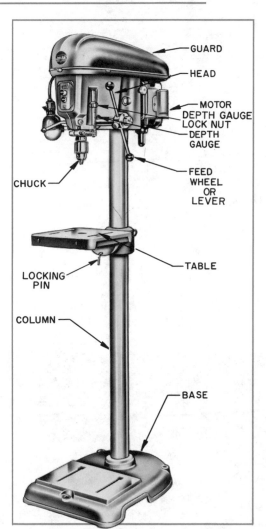

Fig. 10-49. Floor Model Drill Press (Courtesy Delta Div., Rockwell Mfg. Co.)

Principal Parts and Function of Each

1. A cast iron *base* supports the machine.
2. *Column*, made of machined cast steel, holds the table, head, and motor.
3. The cast iron *table* holds the work and is adjustable for height. Some tables may be tilted to angles other than 90°.

4. The machined cast steel *chuck* (three jaw) grips bits and drills securely, and couples or attaches cutter to driving spindle. Chuck is tightened with a chuck wrench or key.
5. *Feed lever* or *wheel*, made of cast steel or iron, raises or lowers spindle in drilling. (See Fig. 10-49.)

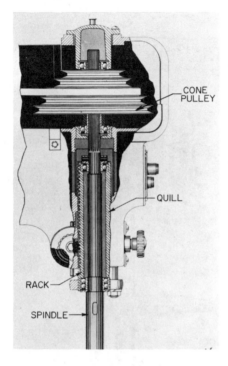

CONE PULLEY

QUILL

RACK

SPINDLE

Fig. 10-49A. Cutaway of Head of Drill Press (Courtesy Rockwell Mfg. Co.)

Fig. 10-50. Mortising Attachment in Place (Courtesy Walker-Turner Div., Rockwell Mfg. Co.)

Fig. 10-49B. Variable Speed Unit on Drill Press (Courtesy Rockwell Mfg. Co.)

Fig. 10-51. Using Shaper Attachment on Drill Press (Courtesy Delta Div., Rockwell Mfg. Co.)

6. *Quill*, made of machined cast steel, permits the vertical motion without interfering with the rotary drive.
7. *Depth gauge* indicates or limits the travel of the spindle.
8. The cast iron *head* houses the pulleys, bearings, spindle, and quill.
9. The *motor* (⅓ to ½ H.P., 1740 r.p.m.) provides the power.
10. The V *belt*, made of rubber and fiber composition, transmits the power.
11. Cast iron or pressed steel *guards* protect the operator from the belt.
12. Steel *feed wheel spring* returns the spindle to the original position.
13. The *spindle lock* holds the spindle at any desired position.
14. The cast aluminum cone *pulley* transmits power and regulates speed.

Maintenance

Some drill presses require periodic greasing while others have sealed bearings. Whenever a drill press is to be idle for a period of time, all machined parts should be coated with a film of oil.

Market Analysis

Capacity

The capacity of the drill press is determined by the distance from the center of the chuck to the column. This distance is expressed as a diameter. Drill press sizes range from 11″ to 17″. The vertical distance is determined by the length of the column and by the travel of the spindle. See Fig. 10-49A.

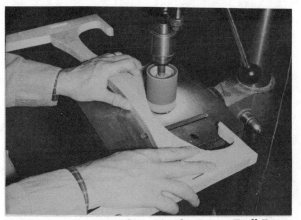

Fig. 10-53. Using Sanding Attachment on Drill Press

Fig. 10-53A. Drum Surform for Removing Stock in Drill Press (Courtesy Stanley Tool Co.)

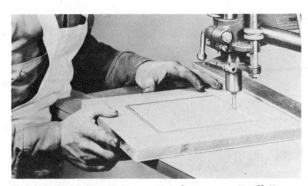

Fig. 10-52. Using Router Attachment on Drill Press (Courtesy Delta Div., Rockwell Mfg. Co.)

Fig. 10-54. Using Planer Attachment on Drill Press (Courtesy Barron Tool Co., Inc.)

Stroke	Drill to Center of Circle	Maximum Distance Table to Chuck Bench Model	Table Model
4″	15″	10½″	39½″
4″	16″	11⅞″	41¾″
5″	17″	26½″	44½″

Attachments

1. Mortiser attachment for cutting mortises, Fig. 10-50.
2. Shaper attachment for cutting moldings, Fig. 10-51.
3. Router attachment for routing, Fig. 10-52.
4. Sanding drums and disks for sanding irregular curves, Fig. 10-53.
5. Rotary planer for surfacing stock, Fig. 10-54.
6. Foot feed enables the operator to use both hands for production.
7. Slow speed attachment for large drill presses for drilling large diameter holes.

Additional Reading

Delta Manufacturing Company, *Getting the Most Out of Your Drill Press*

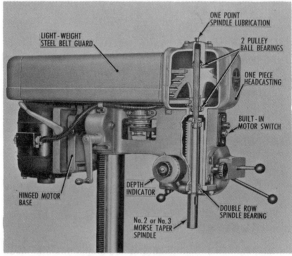

Fig. 10-55. Nomenclature of Drill Press (Courtesy Walker-Turner Div., Rockwell Mfg. Co.)

Topic 97. Using the Drill Press

Classification

Drilling, boring, mortising, routing, shaping, sanding

Fig. 10-56. Using V-Block to Hold Cylinder for Drilling—Note that Entire Set-Up is Clamped to Table

Procedure

Inserting the Drill

1. Select the correct size, round-shank drill for the hole to be cut.
2. Open the chuck so the opening is slightly larger than the diameter of the drill shank. (Turn the sleeve counter-clockwise.)
3. Insert the drill in the chuck making sure that the shank is centered between the three jaws. Tighten the chuck with the key.
4. Remove the key from the chuck before making any further adjustments.
5. Some large drill presses have tapered sleeves which will receive only taper-shank drills. These drills are held in place by friction and pressure. They are

removed by inserting a tapered drift in a slot in the sleeve above the drill shank.

Adjusting the Table

1. Raise or lower the table to the proper height by loosening the table clamp at the column. Care should be taken that the table does not drop.
2. The table should be a distance below the point of the drill equal to the length of the drill extending from the chuck plus the thickness of the stock used as a table pad.
3. The center or clearance hole on the table should line up with the center of the drill bit.
4. Some drill press tables may be tilted at an angle either side of the horizontal. Pins are used to lock the table at predetermined angles.

Adjusting the Spindle Travel Depth Gauge

1. Holes that are to be bored to a desired depth, as in stop-boring, can be measured and regulated by the spindle travel depth gauge.
2. Advance or lower the drill and spindle to the desired depth. Measure the distance in relation to the clearance between the drill point and the table surface or pad.
3. Holding the spindle in this position, adjust the lock nuts on the depth gauge.

Fig. 10-57. Drilling Hole in Irregularly Shaped Piece — Note Use of Clamps

Selecting Proper Speed for Drill Size

1. Adjust the belt to the proper spindle speed for the size drill to be used and the material to be bored. A 1740 r.p.m. motor will give spindle speeds of 600, 1250, 2440, and 5000 r.p.m. In general, large diameter drills are used at low speeds. Very fine drills are run at high speeds. The hardness of stock being drilled is also a factor in selecting the speed. Generally speaking, the harder the material, the slower the speed.

Securing Stock to the Table

1. Long pieces of stock in which small holes are to be cut may be held firmly on the table by hand.

Fig. 10-58. Boring Dowel Hole in End of Apron — Table is Rotated — Note Use of Clamp and Fence

Fig. 10-58A. Drill Press Vise (Courtesy Stanley Tool Co.)

2. Short stock must be held in a drill press vise which is fastened to the table or the work may be clamped in position on the table.
3. Round stock may be held in the drill press vise or in a V block, Fig. 10-56.
4. Irregular stock may necessitate the use of a jig to secure the work in the proper position, Figs. 10-57, 10-58.

Fig. 10-59. Multiple Spindle Drill
— Note the fixture rigged to guide chair seat into position and hold it firmly while the holes for spindles are bored five at a time. (Courtesy Heywood-Wakefield Co.)

Fig. 10-60. Boring a Hole at a Compound Angle
The table is tilted to the desired angle of offset of the leg. The stock is clamped to the table with the diagonal of the layout of the leg position parallel to the front edge of the table. This set-up forms the inward pitch of the hole for the leg. Note: the screw threads have been filed to a cone point.

Drilling a Hole

1. Make an indentation at the exact center. Start the drill into this indentation.
2. Apply a constant feed so that the shavings are carried out of the hole and the drill operates efficiently. Too slow a feed will overheat the drill by friction and too fast a feed may cause excessive pressure which may break the drill or tear the stock.
3. Release the pressure on the feed when approaching the opposite surface on through boring.
4. On deep holes it may be necessary to withdraw the drill from the hole several times to clean the cuttings from the flutes.
5. When drilling a series of parallel holes use a fence as a guide.
6. Large holes may be cut with a hole saw or fly cutter. (See Figs. 10-62 and 10-62A.)

Using the Mortising Attachment

1. Most attachments require a special spindle to receive the bit and chisel. The chisel is fastened to an extension of the quill. See Fig. 10-63.
2. Select the proper size bit and chisel and insert them in their respective holders,

Fig. 10-61. Cutting a Mortise in the End of a Pedestal, Using Mortising Attachment

making sure that the bit projects ⅛″ below the chisel.

3. Mount the fence and hold-down fingers on the table so that the work is in line with the sides of the chisel.
4. Adjust the table to the desired height.
5. Adjust the depth gauge to the proper travel of the spindle for the depth of the mortise.
6. Select the proper speed for the size bit being used. (Generally a slower speed is used than in regular boring.) The larger the hole, the slower the speed.
7. Start the cuts at the end of the mortise and make repeated cuts next to each other until all the waste material has been removed. If the mortise is deep,

the first cut may be made only about half the depth. Make a full cut next to the first one, then cut the first one to full depth.

Using the Shaper Attachment

1. Insert the special spindle or adapter for holding the shaper cutters. A regular chuck should not be used for this operation.
2. Select the shaper cutter for the desired shape to be cut and the proper diameter collar to control the depth of the cut. Fasten these in place on the spindle adapter. Lock the spindle in position.
3. If a collar is not to be used, fasten the shaper fence in the desired position on the table to produce the proper depth of cut in relationship with the vertical axis of the cutter.
4. Raise and lock the table to the desired height.
5. Adjust the spring tension guides to hold the work against the fence and the table.
6. Adjust the speed to 5000 r.p.m.

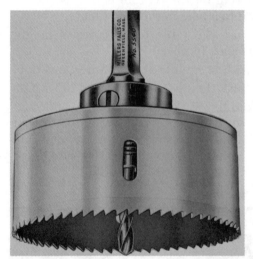

Fig. 10-62. Hole Saw (Courtesy Millers Falls Co.)

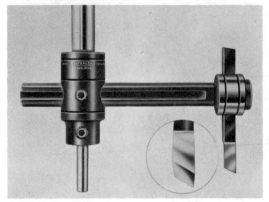

Fig. 10-62A. Fly Cutter (Courtesy Stanley Tool Co.)

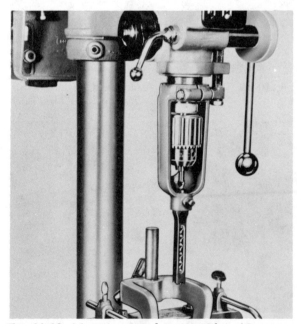

Fig. 10-63. Mortising Attachment in Place (Courtesy Walker-Turner Div., Rockwell Mfg. Co.)

7. Using a scrap piece of stock, make a trial cut. The work should be fed slowly into the cutter from the left side of the table. See Fig. 10-64.

8. If a deep cut is required it is sometimes necessary to make several light cuts to prevent splintering. End grain is cut before sides when cutting on the four edges of a board.

Using the Router Attachment

1. Select the router bit and insert it in the special spindle adapter.

2. Lock the table at the desired height.

3. Locate the special fence in position or clamp scrap stock, straightedges, or guides on the table.

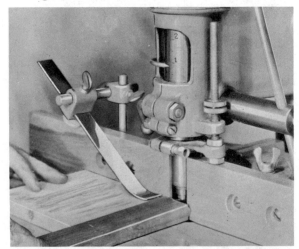

Fig. 10-64. Using Shaper Attachment on Drill Press (Courtesy Delta Div., Rockwell Mfg. Co.)

Fig. 10-65. Using Router Attachment on Drill Press (Courtesy Delta Div., Rockwell Mfg. Co.)

4. Adjust the speed to the highest possible — 5000 r.p.m.

5. If a full length cut is to be made, lock the spindle at the desired depth of the cutter. Make several lights cuts to remove the material in the groove.

6. Feed the work from the left side of the table. If a stop cut is to be made, use stop blocks or marks in the face of the work to limit the length of travel. See Fig. 10-65.

Using a Sanding Drum

1. Secure the sanding drum in the special chuck.

2. Secure a wood table plate on the drill press table. If the drum has a thrust bearing on the bottom end, this should fit into a hole in the wood plate.

3. Adjust the table to the proper height and lock in place.

4. Lock the spindle at the desired position.

5. Adjust the speed to about 1200 r.p.m.

6. Hold the work flat on the table and sand it with light pressure. Make sure that a steady pressure and movement are maintained throughout the length of the sanding. See Fig. 10-66.

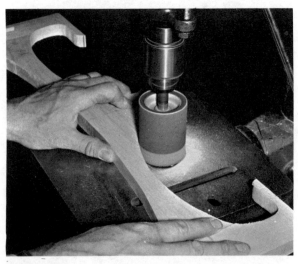

Fig. 10-66. Using Sanding Attachment on Drill Press Chuck has been adapted by securing it to spindle with a cap screw.

Standards and Results

1. Holes and cuts should have clean-cut surfaces and sides and be of proper size.
2. Holes and cuts should be in correct position and at the desired angle.
3. Drill bits should not be overheated.

Safety Considerations

1. Insert only round-shank drills in a three-jaw chuck and round tapered-shank drills in a tapered-shank spindle.

2. Change belt speeds only while machine is stopped.
3. Use correct speeds for all operations.
4. Use clamps or fixtures to hold work.
5. Protect table with a table board.
6. Hold table securely while making table adjustments.

Additional Reading

Delta Manufacturing Company, *Getting the Most Out of Your Drill Press*

Topic 98. Vertical Hollow Chisel Mortiser

Classification

Power-driven, rotary cutting tool within a hollow square chisel

Application

Principle of Operation

The cutting action is a combination of that of the screwless auger bit and the chisel, using the wedge, the inclined plane, and the lever.

Kinds and Uses

The mortiser is used principally in furniture factories and in sash and door plants for production mortising. A wide range of sizes is available to meet production requirements. See Fig. 10-67.

Principal Parts and Function of Each

1. *Motor*, ½ to 2 H.P., 60 cycle, 3600 r.p.m., sealed bearings, provides the power.
2. *Frame*, made of cast steel, holds the motor and table.
3. *Table and fence* are made of cast steel, machined. They support and align the stock.
4. All *hand wheels* are cast iron, machined. Handwheels adjust table height, table to right or left, and table toward or away from frame.

5. *Chuck*, made of steel, machined, holds **bit.**
6. *Chisel holder* is made of cast iron, machined.
7. Adjustable *stops* made of machined steel, regulate travel of table to right and left.
8. *Treadle*, made of either steel or cast iron, lowers the chisel and auger.
9. *Spring*, made of spring steel, returns treadle to the normal "up" position.
10. *Tilting mechanism*, made of machined cast iron, is used to tilt the table 45° to right or left.
11. *Blower*, made of steel with a cast iron casing, removes waste material from the cut.
12. *Depth gauge*, made of steel, regulates depth of cut.

13. *Bit*, made of high carbon steel, bores a hole and carries the shaving through the hollow chisel.
14. *Chisel*, made of high carbon steel, trims the corners of the hole, producing a square opening, Fig. 10-68.

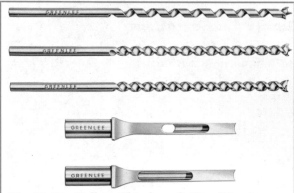

Fig. 10-68. Hollow Chisels and Bits (Courtesy Greenlee Tool Co.)

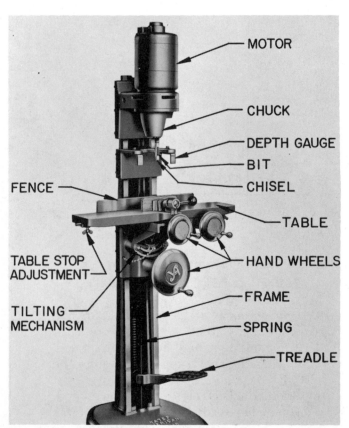

Fig. 10-67. Hollow Chisel Mortiser (Courtesy Yates-American Machine Co.)

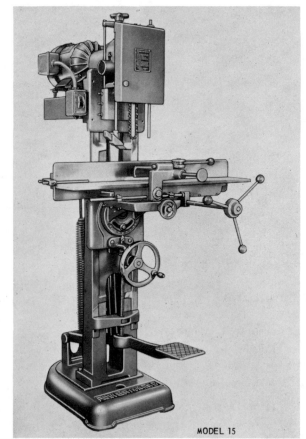

Fig. 10-69. Chain Mortiser (Courtesy Powermatic, Inc.)

Maintenance

All bearings should be lubricated unless they are the sealed type. When a mortiser is to be left unused for a long period of time, all machined parts should be covered with a thin coat of oil. Mortising bits and chisels should be kept sharp; sharpening should be done by an experienced person.

Market Analysis

Capacity

The capacity of a mortiser is determined by (1) the distance from the end of the chisel at its highest point to the surface of the table when in its lowest position; (2) the distance from the center line of the chisel to the fence; (3) the range in the size of chisels which can be accommodated; and (4) the vertical travel of the chisel. Matched bits and chisels are available in sizes as follows: $\frac{1}{4}''$, $\frac{5}{16}''$, $\frac{3}{8}''$, $\frac{7}{16}''$, $\frac{1}{2}''$, $\frac{9}{16}''$, $\frac{5}{8}''$, $\frac{11}{16}''$, $\frac{3}{4}''$, $\frac{13}{16}''$, $\frac{7}{8}''$, and $1''$.

Attachments

Bit guide and spindle extension for changing the machine into a drill press.

Additional Reading

Manufacturers' catalogs

Shaping Circular Forms on the Lathe

Topic 99. Wood Turning

Fig. 11-1. Starting to Turn

Fig. 11-1A. Turning Area of Ridgemount Junior High School, Wayzata, Minnesota, Instructor Robert L. Pearson (Courtesy Form-All Corp.)

Note use of clear plastic guards on front of lathes and back shield chip and dust collector system. This photo shows outboard face plate turning, spindle turning, and inboard face plate turning. Observe the non-skid surfaces on the floor in front of the lathe.

Wood turning is the process of shaping stock into cylinders, disks, and other round and out-of-round forms. This turning is achieved in a lathe or turning machine, which is a power-driven spindle, to which stock may be attached and thus given rotary motion.

When a sharpened tool enters the path of rotation of the stock, it is brought into contact with the high points and produces an arc of a circle on those points, Fig. 11-1. Further advancement of the tool results in the lengthening of the arcs until the circumference of a circle is formed.

The repetition of this procedure along the axis of the rotating stock to some predetermined distance will increase the length of the cylinder to that dimension. The distance from the axis to the cutter; the shape of the tool; and the angle, motion, and sweep of the tool as it is advanced into the work determine the profile of the turning.

Special lathes are used by industry to produce eccentric turned shapes, and to make many, many duplicate turnings.

Fig. 11-2. Turned Bowl (Courtesy Ford Motor Co., Industrial Arts Awards)

Fig. 11-3. Turning a Baseball Bat
This special model for a professional player is roughed on a hand lathe. The original is on the pattern rack and the new bat must conform exactly to model in size and shape. (Courtesy Hillerich & Bradsby Co.)

Fig. 11-6. Industrial Turnings — Semi-Automatic Lathe Turning a Bat (Courtesy Hillerich & Bradsby Co.)

Fig. 11-4. Industrial Turnings—Woodenware (Courtesy Baribeau & Son)

Fig. 11-7. Industrial Turnings — Golf Club Heads
This lathe is designed expressly to turn golf club heads. The persimmon "roughouts" from which the heads are turned are stacked at the left, finished turnings at right. At the right end of the lathe is the iron master pattern of the model being turned. It controls the turning. (Courtesy Hillerich & Bradsby Co.)

Fig. 11-5. Industrial Turnings—Baseball Bat on Semi-Automatic Lathe (Courtesy Hillerich & Bradsby Co.)

When the tool is in contact with the revolving stock at every point on the circumference of the stock, the result will be a concentric

Fig. 11-8. Industrial Turnings — Gun Stocks
This automatic stock carving machine, known as a "Salstrom," performs a carving operation on eight gun stocks at one time. (Courtesy Winchester-Western Div., Olin-Mathieson Chemical Corp.)

circle. When the tool comes into contact with the stock intermittently as the stock rotates it will result in an eccentric turning. This intermittent turning may be controlled and varied by changing the axis of the stock rotation or by changing the reciprocating action of a mechanically-operated cutter.

Speed is a factor in turning. One of the things which governs the selection of the speed is balance of the stock. Once the stock is in balance, the speed of the lathe should be regulated in accordance to the diameter and hardness of the stock being turned. Because peripheral (rim) speed is a factor in cutting, pieces of small diameter may be turned at higher spindle speeds than are recommended for pieces of large diameter. The beginning cuts made in soft wood may be made at higher speed than would be ordinarily used with hard wood because there is less resistance of the material to the cutting action.

Topic *100.* Wood Lathe

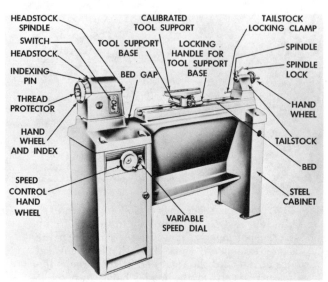

Fig. 11-9. The Wood Lathe and Its Parts (Courtesy Power Tool Div., Rockwell Mfg. Co.)

Classification

Powered rotary driving tool

Application

Principle of Operation

A lathe is a machine on which a face-plate or a spur center is attached to a motor-driven spindle which revolves at adjustable speeds. The work is mounted on the face-plate or between centers and is shaped by turning against chisels or special cutters which cut on the principle of the cutting wedge. The speed of the belt-driven lathe is maintained by step or cone pulleys which operate on the principle of the wheel and axle. When the driving pulley is smaller than the driven pulley, the speed is reduced; when the driven pulley is smaller than the driving pulley, the speed is increased. Speeds may be regulated between 300 and 3600 r.p.m. On some lathes this speed range is attained by the use of a variable speed motor. See Figs. 11-9 and 11-10.

Kinds and Uses

The lathe is used to rotate stock for shaping, sanding, or polishing. It is also used as a holding jig for fluting, reeding, and drilling holes.

Some lathes are made with a gap bed which provides a greater swing (distance from center to bed), permitting larger face-plate turnings, Fig. 11-10.

The usual capacities of lathes are:

Nine-inch swing — thirty inches between centers.

Eleven-inch swing — thirty-six inches between centers.

Twelve-inch swing — thirty-six inches between centers.

Fourteen-inch swing — thirty-six inches between centers

Larger lathes are not usually found in school shops, but some are six feet between centers.

Principal Parts and Function of Each

1. The *head stock*, which contains the driving mechanism, is cast iron with two sealed bearings. If the lathe is a direct drive, the motor is part of the head stock. If it is belt-driven, the pulleys are located in the head stock. The driving mechanism spindle is hollow and extends beyond the head stock at both ends. The inboard end has a right-hand thread for attaching a face-plate while the outboard end has a left-hand thread for attaching a face-plate for outside turning of larger diameters than the swing of the lathe will accommodate.

2. The *live or spur center*, made of unhardened tool steel, has a tapered shank to fit the spindle and supports the stock on the left end when turning between centers, Fig. 11-11. It is called the live center because it turns with the head stock.

3. The cast iron *tail stock* holds the dead center which serves as a pivot.

4. The hardened tool steel *dead center* supports the stock on the right side when turning between centers. There are two

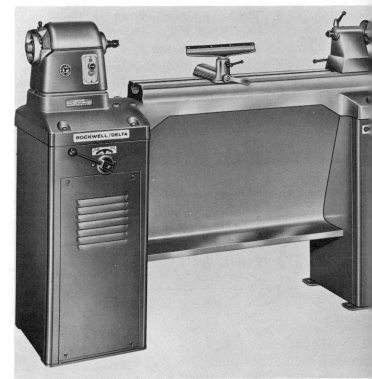

Fig. 11-10. 12″ Gap Bed Wood Lathe (Courtesy Delta Div., Rockwell Mfg. Co.)

Fig. 11-11. Spur Center   Fig. 11-12. Cup Center
(Courtesy Delta Div., Rockwell Mfg. Co.)

Fig. 11-13. Sanding Disk (Courtesy Delta Div., Rockwell Mfg. Co.)

types: cup and cone center. They have a tapered shank to fit the spindle. (See Fig. 11-12.)

5. The *tool rest,* made of machined cast iron, provides support for the lathe tool.

6. The cast iron *bed* supports the head stock, tail stock, and tool rest holder.

7. The cast iron *tail stock hand wheel* increases or decreases the distance the dead center protrudes from the tail stock.

8. The *tail stock clamp* secures the tail stock to the bed.

9. The *alignment screw* on the tail stock adjusts center turning.

10. The *tool rest holder* secures the tool post to the bed.

11. The *tool rest clamp* makes the tool rest secure at the desired height.

12. The *index head* is an adjustable lock for locking the spindle when reeding or fluting. See Fig. 11-18B.

Fig. 11-14. Sanding Drums (Courtesy Delta Div., Rockwell Mfg. Co.)

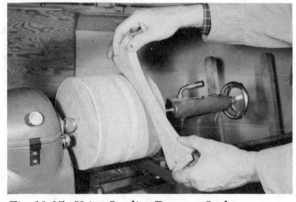

Fig. 11-15. Using Sanding Drum on Lathe

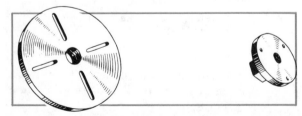

Fig. 11-16. Face Plates (Courtesy Delta Div., Rockwell Mfg. Co.)

13. The *motor* (½ to ¾ H.P., 1725 r.p.m.) provides the power.

14. The *belt* transmits the power.

Maintenance

1. The spurs and points of live centers should be kept sharp.

2. The working edge of the tool rest should be kept smooth. Recondition by draw filing.

3. The original shape of the cup center should be maintained. A cone center should be ground only by an experienced person.

4. Bearings should be kept lubricated.

5. When a lathe is to be left unused for long periods, all machined surfaces should be coated with a protective film of oil or wax.

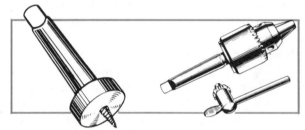

Fig. 11-17. Screwpoint   Fig. 11-18. Jacobs
Face Plate   Chuck
(Courtesy Delta Div., Rockwell Mfg. Co.)

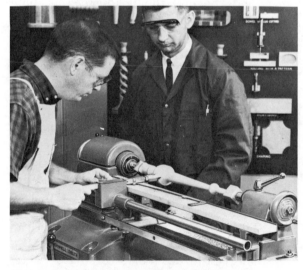

Fig. 11-18A. Turning Duplicator (Courtesy Delta Div., Rockwell Mfg. Co.)

6. The tail stock may vibrate out of line and will need adjusting.
7. Belts may need adjusting or replacing.
8. Wood dust should be blown from the motor periodically.

Market Analysis

Capacity

The capacity of a lathe is determined by the maximum length of stock which can be turned between centers and by the distance from the live center to the bed of the lathe. This is called swing.

Attachments

1. Sanding disk fastens on face plate and is used for sanding convex curves on edges of stock, Fig. 11-13.

Fig. 11-18B. Indexing Head (Courtesy Rockwell Mfg. Co.)

2. Sanding drum or cylinder is mounted between centers for sanding concave curves on edges of stock, Fig. 11-15.
3. Face plates are for holding the stock when doing face-plate turning. There are small spur and screw center plates, left (outside), and right (inside) face-plates, Fig. 11-16.
4. Screw center is used to turn knobs or to do small face-plate turnings, Fig. 11-17.
5. Drill chuck has a tapered shank to fit either the head stock or the tail stock spindle. It serves to hold a drill when drilling holes in turnings.
6. Four-jaw chuck is used in place of live center for holding square or irregularly shaped pieces. (See Fig. 11-22A.)
7. Screw or arbor is for attaching grinding or buffing wheel, Fig. 11-19.
8. Steady rest is to provide support on long between-center turnings, Fig. 11-20.
9. Right angle tool rest is used for turning edge and face on a face-plate without changing set-up of tool rest holder, Fig. 11-21.
10. Floor stand holds tool rest on outside face-plate turning using left face-plate. (See Fig. 11-22B.)
11. Double post tool rest is used for long spindle-turning, Fig. 11-22.

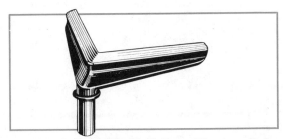

Fig. 11-21. Right Angle Tool Rest (Courtesy Delta Div., Rockwell Mfg. Co.)

Fig. 11-22. Double Post Tool Rest (Courtesy Delta Div., Rockwell Mfg. Co.)

Fig. 11-19. Arbor for Buffing Wheel   Fig. 11-20. Steady Rest
(Courtesy Delta Div., Rockwell Mfg. Co.)

Fig. 11-22A. Four-Jaw Chuck for Holding Square or Irregular Shaped Pieces

Fig. 11-23. Model of Bow Lathe

The most primitive lathe, called the bow lathe, was in reality not a lathe at all, but an arrangement by which one or two loops of a bow string were wrapped around a piece of round stock which was held between two pivot points.

Moving the bow back and forth across and at a right angle to the stock caused the stock to rotate alternately in a clockwise and counter-clockwise direction. The cutting was done when the bow was drawn toward the worker. The operator was required to operate the bow with one hand and hold the cutting tool with the other.

Fig. 11-22B. Floor Stand for Outboard Face Plate Turning

Fig. 11-24. Model of a Pole Lathe

The pole lathe employed much the same principle as the bow lathe, but the string was attached at one end to a flexible pole above the lathe, the other end being attached to a treadle. Depressing the treadle caused the stock to rotate toward the cutter and pulled the end of the pole down. The spring of the pole returned the treadle to the starting position.

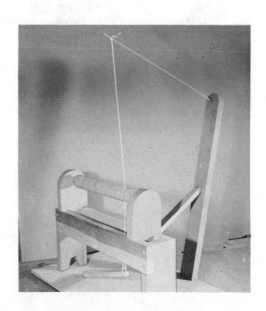

Fig. 11-25. The Great Wheel
The next step in the development of the lathe was connecting the treadle by a crank arm to a large wheel which, in turn, was connected by a belt to a smaller wheel on the head stock spindle, much the same as modern belt-driven lathes. Later, as on this lathe, the large wheel was turned by means of a crank, and a helper was employed. Both of these lathes produced a continuous rotary motion.

Observe how these early craftsmen used to advantage their knowledge of the principles of mechanics. The "Great Wheel" with its very large diameter drove a much smaller wheel at a consequent greater speed. To maintain a reasonable uniformity of speed the heavy flywheel was used. Even the crank on the "Great Wheel" was used because of the mechanical advantage it could provide. (Courtesy Old Sturbridge Village, Inc.)

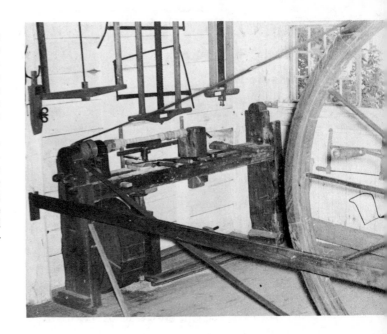

Fig. 11-26. Seventeenth Century Cape Cod Foot Power Lathe
Note the close-up of the wooden cogs on the spur and fly wheels. The tailstock and the tool rest are not adjustable; but are fixed in position. (Courtesy Old Sturbridge Village, Inc.)

Topic *101.* Turning Chisels

(GOUGE, SKEW, ROUNDNOSE, SQUARENOSE, DIAMOND POINT, PARTING TOOL)

Classification

Edge cutting tools

Application

Principle of Operation

The outside, beveled wedge on turning chisels is a cutting wedge. The rotating motion of the lathe provides the driving force. The long handle of the tool provides the necessary lever arm to control the cutting edge. The speed of the turning sets up centrifugal force in the stock, and the turning chisel (the cutting wedge) adjusted at the proper angle serves to release the stock as it is revolved (forced) against it.

Kinds and Uses

1. The *gouge* is a turning chisel used in roughing out cylinders and in turning

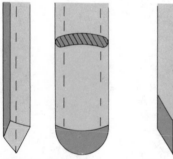

Fig. 11-28. Gouge

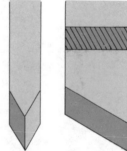

Fig. 11-29. Skew

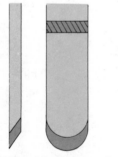

Fig. 11-30. Roundnose

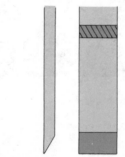

Fig. 11-31. Squarenose

concave surfaces on spindles, Fig. 11-28. Its blade is concave-convex in cross-section, with a rounded, beveled cutting edge. The cutting edge is rounded to prevent the tool from digging into the work being turned. The bevel is approximately 30° which aids in making scraping or shearing cuts. The common sizes of turning gouges are ⅜″, ½″, ¾″, and 1″.

2. The *skew chisel* is a flat turning chisel used in smoothing cylinders, rounding edges, and in making "V" and shoulder cuts, Fig. 11-29. It can be used with either a shearing or a scraping action. The end of the skew forms a 60° to 70° profile which is beveled on both sides to form a cutting angle of approximately 40°. (There are right- and left-hand skew chisels, beveled on one face only, which are scraping chisels used in pattern turning.) The common sizes of skew chisels are ¼″, ½″, and 1″.

3. The *roundnose* is a flat scraping chisel used in roughing and shaping concave surfaces, Fig. 11-30. The end is rounded and has a single bevel of about 30°. The common sizes of roundnose chisels are ⅛″, ¼″, ½″, and 1″.

4. The *squarenose* is a flat scraping chisel used to make flat, straight cuts, Fig. 11-31. It resembles a standard wood chisel in shape but has a thicker and longer blade. The end is square and has a single bevel of about 30°. The most common sizes of squarenose chisel are ½″ and ¾″.

5. The *diamond point* is a flat scraping chisel used to make "V" cuts or beads, Fig. 11-32. The pointed cutting edges are formed by grinding the sides to a desired angle at a bevel of 30°. The most common size of the diamond point is ½″.

6. The *parting tool* is a scraping chisel used to make deep, narrow cuts and

depth cuts for sizing when shaping pro-files, Fig. 11-33. The thickness of the blade is greater at the center than at the edges. The blade is ground at an angle from each edge to the center, thus forming a flat, pointed cutting edge, which reduces binding and friction or heating when cutting. The common sizes of parting tools are ⅛″ and ³⁄₁₆″.

Principal Parts and Function of Each

1. The *blade*, made of carbon tool steel, is the body of the tool.
2. The *bevel* on the blade forms the cutting wedge.
3. The *tang* or tapered end fits into the handle.
4. The *hardwood handle*, 4″ to 9″ long, provides the means of holding the tool and directing and controlling the cutting action.
5. The *brass ferrule* reinforces the handle against splitting.

Maintenance

Sharpening

The blade or cutting wedge should be re-shaped when nicked, broken, or when the bevel is too short. The bevel should be two to two-and-one-half times the thickness of the blade. Turning chisels are dressed with a slipstone. (See Figs. 6-81 and 6-82.)

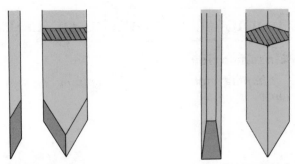

Fig. 11-32. Diamond Point   Fig. 11-33. Parting Tool

Repairing

Damaged handles should be replaced.

Storing

Turning chisels should be stored individually in a rack or case to prevent dulling the keen edge and to insure safety. When left unused for a long period of time, the steel should be coated with a film of oil or wax to prevent rusting.

Market Analysis

Attachments

Wood turner's gauge for parting tool.

Additional Reading

Topic 69, "Grinding Edge Tools"
Topic 71, "Whetting or Honing a Cutting Tool"
Manufacturers' catalogs

Topic *102*. Spindle or Between-Center Turning

Classification

Shaping stock which is revolving against cutter

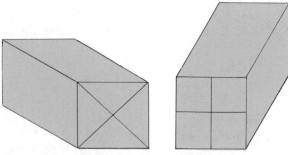

Fig. 11-34. Locating Center with Diagonal Lines
Fig. 11-35. Locating Center with Lines Drawn with Square or Marking Gauge

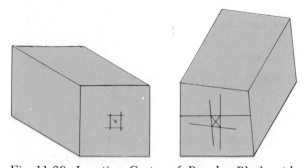

Fig. 11-36. Locating Center of Regular Block with Lines Drawn with Dividers
Fig. 11-37. Locating Center of Irregular Block with Lines Drawn with Dividers

Fig. 11-38. Circle Drawn with Compasses on Uneven Block

Procedure

1. After stock has been selected, cut to size with an allowance of one inch for waste in length and one-quarter inch for waste in diameter. Square the ends and find the center of each end by marking intersecting diagonal lines. Methods of locating centers are shown in Figs. 11-34 through 11-40.

2. Select one end for the live center and, using a backsaw, cut to a depth of one-eighth of an inch on the lines. On the other end, center punch at the point where the lines intersect. When using hard woods, a hole one-eighth of an

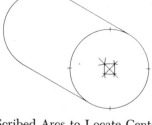

Fig. 11-39. Scribed Arcs to Locate Center on Cylindrical Piece

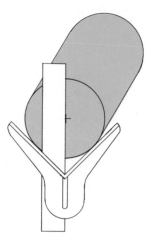

Fig. 11-40. Locating Center of Cylinder with Center Head

inch in diameter and depth may be drilled at each center.

3. Slide the tail stock out of the way.

4. Remove the live center from the headstock. Hold the live center with the right hand. With the left hand, insert the drive-out rod through the headstock spindle and drive out the center. Next, with a wooden mallet drive the live center into the wood so that the spurs enter the kerf made by the saw.

5. With the spur rather firmly imbedded in the stock, replace the live center in the spindle of the head stock.

6. Adjust the tail stock spindle so that it is advanced one inch beyond the tail stock housing. Slide the tail stock until the point of the dead center enters the hole. Lock the tail stock in position. Turn the tail stock spindle-feed handle until the dead center is seated in the wood. Release the pressure slightly and apply a little wax, oil, or soap to the impression made by the dead center on the end of the wood.

Turn the feed handle until the dead center is fairly tight in the original position. Then back off until stock turns freely. Lock the spindle in place.

7. Adjust the tool rest so that it is one-eighth of an inch above the center of the stock and lock in position. Rotate the stock by hand and adjust the tool rest so that it clears every corner of the stock by at least one-eighth of an inch and is reasonably parallel to the stock. Lock the tool rest holder in position. Tool rest should be maintained at a distance of no more than three-eighths of an inch away from the work as stock decreases in diameter.

Fig. 11-41. Rough Turning with a Gouge Using a Scraping Cut

Note the horizontal position of the tool, the placement of the fingers, and the manner in which the gouge cuts the wood being turned.

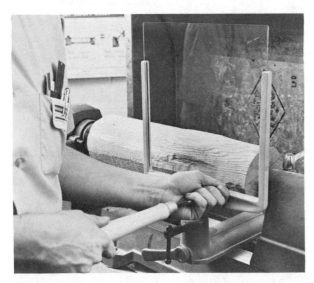

Fig. 11-40A. Spindle Turning Using the Clear Plastic Guard (Courtesy Form-All Corp.)

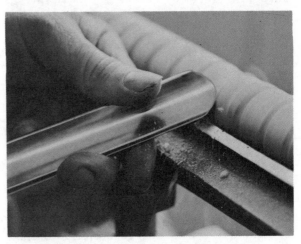

Fig. 11-42. Shearing Cut with Gouge

Note the angle of the cutting tool, the position of the fingers, and the shearing action with which the gouge cuts.

8. Pieces of stock two inches square and over should have the corners removed before inserting piece in the lathe. This can be done with a plane, spoke shave, drawknife, or jointer.

9. Assume a natural position with the feet slightly spread and one foot a little behind the other, and with the weight evenly distributed.

10. Select the large gouge. Grasp the handle well out toward the end with the right hand. With the left hand, hold the blade and guide it along the tool rest. Work from the center toward the ends. It is advisable to get the feel of this position before the lathe is started.

11. Start the lathe on the slow speed (600 r.p.m.)

12. If a scraping cut is to be made, the gouge is held in a horizontal position, using the tip end of the tool to do the cutting, Fig. 11-41. This will produce a rough cut. To avoid long splinters, a series of cuts may be made with the narrow gouge by placing it at approximately 45° on the rest with the tip over the work. Raise the handle to make a ¼" cut. Repeat this about every two inches.

13. If a shearing cut is to be made, lower the right hand about ten degrees; turn the gouge to make a slight angle toward the direction in which the cut is to be made and move the tool along the rest, taking a fine cut, Fig. 11-42.

14. Continue to turn until the piece is cylindrical.

15. Finish turning with skew chisel. Higher speed facilitates smoother cutting and is therefore used for finish turning. Increase the speed to 1600 to 1800 r.p.m.

Fig. 11-44. Shearing with the Skew Chisel

Shearing is accomplished by holding the face of the bevel edge of the chisel flat on the stock with the cut taking place at the center of the bevel. A sharp tool will pare off shavings, resulting in a smooth surface which requires very little sanding.

Fig. 11-43. Scraping with the Skew Chisel

Observe how wood chips and dust are literally being scraped off the stock, resulting in a rather rough turning. Scraping is a forced, tearing action which rapidly wears away the cutting edge, thus necessitating frequent whetting of the chisel.

Fig. 11-45. Cutting a "V" with the Heel of a Skew Chisel

The size of the "V' is determined by the angle at which the skew is held.

The highest speed is used for finishing and polishing and not for turning.

Select a wide skew chisel. With the right hand, grasp the handle close to the end; place the left hand on the blade. With the slope of the bevel pointing in the direction of the cut to be made and resting on the stock with the bevel protruding beyond, draw back on the tool until the center of the bevel is in contact with the stock. Adjust the tool by moving the right hand until the blade is at an angle of approximately 120° to the axis of the stock. Raise the tool handle until the cutting edge begins to cut. (A sharp tool will cut a shaving.) Raising the handle increases the depth of the cut. Beginners should not try a heavy cut. Slide the tool along the rest maintaining the proper angle. Reverse and repeat until stock is turned to proper dimension. See Fig. 11-44.

NOTE: On long, thin spindle turning, a steady rest may be used to reduce vibration or chatter. See Fig. 11-20.

Making "V" Cuts

1. Using a sharp pencil and a rule, lay out the center line and the width of the "V".

2. Place the edge of the skew on the tool rest with the heel down and the cutting edge on the center line of the "V", Fig. 11-45. Score the center line.

3. Slide the skew along the tool rest about one-eighth of an inch from the center line and turn it at a slight angle toward the center line. Cut into the center line. Do the same on the opposite side of the center line. Repeat the steps of this operation until the desired "V" is obtained.

4. If the scraping method is used, the diamond point chisel of the proper size is held in a horizontal position and at right angles with the stock. The chisel is advanced until the desired width and depth are obtained.

Cutting Beads

1. With a sharp pencil and a rule, template, or dividers, lay out the width of the bead. On a wide bead it is advisable to have a center line.

2. Set calipers to the respective diameters of the crest and of the base of the bead.

3. To shape a bead place the edge of the skew on the tool rest with the heel down and the cutting edge on a width line. Score the width line on each side of the bead.

4. From the width lines of the bead, move the skew one-eighth of an inch along the tool rest toward the center of the bead. With the heel doing the cutting, roll the skew to the width line. Repeat this process on both sides until the desired bead is formed. See Figs. 11-46, 11-47, 11-48.

Fig. 11-46. Cutting Beads with the Skew
The bead is being shaped from the high point to the scored width lines.

Fig. 11-47. Layout for Practice Piece for Cutting Beads

Making Concave or Cove Cuts

1. With a sharp pencil and rule or template, mark the center and width lines of the cove.
2. Set caliper to one-sixteenth of an inch greater than the desired diameter.
3. With the parting tool, cut at the center line to this dimension.
4. If the scraping method is used, take a round nose chisel of appropriate size, place it bevel down on the tool rest in a horizontal position, and sweeping the tool from side to side, cut to the desired shape and dimension, Fig. 11-49.
5. If the shearing method is used, place the gouge on its side on the tool rest about one-eighth of an inch on either side of the cut already made by the parting tool. With a rolling motion cut to the center. Continue this process for desired shape and dimension. See Fig. 11-50.
6. If the concave cut is long and gradual as in the handle of a baseball bat, lay out cuts every inch with a pencil and rule or template.

   With a parting tool, cut to the desired depth at each mark, Fig. 11-51. Calipers should be set for each dimension. A wood turner's gauge might be attached to the parting tool after rough cutting. Rough off the surplus stock with a gouge. Use a skew for either a scraping or shearing cut to finished dimensions.

Fig. 11-48. Scraping a Large Bead with the Skew
After depth cuts have been made on each side of the bead, the skew is held flat on the rest and fed in from the high point to the width lines.

Cutting a Long Taper

1. Lay out the length of the taper with pencil and rule, dividers, or trammel points.
2. Set the calipers one-sixteenth of an inch greater than the larger and smaller diameters of the taper.

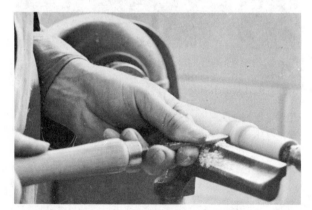

Fig. 11-49. Scraping Cut with the Roundnose Chisel
Hold the chisel flat on the tool rest and pivot the handle to form the arc.

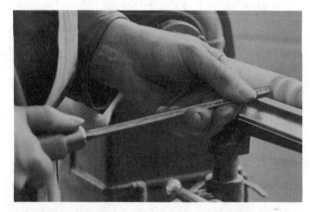

Fig. 11-50. Shearing Cut Using the Small Gouge
The turner who has mastered this method can produce accurate cuts with a minimum of tearing.

3. If a full-size drawing is not available, lay out the taper on paper to determine dimensions of the taper at several points, and cut the proper depth with a parting tool at these intervals, making certain that these cuts are made on the side of the line with the smaller diameter.
4. Rough off surplus stock with a gouge. See Fig. 11-53.
5. Set tool rest parallel to the taper.
6. Use a skew for either a scraping or shearing cut to finished dimensions.
7. Check taper with a straightedge.

Sanding

1. Remove the tool rest for sanding. (See Fig. 11-54.)
2. After a final scraping cut, use # 1, 1/2, and 2/0 garnet paper. After a final shearing cut, very little sanding should be required and then only with 2/0 abrasive.
3. On cylindrical sanding, hold a long piece of sandpaper between both hands and at right angles to the stock, with the right hand over the work. Bear down evenly, moving paper back and forth and lengthwise with the stock.
4. On sanding beads, "V" grooves, and coves, form the paper to fit a small section of the contour of the turning and sand from beneath the piece so that the operation can be seen, Fig. 11-54.

Standards and Results

1. Stock must be turned to prescribed shapes and dimensions. Beads should be round; contours, sharp; sides of "V"s, straight; and shoulders, flat.
2. Surfaces must be smooth and free of sanding marks, defects, and stains.

Safety Considerations

1. When selecting stock for turning, avoid loose knots, checks, cross-grain, splintery stock, or stock improperly glued.
2. Avoid dropping live center when removing from head stock.

3. Check to see that stock is properly centered.
4. Check tail stock to see that it is locked in position, securing work firmly between centers.

Fig. 11-51. Making a Depth Cut with the Parting Tool
Set the calipers to the desired diameter (making a small allowance for sanding) and test frequently while cutting to size with the parting tool.

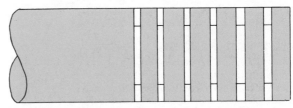

Fig. 11-52. Layout for Practice Piece for Cutting to Depth

Fig. 11-53. Roughing Out a Long Taper by Shearing with the Large Gouge
Work from the larger diameter to the smaller.

5. Rotate stock by hand to determine clearance of tool rest.
6. Avoid loose clothing and dangling ties.

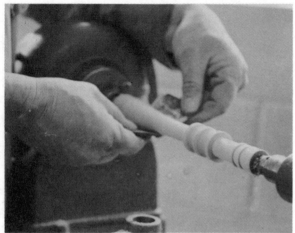

Fig. 11-54. Sanding in the Lathe
Sanding may be done by holding the paper either above or below the turning. Holding the paper below as shown makes it easier to observe the progress of the sanding. Note: The tool rest is removed.

7. Maintain tool rest at proper height and distance from work.
8. Rough turning should be done at a slow speed.
9. Avoid heavy cuts.
10. Keep hands off rough stock which is revolving.
11. Turning chisel should be held always at proper angle with a firm grip.
12. Periodically check the dead center for heating, lubrication, and adjustment.
13. Tools should not be left on bed of lathe while operating lathe.
14. Tools should be kept sharp at all times.
15. Tool rest should be removed before sanding.
16. Eye-protective devices should be used when operating the lathe.

Additional Reading

Delta Manufacturing Company, *Getting the Most Out of Your Lathe*

Topic *103.* Face-Plate Turning on a Lathe

(INBOARD AND OUTBOARD TURNING)

Classification

Shaping stock which is revolving against a cutter

Procedure

In face-plate turning, the stock is mounted on a flat metal plate which is attached to the spindle of the head stock of the lathe. As the plate revolves, the stock is shaped by scraping cuts. The tools used are: the roundnose chisel for concave cuts, the skew chisel for convex cuts, the squarenose for straight cuts, the diamond point for V cuts, and the parting chisel for depth cuts.
1. Band saw a disk ⅛″ larger in diameter than the finished dimensions.
2. Select a face-plate smaller than the disk to be turned.

3. If screw holes are objectionable in the bottom of the finished turning or if there is a possibility of the turning tools striking the screws, a block of wood should be glued to the base of the work. In gluing, a piece of heavy paper should be placed between the glued surfaces in order to simplify separation without damage to the finished turning.
4. Mount the stock to the faceplate, selecting screws of the proper length and diameter to adequately hold the work and yet insure that there is no possibility of the turning tools striking the screws and that the heads of the screws are flush with the back surface of the faceplate. Make sure that the centers coincide. Small objects may be turned on a

screw center; this is a faceplate with one screw in the center.

5. Remove the live center from the lathe and screw the face-plate to the spindle. It is advisable to place a piece of heavy paper between the shoulder of the spindle and the face-plate to facilitate removal.

6. Adjust the tool rest so that it is ⅛″ below the center and ⅛″ away from the turning.

7. Turn the stock through one revolution to see that it clears the tool rest by at least ⅛″ at every point.

8. Adjust to proper speed. It is customary to use the slow speed, 600 r.p.m., but pieces which are 3″ or less in diameter may be turned at a speed of 1200 r.p.m.

9. To turn to diameter, assume a natural position, facing at an angle of approximately 45° to the ways of the lathe with the weight evenly distributed on both feet. Grasp the handle of the turning chisel with the right hand, keeping the hand well out toward the end. With the left hand hold the blade and guide it along the tool rest. Get the feel of this position before the lathe is started.

10. True up the edge with a skew chisel. This is done by holding the tool in a horizontal position — flat on the tool rest. Start at one axis and move the tool across the thickness of the stock. Continue this procedure, taking small cuts and keeping the full width of the blade in contact with the work until the edge is true.

11. To produce convex cuts on an edge, rest the flat side of the skew chisel on the tool rest in a horizontal position and pivot to form the desired arc.

12. To produce a concave cut on an edge, rest the flat side of the roundnose chisel in a horizontal position and pivot to form the desired arc.

13. To produce convex cuts on the face, place the skew chisel as in Step 11 and pivot from the center out.

14. To produce concave cuts on the face, place the roundnose chisel as in Step 12.

Start the cut at the center and work out. Keep the tool perpendicular to the arc of the cut so that the cutting is done with the end of the tool. See Figs. 11-55, 11-56.

15. To produce straight cuts, use a square-nose chisel. Keep the full width of the blade in contact with the work.

16. To produce "V" cuts, use the diamond point chisel.

Fig. 11-55. Inboard Face-Plate Turning
Shaping the inside of a bowl by scraping with the roundnose chisel is a typical application of inboard turning.

Fig. 11-56. Outboard Face-Plate Turning
For diameters too large for inboard turning, the outboard face-plate may be used. Observe that the tool is worked from the center to the right, the opposite of inboard turning.

17. As stock is removed from the turning, the tool rest should be advanced and adjusted to proper angle to keep it within safe working distance.

18. After the turning has been completed, it must be sanded. Use 50 grit garnet cabinet paper to start removal of turning chisel marks. Make the finish sanding with 100 grit garnet paper. See Fig. 11-57.

19. When the turning has been completed, remove it from the lathe; then remove the face-plate from the turning. If a backing block was glued on, remove it by splitting on the glue line with a mallet and chisel. Do not damage the turning.

Standards and Results

1. Turnings should be smooth and without defects.
2. Turnings should be to dimensions and shape specified.
3. Backing block should be split off cleanly on the glue joint.

Safety Considerations

1. Rotate stock by hand to determine clearance of tool rest.
2. Avoid loose clothing and dangling ties.
3. Lathe must be operated at proper speed — the larger the diameter of the stock, the lower the speed and the greater the need for accurate balancing.
4. Rough turning should be done at a slow speed.
5. Avoid heavy cuts.
6. Tools should be kept sharp and properly shaped.
7. Care must be taken not to get chisel caught in work, causing damage to work, tool, or operator.

Fig. 11-56A. Outboard Face Plate Turning Using Clear Plastic Guard (Courtesy Form-All Corp.)

Fig. 11-57. Sanding Concave Surface on a Face-Plate Sanding is done below center and on the down slope of the rotation of the stock. A sanding pad is recommended.

Fig. 11-57A. Portable, Special-Purpose Machine for Face-Plate Turning up to 16″ in Diameter.

8. Turning chisel should be held always at proper angle with a firm grip.

9. Maintain tool rest at proper height and distance from work.

10. Tool rest should be removed before sanding.

11. It is recommended that goggles be worn when operating a lathe.

12. Tools should not be left on bed of lathe when operating lathe.

13. A safe minimum thickness for bowl sides and bottoms is $\frac{3}{16}''$.

14. Screws should be of proper size to fit countersunk holes in face-plate and should be screwed in straight, tight, and flush.

15. To prevent accidents, remove the live center when doing outboard turning.

Additional Reading

Delta Manufacturing Company, *Getting the Most Out of Your Lathe*

Topic *104.* Industrial Turning

Whether it be by hand or machine, turning is based on the same principle. In hand turning the cut is made from the larger diameter to the smaller with the tool shearing the stock with the grain. Automatic shaping lathes follow this identical procedure. Rotating cutter heads containing a multiplicity of knives shear the stock along the entire length of the turning sequence. See Fig. 11-58.

In forming a head or other ornamental shape, the knives always start at the highest point and shear downward, toward the right and toward the left, thus the cut is made as much with the grain as across it, resulting in a smooth surface. See Fig. 11-59.

The six knives are staggered around the short sections of the cutter head and inserted in knife holders designed to hold them at the proper angle back of the center line. This position gives the knives a forward shearing cut. Very rarely are more than one or two knives cutting at the same time, thus reducing strain on the stock.

Some lathes have uniform, double-end drive providing synchronized turning motion on both ends of the stock and making it possible to turn exceptionally delicate pieces with little danger of breaking, chattering, or twisting. This produces work which requires very little or no sanding. All pieces are turned true and uniform in size and shape.

Fig. 11-58. Back-Knife Lathe
The back-knife lathe is used to turn spindles, legs, rounds, and to make slight contour cuts. In this lathe the stock revolves at a high rate of speed in a counter-clockwise direction. The single knife, which is the length of the pattern and ground to the profile of the finished piece, is fed mechanically into the revolving stock, cutting the entire turning to shape. (Courtesy Heywood-Wakefield Co.)

A hollow chuck attachment supports long and slender turnings, permitting the stock to be revolved with or opposite to the rotation of the knives without danger of loosening. The knives revolve at a high rate of speed (2700 r.p.m.) and are advanced into the work which turns slowly (2-30 r.p.m.)

An automatic stock-centering device saves time in centering blanks. The head center holds the turning allowing the cut to be completed over the end of the work thus eliminat-ing the need for an extra inch of stock. As the carriage is pushed forward the centering device automatically recedes out of the way of the knives.

The swing of the automatic lathe is 14″ to 18″. These lathes can accommodate a cut up to 62″ long in one operation. The use of horizontal steady rests, extension plates, and other special attachments allows thinner and longer stock to be turned.

Shaping the knives is a special task. A profile of the desired turning is made into a pattern board which is clamped into a special marking machine and set-up box in which the knife blanks are marked. A perfect fit, corresponding to the pattern board, can then be ground on the knife blanks.

The automatic shaping lathe will handle practically anything in the way of plain or fancy turnings. It will produce round, square, octagonal, hexagonal, or most any other polygonal shape. Among the more common uses are: shaping of table legs, pedestals, piano pillars, lamp standards, standards and posts for bureaus, chiffoniers, table and toilet stands, bedposts and rails, chair legs, casket corners, coffin handles, tenpins, Indian clubs, dumb-bells, ball bats, lawn mower handles, and rollers. Many odd-shaped turnings, such as gun stocks and golf club heads, are produced.

Production on these machines varies from 100 to 600 pieces per day according to size, kind, and style of work being turned. Round turnings are produced on an average of 3 to 10 times faster than they are by hand-operated lathes. Square and many-sided patterns take $\frac{1}{6}$ to $\frac{1}{20}$ the time required by hand sawing.

The knives are fed in behind the stock by means of a lever which the operator controls. His skill is very important. He must feel the cutting action as the knives come in contact with the wood. If he forces the cut a poor turning will result.

Fig. 11-59. The Mattison Lathe
Large, shaper-like knives which revolve at a high rate of speed are advanced into the slowly revolving stock by a series of cams, turning the entire piece in one operation. (Courtesy Mattison Machine Works)

Topic *105.* The Wood Turner

Only a very small number of hand wood turners are employed in industry today. Most woodworking plants have mechanized wood turning and automatic lathes are now widely used. Job opportunities in hand turning are decidedly limited; however, there are still some highly skilled wood turners in the furniture industry. Their training period is from three to four years. Skill in wood-turning is also needed in patternmaking, custom, and specialty shops, as well as small general woodworking shops.

In addition to the common woodworking lathe of the type found in schools and home workshops, business and industry also have semi-automatic and automatic shaping lathes. See Figs. 11-3, 11-5, 11-6, 11-7, 11-8, 11-58, 11-59.

Topic *106.* Joinery

The term *joinery* in its older restricted meaning was the art of constructing doors, windows, stairs, panels, and other closely fitted items of interior woodwork. As commonly used, the term *to join* means to connect, unite, or combine. In woodworking, to join means to connect pieces of wood for the purpose of extending dimension (length, width, or thickness) for the purpose of changing direction, or to couple pieces for the purpose of allowing for motion.

Definition of Wood Joint

A woodworking joint is the place or part in which two separate pieces of wood are joined or united, either rigidly or so as to admit motion. There are ten or twelve basic joints, but the several varieties of these basic joints number more than twenty-four.

Strength and appearance are the basic qualities of a joint.

Types of Wood Joints

Woodworking joints are divided into two basic types: "lay-up" and "assembly" type joints. Lay-up joints are those used for building up the dimensions of stock. Assembly types are those used in assembling members which have been cut to specified shape and dimension. The different types of assembly joints have their respective functions, although some types are used interchangeably depending upon strength considerations and character of design.

Reinforcement of Wood Joints

Practically all joints are held in place by the use of some fastener. Nails, screws, pins, wedges, splines, dowels, corrugated fasteners,

mending plates, and other forms of hardware all serve to reinforce or facilitate the purpose of joints. Glue is the common adhesive used in wood joints where the separate members have been fitted. The strength of the joint is determined largely by the accuracy of the fit, the quality of the glue, and the observance of sound rules for gluing and clamping.

The strength of any given joint depends upon a number of factors, as follows:

1. The ability of a specific kind of wood to stay in shape and place; that is, the degree to which the wood will not twist, cup, bow, swell, or shrink.
2. The degree of dryness of the wood and the extent of utilization of factors controlling the swelling and shrinking in making a joint; for example, chair rungs, spindles and slats, expansion dowels, boats, barrels, tubs, and tanks. The Valiton compressed tenon is another example. See Fig. 12-69.
3. The degree to which the fibers of a particular type of wood can be compressed as in the use of nails, corrugated fasteners, dowels, and splines.
4. The degree of effectiveness of using adhesives with any particular kind of wood.
5. The dimensions of the separate members of the joint.
6. Standard of workmanship.

Some terms used in joinery are:
Arris -- sharp edge formed by the meeting of two surfaces.
Bevel -- a full edge cut at an angle other than 90°, connecting two surfaces in the same plane.

Chamfer — a sloping cut of various angles, cutting two intersecting surfaces but not an entire edge as in a bevel.

Cheek — the broad face or surface of a tenon.

Corner — point where three arrises meet.

Dado — a recess running across the grain of a piece of lumber.

Edge — the narrow faces running with the grain.

Gain — a recess cut in one member to receive another piece. (Locks, hinges, timber, tenons, tongues, etc.)

Groove — a recess running with the grain in a piece of lumber.

Resawing — decreasing stock in thickness by the use of sawing, resulting in two or more thinner pieces of the same length and width.

Shoulder — the end of the stock adjacent to the end of the tenon, where increase in dimension takes place.

Topic *107.* Common Wood Joints

Butt Joint

The *butt joint* is produced by butting or bringing together (end, edge, or surface) of one member to the end, edge or surface of another member, securing and reinforcing with glue, nails, screws, plates, corner blocks, splines, dowels, or other fasteners. The butt joint is a common joint, and is used alone where great strength is not a primary consideration, Fig. 12-1 and 12-2. *Reinforced butt joints* which lock in one or more directions and provide additional gluing surfaces are tongue and groove joint (Fig. 12-3), rabbet joint (Fig. 12-15), scarf joint (Fig. 12-5), half lap joint (Fig. 12-6), cross lap joint (Fig. 12-7), finger joint (Fig. 12-8), dovetail joint (Fig. 12-9), mortise and tenon joint (Fig. 12-11). See also Figs. 12-89, 12-90, and 12-91.

Miter Joint

A miter joint is a butted joint. The two members of equal width are cut at the same angle (less than 90°), and are usually fastened together with glue and reinforced with nails, corrugated fasteners, spline, or dowels. See Figs. 12-4, 12-16, 12-20, and 12-21.

Fig. 12-3. Tongue and Groove Joint

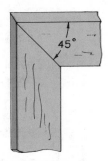

Fig. 12-4. Plain Miter Joint

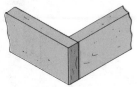

Fig. 12-1. End Butt Joint

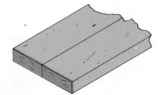

Fig. 12-2. Edge Butt Joint

Fig. 12-5. Scarf Joint

Scarf Joint

A scarf joint is used for extending length. Two members of equal width and thickness are joined at an acute angle (about 15°), in order to obtain maximum bearing surface at the joint, Fig. 12-5.

Half Lap Joints

In the *end lap joint*, two members of approximately equal thickness and usually of the same width, are joined in a modified type of butt joint to extend length or to change direction, Fig. 12-6. Half the thickness of each member is cut away so that when lapped together a thickness equal to that of one member is formed. The *cross lap joint* is an interlocking joint, Fig. 12-7.

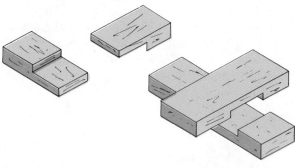

Fig. 12-6. End Lap
         Joint

Fig. 12-7. Cross Lap
         Joint

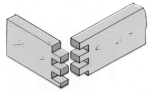

Fig. 12-8. Box or
         Finger Joint

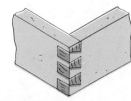

Fig. 12-9. Through
         Dovetail Joint

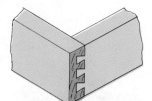

Fig. 12-10. Step Dove-
         tail Joint

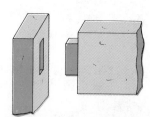

Fig. 12-11. Mortise and
         Tenon Joint

Finger, Box, or Multiple Slip Joint

This joint is made by cutting notches so that the resulting fingers and sockets alternate and the two sections interlock when joined together, Fig. 12-8.

Dovetail Joint

This is a modified finger joint where a reversed, wedge-shaped finger fits into a matched socket. The shape of the finger resembles the spread of a dove's tail, Figs. 12-9, 12-10.

Mortise and Tenon Joint

This is the type of joint where a finger or tenon cut on one member is fitted into a socket or mortise of corresponding dimension in the other member, Fig. 12-11.

There are numerous other special joints which are adaptions or combinations of those which have been described.

Dado Rabbet Joints

A good general rule to follow in laying out dado rabbet joints is to have the rabbet equal to about one-half the thickness of the piece. If the cut is to be made by machine, select the dado head nearest the dimension to one-half the thickness of stock. Since most dadoes are cut with dado heads on the circular saw, this cut should be made first, and the rabbet should be fitted to the dado. Because of the shoulder on the dado rabbet joint, this type joint is stronger than a straight dado. Dado

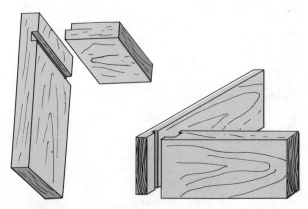

Fig. 12-12. Dado Rabbet Joints

rabbet joints are used in fastening case fronts and backs to ends, such as in cedar chests, top drawer frames to cases, drawer sides and drawer backs. See left of Fig. 12-12. A modified type is used in drawer construction for fastening drawer fronts to ends, Fig. 12-12 right. In this case, the dado in the drawer side is usually ⅛″ wide and ⅛″ deep.

Stop dado rabbets do not run through to the front edge; hence they look like butt joints.

Dowels

Dowels are used to give added strength to a butted joint by providing resistance to cross strain and increasing the gluing surface. Properly fitted dowel pins serve to provide better alignment in assembling pieces to be joined. See Figs. 12-17 and 12-18.

Splines

A *spline* is a narrow strip of thin stock. It is inserted in a groove or keyway in a butted joint with the short grain at right angles to the joining surfaces, Fig. 12-19. Thus, it adds strength to the joint by giving greater resistance against twist or torsion. When the spline is used in panel construction or in applications where strength is not a major factor, the grain usually runs with the length of the spline. In making a spline, cut the thickness by resawing across the end of a board. The length (with the grain) will be equal to the combined depths of the grooves cut in the joint.

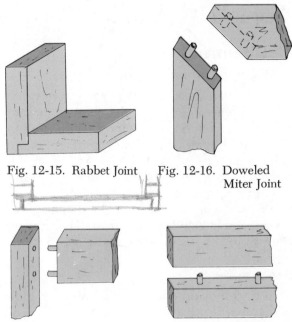

Fig. 12-15. Rabbet Joint   Fig. 12-16. Doweled Miter Joint

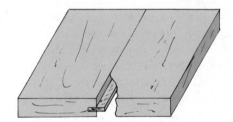

Fig. 12-17. Doweled End Butt Joint   Fig. 12-18. Doweled Edge Butt Joint

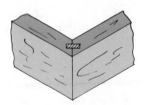

Fig. 12-19. Splined Edge Butt Joint

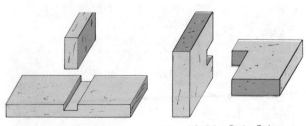

Fig. 12-13. Dado Joint   Fig. 12-14. Gain Joint

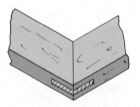

Fig. 12-20. Splined Side Miter Joint   Fig. 12-21. Splined Edge Miter Joint

Topic *108.* Making an Edge-to-Edge Spring Joint

Classification

Joining by fitting and gluing

Production methods in industry rarely use a hand plane on edge-to-edge joints. Stock to be glued is jointed on a jointer. With the use of the newer glues, furniture manufacturers in certain sections of the country use a hollow-ground circular saw blade to square up and smooth edges before gluing. With proper care, joints made in this manner do not have an objectionable glue line, and the bond between the two pieces is stronger than the wood itself.

Procedure

In a well made edge-to-edge joint the glue line is hardly discernible. Any tendency of the joint to open is most likely to occur at the extreme ends. This is due to shrinkage of members. In order to minimize this tendency, each member of the joint is planed in a very slight concave arc, Fig. 12-22. This is done by setting the plane to take a very fine shaving and applying greatest pressure in the center. When the members are brought together there is a slight opening at the center which disappears as pressure is applied by clamping. This clamping sets up compression in the ends which lessens as shrinkage occurs. The spring joint will not open at the ends under normal use.

In gluing up slash- or plain-sawed stock, it is recommended that adjacent pieces be alternated, so that the annual rings are opposite on each piece. This reduces cupping. Cupping may also be reduced by using narrow widths of slash-sawed stock.

1. Match the pieces, giving attention to color, figure, and grain, and mark the members in their respective position.
2. Joint (straight and square) all edges to be joined.
3. Set the hand jointer plane to take a fine shaving and plane the two edges slightly concave.

NOTE: This slight concave may be produced on the jointer by lowering the *rear table very slightly* below the cutters at their highest point and making a *light cut.* This should be done only by experienced workmen.

4. Place the pieces edge-to-edge in a vertical position and sight through from the face side to see if a trace of light shows in the center.
5. Test the joint by swinging each end alternately from side to side to determine if the board pivots on the ends.
6. Use dowels to reinforce an edge-to-edge joint. (See Topic 113, "Reinforcing Joints with Dowels.")
7. Arrange end clamps so that they are approximately two inches from each

Fig. 12-22. A Slight "Spring" is Desirable in an Edge-to-Edge Joint

Fig. 12-23. Position of Clamps in Gluing Spring Joint

end. The center clamps should be on the opposite side. See Fig. 12-23. Also see Topic 126, "Gluing a Joint."

NOTE: It is advisable to smooth the surface of the assembly with a cabinet scraper or scraper plane rather than a plane to prevent tearing of the grain, for:
(1) the highly figured grain pattern in woods, or
(2) the alternate arrangement of slash sawn stock.

Standards and Results

1. There should be no rocking in the joint.
2. The pieces should be in the same plane.
3. The opening in the joint should show only a ray of light before the joint is glued.

Safety Considerations

Observe all safety precautions in the use of hand tools and machines. (See topic on safety.)

Topic 109. Making a Lap Joint — Hand Process

Classification

Joining by fitting and reinforcing with fasteners or adhesives

Procedure

A lap joint is used to extend length or change direction of two pieces of stock. See Fig. 12-24. Half the thickness of each member is cut away so that the surfaces are flush. It is used for house, sill, and plate construction; stretchers; bases, stands and frames.

1. Square the ends of the stock to be joined. The two pieces of stock of equal thickness on which the joint is to be made are laid side by side; one member is face up and the other face down, Fig. 12-25.
2. From the squared end of each, measure and mark with a sharp knife the width, W, Fig. 12-25.
3. Use a try square and mark a knife line AB across the surface of the two boards.

To check your accuracy, lay one piece over the other at right angles.

4. From points A and B, square lines down the edge, half the thickness of the board. Do this on both edges of each piece.
5. Set a marking gauge to one-half the thickness of the stock. Measure from the face. Mark along the edges and ends of each piece to be cut.
6. Secure stock in vise with the end grain up. Use a back saw and cut on the waste side of the line for the cheek cut.
7. Lay the piece on a bench, and with the back saw cut on the waste side of the cross lines to the depth of the cut just made. If the cuts have been accurate, the two pieces should fit together to make an extended surface or a right angle. If the pieces are not even, pare the cut surface with a chisel.

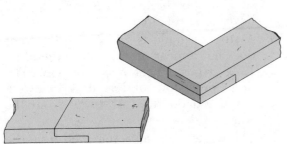

Fig. 12-24. End Lap Joints — (Left) to Extend Length and (Right) to Change Direction.

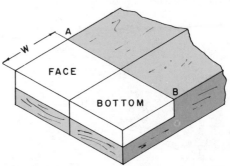

Fig. 12-25. Laying Out an End Lap Joint

8. To make a cross lap joint, the same procedure of layout is used, but the measurements are made from the midpoint of the surface of each piece. The depth cut is made in several places and the waste material is removed with a chisel. See Fig. 12-12.

9. Lap joints are made secure by reinforcing with glue, nails, or screws.

Standards and Results

1. The two members of this joint should fit together snugly. There should be no space between surfaces, edges, or between lapping surfaces at the center point.

2. The joint should not be forced together.

3. A loose-fitting joint or one that is too tight indicates poor work.

4. "Standards and Results" listed for fasteners used should be observed.

Safety Considerations

Observe all safety precautions in the use of the knife, chisel, and saw. (See topic on safety.)

Topic *110*. Making a Dado Joint — Hand Process

Classification

Joinery by fitting and gluing

Procedure

A dado is a recess cut across the grain, into which another board is to fit. It is commonly found in case construction.

1. Locate position of joint by measuring desired distance from the nearest end.

2. With a try square and sharp knife, mark a line across the width of the board.

3. From the line just made, measure and mark the thickness of the board that is to fit into the dado.

4. With the try square and knife, mark this line to define the width of the dado. Continue these lines to the depth of the joint on the sides of the board.

5. A marking gauge set to the depth of the joint is used to mark the depth of cut on both edges, Fig. 12-27.

6. The dado cut is made in much the same manner as a cross-lap cut. A stop is clamped to the cutting line to enable the back saw to be guided squarely and on the waste side of the line. Several cuts are made into the waste material.

7. To remove waste material, use a chisel with a blade a little narrower than the width of the dado.

8. Set a router plane to the depth of the dado and trim the bottom surface. See Fig. 12-7.

9. Try the second piece for fit. Too tight a fit can be made a perfect fit by removing a few shavings from the underside of the shelf. Too loose a fit will have to be repaired.

10. A stopped dado is one where the joint does not appear on the front edge, Fig. 12-28. It is a neater looking job. The same procedure of layout is followed, but the dado stops ⅜″ to ½″ from the edge.

11. The waste material is removed from the dado with a chisel near the stop and the remainder is cut with the back saw.

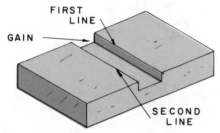

FIRST LINE

GAIN

SECOND LINE

Fig. 12-27. Dado Joint

12. The board that is to fit the stopped dado is notched on the front edge. This notch must be equal to the width of the stop on the front edge of the dado and as deep as the dado.

13. The joint may be reinforced with glue, nails, or screws. See Topic 126, "Gluing a Joint;" Topic 129, "Driving Nails;" and Topic 132, "Driving Wood Screws."

14. The machine process for making a dado is described in Topic 49, "Using the Circular Saw."

Standards and Results

1. A dado joint must fit snugly.
2. The depth of the recess must be even.
3. The notched edge should fit snugly to the surface of the second piece.

Safety Considerations

1. Always chisel away from your body.

2. Keep both hands on the chisel.

3. Observe precautions in the use of hand tools. (See topic on safety.)

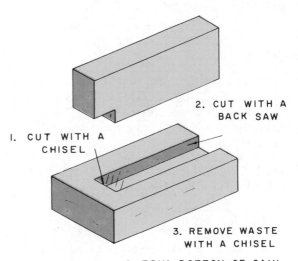

1. CUT WITH A CHISEL
2. CUT WITH A BACK SAW
3. REMOVE WASTE WITH A CHISEL
4. TRIM BOTTOM OF GAIN WITH A ROUTER PLANE

Fig. 12-28. Stopped or Blind Dado Joint

Topic *111.* Making a Rabbet Joint — Hand Process

Classification

Laying out and cutting a recess

Procedure

A rabbet is the recess that is cut along the end or edge of a board. It is commonly used in panel and drawer construction. The recess is usually one-half to two-thirds the thickness of the stock. See Figs. 12-29, 12-30.

1. Square the end or edge on which the joint is to be made.

2. Lay the board on which rabbet is to be cut, face down.

3. From the squared end or edge measure the thickness of the board which is to fit the rabbet.

4. Mark this thickness on the upper surface of the board.

5. With a try square and sharp knife square a line across the length of the rabbet for the cut.

6. Square a line down each edge to the depth of the rabbet.

7. Set a marking gauge to this depth and mark the sides and end.

Cutting an End Rabbet

1. Using a back saw and with the board held securely on a bench hook, make several cuts to the depth of the rabbet. Make sure the saw kerf is on the waste side of the line. It is good practice to clamp a piece of stock to the line to insure a square cut.

2. Remove the waste with a chisel.

3. Smooth the bottom with a chisel, rabbet plane or plow. Be careful to make a square edge and not to pare beyond line.

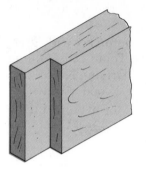

Fig. 12-29. End Rabbet

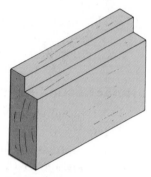

Fig. 12-30. Side Rabbet

Cutting a Side Rabbet

The side rabbet is usually cut on a machine but may be cut with a rabbet plane when it is a hand operation.

1. Set the plane to cut an even shaving.

2. Beginners should gauge a depth line with the marking gauge as previously described under cutting an end rabbet.

3. A stop may be clamped along the surface to act as a guide for planing parallel to the edge.

Standards and Results

1. The rabbet should form a 90° angle and should be parallel to the face surface.

2. The rabbet should be the correct width and depth.

Safety Considerations

Observe safety precautions for all hand tools. (See topic on safety.)

Topic *112.* Dowels — Wood and Metal

Classification

Aligning and reinforcing pins

Composition or Description

Wood dowels are cylindrical pieces of birch, beech, maple, or oak, sometimes with spiral grooves or flutes cut or pressed into the surface, Fig. 12-31.

Metal dowels, sometimes called dowel pins, are made of brass or steel. They are in two pieces and are screwed into the wood. Metal dowels are used by patternmakers on split patterns.

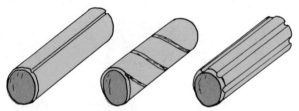

Fig. 12-31. Types of Dowels

Properties

Wood dowels add strength to an edge-to-edge joint and reduce twisting. Dowels with spiral cuts in the surface permit the application of a greater quantity of glue, making for a stronger joint. Dowels with flutes pressed into the surface are called expansion dowels. They are made of lumber that is not thoroughly dried, but which has been compressed. When used with hot or cold animal glue they expand and make a stronger joint.

Uses

Wood dowels are used in applications similar to that of the mortise and tenon joint; in edge-to-edge and miter joints; in segments, reinforcements, and pinning; and in temporary joints as in table leaves. In addition to joinery, they are used for spindles, crates, racks, and other articles requiring wood pieces of their shape and size.

Metal dowels are used to prevent side slip and are not intended to be used on a glued joint.

Market Analysis

Shapes

Wood dowels are made smooth, spiral, fluted, and grooved.

Metal dowels are made smooth. The male piece has a square shoulder on the end; the female pieces has flutes. This is to permit each part to be fastened into the wood.

Sizes

Wood dowels are available in the following diameters: $\frac{1}{8}''$, $\frac{3}{16}''$, $\frac{1}{4}''$, $\frac{5}{16}''$, $\frac{3}{8}''$, $\frac{7}{16}''$, $\frac{1}{2}''$, $\frac{9}{16}''$, $\frac{5}{8}''$, $\frac{3}{4}''$, $\frac{7}{8}''$, $1''$ and in various other diameters up to $3''$. The lengths available are $12''$, $18''$, $2'$, $3'$, and $4'$. Metal dowels are available in the following sizes: $\frac{11}{64}''$, $\frac{3}{16}''$, $\frac{7}{32}''$, $\frac{5}{16}''$, $\frac{13}{32}''$, $\frac{9}{16}''$, and $\frac{13}{16}''$.

Sales Units

Dowels may be bought in any desired quantity, but the most economical way to purchase them is in bundles of 100 and 200. Dowels made be made by the use of a dowel cutter.

Metal dowels are packed in lots of 100.

Maintenance

Store in a dry place either in a horizontal or vertical position.

Fig. 12-31A. Reducing the Diameter of a Dowel and Scoring It Along Its Length by Driving It through a *Dowel Plate*

Topic *113.* Reinforcing Joints with Dowels

Classification

Joinery by fitting and reinforcing

Procedure

A dowel is used to strengthen a butt joint, and as a substitute for mortise and tenon joints in joining aprons and legs in table and chair construction.

Making an Edge Dowel Joint

1. The two surfaces to be fitted together to make the joint are squared to proper dimensions. The two pieces must fit closely together for a dowel will not hold in a poorly fitted joint.

2. Set a marking gauge so that a center line may be drawn along the edge to be joined as in Fig. 12-33. Care must be taken to insure that all measurements are taken from the face of each piece.

3. Measure and mark the position of each dowel. Place the two pieces together so that the jointed edges are as in Fig. 12-33. With a try square and sharp pencil or knife, mark the position of the dowels on each member by drawing a line across the jointed edge of each piece. Dowels should be about two inches (2″) from the end on edge joining and 12″ to 14″ apart.

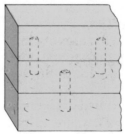

Fig. 12-34. Alignment of Dowels — Butt Joint   Fig. 12-35. Alignment of Dowels — Segments of Circle

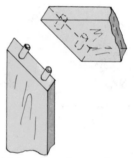

Fig. 12-36. Alignment of Dowels — Miter Joint

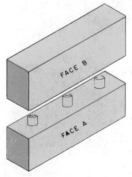

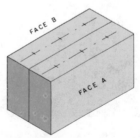

Fig. 12-32. Butt Dowel Joint   Fig. 12-33. Layout for Dowels

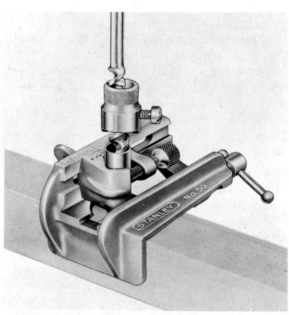

Fig. 12-37. Dowel Jig (Courtesy Stanley Tool Co.)

4. Select the size of dowel to be used. It should be about one-third to one-half the thickness of the board.

5. Make a small hole with a brad awl at the point where lines intersect. It is very important that this be done accurately to have the dowels line up.

6. Set the dowel jig so that it will guide the bit to the proper position, Fig. 12-37. Protect the surface from marks by the jig. Bore the holes with an auger bit or dowel bit the size of the dowel. After the hole has been started, check with a try square to see that the holes are being cut accurately. Slightly countersink holes in each piece to facilitate insertion of dowel and allow space for excess glue.

7. Dowels should not be more than three inches in length so a stop gauge is used with an auger bit to insure even depth of holes, Figs. 12-38, 12-39, 12-40.

8. Cut the dowels ⅛″ shorter than the total depth of both holes. Too short a dowel may cause a depression in the wood surface from shrinkage at a later date. If spiral dowels are not used, a groove should be cut along the length of the dowel to allow glue and air to escape from the hole while the dowel is being inserted, Fig. 12-31.

9. Point the tip of each dowel to allow easy insertion in the hole, except in expansion dowels which are smaller on the ends.

10. Make a dry run to test fit.

Fig. 12-38. Bit Gauge

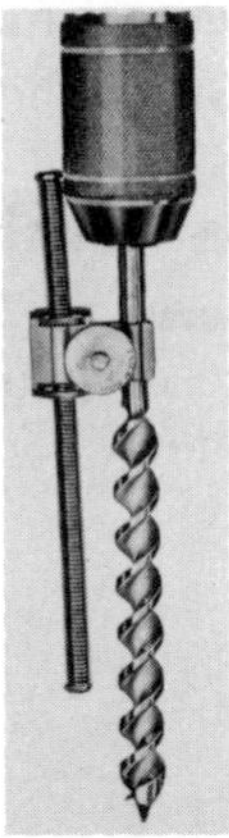

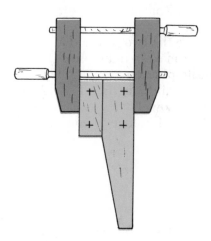

Fig. 12-39. Bit Gauge
(Courtesy Stanley Tool Company)

Fig. 12-41. Dowel Layout in Leg and Rail

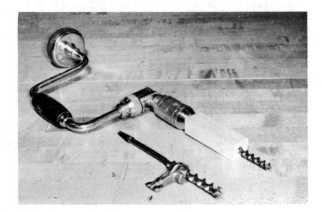

Fig. 12-40. Bit Stops

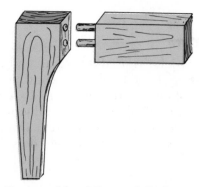

Fig. 12-42. Assembly of Leg and Rail

11. With a small, chisel-like stick put glue inside the holes of one member of the joint.
12. Dip the end of the dowel in glue and drive in solid with a mallet. Use light blows.
13. Spread a thin layer of glue in the holes and on the surface of each member of joint. Cover the entire surface with a thin, even film.
14. Fit the joint together. Tighten the joint with clamps.
15. Check with square and straightedge to see that members of joint are in line.
16. Wipe off all surplus glue with a damp paper towel.
17. Put aside to dry.

Using Dowels to Reinforce a Butt Joint on a Leg and Rail

1. Be sure the two pieces that are to fit together make a tight joint.
2. Locate position of rail on leg.
3. Clamp rail to leg. See Fig. 12-41.
4. Locate dowel holes in the end of rail as in Step 2 for edge-to-edge dowel joints.

Dowels should be no closer to the edges than 2½ times their diameter.
5. Determine how far you want the rail to set back from the face of the leg and add this distance to the previous setting of the marking gauge. Mark legs.
6. Square lines across from end of rail to leg. Lines will intersect at center of dowel holes.
7. Continue steps as outlined in edge-to-edge doweling. See Fig. 12-42.

Standards and Results

1. All joints should make a snug fit. A good glued joint will not show a hair line.
2. All excess glue should be removed.
3. All pieces should be in the same plane.
4. Dowel holes should be correctly positioned and square with working surfaces.
5. Stock should not show clamp marks.

Safety Considerations

Observe all necessary safety precautions in the use of hand tools and storing stock and equipment. (See topic on safety.)

Topic *114.* Making a Miter Joint

Classification

Joinery by reinforced, matched, angular butting

Procedure

A miter joint is used where all end grain is to be covered and to obtain a continuous profile of moldings and matching. It is usually thought of as 45° but includes all joints made up of beveled edges or ends. It is a weak joint if not strengthened by a spline, dowel, miter nails, or corrugated fasteners. Miter joints are used on picture frames, door casings, moldings, and segment construction.

1. The length of the mitered piece is determined by the outside limits of the object to be framed. In a picture frame,

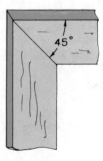

Fig. 12-43. Miter Joint

it would be the length of the picture plus two times the width of the molding minus two times the width of the rabbet.

2. A miter is most accurately cut in a miter box, Figs. 12-44 and 12-45. This can usually be set for cutting any angle between 30° and 90° with stops at increments of 5°. Locks are provided on some miter boxes to lock the saw guide at any angle between the limits of the box. A wood miter box can be made as shown in the diagram, Fig. 12-45. The work should be held securely in the miter box while the cut is being made.

3. The joint should form a close fit. If there is any opening, the joint may be resawed or planed. To resaw, the joint is clamped in position on a board and a back saw or fine-toothed crosscut saw is run between the joint. This trims the high spots from each piece. This may also be done while stock is in a miter vise. One should never try to trim a miter joint by sanding or by planing. Such fitting is a difficult operation.

When a board is to be cut on an angle and no miter box or jig is available, the board is laid out by squaring a pencil line across its width. Measure the width of the board along one edge and square another pencil line. Diagonals from the corners of this square will form the 45° angle for the miter. This joint may be cut accurately by clamping a board close to the diagonal line to act as a saw guide, Fig. 12-44.

4. In gluing a miter joint, most of the exposed surface to be glued is end grain. To prevent this porous surface from absorbing all the glue, a seal coat of glue is applied and allowed to set on the open pores. After this has hardened sufficiently, a good coating of glue is applied. Some sort of a jig, miter clamp, or clamping board should be used to hold the joint in position, Figs. 12-47, 12-48, and 12-49.

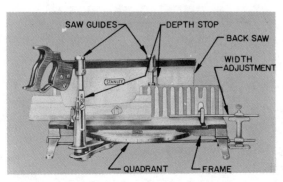

Fig. 12-44. Miter Box (Courtesy Stanley Tool Co.)

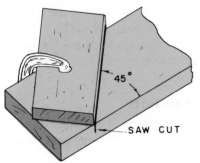

Fig. 12-46. Use of Board as Guide to Cut a Miter

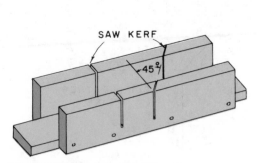

Fig. 12-45. Homemade Miter Box

Fig. 12-47. Miter Vise (Courtesy Stanley Tool Co.)

5. Some method of reinforcing the glued joint must be used. Nails, screws, special miter hardware (corrugated fasteners or chevrons), dowels, or splines may be selected, according to the use of the joint. Nails, screws, or dowels may be inserted in the open ends of the joint, while it is held in the clamping jig, and before the glue is set. See Figs. 12-50, 12-51, and 12-52.

6. If a spline is to be used to reinforce the miter joint, a kerf may be cut in each member the width of each joint face before assembly and a spline is fitted and glued in the joint. Fig. 12-50.

In an alternate method, which uses a *slip feather spline* (Fig. 12-51), the frame is first assembled and glued. When the joint is dry, a kerf is cut in each outer corner and a spline is fitted and glued into the kerf.

In both methods, the grain of the spline should be at a right angle to the face of the joint for strength.

7. A doweled miter joint always has the dowels at right angles to the miter cut.

8. Sometimes a lap miter joint is used with fasteners inserted such as nails, screws, corrugated fasteners, etc. from the back edge to increase strength.

Standards and Results

1. In a good miter joint, no space should appear between the joining wood surfaces.

2. The inside and outside corners should be flush, and the face surface should be in the same plane.

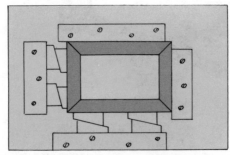

Fig. 12-48. Homemade Miter Frame

3. In figured grain, the markings should be matched as closely as possible.

4. Grain in splines should be at right angles to frame parts.

Safety Considerations

Observe all safety precautions in the use of hand tools. (See topic on safety.)

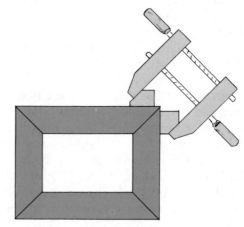

Fig. 12-49. Method of Clamping a Mitered Joint

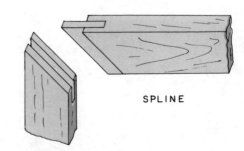

SPLINE

Fig. 12-50. Miter Spline

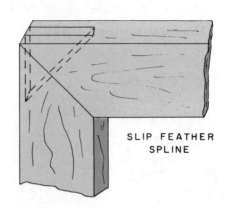

SLIP FEATHER SPLINE

Fig. 12-51. Feather Spline

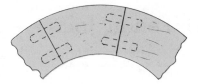

Fig. 12-52. Doweled Miter Joint

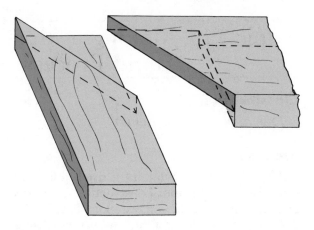

Fig. 12-53. Lap Miter Joint

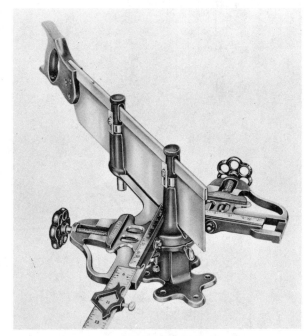

Fig. 12-54. Miter Machine (Courtesy Stanley Tool Co.)

Fig. 12-54A. Wood Trimmer

The wood trimmer is used for cutting cross grain square with the face and at angles up to 45° either side of 90°

Topic 115. Making a Mortise and Tenon Joint — Hand Process

Classification

Joinery by fitting and gluing

Procedure

A mortise and tenon joint is used in joining rails and stiles in door construction, and legs and aprons in table construction, Fig. 12-55. It is one of the oldest joints and is very strong when constructed so that the tenon and the stock remaining on each side of the mortise are of equal strength. A standard practice is to make the tenon about one-third to one-half the thickness of the thinner piece of the joint, with the width no more than six times the thickness of the tenon, Fig. 12-56. Wider tenons weaken the mortise. Multiple tenon construction is recommended because of greater strength. It is advisable to leave a space between the mortises equal to the thickness of the thinner piece.

There are many variations of the tenon joint, such as the through tenon, haunched tenon, miter tenon, and blind tenon. The steps which follow outline the procedure for making a blind tenon.

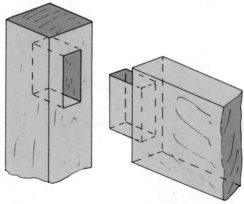

Fig. 12-55. Mortise and Tenon Joint

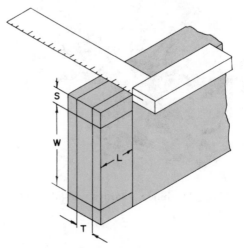

Fig. 12-56. Layout of Tenon

Laying Out the Tenon

1. Select face side of both pieces on which mortise and tenon will be laid out. Work from this side.
2. Determine the length of the tenon. In a blind tenon joint the tenon should be no longer than two-thirds the width of the thicker piece. Square a line around the length of the tenon using a sharp knife and a try square, *L* in Fig. 12-56.
3. Set the marking gauge to the desired thickness of the cheek. This is determined by subtracting the thickness of the tenon from the thickness of the rail and dividing by two. Mark the sides and ends of the tenon from the face side. Reset the marking gauge by adding the thickness of the tenon to the orig-

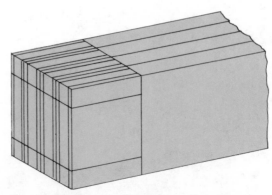

Fig. 12-57. Layout of Tenons on Four Pieces

inal setting. Holding the head against the same face, mark the opposite side. (This could be done in one operation if a mortise gauge were used.) See *T* in Fig. 12-56.

4. The shoulder *S* is determined by the position of the tenon. Generally the shoulder of a tenon is equal to its thickness; however some prefer to make all shoulders ½″. If more than one tenon is to be made of the same size, the rails should be laid side by side and clamped together so that the length and shoulders can be marked together, Fig. 12-57.

Laying Out the Mortise

As in making the tenon, if more than one mortise is to be made, the pieces should be clamped together and marked at the same time to insure alignment. Do all laying out from the face side of stock. See Fig. 12-58.

1. The length *L* of the mortise is determined by the width of the tenon.
2. The shoulder *S* is equal to the shoulder of the tenon.
3. The width *W* is equal to the thickness of the tenon.
4. Mark the length of the mortise with a sharp knife and a try square.
5. Set the marking gauge to the width of the tenon shoulder and gauge the width *W*. Each shoulder must be gauged from the same face. (Again, this may be done in one operation if the mortise gauge is used.)

Cutting the Mortise

The mortise is cut first because it is easier to fit the tenon to the mortise than vice-versa.

1. To remove the waste stock a doweling jig is a convenient tool. Select a bit which is ¹⁄₁₆″ smaller than the width of the mortise and set the dowel jig so that the bit is centered in the waste. Attach a bit gauge to the bit so that all holes will be bored ⅛″ deeper than the length of the tenon. Bore the hole at the end nearest the end grain, then bore the hole at the opposite end. Continue to bore holes close together until all waste has been removed, Fig. 12-59.
2. With a reasonably wide, sharp chisel carefully pare the sides of the mortise. A straight, evenly cut mortise is necessary for a good joint. Do not make the mortise wider than the width lines.
3. The ends of the mortise are cut to the straight shoulder with a chisel narrower than the width of the mortise.
4. Another method of cutting a mortise by hand is to use a mortise chisel ¹⁄₁₆″ narrower than the width of the mortise. Start to cut from the center and work to each end as shown in the diagram, Fig. 12-60.

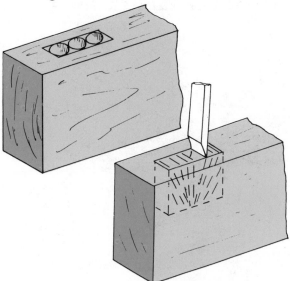

Fig. 12-59. Holes Bored for Mortise   Fig. 12-60. Steps in Chiseling Out a Mortise

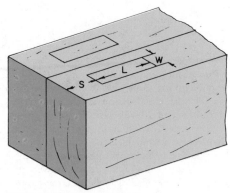

Fig. 12-58. Layout of Mortise

Cutting the Tenon

1. Cut the cheeks of the tenon with a back saw, Fig. 12-61. Fasten the rail in the vise at a convenient angle as shown in the diagram. Be sure to start the saw cut on the waste side of the gauged line and stay within the limits.
2. Cut the width of the tenon.
3. Cut the shoulders on the face and back side. These shoulders are determined by the length of the tenon. A miter box is best used with a stop to insure equal length and a square shoulder on all members.

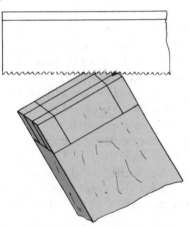

Fig. 12-61. Cutting Cheeks of Tenon

4. Cut shoulders on top and bottom using the same stop for length as above.
5. Chamfer the ends of the tenon as in Fig. 12-62 to allow for easier insertion and for a small glue pocket.

Fitting the Joint Together

1. The members should make a snug fit. Too tight a joint will cause the mortise to bulge or the wood surrounding the mortise to split. Too loose a joint will not hold.
2. The shoulders of the tenon must be perfectly square around the rail so that a snug fit is made with the joining surface. An uneven tenon shoulder may be pared with a sharp chisel, Fig. 12-63.

Standards and Results

1. The joint should be tight and at the correct angle.
2. Opposite shoulders should be parallel.
3. The tenon should not be forced into the mortise as it will cause splitting.
4. Friction of joint should hold the two pieces together.

Safety Considerations

The process is not dangerous if normal precaution is exercised in the correct use of the knife, chisels, and saw. (See topic on safety.)

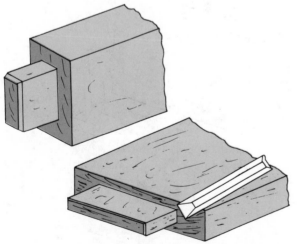

Fig. 12-62. Completed Tenon   Fig. 12-63. Paring shoulders of a Tenon with Chisel

Interesting Fact: The mortise and tenon, as applied to millwork and furniture, dates back to days before written history, for this construction is evident in articles excavated from tombs of ancient Egyptian rulers. Although it is still the prevailing method of construction in Europe, dowel construction is more commonly used in this country, principally because the development of production equipment for the latter method has proceeded more rapidly than has high production mortising equipment.

Topic *116.* Making a Mortise and Tenon Joint — Machine Process

Fig. 12-64. Mortising Attachment (Courtesy Delta Div., Rockwell Mfg. Co.)

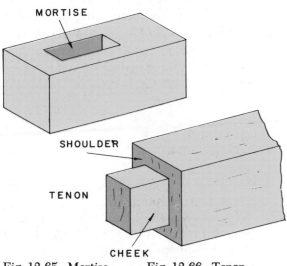

Fig. 12-65. Mortise   Fig. 12-66. Tenon

Classification

Joinery by fitting and gluing

Procedure

Follow the layout procedure as in hand joining. See Figs. 12-65, 12-66.

Cutting the Mortise

1. Select the proper size hollow chisel for the width of the mortise. Insert it in either a mortiser Fig. 10-67 or in an attachment on the drill press, Fig. 12-64. Adjust the table and guide so that the shoulders for the cut will be at right angles with the table guide. The bit should be about ⅛″ below the cutting edge of the chisel to prevent overheating.

2. Locate the work on the table so that when the chisel is lowered the cut will be made between the gauged lines. Adjust the fence so that the gauged lines will be parallel to the cutting edges of the chisel. The face side of the work is usually towards the fence; all pieces must be set in the same position.

3. Secure the lock-down lever so that the work will not be raised when the chisel is withdrawn.

4. Set the depth gauge or the stop to cut to the desired depth.

5. When making more than one mortise, clamp stops to the table to limit the lengths of the mortise in each member.

6. Start the cut at one end of the mortise, and make a partial depth cut at the first position to prevent binding the chisel on withdrawal. Make repeated adjacent cuts until all waste has been removed. On the last cut there should be enough stock for the chisel to take a full bite thereby insuring a straight cut.

Cutting the Tenon on a Circular Saw

1. The surfaces on all tenon stock must be square with each other and of the same thickness and length. Any slight variation in these dimensions will cause a variation in the size of the tenon.

2. If more than one tenon is to be cut and all pieces of stock are of proper dimension, it is only necessary to lay out the first piece to the exact dimensions.

3. To cut the cheeks, set the rip fence so that the distance from the fence to a

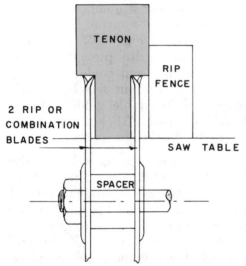

Fig. 12-67. Set-Up for Cutting Tenon on Circular Saw Using Two Saw Blades

Fig. 12-68. Tenoning Jig (Courtesy Delta Div., Rockwell Mfg. Co.)

saw tooth bent away from the fence is equal to the length of the tenon. Lock in position.

4. Set the crosscut or combination saw to a height above the table equal to the waste stock to be removed. It is good practice to make a test nick near the end of the tenon to insure the correct height. Too high a saw blade will make too thin a tenon. When the correct height has been obtained, the stock should be moved to its cutting position against the miter gauge and a nick made to check the proper length of the tenon. When the setting is correct, lock the blade-raising mechanism in position.

5. Make the shoulder cheek cuts first; then by repeated cuts (close together) remove the waste on one side.

6. Turn the stock over and repeat for the opposite side.

7. After opposite cheeks have been cut to one dimension on all pieces, reset the saw height to cut the shoulders on the edges of the stock. Do not move the rip fence.

8. Repeat the operation of removing waste by starting at the shoulder cut and working toward the outside end.

9. The cheeks of the tenon may be smoothed by carefully paring with a sharp chisel. Do not remove too much material or the tenon will be too thin.

10. If a dado head (Figs. 5-44A and 5-44B) is available, the process of removing the waste may be speeded by reducing the number of cuts.

Cutting Identical Tenons

1. All shoulders are cut as in the above process.

2. Two rip or combination blades of the same size are mounted so that the space left between the blade when cutting is equal to the thickness of the tenon. NOTE: The spacer must take up allowance for the saw set. See Fig. 12-67.

3. Set the stock to be cut upright in a tenoning jig so that it will be held securely while the work is being passed over the saw blade. See Fig. 12-68.

Regardless of how the tenon is cut, a ⅛" chamfer should be cut on the end of the tenon.

Standards and Results

1. Cuts should not run into shoulder of tenon.
2. Edges of both mortise and tenon should be smooth.
3. Tenon should fit the mortise snugly.
4. Mortise should be ⅛" deeper than tenon to allow for glue.
5. End of tenon should have ⅛" chamfer on all edges.
6. Shoulder of tenon should fit flush against mortised members.

Safety Considerations

1. Observe all standard safety precautions in the use of the circular saw, drill press, or mortiser. (See topic on safety.)
2. Clamp stock securely on the mortiser.
3. Keep fingers out from under mortising chisel.

Fig. 12-69. Valiton Compressed Tenon Joints

In this method the conventional tenon is placed in the Valiton machine and in one operation is compressed toward the center from three different directions. When the tenon thus compressed is inserted into a glue-lined hole, the moisture in the glue causes the tenon to expand back to its original size. The swelling of the tenon makes a tight joint. This process requires glues that have a high moisture content. Valiton dowels of varying diameters and lengths can be purchased. (Courtesy Heywood-Wakefield Co.)

Topic *117*. Making a Dovetail Joint—Hand Process

Classification

Joinery by lock fitting

Procedure

1. Study Fig. 12-70, noting particularly the names of the parts of the dovetail joint.
2. The *pins* may be the same size as or smaller than the tails and are usually designed this way for better appearance. However, more strength is gained by having the pins wider than the tails. This type of layout is recommended for softwood construction.
3. A good rule to follow in laying out the pins is to make the base width of the pin ¾ the thickness of the thinner piece (W = ¾t). The distance from center to center of the pins is between two and three times that width (CC = 2–3 W). The outside pins are ⅛" wider than one-half the width of the center pins. No pin should be less than ¼" wide. The pins are laid out with a T-bevel, which has been set to an angle having a ratio of 1 to 6, as shown in Fig. 12-72.

Laying Out the Pins

1. Square the ends of the two members to be joined.
2. Square a line around the ends of each piece at a distance equal to the thickness of the opposite member. Use a sharp knife or sharp, hard pencil.
3. Determine the number of pins and sockets. Applying the formula recommended above on a board 6" wide and ¾" thick, (W = ¾t), you would have ¾ times ¾ which is ⁹⁄₁₆". Using 2½ as the midpoint between 2 and 3 in order to determine the center-to-center spacing (CC = 2½W) and applying the dimensions— 2½ times ⁹⁄₁₆" = 1¹³⁄₃₂", or in round numbers 1½".

   To determine the number of pins or sockets, divide the width, in this case,

6" ÷ 1½" = 4 pins. Since there is to be a half pin on each edge, there will be three full pins and two half pins.

4. Since each outside pin will be ⅛" wider than one-half the center pins, lay out a ⅛" line along the outside edges.
5. Divide the space remaining into four equal parts and mark on the line laid out in Step 2. These marks indicate the center of the pins.
6. Measure and mark one-half the width of each pin (in this case ⁹⁄₃₂") on each side of the points located in Step 5 and also on the inside of the ⅛" marks on both edges.

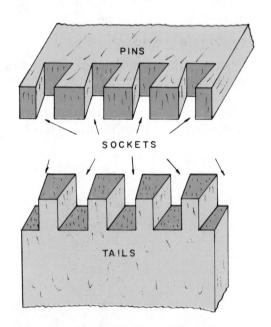

Fig. 12-70. Nomenclature of Dovetail Joint

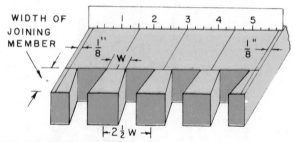

Fig. 12-71. Layout of Pins

7. From these measurement points, lay out with a T-bevel the side of the pins with the ratio of 1 to 6.

To set the T-bevel, make the layout shown in Fig. 12-72. Square a line across the width of a board. At the 6″ mark square a line at a right angle and

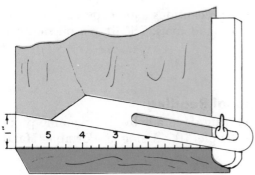

Fig. 12-72. Laying Out the Slope of the Pins

Fig. 12-73. Blind or Stop Dovetail

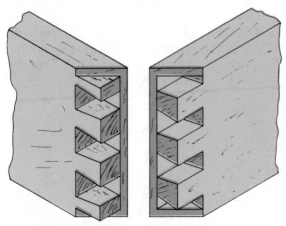

Fig. 12-74. Blind Miter Dovetail

measure in 1″ on this line. Draw a line from this 1″ mark to the beginning of the 6″ line. With the head of the T-bevel along the edge of the board, adjust the blade so that it coincides with the line.

8. Complete the layout of the pins on one surface. Square lines across the end with a try square. Complete the layout on the other surface.

Cutting the Tails or Pins

1. Select a small auger bit to bore into the waste at the depth of the tails. This is to facilitate removing the stock at the base. **CAUTION:** Care must be taken not to split the stock.

2. With a back saw or dovetail saw cut on the waste side of the layout of the pins.

3. The sockets formed by cleaning the waste between the pins may now be removed with a coping saw or by chiseling half way on one side then turning the face stock over and removing the remaining half. Care must be taken to keep the sides of pins square with no undercutting.

Laying Out the Tails on Joining Side

1. The cut dovetailed piece is used as a template to mark the tails on the second member.

2. Stand the two boards on edge and at right angles to each other in the way they will fit in the finished joint.

3. Mark the shape of the pins with a sharp knife or sharp, hard pencil by tracing around the cut pins.

4. Square the depth of the pins along the width of the board with a sharp knife and try square.

5. Duplicate the markings on the reverse side using the T-bevel and square.

6. Cut tails as on first piece, making sure to cut on the waste side of the line.

7. Fit the pieces together, taking care not to force any part out of position.

Cutting a Half-Lap Dovetail

Blind or stop dovetails have tails which do not project through the joint. This type of dovetail is used in face and drawer front construction. The side members lock into ⅔ to ¾ the thickness of the front piece. See Figs. 12-73, 12-74.

1. The method of layout is the same as above.
2. Cutting must be done with a chisel except for part way down the diagonal side which may be made with a fine tooth saw.

Standards and Results

1. The joint should fit tightly and at the correct angle.

2. The tails should not be forced into the grooves causing splits.
3. The width of the joining pieces should fit flush.

Safety Considerations

Normal precautions should be exercised in the use of hand tools. (See topic on safety.)

Additional Reading

For cutting dovetails by the machine process, see Topic 79, "Using a Portable Hand Router"

Topic *118.* Laying Out and Cutting Dovetails on a Pedestal Leg

Classification

Joinery by lock fitting

Procedure

A general rule for determining the size of dovetails is to make: (1) the length of the pin ¼ the diameter of the pedestal, (2) the width of the pin at the widest point ¾ the thickness of the leg, and (3) the taper of the pin 6 to 1.

Example:
(1) $L = \frac{1}{4}d$ $\frac{1}{4} \times 3 = \frac{3}{4}$
(2) $W = \frac{3}{4} \times 1\frac{1}{4} = {}^{15}\!/_{16}$
(3) Taper = 6 to 1 ratio

The pin is cut first and then the socket is laid out and cut to fit.

Laying Out and Cutting the Pin on the Leg

1. Lay out the center lines on the ends of the legs, Fig. 12-75. With a square, knife, marking gauge, and T-bevel lay out the pins. See Topic 117, "Making a Dovetail Joint."
2. With a back saw cut the shoulder and cheek. Make sure that the cuts are made on the waste side of each line. Trim to the line with a sharp chisel.

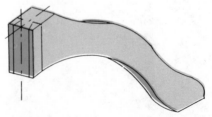

Fig. 12-75. Layout of Pin on Leg

3. Step 2 may also be made on the circular saw by first making the cheek cuts and then the shoulder cuts. To do this tilt the saw to the proper angle and adjust the fence to the desired distance. With the joint end of the leg down, make the cheek cut.

Adjust the saw blade to the vertical position and proper height. Set the rip fence to the required distance. Place the leg on its side, and make the shoulder cut. Repeat for the other shoulder.

Laying Out the Center Lines of the Socket Cuts

1. Divide the end of the cylinder into three equal parts. See Fig. 12-76. This may be done with compasses or dividers by setting to the radius of the cylinder and stepping off the six equal divisions on the outer circumference.

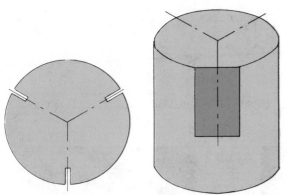

Fig. 12-76. Layout of 120° Angles for Template

Fig. 12-77. Flat on Pedestal

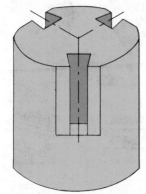

Fig. 12-78. Sockets on Pedestal

2. With a square and pencil mark the center lines at alternate points along the face of the spindle (a distance equal to the length of the shoulder of the leg).

Laying Out and Cutting the Flats

1. On the end of the cylinder measure one-half the thickness of the leg each side of the center line, forming a chord the length of which will be equal to the thickness of the leg.

2. Square these lines down the face of the cylinder a distance equal to the length of the shoulder of the leg, *L* in Fig. 12-77.

3. Set the combination square equal to the length of the shoulder of the leg, and with a knife mark the length of the shoulder for the flat by connecting the lines. With a sharp knife make an undercut on the line just made.

4. With a back saw cut at right angles along the undercut just made until the saw kerf reaches the width lines.

5. With a chisel and mallet remove all waste stock within the area just laid out. Finish with a shearing cut.

Laying Out and Cutting the Sockets

1. Lay out the socket on the end of the pedestal. This may be done with a knife and T-bevel, Fig. 12-78. Square these lines down the face of the flats the length of the shoulder. Remove the waste for the socket by boring or using a mortiser. Trim to the exact size with a chisel.

2. Make a partial fit by testing and paring with a chisel where necessary. **CAUTION: Do not force the fit.**

To test for proper fit, coat the sides and end of the pin with chalk, and assemble the joint. Surfaces of the socket most heavily marked by chalk indicate spots that need trimming. A well-fitted joint will have a light, even coating of chalk on all contacting surfaces.

Standards and Results

1. The pin should fit snugly in the socket.
2. The shoulder of the leg and the flat cut on the spindle should make a tight joint.
3. Legs should be properly spaced on the spindle — at right angles and perpen-

dicular to the axis of the pedestal.
4. All feet should set flat on tested surface.

Safety Considerations

Observe all safety precautions in the use of hand tools. (See topic on safety.)

Topic *119.* Making a Coped Joint

Classification

Joinery by profile butting

Procedure

A coped joint is usually used in joining inside corners of moldings. See Fig. 12-79. The end of one member is cut to fit the contour of the shaped surface of the other member.

Mitering Method

1. After the first member has been squared at one end and cut to length, fasten in place. The two inside faces, top and back, should fit snugly and not be canted.
2. Place the second member in the miter box so that the bottom edge of the molding is up and the back of the molding fits against the miter fence. The 45° angle cut should be made so that the contour of the work will show a profile on the face of the molding. See Fig. 12-80.

3. With a coping saw cut on the face profile. Hold the coping saw parallel with the top edge of the molding and undercut at a slight angle to make a tight fit on the face.
4. Place the second member in position. It should fit the contour snugly. If any

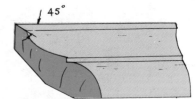

Fig. 12-80. Miter Cut Made, Ready for Cope Cut

Fig. 12-81. Molding Comb or Contour Gage (Courtesy Arco Tools, Inc.)

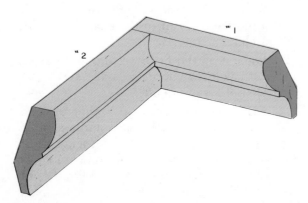

Fig. 12-79. Coped Joint

obstructions exist they may be undercut with a knife or file. Be sure that the top edge and the back are held so that the members form a 45° angle with the corner.

5. Fasten the second member in place. Nails should be driven into two adjacent surfaces. It should look like a mitered joint. Nailing will not open up a properly fitted joint.

Template Method

1. A molding comb (Fig. 12-81) or stock of thin sheet material is fitted to the molding.

2. The profile so made is used to transfer contour to the piece to be joined.

Standards and Results

1. There should be no openings in the fitted members.
2. The pieces should form a perfect corner with no gaps.
3. There should be no hammer marks or splits showing on the face of the work.
4. Nails should be set below the surface.

Safety Considerations

1. Observe all hand-tool safety precautions.
2. If ladders or staging are used make certain they are safe. (See topic on safety.)

Topic 120. Making Finger Joints to Support Table Leaves

Classification

Joinery by fitting and pinning.

Procedure

1. Finger joints are used on a swing leg or rail, to support drop leaves of a table.
2. To use this type of joint, an apron which is fixed and solid is needed. The apron

with the finger joint (or joints if more than one support is used) should be on the outside and adjacent to the fixed apron. See Fig. 12-82.

Laying Out the Arcs on the Ends of the Pieces

1. Locate the center of the thickness on the top and bottom edges and near the end of both pieces of stock which will be used to make the joint.
2. Set a pair of dividers to an opening equal to one-half the thickness of the fixed apron.
3. Place one leg of the dividers on the center line at a distance from the end of the pieces which is equal to the radius of the circle. See Fig. 12-83.

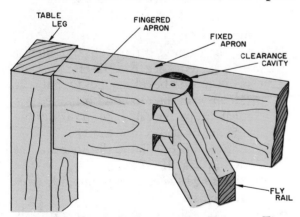

Fig. 12-82. Fly Rail Construction Using a Finger Joint

Fig. 12-83. Determining the Arc of the Ends

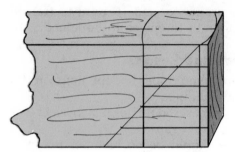

Fig. 12-84. Laying Out the Fingers

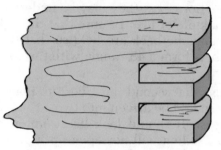

Fig. 12-85. Cutting the Fingered Apron

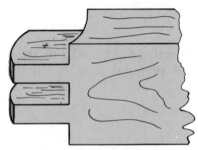

Fig. 12-86. Cutting the Fly Rail

4. Using the same center, increase the radius to a distance from the center to a corner.
5. Relocate the center so that the new radius scribes an arc tangent to the end of the piece.
6. Draw as much of a complete circle on the edge of the stock as the thickness permits. Do this on the opposite edge and on both pieces.
7. Where the arcs meet the faces of the pieces, square lines down both faces to the opposite edge. See Fig. 12-84.

Laying Out the Width of the Fingers

For maximum strength, fingers are usually laid out as close to 1″ as possible. There should be an odd number of fingers, so that the fingered apron has a finger at each edge.
1. Divide the width of the apron into an odd number of equal divisions. This may be done with either a pair of dividers or a rule. Fig. 12-84 shows a diagonal line drawn so it can be conveniently divided into 5 equal parts.
2. On these divisions, square lines in from the end to the line previously drawn on the faces, as shown in Fig. 12-84.
3. Lay out the matching fingers on the fly rail.

Cutting the Fingered Apron

1. Shape the arc on the end of the pieces with a smooth plane, file and sandpaper, or a suitable shaper cutter if available.
2. Using a back saw and chisel or a band saw, remove the stock within alternate divisions. Be careful to stay on the waste side of the line.
3. To cut the inside arc on the center cavity, clamp the stock upright in the vise, and place a handscrew across the stock at a position even with the inside end of the fingers. The handscrew prevents the stock from splitting.
4. Select a chisel slightly narrower than the width of a finger; hold the bevel side down, and work from each face toward the center. Cut the concave arc in the center cavities. See Fig. 12-85.

Cutting the Fly Rail

1. Cut the cavities to match the fingers previously cut. See Fig. 12-86.
2. Use an inside-bevel gouge to cut the inside arcs on the top and bottom edges.
3. Repeat Steps 3 and 4, for cutting the inside arc on the center cavity.
4. The two pieces should fit together as shown in Fig. 12-87.
5. If the fingers need trimming, do this with a chisel.
6. After the pieces have been properly fitted and while they are in the correct

position, using the center point of the arc, bore a ¼″-diameter hole from the top edge down to halfway through the bottom finger. Care must be taken to bore the hole at right angles to the edge of the apron; otherwise, the fly rail will not swing plumb.

7. Apply a coat of wax to a ¼″, hardwood dowel or steel pin and insert it in the hole just drilled.

Laying Out and Cutting Clearance Cavity

In order for the fingers to clear the fixed apron, a cavity must be cut in it.

1. Clamp the movable apron to the fixed apron in the exact position they will occupy when in use.

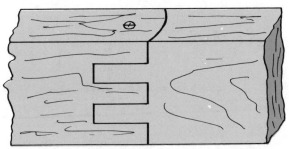

Fig. 12-87. The Assembled Joint on the Fly Rail

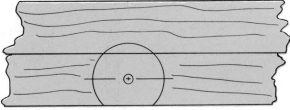

Fig. 12-88. Laying Out the Clearance Cavity of the Fixed Apron

2. The cavity may be laid out by setting the dividers at the same arc as that of the ends of the fingers. Placing one point at the center of the dowel pin, scribe the arc on the top edge of the inner apron. Using the center on the lower edge, scribe the same-size arc on the underside of the inner apron. See Fig. 12-88.

3. Remove the clamps and separate the pieces.

4. Square lines down the face, connecting the ends of the two arcs.

5. Cut and smooth the cavity, using chisel, file and sandpaper.

6. If the fly rail swings smoothly, when the two aprons are clamped in the correct position, fasten it permanently, using glue and reinforcing that with screws driven from the inside of the aprons.

Standards and Results

1. If layout and cutting have been done accurately, the fly rail should swing out to a 90° angle with the inner apron and in a plumb position.

2. Joints between the fingers should be reasonably tight.

3. The top and bottom edges of the fly rail and the aprons should be flush.

Safety Considerations

This process is not dangerous if normal precaution is exercised in the correct use of chisels, gouges, planes, hand saws, band saws, and bit and brace. See topic on safety.

Topic *121.* Joints Commonly Used in Table Construction

1. *Edge-to-edge spring joint* (Topic 108,) or *dowel butt joint* (Topic 113,), used in joining tops.
2. *Mortise and tenon joint* (Topics 115 and 110) or *dowel joint* (Topic 113), used to assemble legs, rails, and aprons.
3. *Dovetail joint* (Topic 117), *rabbet joint* (Topic 111), and *dado rabbet joint* (Fig. 12-12), used in drawer construction.
4. *Reinforcing joints*, Figs. 12-89 — 12-91.
5. *Rule joint*, used between the center-board and the drop leaf on a table. This provides a moveable joint with an attractive molded edge on the center-board when the leaf is down, yet closes to a flat, horizontal surface when the leaf

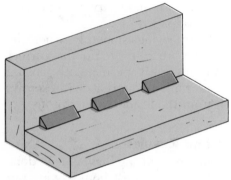

Fig. 12-89. Edge Butt Joint Reinforced with Glued Corner Blocks

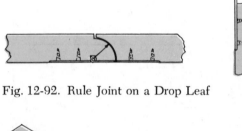

Fig. 12-92. Rule Joint on a Drop Leaf

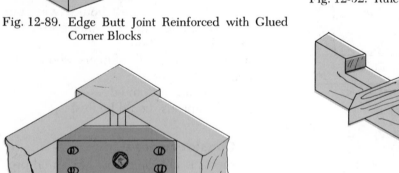

Fig. 12-90. End Butt Joint Reinforced with Corner Brace Fastened with Screws

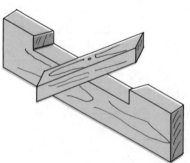

Fig. 12-93. Pivot Support for Drop Leaf

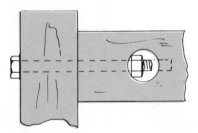

Fig. 12-91. End Butt Joint Reinforced with Through Bolt

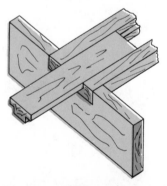

Fig. 12-94. Pull-Out Support for Drop Leaf

is raised. It must be used in conjunction with a pair of table-leaf hinges. (See Fig. 12-92.)

6. *Finger joint* (Topic 120,), *pivot support* (Fig. 12-93), or *pull-out support* (Fig. 12-94), used for supporting drop leaves of a table.

7. Dado joint (Topic 110) used for fastening drawer frames to sides or aprons.

8. Fastening table tops, Figs. 12-95 and 12-96, shows a method allowing greater expansion.

9. Drawer guides.

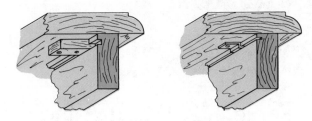

Fig. 12-96. Table Top Fasteners Which Allow for Expansion

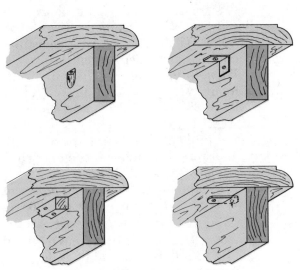

Fig. 12-95. Methods of Fastening Table Tops

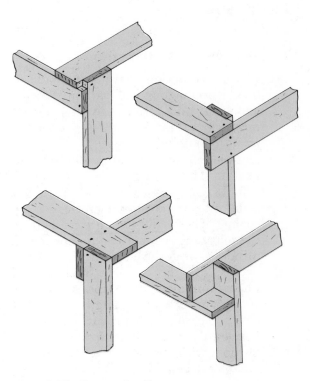

Fig. 12-97. Corners for Crates

Topic *122.* Wood Adhesives (Glue)

(SYNTHETIC RESIN, ANIMAL, CASEIN, FISH, VEGETABLE, BLOOD ALBUMIN)

Classification

Adhesive

Composition or Description

1. Liquid synthetic resin glue is made of *urea,* (a compound of carbon dioxide, ammonia, and formaldehyde); *phenol resin,* (a coal tar derivative); and *melamine formaldehyde.*
2. Hot-melt adhesives are solid prior to heating. The application of heat 250° to 425° F. changes the material to a liquid state. After removal of heat, they set by cooling. These adhesives are made from the following: coumarone indene, rosin, mineral, vegetable, and petroleum waxes, alkyds, terpene resins, and phenol-formaldehyde resins. All of these resins are of low strength and melt easily. To make them into useful adhesives, they are mixed in limited proportions with one or more of the following: ethyl cellulose, polyvinyl acetate, butyl methyl acrylate, polyethylene, polystyrene, styrene copolymeres, and polyisobutylene.
3. Animal glue is made from hides, hoofs, bones, sinews, and hide fleshings.
4. Casein glue is made from curds of milk called *casein,* hydrated lime, and sodium hydroxide.
5. Fish glue is made from scales, heads, backbones, fins, and tissues of fish.
6. Vegetable glue is made from starch and from protein of soybeans.
7. Blood albumin glue is made from beef blood to which an alkali is added.
8. Most glues range in color from white to yellowish-brown.

Properties

1. *Synthetic resins* are of two major types: thermosetting and thermoplastic.

   a. Thermosetting synthetic resin glues (These glues set by catalytic action, and, once set, they cannot be reworked.)

   Resorcinal formaldehyde glues are liquid and set at temperatures of 75° to 80° F. They are resistant to moisture, chemicals, and micro-organisms.

   Phenol-formaldehyde glues are available in two types: *Hot press* (set at 240° to 320° F.) and *intermediate* (set at 210° F. or less). These glues hold under prolonged or alternating exposure to moisture, heating, and cooling. They are highly resistant to heat.

   Melamine-formaldehyde glues are of two types: *Hot press* (set at 230° to 300° F.) and *intermediate* (set at 120° to 200° F.). Intermediate may be used at 70° F. if the assembly is left unclamped for ½ hour after glue is applied (to permit proper penetration and curing) and then closed and clamped for one hour. Hot press melamine glue joints have good durability, but intermediate is somewhat less durable.

   Urea-formaldehyde glues are of two types: *Hot press* (require 240° to 260° F. and set in three to five minutes) and *cold press* (hardwoods 90° for three hours — 70° for six hours; softwoods 90° for two hours or 70° for four hours). They are not recommended when the temperature of the wood is below 70° F. They resist cold water but cannot withstand high temperatures and humidities.

304

Epoxy resin glues can be used to bond metal, wood, glass, ceramics, plastics, and hard rubber. The bond can be accomplished from 70° to 250° F., requiring only pressure sufficient to hold the assembly in place. They have excellent strength and good resistance to weather, moisture, weak acids, corrosive salts, and petroleum products.

b. Thermoplastic synthetic resin glues

(These glues set by evaporation of the solvent, and they may be reworked by heating or by adding a solvent.)

White resin glues such as *polyvinylacetate resin emulsion glues* set in one hour at 70° F., making a colorless glue line. They remain elastic, limiting their use in highly stressed joints, but often their use gives an advantage over more rigid glues. They are not water-resistant and cannot withstand high temperatures.

Aliphatic resin glues have good heat resistance, cold flow, and creep resistance, may be used at temperatures as low as 45° F., and they can withstand temperatures up to 250° F.

Hot-melt adhesives are waterproof, flexible, and require no surface preparation or clamping. It is a good gap filler in loosely fitted parts (will not take stain), but it is not shock resistant. Its strength is between 200 and 300 p.s.i., which is much lower than most other glues, but ample for some gluing jobs. Materials to be glued should be 70° F. except metals and glass which should be 150° F. Hot-melt adhesives set in 60 seconds (joint must be assembled in 20 seconds). For best results stock should be preheated (1) in a caul box, (2) with a flat iron, or (3) heat lamp to prevent chilling of the glue before the joint is tight. Some hot-melt adhesives cannot withstand temperatures over 130° F. and lacquer finishes will soften the glue and cause joint opening.

2. All *animal glue* except liquid hide glue must be soaked in water overnight and then heated. Repeated heatings cause loss of strength. Hot glue sets quickly. Liquid hide glue is ready to use at room temperature but sets slowly. Hide glue has great strength and does not stain. It has poor resistance to moisture.

3. *Casein glue* has fair resistance to moisture, but some types stain wood.

4. *Fish glue* is ready to use at room temperature, is slow to set, is good for joining wood but has poor resistance to moisture. It crystallizes with age.

5. *Vegetable glue* is ready to use at room temperature, sets rapidly, is excellent for interior plywood and veneers but has poor resistance to moisture.

6. *Blood albumin* flakes are dissolved in water. This glue sets rapidly, is waterproof and stainless, but the wood must be heated.

Fig. 13-A. Glue Viscosity Test (Courtesy Timber Structures, Inc.)

Dielectric Gluing

The principle of dielectric heating is based on the fact that disturbed molecules cause friction and create heat. This disturbance is caused by very high frequency cycle charge which moves the molecules of glue at such a high speed that the friction generates heat and the glue bond is completed in a matter of seconds.

Recorcinal, phenol-formaldehyde, and urea-formaldehyde resins are relatively unaffected by weather conditions and can easily be cured with dielectric heating.

Uses

While glue is first of all an adhesive, it is widely used as a sizing. The best glue for a given use depends upon the materials to be sized or joined and the conditions of use. Under ideal conditions, a properly fitted joint should withstand approximately 1000 p.s.i.

In the woodworking industry, the greatest uses of hot-melt adhesives are edge banding of veneer or plastic lamination of furniture tops made of plywood or particle board cores, the application of corner blocks, drawer stops, and decorative objects. It is not recommended for joining structural members such as furniture joints. Other applications for hot-melt adhesives are on ceramics, leather, cloth, metals, glass, and most types of plastics. The glue is usually melted and applied with an electric glue gun. See Fig. 13-B.

Market Analysis

Shapes

1. Synthetic resin glue is available in powder, liquid, paste, or as a powder to which a catalyst must be added, and in paper film form.

Fig. 13-C. Scarf-Joint Test (Courtesy Timber Structures, Inc.)

Fig. 13D. Dielectric Gluing of Edge Banding

Fig. 13-B. Glue Gun for Hot-Melt Adhesives (Courtesy U.S.M. Corp.)

Fig. 13E. Dielectric Gluing of Miter Joint

Hot-melt adhesive is available in many different forms, such as sticks, tapes or ribbons, films or thin sheets, granules, pellets, cylinders, cubes, blocks, and cords.
2. Animal glue is available in liquid, flake, pearl, bead, sheet, stick, powder, cake, ground, and shredded form.
3. Casein glue is available in powder form.
4. Fish glue is available in liquid form.
5. Vegetable glue is sold in either powder or liquid form.
6. Blood albumin glue is sold in flakes.

Grades
1. Packers' glue is considered the best grade of animal glue, followed by renders' glue and extracted bone glue.
2. The other types of glue are ungraded.

Sales Units
1. Synthetic resin glue in powdered form is available in 4-ounce, 8-ounce, 1-pound, 5-pound, 10-pound, and 25-pound, cans. Liquid form is available in ¼-pint, pint, quart, gallon, and 5-gallon cans, and in 55-gallon drums. Paper film form is available in sheets. Small containers (1-ounce) of epoxy resin glue are available.
2. Powdered or flake animal glue is available in 1-pound, 10-pound, and 25-pound packages and in 100-pound barrels; liquid glue in tubes and in ¼-pint, ½-pint, pint, quart, and gallon cans.

3. Casein glue is available in containers of 4 ounces, 8 ounces, 1 pound, 5 pounds, 10 pounds, 25 pounds, 50 pounds, 100 pounds, and 300 pounds.
4. Fish glue is sold in tubes and in ¼-pint, ½-pint, pint, quart, and gallon cans.
5. Vegetable glue is not commonly used in school shops.
6. Blood albumin glue requires extensive equipment and is not commonly used in school shops.

Maintenance
All liquid glues except hot animal glue should be kept tightly covered. When thermoplastic synthetic resin, animal glues and fish glues become too thick for use, add warm water to bring to consistency of light cream.

Additional Reading
Department of Agriculture (Forest Products Laboratory), *Synthetic Resin Glues, Woodworking Glues of Natural Origin, Strength of Commercial Liquid Glues, Vegetable Glue, Casein Glue, and Blood Albumin Glues.*

Franklin Glue Co., *Your Glue Problems — Their Costs and Solutions.*

National Glue Manufacturers Association, *Animal Glue in Industry.*

Manufacturers' pamphlets

Table 19

Glues and Their Properties

Type of Adhesive	Form and Mixing Procedure	Use	Setting Time	Durability	Temperature	Stain	Cost	Shelflife	Clamping Pressure
Hot Animal Glue	Sheets, flakes, or chips. Soak in water for 8 hours. Heat in double boiler to 140°-160° F.	Interior	2 Minutes	Non-water resistant	70° F.	No	Medium	Unlimited before heating	Dense woods (oak, maple, birch, cherry) 200 p.s.i.
Liquid Animal Glue	Liquid, no mixing required.	Interior	4 Hours	Non-water resistant	70° F.	No	Medium	6 months	
Polyvinyl Acetate	Liquid, no mixing required.	Interior	20 Minutes to 1 Hour	Non-water resistant	70° F.	No	Medium	1 year	Medium density woods (poplar, yellow pine) 150 p.s.i.
Aliphatic Resin	Liquid, no mixing required.	Interior	20 to 40 Minutes	Slightly water resistant	40° - 90° F.	No	Medium	1 year	
Vegetable (starch)	Powder or liquid. Mix powder with water, use liquid as purchased.	Interior	4 to 6 Hours	Non-water resistant	70° F.	Yes	Low	1 year	Low density woods (bass, white pine, spruce) 100 p.s.i.
Vegetable (soybean)	Powder, mix with water.	Interior	2 to 3 Hours	Non-water resistant	70° F.	Yes	Low	1 year unmixed, 3 hours mixed.	
Casein	Powder, mix with water.	Interior/Exterior	4 to 6 Hours	Water resistant	34° - 90° F.	Some	Low	1 year unmixed, 4-6 hours mixed.	
Urea (Powder)	Powder, mix with water.	Interior/Exterior	4 to 6 Hours	Water resistant	70° F.	No	Low	1 year unmixed, 4-6 hours mixed.	
Urea (Liquid)	Liquid, mix with powdered catalyst.	Interior/Exterior	2 to 6 Hours	Water resistant	70° F.	No	Low	1 year unmixed, 2-12 hours mixed depending upon catalyst used.	
Resorcinal	Liquid, mix with powdered catalyst.	Exterior	2½ Hours	Waterproof	70° F.	No	High	1 year unmixed, 3 hours mixed.	
Phenol	Liquid, no mixing required.	Exterior	2 to 5 Minutes	Waterproof	300° F.	No	Medium	3 months	
Phenol Resorcinal	Liquid, mix with powdered catalyst.	Exterior	2 to 6 Hours	Waterproof	70° - 90° F.	No	High	1 year unmixed, 3 hours mixed.	
Melamine	Powder, mix with water.	Exterior	16 to 18 Hours at 75°	Waterproof	Hot Press 240° - 260° F.	No	High	1 year unmixed, 10-15 hours mixed.	
Melamine Urea	Powder or liquid, mix powder type with water.	Interior/Exterior	4 Hours at 75°	Water resistant	Hot Press 250° - 300° F.	No	Medium	1 year unmixed, 3-10 hours mixed.	
Epoxy	Liquid, mix with catalyst.	Exterior	6 to 8 Hours	Waterproof	70° F.	No	High	Unlimited unmixed, 1-2 hours mixed.	
Blood Albumin	Powder, mix with water.	Exterior	2 to 5 Minutes	Waterproof	Hot Press 230° - 280° F.	Yes	Low	Unlimited unmixed, 4-12 hours mixed.	

Topic *123.* Hand Screw

Classification

Adjustable holding tool

Application

Principle of Operation

The hand screw works on the principle of the screw and lever, Fig. 13-1. It is designed for holding stock under pressure. The two jaws are adjusted for size opening by simultaneously revolving the two spindles. Compression is applied by tightening the middle spindle. Tightening the end spindle causes the jaws to pivot on the middle spindle, resulting in leverage which produces additional compression at the open end of the jaws. See Topic 33, "The Screw." In order to secure uniform pressure the jaws must be parallel.

Kinds and Uses

Hand screws serve as an adjustable, pressure device and as an aid in securing stock in position for work.

Length of Jaw	Opening
4″	2″
5″	2½″
6″	3″
7″	3½″
8″	4½″
10″	6″
12″	8½″
14″	10″
16″	12″
18″	18″

Some manufacturers indicate the sizes of hand screws with numbers which range from 4/0 for the smallest to 5 for the largest size.

Principal Parts and Function of Each

1. Jaws are made to serve as gripping levers for holding stock between their openings. They are made of oiled maple or cast of a magnesium alloy steel.
2. Adjustment spindles are made of cold-drawn steel. One-half of the spindle has right-hand threads; the other half has left-hand threads. Revolving the spindle advances or retracts the jaws simultaneously. Wooden spindles are made of ash or hickory and have right-hand threads throughout their length.
3. Pivot nuts, made from cold-drawn steel, are fitted into the jaws to hold the threaded spindle.
4. The maple handle is fastened to the spindle to afford a better grip.

Maintenance

Hand screws should be stored on racks with jaws not under pressure. The jaws should be clean and free from glue (coat with wax). A drop of oil should be applied to the spindle periodically.

Market Analysis

Capacity

Hand screws are made with jaw openings from 0 to 18″.

Additional Reading

Cincinnati Tool Company, *A Clamp for Every Purpose*
Manufacturers Catalogs

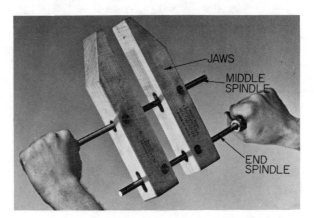

Fig. 13-1. Hand Screw (Courtesy Adjustable Clamp Co.)

Topic *124.* Bar Clamps

(WOOD, I-BAR, PIPE, DOUBLE BAR, CABINET)

Classification

Adjustable, rigid holding tool

Application

Principle of Operation

Clamps operate on the principle of the screw. Pressure is applied and maintained by means of tightening a screw.

Kinds and Uses

Bar clamps are used in clamping wide, glued-up sections such as table tops and in holding parts in assembly.

1. Single bar clamps are made in several types.

   Wood cabinet clamps have 2¼″ jaws, and are made with maximum openings of 18″, 28″, 38″, 48″, 60″, and 72″. See Fig. 13-2.

   Steel bar cabinet clamps have 3½″ jaws and are made with openings of 6″ to 24″ by 2″ increments. See Fig. 13-5.

   I-bar clamps have 2″ jaws. The length of opening may be from 2′ to 8′ by 12″ increments, see Figs. 13-5 and 13-6.

   Steel bar clamps have 2″ jaws with a length of opening from 2′ to 8′ by 12″ increments, see Fig. 13-7.

   Eccentric clamps are the same as steel bar clamps except that the screw is replaced with a cam locking device.

2. *Cabinet bar clamps* have leather buffers or padded jaws to prevent marking the edges in fine cabinet work.

3. In gluing thin stock, double-bar clamps or piling clamps are used to prevent buckling or the bend-back of the single bars, Fig. 13-8.

   Double pipe bar clamps — the length of opening is determined by the length of pipe. Jaws are 3½″, Fig. 13-8.

Fig. 13-3. Eccentric Clamp

Fig. 13-2. Wood Bar Cabinet Clamp (Courtesy Adjustable Clamp Co.)

Fig. 13-4. Steel Cabinet Clamp

Piling clamps are similar to double bar clamps, Figs. 13-9 and 13-10. Piling clamps are used in quantity gluing where stock is "piled" one on the other. The clamp is placed between the layers of stock; one screw clamps the above layer and the opposite screw clamps the lower layer. Openings: 6″ - 24″, 12″ - 30″, 18″ - 36″, 24″ - 42″, 30″ - 48″, 42″ - 60″, and 54″ - 72″.

4. *Joiner bar clamps* are used in clamping narrow stock.

Fig. 13-5. Warp Being Clamped into This Top, Indicated by Light Showing under Clamps (Courtesy Adjustable Clamp Co.)

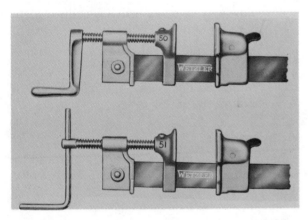

Fig. 13-7. Steel Bar Clamps (Courtesy Wetzler Clamp Co., Inc.)

Fig. 13-6. I-Bar Clamps (Courtesy Adjustable Clamp Co.)

Fig. 13-8. Double Bar Clamps (Courtesy Adjustable Clamp Co.)

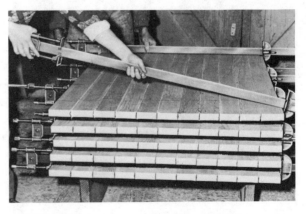

Fig. 13-9. Piling Clamps (Courtesy Wetzler Clamp Co., Inc.)

5. *Clamp fixtures* may be purchased separately to fit wood strips and pipe, Figs. 13-11 and 13-12.

Principal Parts and Function of Each

1. The bar — made of wood, rectangular steel, I-shaped bar or pipe — holds and guides clamping mechanism and serves to regulate the length of opening and provide stiffness.

2. Movable forged steel *dogs* grip the bar and adjust for length of opening.

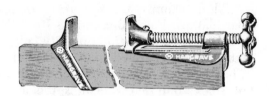

Fig. 13-12. Wood Bar Clamp Fixture (Courtesy Cincinnati Tool Co.)

3. *Clutch or pressure plates*, made of tempered steel, grip the I-bar or pipe (some bars have notches into which the steel dogs catch at fixed intervals).

4. *Sliding steel dogs* provide the pressure plate for screw.

5. *Screw*, made of cold-drawn steel, transmits pressure to dogs or jaws.

6. *Handle, crank, wing, or wheel* aids in turning the screw.

Maintenance

Bar clamps should be oiled when stored to prevent damage and rusting. The screw should be oiled periodically.

Market Analysis

Capacity

Bar clamp openings are determined by length of the bar or pipe. I-bars are available in openings of 0 to 8 feet. Pipe bars may be of any convenient length. Cabinet bar clamps have longer jaws than regular bar clamps.

Additional Reading

Adjustable Clamp Company, *Clamps*
Cincinnati Tool Company, *A Clamp for Every Purpose*

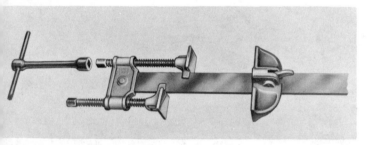

Fig. 13-10. Piling Clamps (Courtesy Wetzler Clamp Co., Inc.)

Fig. 13-11. Pipe Clamps (Courtesy Adjustable Clamp Co.)

Topic *125.* C-, Band, Miter, and Spring Clamps

Classification

Adjustable holding tool

Application

Principle of Operation

Pressure is applied by means of a screw or spring. See Topic 33, "The Screw."

Kinds and Uses

1. C-clamps, carriage clamps, and machinist's clamps are used in clamping small work. See Figs. 13-13 through 13-19.

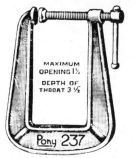

Fig. 13-16. C-Clamp, Deep Throat

Fig. 13-17. C-Clamp, Square Throat

(Courtesy Cincinnati Tool Co.)

Fig. 13-13. C-Clamp

Fig. 13-14. C-Clamp, Regular Throat

(Courtesy Cincinnati Tool Co.)

Fig. 13-18. Carriage Clamp (Courtesy Cincinnati Tool Co.)

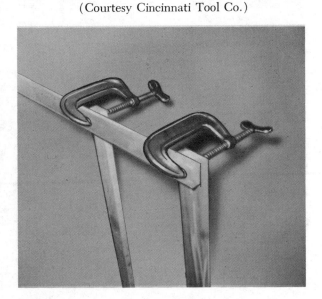

Fig. 13-15. C-Clamps, Round Frame (Courtesy Adjustable Clamp Co.)

Fig. 13-19. Machinist's Clamps (Courtesy Adjustable Clamp Co.)

Table 20
Sizes of C-Clamps

	Opening Between Jaws	Depth of Throat Opening
Regular Throat	¾″	⅝″
	2″	1″
	2½″	1⅜″
	2″	2″
	3″	2⅜″
	4″	2¾″
	6″	3⅝″
	8″	4½″
	10″	5⅜″
	12″	5¾″
Medium Throat	1″	1⅛″
	1½″	1½″
	2½″	2½″
Round Frame	⅝″	⅞″
	1¼″	1⅛″
	4″	5″
	5″	5″
	6″	6″
Deep Throat	1″	3½″
	1½″	3½″
	2½″	4¾″
	2½″	6¼″
Square Frame	1″	1½″
	1½″	2″

Table 21
Sizes of Carriage Clamps

Opening Between Jaws	Depth of Throat Opening
2½″	1¾″
3″	1⅞″
4″	2⅛″
5″	2½″
6″	2¾″
8″	3¼″
10″	3⅝″
12″	3⅝″ to 6″

Table 22
Sizes of Machinists' Clamps

Opening Between Jaws	Depth of Throat Opening
2″	2½″
3″	2½″
4″	2½″
5″	2½″
6″	2½″
8″	2½″
10″	2½″
12″	2½″

Fig. 13-20. Miter Clamp, 4 Corner (Courtesy Cincinnati Tool Co.)

Fig. 13-21. Miter Clamps (Courtesy Adjustable Clamp Co.)

2. Miter clamps provide a right angle for squaring and clamping flat, mitered corners. There are three types: miter vise, miter frame, and miter clamp. See Figs. 13-20 through 13-23.

3. Band clamps, made of canvas or flexible steel, are used in clamping round and irregularly shaped objects such as furniture, tanks, and columns, Fig. 13-24.

4. Spring clamps are quick-release clamps used for holding small pieces, Fig. 13-27.

Table 23
Sizes of Spring Clamps

Length of Jaws	Jaw Opening
4″	¾″
6″	1½″
9″	2¾″
12″	4″

C, Carriage, and Machinist's Clamps — Principal Parts and Function of Each

1. *Frame* of C-clamps, made of malleable iron or forged steel, forms the opening between fixed and adjustable jaw.
2. *Screw*, made of cold-rolled steel, transmits pressure to steel swivel or plate.
3. *Steel swivel* serves as adjustable jaw.

Band Clamps — Principal Parts and Function of Each

1. The *frame*, made of pressed steel, secures the flexible steel or canvas band.
2. The pressed-steel *base* provides the plate for tightening the flexible band.
3. The *screw*, made of cold-rolled steel, transmits pressure to base.

Miter Clamps — Principal Parts and Function of Each

1. Steel *jaws* serve as pressure plates.
2. *Screws* transmit pressure to jaws.
3. *Corner miter clamps* have four aluminum alloy corner blocks and four screws and nuts.

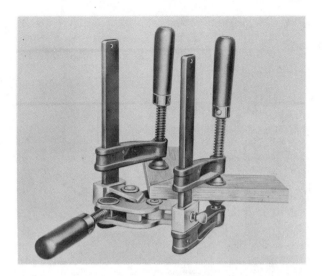

Fig. 13-22. Miter Clamp (Courtesy Wetzler Clamp Co., Inc.)

Fig. 13-23. Miter Clamp (Courtesy Stanley Tool Co.)

Fig. 13-24. Band Clamp (Courtesy Adjustable Clamp Co.)

4. *Jorgensen miter clamp* has two steel jaws with a ⅜″ diameter binding pin, and is used to lock any miter angle together.

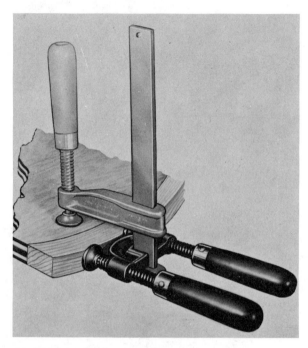

Fig. 13-25. Cross Clamp — Used with Quick Action Clamp (Courtesy Wetzler Clamp Co., Inc.)

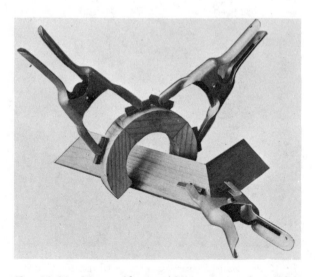

Fig. 13-26. Spring Clamps (Courtesy Arvids Iraids)

Spring Clamps —
Principal Parts and Function of Each
1. One-piece steel *jaws* and handle are shaped to fit the hand and provide gripping pressure.
2. Steel *spring* provides pressure.

Maintenance
Clamps should be stored on racks when not in use. The screw should be oiled periodically.

Market Analysis
Capacity
1. C-clamps are made with throat openings from ⅝″ to 6¼″ and depths of ¾″ to 2½″.
2. Carriage clamp throat openings are 1¾″ to 6″ and have a depth of 2½″ to 12″.
3. Machinist's clamps have throat openings of 2½″ and jaw openings of 2″ to 12″.
4. In band clamps the length of band determines the size of object which can be clamped. Bands are 10 to 30 feet long.
5. Spring clamps are made with the following jaw opening: #1 − 1″, #2 − 2″, #3 − 3″, #4 − 4″.
6. Miter clamps are limited to the opening of the jaws.
7. Miter vise will open to 3½″ wide.
8. Jorgensen miter clamps have a distance between centers of 2″ - 6″.

Additional Reading
Manufacturers Catalogs

Fig. 13-27. Use of Spring Clamps (Courtesy Adjustable Clamp Co.)

Topic *126.* Gluing a Joint

Classification

Fastening by adhesion

Procedure

1. Test all surfaces to be glued together for accuracy of fit. Glue cannot compensate for a poor fit. The closer the members fit together, the better the glue will hold. A good glued joint is generally stronger than the wood itself.

Fig. 13-28. Position of Clamps in Gluing Spring Joint

2. After members of the joint have been fitted properly, they should be assembled in a dry run. Check to see that adjacent pieces are marked with corresponding numbers or letters so that exact reassembly will be quick and easy.

3. Adjust clamps to tighten joints and retest for proper fit. Protective blocks should be used under clamp jaws to prevent marring the finished surface. Check to see that the work is locked square and flat. See Fig. 13-28.

4. Disassemble and apply a thin layer of glue to each member of the joint. Some glues set in a short time. If the glue which you are using is one of these, work fast. Use paper inserts or some other means of insuring that hand screws, straight edges, or protective blocks are not unintentionally glued to the work.

Fig. 13-29. Taylor Clamps

Previously fitted stock is joined into large blanks for table tops, case tops, and other long furniture surfaces and held in large Taylor clamps until dry. It takes these revolving clamp gluers about one-half hour to complete the cycle. (Courtesy Heywood-Wakefield Co.)

Fig. 13-30. Gluing Chair Backs

Pieces of stock are tongued and grooved, then lined with glue. They are fitted in a gluing form and clamped until the glue sets. The excess glue at the joints is sanded away in later operations. (Courtesy Heywood-Wakefield Co.)

5. Quickly apply pressure with clamps to bring the joint together. Do not force out the glue by excessive pressure. See Topic 33, "The Screw." *Check to see that your work is flat and square.*

6. Wipe all excess glue from the surface with a damp paper towel. If this glue is left to harden, it will have to be removed with a glue scraper or chisel which causes additional work and may cause trouble in finishing.

7. Set the work aside for the glue to dry. Some glues harden in one hour while others take four to eight hours to harden. Follow the directions of the manufacturer.

8. Room temperature should be at 70° F. for most desirable gluing conditions.

Standards and Results

1. A good glue joint should fit so closely that no glue line shows between the pieces.

2. There should be no warp clamped into the assembly. See Fig. 13-5.

Fig. 13-32. Industrial Assembling — Clamping a Dresser in a Hand-Operated Press (Courtesy Heywood-Wakefield Co.)

Fig. 13-31. Industrial Assembling — Frame Being Clamped in Pneumatic Press (Courtesy Heywood-Wakefield Co.)

Fig. 13-33. Industrial Assembling — Attaching Glue Blocks to Drawer Clamped in Hand-Operated Press (Courtesy Heywood-Wakefield Co.)

3. Work should be square.
4. There should be no excess glue left on the surface.

Safety Considerations

1. Excess pressure should not be applied to any clamp fixture to cause deformation or breakage.
2. Employ assistance when handling awkward or heavy projects.
3. See topic on safety.

Additional Reading

Department of Agriculture (Forest Products Laboratory), *Important Factors in Gluing With Animal Glue, Strong and Weak Glue Joints,* and *Occurrence and Removal of Glue Stains*

Department of Agriculture, *Wood Handbook,* pp. 233-244

Topic *127.* Claw Hammer

Classification

Driving and withdrawing tool

Application

Principle of Operation

The hammer works on the principle of the lever, whether driving or withdrawing nails.

Kinds and Uses

The hammer is used to drive and withdraw nails and as a lever in driving apart pieces that have been nailed, Fig. 13-35. Claw hammers are available in head weights of 5 ounces, 7 ounces, 10 ounces, 13 ounces, 16 ounces, and 20 ounces. They are available with straight or curved claws.

Principal Parts and Function of Each

1. The *handle* is used in holding the hammer when either driving or withdrawing nails. Handles are made of hickory, ash, fiber glass, or leather-covered steel.
2. The *head* of the hammer does the driving or withdrawing. The heavier the head, the greater the force exerted in driving nails. The head of a hammer is composed of several parts. (See Fig. 13-35.) High-grade steel is drop forged to shape, then semi-hardened and tempered.

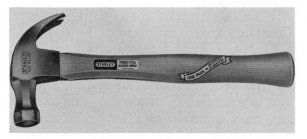

A. Curved claw with octagon neck and poll and wooden handle.

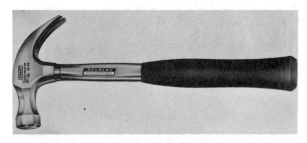

B. Curved claw with neoprene rubber handle.

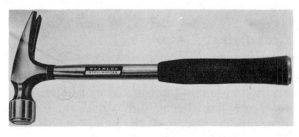

C. Ripping claw for heavy-duty, exceptional driving and pulling power.

Fig. 13-34. Claw Hammers (Courtesy Stanley Tool Co.)

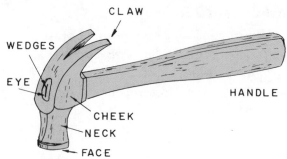

Fig. 13-35. Nomenclature of Claw Hammer

Maintenance

Cleaning

The face of a hammer head may become gummy from use. This gum may be cleaned off with steel wool or fine sandpaper. Handles may also get dirty and sticky and may be cleaned with sandpaper.

Repairing

Wooden handles may dry out and shrink, causing a loose head. This may be overcome by driving the wedges further into the handle. Immersion in water provides only a temporary solution. A more permanent repair may be obtained by soaking the handle in a commercial wood stabilizer such as ethylene glycol. (See Topic 3 on wood stabilization.)

Replacing Parts

Wooden handles may break and need replacing.

Market Analysis

Attachments

Hammer nail clip which fits onto the head of a hammer to hold a nail until the first blow is struck. This frees one hand to hold stock in overhead nailing.

Topic *128.* Nails

Classification

Fasteners

Composition or Description

Nails are made of steel, iron, copper, zinc, brass, and aluminum. Iron nails are sometimes coated with zinc, copper, brass, cadmium, or resin.

Properties

Wire nails are a steel gray color unless coated to increase resistance to rust or to give additional holding power. They are designed so that when driven into wood they force, bend, break, or split the fibers. The bent fibers tend to return to their normal position, thus pressing against the nail and wedging and gripping it tightly as shown in Fig. 13-36. See "Factors Affecting the Holding Power of Nails," pp. 326-327.

Uses

Nails are usually used to fasten two or more pieces by driving into or through the separate pieces of wood or other materials.

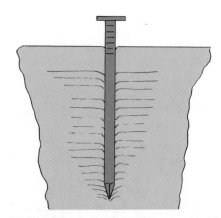

Fig. 13-36. Action of Wood Fibers to Hold Nail

Market Analysis

Shapes —
According to Methods of Manufacture

1. *Wrought iron nails* — each nail made by hammering or forging a hot piece of metal into shape.
2. *Cut nails* — heavy mechanical shears cut tapered strips from sheets of steel.

3. *Wire nails* — drawn from cold wire.

Shapes — According to Head Form and Diameter of Wire

1. *Common nails* — large, flat-headed wire nails of a standard gauge wire for any given length. Usually plain but may have spiral grooves or ring grooves, Fig. 13-37.

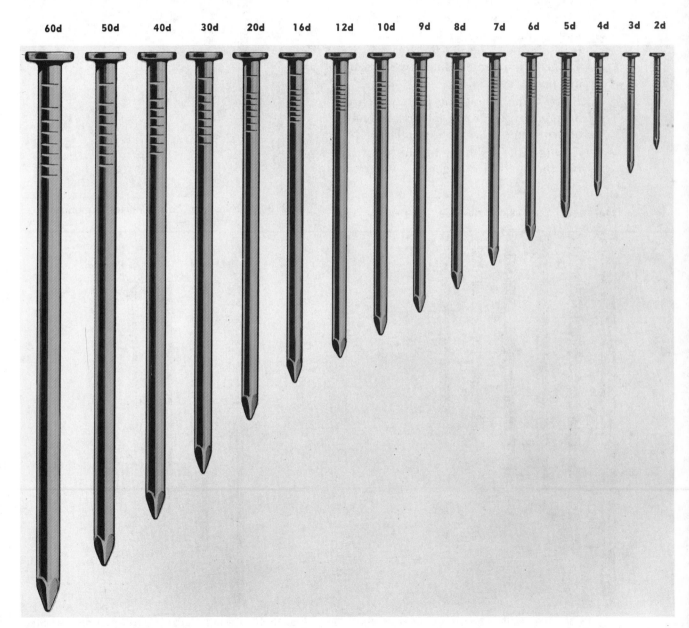

Fig. 13-37. Common Nails (Courtesy American Steel & Wire Co.)

2. *Spikes* — larger sizes of common nails: 16d to 60d.

3. *Box nails* — similar to common nails but smaller in diameter with a thinner head, Fig. 13-38.

4. *Wire nails* — similar to common nails but gauges of wire differ from those of common nails. These are ordered by length in inches and by gauge of wire as explained under *size*.

5. *Finishing nails* — small head on wire nail so that it may be set below the surface of the wood on finish work, Fig. 13-39. These are classified by the standard penny system.

6. *Brads* — small finishing nails which are ordered by length in inches and gauge of wire, just as are wire nails.

7. *Casing nails* — similar to finishing nails but the heads are larger to give greater

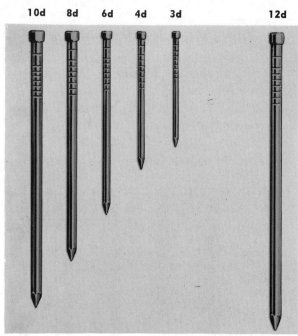

Fig. 13-39. Finishing Nails (Courtesy American Steel & Wire Co.)

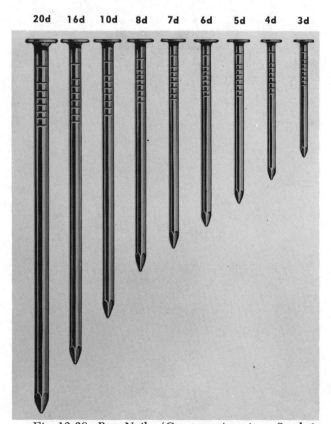

Fig. 13-38. Box Nails (Courtesy American Steel & Wire Co.)

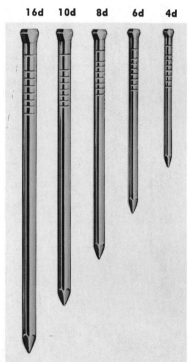

Fig. 13-40. Casing Nails (Courtesy American Steel & Wire Co.)

holding power, Fig. 13-40. These are also classified by the standard penny system.

Shapes — According to Point (See Fig. 13-41)

1. *Common or regular diamond* — medium sharpness for general use.
2. *Long diamond* — for speed driving.
3. *Blunt* — for dense wood and masonry.
4. *Chisel* — large spikes for hardwood.
5. *Round* or *pointless* — used for fabric and carpeting to prevent tearing.
6. *Needle* — used to prevent tearing and for speed nailing.
7. *Duck bill* — usually on smaller nails which are to be clinched.
8. *Side* — for clinching in hardwood and to minimize splitting.
9. *Cruciform* — to prevent splitting.

Special Shapes

Nails are shaped for special uses, such as boat nail, American Duplex nail, escutcheon pin, cement or concrete nail, shade roller nail, and innumerable others. See Fig. 13-43.

Sizes

1. The sizes of wire nails most commonly used are indicated by numbers and the term *penny* (abbreviated as "d"). Each size of a common nail has a standard gauge wire. It will be noted that the larger the wire gauge number the smaller the diameter of the nail.
2. Sizes of all wire brads and of wire nails which deviate from the penny system are usually indicated by length in inches and by gauge of wire. For example, a wire nail that is 1″ long and made of #15 wire is actually classified as a 2d common nail, but a wire nail that is 1″ long and made of #17 wire is classified as a 1″ #17 wire nail.

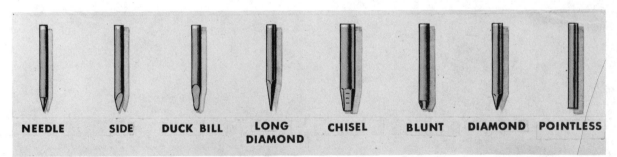

NEEDLE   SIDE   DUCK BILL   LONG DIAMOND   CHISEL   BLUNT   DIAMOND   POINTLESS

Fig. 13-41. Types of Points (Courtesy American Steel & Wire Co.)

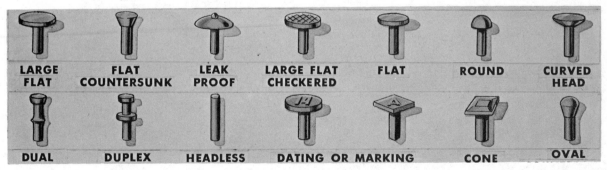

LARGE FLAT   FLAT COUNTERSUNK   LEAK PROOF   LARGE FLAT CHECKERED   FLAT   ROUND   CURVED HEAD

DUAL   DUPLEX   HEADLESS   DATING OR MARKING   CONE   OVAL

Fig. 13-42. Types of Heads (Courtesy American Steel & Wire Co.)

Sales Units

1. Most nails may be purchased by the pound, but are sometimes sold in 5-pound packages. Nails may also be purchased in 100-pound units in a wooden keg or cardboard carton.
2. Small wire nails, brads, and escutcheon pins are usually sold in ¼-pound, ½-pound, and 1-pound packages.

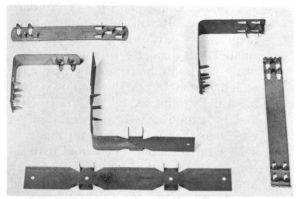

Fig. 13-42A. Fasteners for Crate Corners (Courtesy Acme Steel Co.)

Fig. 13-42B. Corrugated Fasteners (Courtesy Stanley Tool Co.)

Maintenance

Nails should be stored in a dry place to prevent rusting.

Additional Reading

Department of Agriculture (Forest Products Laboratory), *The Effect of Nail Points on Resistance to Withdrawal.*

Interesting Fact: Nails were first made in England in the fifteenth century. In this country they were hand-forged until about 1800 after Jacob Perkins of Newburyport, Massachusetts, invented a nailmaking machine in 1790, which superseded the hand manufacture of cut nails. It could make 200,000 nails per day, and was a major pioneering step in an industry which today has capacity to produce more than 1.2 million tons of nails and staples annually.

Wooden pegs, called trunnels, were used by the Pilgrims in the construction of their buildings instead of nails.

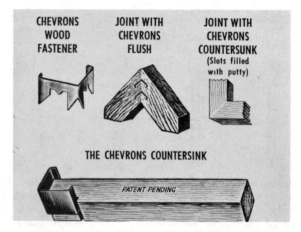

Fig. 13-42C. Chevrons (Courtesy Chevron Div., Everard Tap and Die Corp.)

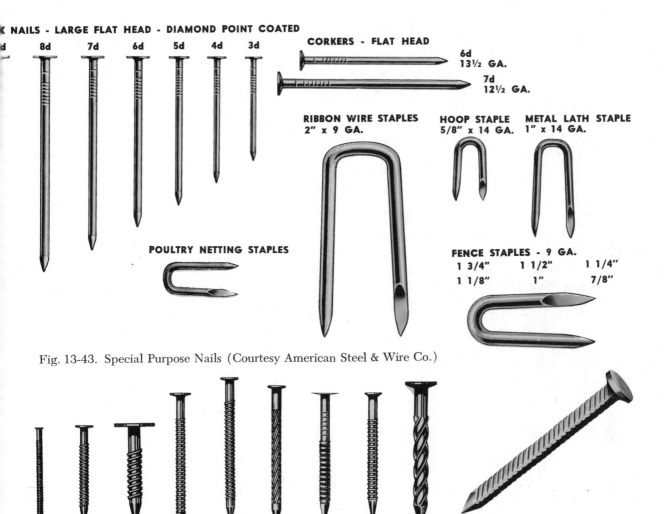

K NAILS - LARGE FLAT HEAD - DIAMOND POINT COATED

8d   7d   6d   5d   4d   3d

CORKERS - FLAT HEAD

6d
13½ GA.

7d
12½ GA.

RIBBON WIRE STAPLES
2" x 9 GA.

HOOP STAPLE
5/8" x 14 GA.

METAL LATH STAPLE
1" x 14 GA.

POULTRY NETTING STAPLES

FENCE STAPLES - 9 GA.
1 3/4"   1 1/2"   1 1/4"
1 1/8"   1"   7/8"

Fig. 13-43. Special Purpose Nails (Courtesy American Steel & Wire Co.)

Fig. 13-43A. Special-Purpose, Stronghold® Nails
(Courtesy Independent Nail Corp.)

Fig. 13-43B. Scotch Truss Nail,
Available in Many
Sizes and Designs
(Courtesy Armo Steel
Corporation)

Topic *129.* Driving Nails

Classification

Fastening

Procedure

1. Nails are used to fasten wood, metal, asbestos, slate, plaster board, and composition board to wood. Generally, wood is the base into which nails are driven.

2. Select the proper nail. (See Topic 128, "Nails".)
3. Select hammer in accordance with size of nail.

Locating Position of Nail

1. If conditions permit, it is best to locate nails at least ¾" from the edge or end of the board. If this is not possible, a hole slightly smaller than the diameter of the

nail should be drilled through the first piece to prevent splitting.

2. If strength is the only consideration, the nails should be staggered so that adjacent nails are not in line with each other in the same grain.

3. If appearance is a major consideration, the nails should be in perfect alignment and spaced equally.

4. Avoid nailing into knots or other defects.

Driving Nails

1. Take a position so that the nail can be sighted and driven at the proper angle.

2. Hold the nail with the forefinger and thumb of one hand and with the other hand grasp the handle of the hammer so as to gain maximum leverage, Fig. 13-44.

3. The nail should be struck squarely on the head, using forearm action. Begin with light taps to start the nail and increase the force of the blows as the nail penetrates deeper, lessening the force as head approaches the surface. Light hammer blows cause the nail to hold better because the wood fibers into which the nail is being driven are bent rather than torn.

4. Splitting may be prevented and nails driven easier if holes slightly smaller than the diameter of the nails are drilled in the piece being fastened.

5. If nail bends while being driven, remove and discard.

6. If a nail tends to follow the grain, withdraw and relocate the nail or drill out the hole.

7. Heads of most nails are usually driven flush with the surface of the material being held.

8. Finish and casing nails are usually set below the surface with a nail set.

Toe nailing is the method used to fasten two pieces of stock together, when the contact of the butted surface is small and the pieces are running at an angle which would not permit straight driving of nails. Nails driven at an angle greater than 30° from the perpendicular do not permit enough depth of penetration into the second piece. Nails driven at an angle less than 30° may cause splitting of the first piece. Contrary to popular opinion, toe nailing does not have the holding power of straight nailing. It is usually used, in house construction, to fasten the lower ends of studs to the sole, to fasten fire stops to studs, or to fasten corner braces to studs.

Factors Affecting the Holding Power of Nails

The following statements apply only if there is no splitting in the wood. They need to be modified, if drilling is necessary.

1. As the length of the nail is increased, the holding power is increased.

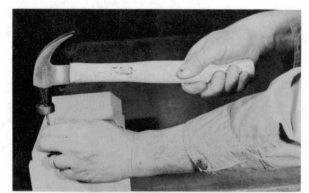

Fig. 13-44. Driving a Nail — Note the Manner of Holding the Hammer

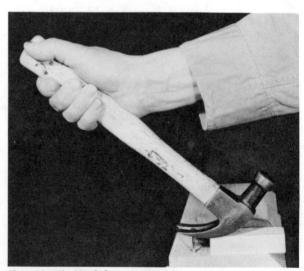

Fig. 13-45. Withdrawing a Nail

2. As the diameter of the nail is increased, the holding power is increased.
3. The sharper the point, the greater the holding power.
4. The density of the material the nail is driven into affects the holding power, *i.e.*, a nail driven into oak has a greater holding power than an identical nail driven into pine.
5. The surface of the nail affects the holding power, *i.e.*, smooth nails do not have as great a holding power as sand blasted, galvanized, spirally or annually grooved nails.

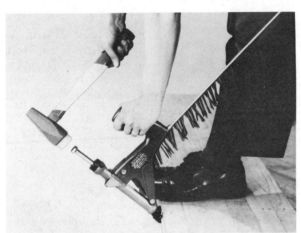

Fig. 13-46. Production Technique in Floor Nailing
This machine feeds nails at the proper angle, drives and sets nails, and drives flooring strip snugly into place — all in one operation. Tongue and groove floors may be laid better, faster, and without dented or mashed edges. (Courtesy Independent Nail & Packing Co.)

6. The driving force affects the holding power; in general, a moderately slow blow is preferred.
7. Greatest holding power is obtained when the nail is driven at right angles to the fibers.
8. Nails driven into dry wood have greater holding power than those driven into wet wood.

Standards and Results

1. There should be no splitting of the material being fastened.
2. The heads of nails should not protrude above the surface of the work.
3. Nail points should not protrude from any surface or force out stock.
4. There should be no hammer marks on the face of the material.
5. There should be no bent nails driven into the surface.

Safety Considerations

1. Points of nails should not protrude through a board, unless they are clinched.
2. Avoid glancing blows. Flying nails are very dangerous.
3. When the nail is started, withdraw fingers to avoid mashing.
4. Whenever possible avoid driving against a springy surface.
5. See topic on safety.

Additional Reading

Housing and Home Finance Agency, *Technique of House Nailing*

Topic *130.* Screwdrivers

(COMMON, OFFSET, OFFSET RATCHET, SPIRAL, RATCHET, STUBBY, REPLACEABLE BIT, SCREW DRIVER BIT, ELECTRIC, PNEUMATIC)

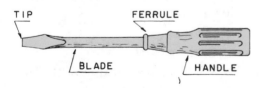

Fig. 13-49. Nomenclature of Screwdriver

Fig. 13-50. Offset Screwdriver (Courtesy Stanley Tool Co.)

Fig. 13-52. Ratchet Offset Screwdriver (Courtesy Stanley Tool Co.)

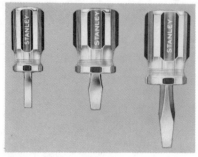

Fig. 13-53. Stubby Screwdrivers (Courtesy Stanley Tool Co.)

Fig. 13-54. Spiral Ratchet Screwdriver (Courtesy Millers Falls Co.)

Classification

Driving and withdrawing tool

Application

Principle of Operation

The screwdriver works on the principle of the wheel and axle. The handle represents the wheel and the blade and tip represent the axle. Hence, the larger the diameter of the handle, the greater the mechanical advantage. The manner in which the hand, wrist, and arm are used may also increase the mechanical advantage. See Fig. 13-49.

Kinds and Uses

1. *Common screwdrivers* are used to drive and withdraw screws. They are available in blade lengths from 1¼″ to 18″ and in blade diameters from 1/16″ to ½″.

2. *Offset screwdrivers* are available in lengths of 3″ to 6″. They are used for driving or loosening screws in cramped quarters. The body is made with one or two tips at each end, Fig. 13-50.

3. *Ratchet screwdrivers* are similar to a common screwdriver except there is a ratchet located at the handle end of the blade. This permits turning the handle a full turn of the wrist then returning to the original position without removing the screwdriver tip from the screw.

4. *Offset ratchet screwdrivers* are available only in a 4″ size. They are similar to the regular offset screwdriver except for the ratchet action which permits back-and-forth motion without removing the screwdriver tip from the screw, Fig. 13-52.

5. *Stubby screwdrivers* are identical to a common screwdriver except the blade

is much shorter to allow use in close quarters, Fig. 13-53.

6. *Spiral ratchet screwdrivers* are available in lengths of 10¼″ to 18″. They are used to speed up the operation of driving or withdrawing screws. They work on the principle of the inclined plane, Fig. 13-54. When pushing down on the handle, the double spiral grooves in the shaft turn the blade to drive or loosen the screw, depending on the position of the ratchet. Some types have a spring on the handle for quick return. Spiral screwdrivers are equipped with a chuck that permits the changing of bits.

7. Screwdriver bits are available in tip widths of ³⁄₁₆″ to ¾″, by 16ths. They are used in bit braces when greater force is required in driving or withdrawing screws and also to speed up the operation, Fig. 13-55.

8. *Replaceable bit screwdrivers* are recommended for driving case-hardened screws which might cause wear on the tip of ordinary screwdrivers. Bits are made in a number of sizes which fit a common handle.

9. *Electric screwdrivers* are used in production work. They are manufactured in four speeds: 500, 800, 1600, and 2500 r.p.m. The 1600 r.p.m. is recommended for all-purpose use. They are equipped with a clutch which slips when screws are properly seated.

10. *Pneumatic screwdrivers* are similar to the electric but are driven by air pressure, Fig. 13-57.

11. All of the above types of screwdrivers come in regular, Phillips, or cross tips, Fig. 13-55 and 13-56.

Phillips screwdriver tips are available in four sizes: #1, #2, #3, and #4.

Screws with a wire size of from 0 to 4 — use #1.

Screws with a wire size of from 5 to 9 — use #2.

Screws with a wire size of from 10 to 16 — use #3.

Screws with a wire size over 18 — use #4.

Principal Parts and Function of Each

1. The wood or plastic *handle* is shaped for grip in twisting.

Fig. 13-55. Screwdriver Bit (Courtesy Stanley Tool Co.)

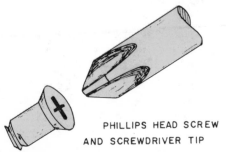

PHILLIPS HEAD SCREW
AND SCREWDRIVER TIP

Fig. 13-56. Phillips Head Screw and Screwdriver Tip

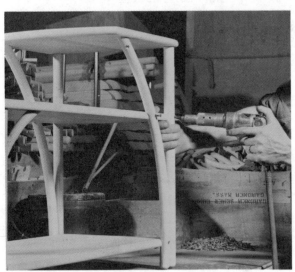

Fig. 13-57. Pneumatic Screwdriver
This worker is using a pneumatic screwdriver to assemble a step table with screws. Operated by compressed air, the screwdriver bit is disengaged by a friction clutch when the screw is seated properly. (Courtesy Heywood-Wakefield Co.)

2. The *ferrule,* made of pressed-steel or brass tubing, strengthens the handle against splitting when great force is applied.
3. The *tip* is the part of the blade which fits the slot of the screw. The *blade* is made of carbon steel with a hardened tip.

Maintenance

1. Keep screwdriver handles clean and smooth.
2. Screwdriver tips should be ground so that the sides are straight and parallel.
3. Metal blade and tip should be covered with a thin coat of oil when not to be used for long periods of time.
4. Spiral and ratchet screwdrivers should be lubricated periodically.

Market Analysis

Capacity

Screwdrivers should fit the slot of the screw snugly, and the tip should not protrude beyond the diameter of the screw head.

Additional Reading

Manufacturers Catalogs

Topic *131.* Wood Screws

Classification

Spiral fasteners

Composition or Description

Screws are made of steel (either galvanized or plated), brass, copper, bronze, cadmium, aluminum, monel, or stainless steel.

Properties

Screws made of steel and cadmium are strong and brittle. Those made of brass, copper, and aluminum are not as strong but have better resistance to corrosion. Those made of monel or stainless steel are high-strength, special-purpose screws. A screw taps its own internal thread when being driven into wood.

Uses

Screws are used to fasten by being turned into or through a piece of material when greater strength than a nailed joint is desired. Screws permit pieces to be taken apart without injury to either member. Drive screws, Fig. 13-58B, can be driven at least partially by a hammer and thus combine driving ease of a nail with some of the holding power of a screw. Most must be seated with a screwdriver. Full bodied threaded screws can be used for fastening wood or composition board for greater holding power.

FLATHEAD   ROUNDHEAD   OVALHEAD

Fig. 13-58. Screw Heads
There are many special shapes of screw heads, but the most common are flat, round, and oval.

STRAIGHT SLOT   PHILLIPS SLOT

Fig. 13-58A. Types of Slots on Standard Wood Screws

13-58B. Drive and Self-Tapping Screws

Market Analysis

Shapes

There are many specialty shapes of screws, but the common shapes usually refer to the shape of the head, such as flat head, round head, and oval head, see Fig. 13-58. Some screws are made of hardened steel and are self-tapping, see Fig. 13-58B.

Sizes

Screws range in lengths from ¼″ to 5″ and in wire gauges from 0 to 24. A ¼″ screw is made in wire gauges from 0 to 4, while a 1¼″ screw is made in gauges from 4 to 18. The larger the gauge number, the larger the diameter of the wire.

Sales Units

Screws may be bought in any desired quantity, but the economical way to purchase them is by the box, containing 100 screws. Handy assortments may be purchased in lesser amounts.

Cost

For any given size, flat-head screws are cheapest. Round- and oval-head screws usually cost 10% more than flat-head screws.

Maintenance

Store in a dry place.

Additional Reading

Manufacturers Catalogs

Table 24
Screw and Screw Hole Chart

Gauge No. Wire Size	Counter-bore for head Drill Size	Shank Hole Drill Size	Pilot or Lead Hole Drill Size	
			Hard Wood	Soft Wood
0	.119(⅛)	1/16	3/64	
1	.146(%₆₄)	5/64	1/16	
2	1/4	3/32	1/16	3/64
3	1/4	7/64	1/16	3/64
4	1/4	1/8	3/32	5/64
5	5/16	1/8	3/32	5/64
6	5/16	9/64	3/32	5/64
7	3/8	5/32	1/8	3/32
8	3/8	11/64	1/8	3/32
9	3/8	3/16	1/8	9/64
10	1/2	3/16	5/32	9/64
12	1/2	7/32	3/16	9/64
14	1/2	1/4	3/16	11/64
16	9/16	9/32	15/64	13/64
18	5/8	5/16	17/64	15/64
20	.650(¹¹⁄₁₆)	11/32	19/64	17/64
24	.756(¾)	3/8	21/64	19/64

Topic *132.* Driving Wood Screws

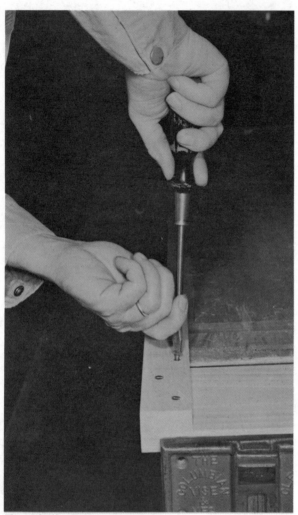

Fig. 13-59. Driving a Screw

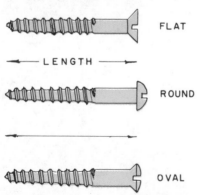

FLAT

←— LENGTH —→

ROUND

OVAL

Fig. 13-60. Length of Wood Screws

Classification

Fastening

Procedure

1. Select the proper size, type, and quantity of screws for the job. Keep in mind that wherever possible, two-thirds of the length of the screw should be in the second piece and that the diameter should be large enough to withstand the probable strain. Oval-head or round-head screws are usually used where the head of the screw will show.

2. Locate the screws not closer than one-half inch from the end of board if possible. Arrange in straight line for appearance and stagger for strength.

3. Drill holes in the first piece the size of the shank or smooth part of screw. These are called shank holes. Countersink for flat- and oval-head screws.

4. When fastening hard materials — such as maple, oak, birch, or walnut — pilot holes should be drilled in the second piece. These holes may be located by holding the pieces in position and marking through the holes in the first piece with an awl. See Figs. 10-25, 10-26, and 13-61.

5. Drill holes in second piece the size of the root diameter (base of thread) of the screw. This is called the pilot hole.

6. Select screwdriver with a blade tip as wide as the diameter of the screw head and one that fits the slot snugly.

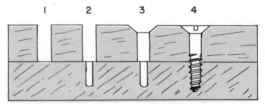

Fig. 13-61. Shank, Pilot, Countersink, and Screw Holes

7. Secure pieces to be fastened and place screw in holes. Drive by turning screw in clockwise direction until the two pieces are held firmly in place and the head is seated, Fig. 13-59. Soap or wax may be applied to the screw threads as a lubricant for easier driving.

Standards and Results

1. Slot of screw should not be burred.
2. There should be no splitting of the materials being fastened.
3. There should be no screwdriver marks showing.
4. Care must be taken to avoid stripping out stock and breaking screw off in stock.

Safety Considerations

1. Be careful screwdriver doesn't slip and cut the hand.

2. Don't rub fingers over head of screw as small slivers are sometimes raised on the head of the screw by the screwdriver.
3. See topic on safety.

Additional Reading

Graham, Paul, *"Encyclopedia of Fasteners" Furniture Production*, April, 1959

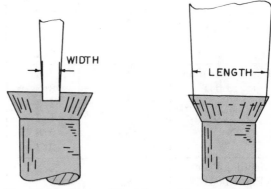

Fig. 13-62. Proper Fit of Screwdriver Tip

Topic *133*. Corner Irons (Braces), Flat Corner Irons, Mending Plates, T-Plates

Classification

Fasteners and reinforcements

Composition or Description

These braces are stamped out of wrought iron, steel, or brass plate. The wrought iron is usually galvanized or plated to prevent rusting.

Properties

These braces and plates add stiffness and distribute the strain.

Uses

This type of hardware is used as a reinforcement to strengthen joints or cracks and hold

two or more pieces together or in place. The head of the screws should fill the countersunk hole and fit flush with the surface.

Fig. 13-63. Corner Brace (Courtesy Stanley Tool Co.)

Market Analysis

Sizes

Table 25
Sizes of Fasteners and Reinforcements
(Given in Inches)

	Side Lengths	Lengths
Corner Braces (Fig. 13-63)	1	1/2
	1½	1/2
	2	5/8
	2½	5/8
	3	3/4
	3½	3/4
Flat Corner Irons (Fig. 13-64)	1½	3/8
	2	3/8
	2½	3/8
	3	1/2
	3½	5/8
	4	3/4
Mending Plates (Fig. 13-65)	2	5/8
	2½	5/8
	3	3/4
	3½	3/4
	4	3/4
T-Plates (Fig. 13-66)	2½ x 2½ x ½ wide	
	3 x 3 x ⅝ wide	

Grades

Braces are made of brass, steel, and galvanized iron. The strength is dependent mostly upon the thickness of the metal.

Sales Units

They may be purchased singly, in cards of 3, by the dozen, or in boxes of 24.

Maintenance

Braces should be stored in a dry place, and straightened out when bent. Braces which are not rust-resistant should be painted, when used in places exposed to moisture.

Additional Reading

Manufacturers Catalogs

Fig. 13-65. Mending Plate (Courtesy Stanley Tool Co.)

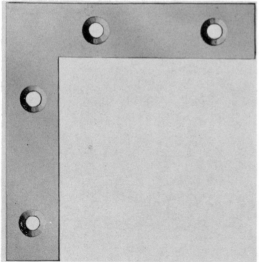

Fig. 13-64. Flat Corner Iron (Courtesy Stanley Tool Co.)

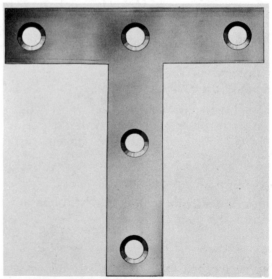

Fig. 13-66. T-Plate (Courtesy Stanley Tool Co.)

Topic *134.* Hinges

Classification

Mechanical fasteners which permit a fixed motion

Composition or Description

Hinges are made from malleable iron, steel, bronze, brass, brass plate, and chromium plate. Hinges usually have two leaves and a pin which ties them together and permits motion according to their particular design.

Properties

The hinge is a movable fastener which permits motion or change of direction. The appearance, the amount of motion, and the strength are determined by the design of the hinge and the material from which it is made.

Uses

A hinge is used as a joint permitting the movement of one of two members. Hinges are used to hang a door or gate and as a movable fastener for a table leaf, desk or chest cover.

Fig. 13-67. Hook and Eye

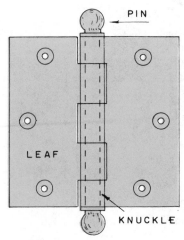

Fig. 13-68. Hinge Nomenclature

Market Analysis

Shapes

1. The *hook and eye* is the simplest form of hinge, Fig. 13-67. The hook is screwed into one of the matching pieces and the eye screwed into the other matching piece.

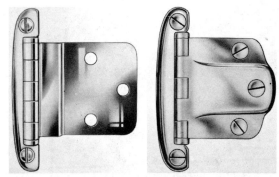

Fig. 13-69. Semi-Con-   Fig. 13-70. Cabinet
cealed Hinge   Hinge
(Courtesy Stanley Tool Co.)

Fig. 13-71. Box Hinge (Courtesy Stanley Tool Co.)

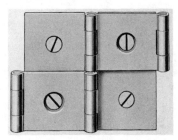

Fig. 13-72. Double Action Screen Hinge (Courtesy Stanley Tool Co.)

Fig. 13-73. Table Hinge (Courtesy Stanley Tool Co.)

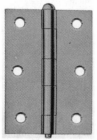

Fig. 13-74. Narrow Cabinet Hinges (Courtesy Stanley Tool Co.)

Fig. 13-75. Back Flaps (Courtesy Stanley Tool Co.)

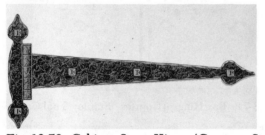

Fig. 13-76. Cabinet Strap Hinge (Courtesy Stanley Tool Co.)

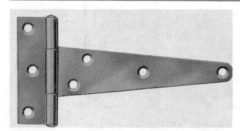

Fig. 13-77. T-Hinge (Courtesy Stanley Tool Co.)

2. *Butt hinges* or "butts," as this hinge is commonly called, are made in many variations. They may have a plain or fancy leaf, fixed or loose pin, a dull or bright surface. Butt hinges are probably the most difficult to apply. See Fig. 13-68. The leaves are fitted into a recess, called a *gain*, which conceals the leaves. Only the knuckle is exposed when the hinge is closed.

3. *Surface hinges* are fixed-pin-butts whose leaves are applied to the exposed surface. These are easy to apply except the table hinge when applied to a molded edge. See Figs. 13-69 through 13-76 and Figs. 13-80 through 13-85.

4. *Swaged hinges* make tighter joints between the separate members.

Fig. 13-78. Butt (L) and Swage (R) Hinges

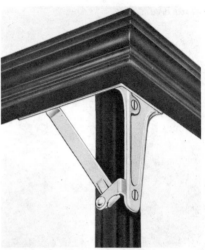

Fig. 13-79. Brass Card Table Hinge (Courtesy Stanley Tool Co.)

Fig. 13-80. Half Surface Butt Hinge

5. A hinge used in heavy or rough work is shown in Fig. 13-77.

6. There are many *special hinges.*

Invisible pivot hinges are fitted into the top and bottom edge of the door and frame. They are easy to apply but are not very strong.

Invisible hinges, also called *soss hinges,* are used on small cabinet construction. They are cast and not very strong. Soss hinges are used on reproductions of Duncan Phyfe, Empire, and Victorian card tables where the top folds down.

Fig. 13-81. Soss Hinge (Brodhead-Garrett)

Sizes

Table 26
Sizes of Hinges

| Name | Size of Leaf | |
	Length	Width
Fixed pin, brass butts	½″ to 2″ by ¼″	½″ to 1⅜″ by ⅛″
Table Hinge	1″ to 2″	2⅝″ to 3¹³⁄₁₆″
Strap hinges	4″ x 1″ 6″ x 1³⁄₃₂″	
T-Hinge	2″ x 2″ 3″ x 2⅜″ ⅝″ x ⅝″ 1″ x ¾″ 1¹¹⁄₁₆ x ¾″	
Invisible or Soss	1¾″ x ½″	
Cabinet Hinges	⅝″ lip offset	

Fig. 13-82. Half Surface Hinge (Courtesy Stanley Tool Co.)

Fig. 13-84. "H" Hinge   Fig. 13-85. "H-L" Hinge
(Courtesy Stanley Tool Co.)

Sales Units

Hinges are usually sold singly, in pairs, or by the dozen.

Maintenance

Lubricate flexible joint.

Additional Reading

Topic 158, "Fitting and Hanging a Door"
Manufacturers Catalogs

Topic *135.* Hanging a Cabinet Door with Fixed-Pin Butts

Classification
Joinery and assembly.

Procedure
The following rule, although flexible, is a good guide for locating fixed-pin butt hinges. When only two hinges are used, the distance from the top of the door to the center of either hinge is 2″ to the foot of door length. This is the same as 1/6 the length of the door. As an example, the center of the upper hinge on a 24″ door would be 4″ down from the top edge. The lower hinge is usually the same distance up from the bottom.

Fitting the Door to the Opening
1. Plane the door to fit the opening. It is good practice to plane the door so it is approximately $\frac{1}{16}$″ smaller than the opening on all four sides. Clearance on all four edges is about the thickness of a nickel. This will allow for both finish and expansion.
2. On the edge of the door opposite the hinged side, plane a slight bevel toward the inside. This is done so that the door will not bind as it swings open and closed.

Laying Out and Cutting Gains on the Door
1. Locate the center of the gain on the edge of the door. From this point, measure up a distance equal to one-half the length of the hinge, and mark with a sharp knife.
2. Place the end of the leaf of the hinge on this line, and mark the opposite end.
3. Set a butt gauge or marking gauge equal to the width of the leaf, not including the knuckle. See Fig. 13-86.
4. Mark the width of the leaf on the edge of the door.
5. With a knife and try square, square the marks indicating the end of the leaf to the line indicating the width of the leaf.

6. Set the second bar of the butt gauge (or a marking gauge) equal to the thickness of the leaf, and mark a line on the face of the door.
7. With a chisel and a mallet, rough out the waste within the marked area. Best results are obtained when the chisel is used with the bevel side down.
8. Pare the gain to the finished depth with either a chisel or router plane.
9. Place the leaf of the butt in the gain. Locate the center of one screwhole and fasten with one screw.
10. Do the same to the other hinge(s).

Laying Out and Cutting Gains on the Case
1. Place the door in the proper position, using a piece of $\frac{1}{16}$″ cardboard under the door and on the edge opposite the butts.
2. With a thin-bladed sharp knife, mark the top and bottom edge of the leaves.
3. From the front of the case, square these lines to a distance equal to the width of the leaves.
4. Connect the ends of these two lines, using a butt gauge or marking gauge.
5. Mark the depth of the gain on the front of the case, as in Step 6 above.
6. Repeat Steps 7, 8, and 9, as above.
7. Do the same on the other gains.
8. Holding the door open with the leaves in the newly cut gains, insert one screw in each leaf.
9. If the door swings properly, insert the remainder of the screws in the leaves. If the door tends to swing open, it may be due to the leaves being set too deep. This can be remedied by padding the gains with thin cardboard to bring the surface of the leaves flush with the surrounding area. If the door binds, remove the leaf and cut the gain deeper.

Standards and Results

1. Leaves should fit tightly in the gains.
2. Leaf surfaces should be flush with the surrounding area.
3. Screwheads should be flush with the surface of the leaf.
4. Door should swing freely and stay in any position.

Safety Considerations

Observe all precautions in the use of hand tools. (See topic on safety.)

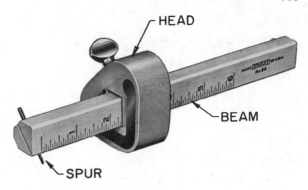

Fig. 13-86. Boxwood Marking Gauge (Courtesy Stanley Tool Co.)

Fig. 13-87. Butt Gauge

Topic *136*. Veneer and Transveneer

Classification

Surface enrichment

Veneering is a process of applying very thin sheets of wood ($\frac{1}{28}''$ to $\frac{1}{20}''$ in thickness) to a core for the purpose of obtaining greater strength and a more attractive surface. Flat, veneered stock consists of (1) a core, ordinarily yellow poplar or particleboard; (2) crossbanding — a layer of inexpensive veneer with the grain running at right angles to each face of the core; and (3) the face veneers, which are glued with the grain running in the same direction as that of the core. Exposed faces are generally figured veneers. These veneers are produced by three methods: slicing, rotary cutting, and sawing. Sawing is not widely used due to the great amount of waste created by the saw cut.

Composition or Description

Classes of Veneer

1. *Face veneers* are sometimes called fancy veneers. These veneers have attractive grain, figure, and color.

2. *Commercial veneers* are usually domestic woods and are not selected for color or grain as this class is usually used for crossbanding and backing.
3. *Veneers for packaging and boxing* are made of domestic woods and are selected for their hardness; defects such as knots are permissible in this class.

Transveneer

Transveneer is a film of lacquer of paper thickness on which color prints are made from photo engravings of actual wood, marble, and leather. This film is covered with a paper coating. Unlike a decalcomania, the *film must be cemented to the surface* to be covered. The paper coating is then soaked with warm water and removed. Transveneers are used on furniture, radio and television cabinets, and automobiles.

Properties

Veneer strips or sheets are flexible, weak, and easily split. When applied to a core with a sheet of crossbanding under the face veneer,

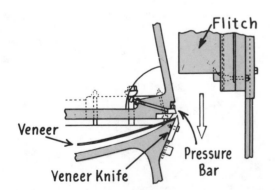

Fig. 14-1. Schematic of Veneer Slicer (Courtesy Simonds Saw & Steel Co.)

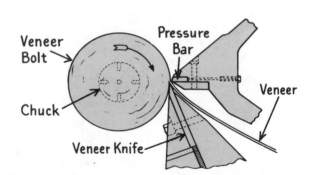

Fig. 14-2. Schematic of Veneer Lathe (Courtesy Simonds Saw & Steel Co.)

the completed piece is stronger than solid wood of the same dimension, has a greater variety, and standardization of grain pattern.

Transveneers should not be applied over open-grained woods.

Uses

1. Veneers are used in the construction of furniture, panels, casework, boats, airplanes, and in the manufacture of plywood.
2. Transveneers are strictly decorative applications.

Market Analysis

Shapes and Sizes

1. Veneers are available in sheets in thicknesses $\frac{1}{28}''$, $\frac{1}{24}''$, and $\frac{1}{20}''$ in widths from 4″ to 24″ and 3′ to 12′ lengths.
2. Transveneers are available in sheets 24″ x 32″ and 32″ x 48″ and $\frac{1}{100}''$ thick. They are sold by the square foot.
3. Tapes

Grades

Select, standard, and common.

Sales Units

Veneer sheets are sold by the square foot. A *flitch* is several sheets of veneer cut from one log and sold as a unit. Matched veneers are available in taped, matched patterns. Tapes are sold by the lineal foot.

Maintenance

Veneers should be stored flat and in a place where they will not dry out.

Fig. 14-3. Veneer Slicer

The workmen are turning over a slice of mahogany veneer which has just been cut. After the log is cut into a *flitch* or rectangular block, it is steamed to saturation. A long knife takes a shearing cut to slice a veneer strip the entire length of the flitch. (Courtesy U. S. Forest Service)

Additional Reading

Di-Noc Company, *Transveneer Plastic Veneer*

The Veneer Association, *Veneers — Their Manufacture* and *Veneers — The Industry and Its Salesmen*

Hardwood Plywood Manufacturers' Association, *Where to Buy Veneer*

Interesting Fact: Furniture found in the tombs of the ancient Egyptians was made by gluing thin woods to the face of solid wood.

Topic *137.* Veneering a Surface

Classification

Decorative banding and facing

Procedure

Preparing the Core

1. Glue up several pieces of stock edge-to-edge for proper size of core.
2. Dress stock reasonably smooth and parallel.
3. Scratch the surfaces of the core with a toothing plane. (This step may be omitted when modern resin glues are used.)

Preparing the Veneer

1. Lay out veneer for direction of grain, matching, and arrangement of figure.
2. With a veneer saw (Fig. 5-20) or knife cut each piece of veneer slightly larger than the core.
3. Select two pieces of heavier stock with smooth faces and straight edges. Place veneer between these pieces with edge to be jointed protruding $\frac{1}{16}''$ or less. Joint this edge with a jack plane. This

step applies to crossbanding as well as to face veneers.

4. Arrange jointed pieces of surface veneer edge-to-edge according to desired pattern and tape (on the good surface) with veneer tape, which is a paper or cloth water soluble gummed tape. Crossbanding is not held together with tape as the glue on the core and the glue on the underside of the face veneer will hold it in place.

Assembly and Gluing

1. Procure two slightly oversize *cauls*. A caul is a wood, zinc, aluminum, or (less frequently) galvanized iron mold conforming in shape to the core, which serves to distribute pressure and heat. Place one caul in the veneer press.
2. Cover the exposed surface of the caul with newspaper to prevent glue from adhering to the caul. Care must be taken

Fig. 14-4. Joining Edges of Veneer

Fig. 14-5. Rotary Cutting of Veneer (Courtesy U. S. Forest Service)

to avoid uneven thickness or overlapping of newspaper, as this will result in an indentation in the face veneer.

3. Place the face veneer on the newspaper in the caul, taped side down. Coat the exposed surface of the veneer with glue.

4. Coat one side of the crossbanding and set in position on top of the face veneer with the grain running at right angles to the grain of the face veneer.

5. Coat the exposed surface of the crossbanding and one surface of the core with glue. Place the core in position on top of the crossbanding with the grain running at right angles to the grain of the crossbanding (in the same direction as the face veneer).

6. Coat the exposed surface of the core with glue. Coat one surface of the second piece of crossbanding with glue and set in position on top of the core with the grain running at right angles to the grain of the core.

7. Coat the exposed surface of the crossbanding with glue. Coat the untaped side of the back face veneer with glue and place on top of the crossbanding with the grain running at right angles to the grain of the crossbanding, and in the same direction as the opposite face veneer.

8. Cover the taped side of the back face veneer with newspaper, being careful to

avoid uneven thickness and overlapping of newspaper.

9. Place the second caul on top of the newspaper. Veneer pins or brads can be driven into the waste area to prevent slippage of the laminations when pressure is applied.

10. Insert 2 x 4's or heavier material under the screws of the press and apply sufficient pressure to insure all glued surfaces have even contact.

Fig. 14-7. Veneer Leaving Drier

The dried sheets are stacked in the form of the original flitch to provide for later matching. (Courtesy Palmer & Parker Lumber Co.)

Fig. 14-8. Veneer Sheet Gluing Machine

The woman at the right feeds dry veneer into the machine which coats them on both sides with a heavy coating of glue. The man takes each glue covered sheet and sandwiches it between two dry sheets of veneer. (Courtesy U. S. Forest Service)

Fig. 14-6. Veneer Entering Drier

After veneer strips are sliced from a flitch, they are passed through a drier and in a matter of minutes are dried by circulating hot air. (Courtesy Palmer & Parker Lumber Co.)

NOTE: For small surfaces, the assembly may be made on a benchtop or other flat surface and a series of handscrews may be used instead of a veneer press. Apply pressure, working from the center toward the edges, being careful to secure evenly distributed pressure.

Standards and Results

1. Veneer joints should be tight and no glue line should be visible.

2. There should be no air pockets under the veneer to cause blisters on the sur-

face. (If a blister appears, the veneer should be slit, glue forced under the surface, and the piece reclamped.)

3. Surface should be smooth and free of depressions.

Safety Considerations

Observe all safety precautions in the use of tools.

Additional Reading

Manufacturers Catalogs

Topic *138.* Inlay and Insets

Classification

Surface decoration

Composition or Description

Inlay may be of plastic, pearl, metal, ivory, bone, or wood. Wood inlay is made up of one or more sheets of veneer cut and glued together to form a pattern. As often as not, the pattern is of different colors and shapes. When this built-up unit is sawed into narrow strips $\frac{1}{20}$ of an inch in thickness, the resultant strips are inlay line. Flat pictorial patterns formed of veneer woods of different colorings with the face glued to a paper or cloth is called an inset.

Properties

Inlays are flexible because of the grain structure of the wood but are brittle and weak because of the method of fabrication. Their function is purely decorative.

Uses

Inlay is used in furniture, panels, and casework.

Market Analysis

Shapes and Sizes

1. Inlay line is available in 12″ and 36″ lengths and in widths from $\frac{1}{16}$″ to $1\frac{1}{4}$″.

2. Insets are available in various shapes and sizes.

Sales Units

Inlay lines are sold by the running foot or yard; insets by the unit.

Table 27
Woods Used for Inlay and Their Colors

Amaranth	Purple
Avodire	Light straw
Benin	Golden brown
Boxwood	Lemon yellow
Bubinga	Reddish-brown
Coco Bolo	Brown with red streaks
Dao	Light brown with dark streaks
Ebony	Black
Holly	White
Koa	Brown
Maple	White-tan
Narra	Brown
Prima Vera	Yellowish-white
Rosewood	Brick red, deep purple to black
Satinwood	Light yellow
Sycamore	Cream to light tan
Teak	Tan
Tulip	Red and yellow
Vermillion	Bright red
Walnut	Chocolate brown
Zebra	Tan with dark brown stripes

Maintenance

Inlay should be stored in a dry place.

Interesting Fact: American holly, widely used in inlay, is an evergreen with broad elliptic, oval leaves. The wood is durable, white, and hard, but rather weak and brittle.

Topic *139*. Applying Inlay and Insets

Classification

Applying decorative units

Procedure — Lines or Borders

Cutting the Gains (Machine process)

1. Locate accurately the position of the inlay line.
2. If the line runs parallel to an edge or end, cut the gain with an electric router if one is available.
3. Select a cutter with a diameter equal to the width of the inlay. The inlay should be inserted with a press fit.
4. Set the cutter so that it will cut a gain slightly less in depth than the thickness of the inlay. This is so that the inlay may be sanded even with the surrounding surface after it is inserted and glued.
5. Set the fence so that the gain will be cut at the desired distance from the edge of the stock. Edge must be previously finished.
6. Make a trial run on a scrap piece of stock.
7. Cut the gain. Care must be taken not to go beyond the line at the end of each cut.
8. Corners and ends will need to be cut square. Use a marking gauge, square, and knife to lay out the cut. Remove the waste material with router plane or a chisel.
9. Fit the line into the gains making sure each section is of proper length and the joints are tight. (This is called *dry run*.)
10. If the inlay line runs into a corner, the ends of each piece must be mitered. This may be done with either a knife or chisel.
11. Remove the pieces and apply a thin coating of glue to the bottom and sides of the gain.

12. Inlay may be pressed into the gains by using the bell face of a claw hammer and pressing with a rubbing motion. Inlay may be held in place with veneer tape until the glue sets. This is done only when the inlay springs out of the gain.
13. If several pieces are to be inlaid to form a design, glue in one piece at a time.

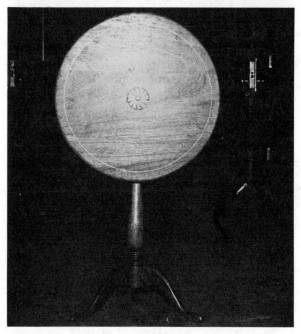

Fig. 14-9. Table Tops with Inlay Line and Insert

Cutting Gains (Hand process)

1. If an electric router is not available, the gain can be laid out with a mortise gauge or two marking gauges. Set one spur to mark one side of the gain and the other spur to mark the opposite side. Cut the lines with a sharp, thin knife blade. Then make a V cut on the waste side of each line. Remove the waste material with either a router plane or a chisel. Proceed as in steps 7-13 of *Machine process*.
2. If the line does not run parallel to an edge or end, the gain may be laid out with a metal template, French curve, or compass. Use a sharp, hard pencil to make the line.
3. Remove stock as described in step 1 to a depth slightly less than the thickness of the line. This is so the inlay may be sanded even with the surrounding surface after it is inserted and glued.

Applying Insets or Inlays

1. Some inlays are set into a piece of veneer. This is done to protect the edges in handling. They may be separated with a sharp knife.
2. The face side of the inlay is always covered with a cloth or paper tape.
3. File a slight taper away from the face side on all edges. Use a mill file.

4. Locate the position of the inlay and trace around it with a sharp, hard pencil.
5. With a sharp knife cut on the inside of the line, straight into the surface, then make the V cut.
6. Remove the waste within the area marked by the knife lines with either a router plane or a chisel.
7. The depth of the gain should be slightly less than the thickness of the inlay. This is to allow for later sanding. Proceed as in steps 7-13. Inlay may be held in place until the glue has set by placing a block over it and weighting it down or by clamping it.

Standards and Results

1. All joints should be tight.
2. Inlay should be slightly above the surface for sanding.
3. Inlay should be tightly glued into the gain.
4. Lines should not be wavy or irregular but positioned as intended.
5. No glue line should show.
6. Shoulders of gains should not be chipped.

Safety Considerations

Observe all precautions in the use of hand tools and electric router.

Additional Reading

Topic 79, "Using a Portable Hand Router"

Topic *140.* Plastic Laminates

Classification

Plastic covering material

Composition or Description

The base material is cellulose, cotton, nylon, or glass fabric. This base material is covered with a resin binder, and after being subjected to heat and pressure forms a hard, strong panel. Several brands are available in a variety of patterns and colors.

Properties

Plastic laminates are tough and strong but quite brittle. Because of these properties they resist most abrasive wear, denting, and cracking. Strong, yet light in weight, plastic laminates may be sawed, drilled, routed, and the edges may be planed; but because of their brittleness, care must be taken to prevent chipping. Normally, they may be bent to fit curved surfaces as small as a radius of 8"; however, with heat and the proper equipment, they can be bent to a radius under 1". Plastic laminates are non-conductors of electricity; consequently they are good insulators. They resist heat, alcohol, water, and fruit acids.

Uses

Plastic laminates are commonly used in the home for tops of kitchen counters, kitchen table tops, coffee table tops, and bar tops. They are also commonly used in restaurants as counter and table tops. Because of their insulating properties they are also used in electrical work.

Market Analysis

Shapes

Sheets, rods, tubes, and molded shapes.

Sizes

Available in sheets .010 to 6" thick but usually less than $\frac{1}{16}$" thick. Second quality pieces may be purchased in smaller random lengths and widths. Sheets are available in the following sizes:

24" wide x 6', 8' long
30" wide x 6', 8', 10', 12' long
36" wide x 6', 8', 10', 12' long
48" wide x 8', 10' long
60" wide x 12' long

Maintenance

1. Plastic laminates are usually cleaned with a damp rag, but may be cleaned with any household soap or detergent.
2. Store in a horizontal position to prevent buckling, curling, and chipped surfaces.
3. Surfaces covered with plastic laminates may be waxed periodically to preserve their luster and to minimize scratching.

Additional Reading

Manufacturers Catalogs

347

Topic *141.* Contact Cement

Classification

Adhesive

Composition or Description

Contact cement is a synthetic resin produced in either liquid or paste form. The most common type of contact cement is referred to as clear, but is slightly amber in color.

Properties

When two surfaces coated with contact cement (and allowed to dry) are placed in contact the bond is immediate and permanent, and it is practically impossible to move or separate the two parts. Contact cement will adhere to most surfaces, but once it has dried it will not adhere to another surface not so coated. Because of this property it is possible to make a perfect alignment of two coated and dried surfaces by inserting a sheet of paper between them. The paper is withdrawn carefully and the surfaces bond on contact. It is recommended that contact cement not be used at temperatures below 70° F. *Because of the toxic fumes, contact cement should be used in a well-ventilated room.*

Uses

Contact cement is used to adhere any combination of wood, glass, leather, paper, cloth, rubber, fiberglass, metal, or plastic laminates. It is most commonly used to adhere plastic laminates to plywood, but is also used widely to adhere aluminum or plywood panels to walls.

Market Analysis

Shapes

Liquid or paste.

Sizes

Most commonly available in pints and quarts, but also available in gallons.

Maintenance

Do not store or use in extreme heat or cold.

Additional Reading

Manufacturers Catalogs

Topic *142.* Bending Wood to a Form

Classification

Shaping

Procedure

Wood may be bent to a shape by the use of three methods: plasticizing by steaming, laminating, or (where strength is not a factor) by relief kerf cutting. In all cases it is important that straight, clear grain be used. The grain is reformed to follow a curve which makes a stronger, clean-surface piece than one that has been cut to shape. For parts requiring severe bendings, stock cut so that the annual rings are flatwise bends with less breakage than if the grain is edgewise to the bending form. Holes or mortises should not be cut prior to bending and the end grain of stock which is shaped or cut to length should be painted or coated to prevent checking.

Steaming Method

1. When wood is bent the fibers within the piece must undergo change. Those on the inside of the curve are made shorter or compressed and the fibers on the

outer radius are stretched. In order to accomplish this change, the fibers within the board must be made pliable. This is done by steaming.

2. Stock to be bent should be dried to no less than 12% to 15% moisture content.

3. Surface finish all stock slightly larger than final size to allow for shrinkage.

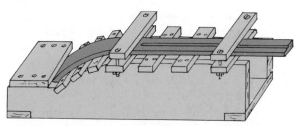

Fig. 15-1. Steaming Wood
This workman is removing stock which has been processed in a steam oven preliminary to bending. (Courtesy Heywood-Wakefield Co.)

Fig. 15-2. Bending a Water Ski

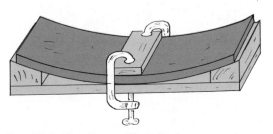

Fig. 15-3. Bending a Chair Back

4. Prepare the steaming equipment. Steaming action is more effective when wood is not immersed in water. Therefore some method of supporting wood above the water level should be devised.

5. The volume of water should be great enough to maintain a constant supply of steam during the complete process.

6. Steaming time should be judged by the thickness of stock; 1 hour for each 1″ thickness is a good rule. Steaming lessens the strength of wood and excessive heat should be avoided.

7. Tanks, boilers, and pipes may be rigged up as chambers in which to hold the wood for steaming. Care should be

Fig. 15-4. Hydraulic Bending Press Using Platen
Steamed stock (or unsteamed wood of *exactly* the the right moisture content) is placed between cauls or metal forms, which are hollow on the inside like a radiator. Tons of pressure are hydraulically applied and the heated cauls cause the moisture in the stock to turn to steam, thus the stock is self-steamed. No separate drying is necessary after the bent wood is removed from the press as the heat sets the bends and reduces (dries) the moisture content during the hour it is between the cauls. (Courtesy Heywood-Wakefield Co.)

Fig. 15-5. Bending Press Closed (Courtesy Heywood-Wakefield Co.)

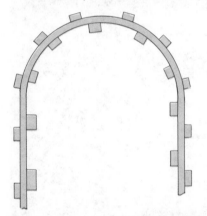

Fig. 15-6. Laminating Form with Glue Blocks

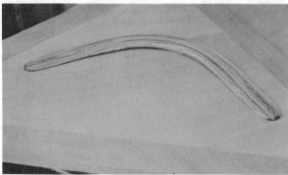

Fig. 15-7. Laminated Boomerang

taken that the water condensed from the steam does not touch the wood.

8. When only a portion of a piece of stock needs to be plasticized and bent, boiling water may be more convenient than steaming. The effectiveness of boiling or near boiling water is approximately equivalent to steaming. Steaming is the preferred method, since boiling is apt to cause saturation of the cells, which makes bending more difficult. It may also cause discoloration of the stock.

9. As soon as the wood is pliable it is bent to shape. The forming die should be slightly smaller in radius than the finished bend to allow for spring-back.

10. The method of securing the piece in the form should be adequate to hold the piece in place and to allow air to circulate for efficient drying.

11. After bending, wood must remain in the forms until it is sufficiently dry to retain its shape. This varies from a fractional part of an hour under industrial conditions to a week or so in a school shop.

12. There are four basic industrial types of bending machines used in furniture manufacture.

   a. The simplest form of machine bending or forming is done on the platen press by use of heat. It is used to make such parts as flat curved chair backs. The pieces are bent, then dried in the press in short periods of time by use of heat. See Figs. 15-4 and 15-5.

   b. The ram type bending machine has hinged arms which permit the workpiece to be wrapped around a mandrel as it bends to make a horseshoe-like bend. The shaped parts are clamped in retainer pans to restrain the outer surface and prevent stretching while the inside radius compresses the wood fibers.

   c. The third type is called a pretzel bend. This is done on small diameter, round pieces bent over, around, and under the form to one continuous leg shape. Both ends must be bent into the form at approximately the same rate to obtain symmetrical curves and avoid breaking. Metal restraining straps with clamps on each end retain end pressure and wrap with the workpiece on the outside of each radius to secure inside compression and avoid outside stretching which may cause breakage. Parts must remain clamped in the bending form with restraining straps until the wood is dry. This usually takes 24 hours.

    d. The fourth type of bending is made with a pusher mechanism. With one end restrained, the workpiece is pushed around the form on a turntable similar to metal bending, except the parts must be left in the form until they dry to 6 to 8% M.C., Figs. 15-8 and 15-9.

13. If a piece is bent and dried in the form, then placed in extremely dry air which further dries out the moisture content of the wood, the bend will increase. If the piece picks up moisture, it will tend to slightly straighten back to its original shape. If a part fractures on the outside of the bend, it is too dry. If it compresses too much and wrinkles on the inside, it has been steamed too much.

Laminating Method

1. Thin strips may be built up and glued with the grain running parallel to the bend; then clamped in a form to dry.

    When larger surfaces, such as seat forms or chair backs are to be laminated, it is sometimes necessary to strengthen the piece by crossing the grain pattern in alternating layers, thus requiring an odd number of sheets.

2. Glue must be spread evenly between each layer of lamination and clamped into the form in such a manner that the entire piece will be of even thickness and strength.

3. If a sharp radius is desired or if the strips to be laminated are too thick to bend dry, steam bending is necessary. The bent pieces are then laminated.

4. Prepare the wood or metal form to a radius slightly less than the required curve, to allow for spring-back.

5. Formed pieces are clamped together by mechanical, hydraulic, or air pressure. One type of form is composed of two pre-shaped sections which fit together. Another type of form has an under die of desired shape and an outer flexible band which follows the bend and equalizes the pressure along the curve thus preventing splintering.

Fig. 15-8. Bending with Steel Band and Dogs
The flexible steel band draws the steamed wood into shape around the steel ring form and the clamps are driven into position to hold the wood to shape until it has dried and set. (Courtesy Heywood-Wakefield Co.)

Fig. 15-9. Bending with Steel Band and Dogs

6. Apply glue to the surfaces to be joined and place in position in the forming jig. Use enough clamps to provide evenly distributed pressure.

7. Allow to stand under pressure until the glue has set.

Saw Kerf Method

Where the ends are fixed, only the face of the bent piece is to show, and strength is not a factor, a bend may be made by making saw kerfs in the back side of the piece.

1. Measure the radius of the bend.

2. Lay out this length on the board to be bent, starting the measurement at the point at which the curve is to begin.

3. At point A in Fig. 15-10, make a saw cut part way through the board. Try a depth of ¾ the thickness of the stock. The depth may vary according to the sharpness of the bend.

4. Lay the board on a flat surface with the kerf side up. Raise one end of the board, closing the saw kerf, and measure the distance "B." Divide this distance "B" into the radius of the bend to find the number of saw kerfs which need to be cut for a bend of 90°.

5. A stop should be used to make certain that all saw kerfs are the same depth and width if a hand saw is used.

6. A miter box with a depth gauge may be used for a fine kerf or a circular saw for a larger kerf.

7. For maximum strength, saw cuts should be closed up on the inside surface after bending. A heavy coating of glue applied in the saw kerfs before bending will help to hold a rigid, stronger bend.

Standards and Results

1. Upon removal from the form, stock should be of desired curvature and dimension and free of twist.

2. There should be no surface splinters, cracks, or flat spots.

3. All laminations should be securely joined.

4. All saw kerfs should be of proper width and depth.

5. There should be a minimum loss of strength at the bend.

Safety Considerations

1. Care should be taken in the proper venting of the steaming device and in its use.

2. Use exceptional caution in the use and handling of boiling water and live steam.

3. Care should be taken when making sharp bends to avoid stock slipping out of form or snapping.

4. Observe usual cautions in clamping.

5. Use asbestos or leather gloves in handling steaming equipment and steamed stock during the steaming process.

6. See topic on safety.

Additional Reading

Department of Agriculture (Forest Products Laboratory), *Bending Solid Wood to Form*, and *Some Methods of Gluing Light Laminated or Plywood Curved Shapes from Veneer*

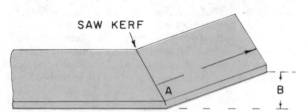

Fig. 15-10. Bending with Single Saw Kerf

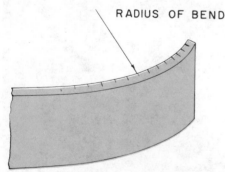

Fig. 15-11. Bending with Multiple Saw Kerf

Topic *143*. Structures

Wood has a long history as a structural material. It has long served as the basic framework or skeleton for buildings, scaffolding, bridges, trestles, piers, docks, boats, planes, wagons, freight cars, and other vehicles and conveyances. Wood frame construction is used in concrete-form making, in crating, and

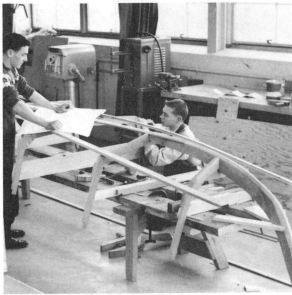

Fig. 16-1. Building a Boat
These boys are building up the skeletal structure of a boat. Note the keelson (long, backbone-like piece) and the frames.

Fig. 16-2. Building a Model House

Fig. 16-3. Scale Models of Houses — Scale 1″ = 1′

Fig. 16-4. Covered Wooden Bridge

This reproduction, to scale, of an old New England bridge is pinned together with pegs, called *trunnels*.

Fig. 16-5. Scale Model of Bridge Foundation

in the making of stage scenery. A wood framework is basically an open structure employing scientifically tested principles of bracing and trussing.

In the construction of buildings there are standard methods of framing such as balloon, modern braced, and platform. There are also standard methods of framing boats, planes, gliders, and other vehicles. In addition to the conventional practices, there are building codes governing the methods to be used. The development of laminated arches, and the use of post and beam construction has increased the popularity of wood in building construction.

In the transportation field, the use of wood structures has lessened considerably due to the increased use of light, strong metals.

Wood structures include more than the skeletal framework. Doors, windows, floors, sheathing, shingling, planking, and siding are also related aspects of the comprehensive field of wood structures.

Principles of carpentry are basic to structural woodworking in any of the respective fields.

House Design

Wood framing is an old tradition that is becoming stronger with the passing years. Of every ten houses built today eight of them are framed with wood. Although basic principles and framing members have remained the same, many refinements in framing have taken place, and new and radically different

house-framing techniques already have been developed. The high strength of wood in proportion to its weight, plus its flexibility and beauty, assures its continued popularity in the construction of buildings.

Though house styles appear to change slowly, outwardly the wood frame house of today bears little resemblance to its counterpart of the previous century. The modern house is lighter, more graceful, more striking in appearance — as well as more functional. The influence of American designers like Frank Lloyd Wright and the demonstrated effectiveness of the graceful Japanese style house are having a marked effect on modern American house design.

Quality framing lumber is being used with a view toward letting the structure itself provide the decoration. Ceiling joists and studding are being left exposed. Some rooms are partitioned simply with a curtain of exposed finished studs decorated in various ways. Trussed rafter construction is becoming widely used because it eliminates the need for load-bearing walls. Post and beam construction carries the structural load on a few supports. Besides providing greater height it permits more flexible planning of room layout and easy future expansion. Interior walls can be used as attractive storage space rather than for roof support. On the exterior, studs are exposed as frames for picture windows. Wide overhangs make the house look larger and more handsome. They keep summer sun out and let winter sun in.

Glued wood arches and beams of much greater lengths than standard solid members are appearing with increased frequency. In both houses and larger structures the use of laminated lumber is becoming more widespread. Their use permits post-free interior areas of heretofore undreamed of dimensions and unusual attractiveness.

New lumber products will promote the inclusion of large panels for walls, floor sections, and roofing. The never-ending research in wood and wood products will further the use of plywood of new and different forms and sizes. Plastic laminated plywood is widely used in buildings.

A-Frame House

A development in house construction, which is enjoying increased popularity, is known as an *A-Frame* house. Shown in Fig. 16-6, it is

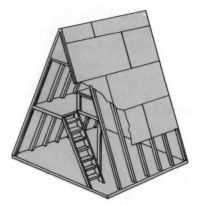

Fig. 16-6. A-Frame House

designed to incorporate the roof and wall structure in one unit. This type of construction is ideal for use in areas which have heavy snowfall, as the steep pitch sheds the snow. Because it is essentially a braced triangle, it is a very rigid and strong structural unit. It has the disadvantage of decreased headroom close to the interior walls. Because it is relatively taller than other building designs, it may offer greater resistance to wind.

Topic *144.* The Carpenter

Carpentry is that branch of the woodworking industry which is concerned with the building of structures. Structures include the forms into which concrete is poured for foundations, bridges, and buildings; scaffolds and platforms; and most commonly, the building of frame houses. Form making is a special skill and many carpenters do only this type of construction. Carpenters lay the wood sills, joists, and floors; erect studs and rafters; apply sheathing, siding, and roof boards. All the finish woodwork (doors, window trim, stairs, finish floors, moldings, and cabinet work) is carpentry. Repairs and alterations are important aspects of carpentry.

A qualified carpenter must be skilled in the use of a wide variety of hand tools and portable machines. He must know the characteristics of many different kinds of building materials, he must be familiar with the basic systems of frame construction, he must know and use the tools and practices for layout, he must know enough about structural design to recognize the purpose and use of each member, he must be able to read plans and blueprints, and he must be able to estimate the amount and cost of materials, and the time necessary to complete a job.

The carpenter's work is often dependent upon weather conditions and progress of construction. Much of his work is done in conjunction with other tradesmen such as masons, plasterers, plumbers, electricians, etc.; as a consequence he should have a general knowledge of the work they will be doing.

Carpenter's helpers are those handymen who do some of the routine jobs, assist the carpenter with heavy or long pieces, or carry out specific tasks under close supervision.

A knowledge of the general principles of carpentry may be acquired and an interest awakened in industrial arts classes. Specialized training may be had in trade and vocational courses, and many carpenters have had on-the-job training only. Since there is such a multiplicity of skills needed to be successful, carpenters are always in demand and their wage scale compares favorably with that of other skilled workers.

Topic *145*. Leveling Tools

(PLUMB AND LEVEL, LINE LEVEL, PLUMB BOB, LEVEL SIGHTS, PLASTIC HOSE)

Classification

Layout or testing devices for checking horizontal or perpendicular surfaces

Application

Principle of Operation

1. The level consists of a crowned glass tube containing a spirit liquid in which is encased an air bubble. The glass is set with the crown up which causes the bubble to seek the highest point on center. This position is marked by etched lines in the glass.

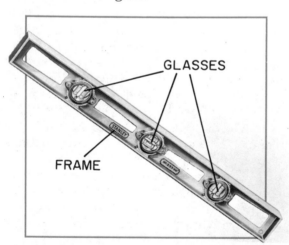

Fig. 16-7. Aluminum Level (Courtesy Stanley Tool Co.)

2. A plumb bob suspended on a string from a fixed position will locate a point directly below the point of suspension.

Kinds and Uses

Levels are commonly named according to their use. (See Market Analysis.)
1. A level is used in laying out foundations, calculating grades, and setting framing members to the horizontal and vertical. Some levels have a glass set to test for 45° angles. (See Fig. 16-8.)
2. A plumb bob is used in determining a vertical position, Fig. 16-11.

Principal Parts and Function of Each

1. *Glasses* are set in the frame. When the bubble in the respective glass is centered between the marks, the piece be-

Fig. 16-8. Torpedo Level (Courtesy Stanley Tool Co.)

Fig. 16-9. Line Level (Courtesy Stanley Tool Co.)

ing tested is either plumb (vertical) or level (horizontal).

Glasses are available in two types: ground and proved. *Ground glasses* are made of glass tubing internally ground to a barrel shape so that the high point is in the center. The bubble settles slowly and is very accurate. Ground glasses are used in precision tools such as machinist's levels and surveyor's transits. *Proved glasses* are made of glass tubing bent slightly so that the high point is exactly in the middle. The bubble settles quickly and with sufficient accuracy for carpentry work.

2. The *liquid* in the level is alcohol.
3. The *frame*, which forms a straightedge to aid in testing a surface, is made of cast iron, aluminum, cherry, or mahogany, well seasoned to insure against warping.
4. The *plumb bob* is made of machined brass or steel, and is designed so that the point will hang directly below the point of suspension.

Maintenance

Levels should be checked periodically for accuracy. The better levels have an adjustment for position of bubble. Broken glass may be replaced.

Market Analysis

Sizes

Levels are made in various sizes and shapes according to their use by craftsmen.

1. Carpenter's levels are from 12″ to 30″ long, Fig. 16-7.
2. Mason's levels are 48″ long.
3. Torpedo levels, which have tapered oval sides and are used by inspectors and mechanics, are 9″ long, Fig. 16-8.
4. Machinist's levels, made from cast iron, are from 6″ to 24″ long.

Fig. 16-10. Pocket Level (Courtesy Stanley Tool Co.)

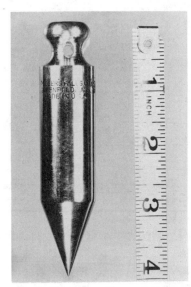

Fig. 16-11. Plumb Bob (Courtesy Millers Falls Co.)

5. Line levels, round or hexagonal in shape, are made from plastic, aluminum, or bronze and are 3¼″ long, Fig. 16-9.
6. Pocket levels in brass are 2″ to 3½″ long, Fig. 16-10.
7. A substitute for a line level or transit is a plastic, transparent hose or a hose with glass tubes fitted to both ends. Liquid filling the hose will determine a level position at each end.

Attachments

Level sights are used in conjunction with a level to sight a line or level a wall.

Additional Reading

Manufacturers Catalogs

Topic 146. Laying Out Batter Boards

Four frames, called *batter boards,* are erected outside of the corners of the proposed foundation. Lines are stretched from adjacent sets of batter boards, indicating position of footings and/or foundation. From these intersecting lines a plumb bob may be dropped to determine the exact corners of the foundation and for plumbing the wall. This method is most commonly used with stone or block foundations.

The large triangle on the ground in Fig. 16-15 is made by carpenters to check the squareness of the corners. The sides of the triangle are 6', 8', and 10' respectively. This is commonly called the 6-8-10 method of layout.

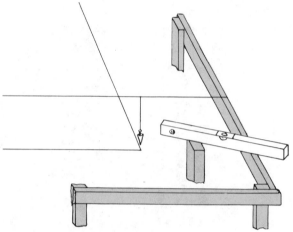

Fig. 16-12. Leveling Batter Boards

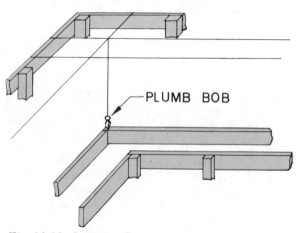

Fig. 16-13. Locating Corners

Fig. 16-14. Laying Out the Foundation

Fig. 16-15. Checking Squareness of Corners

Topic *147.* House Framing

Builders are well aware of the need for stability in any building they erect. A completed building itself represents considerable weight, i.e. many tons. Furniture and equipment add a significant weight. Snow loads increase the weight even more. *Unless proper engineering procedures are followed, the building weight will cause movement of the soil.* Uneven moving will cause uneven settling, which causes distortion of framing affecting walls, windows, doors, plaster, etc. Nature has demonstrated to man that large animals like an elephant have broad feet to provide stability. Adopting this principle, man erects *foundations* for buildings on a broad base called *footings.* He also recognizes the quality of the soil and its reaction to composition.

Factors Determining the Size of Foundation Wall, and Footings

There are two types of loads in building construction that must be adequately supported by the foundation wall and footings; namely, the dead and the live loads.

1. The *dead load* is the weight of the material which forms the structural walls and roof.
2. The *live load* is the weight of the furniture and moveable items in the building, plus the wind and snow loads on the exterior.

The sum total of these weights must be supported by the footings. *Footing size will also be governed by the bearing quality of the soil.* Table 28 indicates the safe loading of soil types.

Table 28
Safe Loading of Soil Types

Type of Soil	Safe Load in Lbs./Sq. Ft.
Ledge rock	200,000
Hard pan and compact gravel	20,000
Compact sand and gravel	12,000
Firm sand and clay	8,000
Loose gravel	8,000
Coarse sand	6,000
Fine sand	4,000
Soft clay and loam	2,000

Adapted from *Architectural Graphic Standards*

The *actual load* on a floor may be calculated by the weight of the material, and the weight of the intended live load. However, it is common practice to use the following weights for small house construction:

Lbs./Sq. Ft.	Type of Load
10	dead load of floor
20	dead load of floor and plastered ceiling
20	live load attic storage
30	live load sleeping area
40	live load living area
20	dead load partition wall

Roof loads will vary according to climatic conditions of snow and wind loads.

Area	Lbs./Sq. Ft. Snow and Wind Load
Northern States	40
Central States	30
Southern States	20

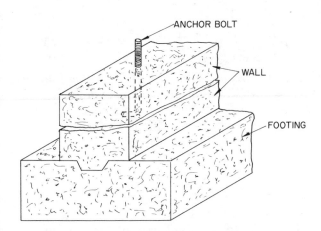

Fig. 16-16. Footing, Wall and Anchor Bolt

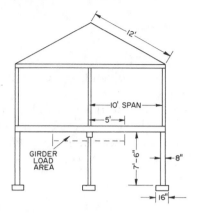

Fig. 16-16A. Building Structure

Fig. 16-16B. Forms for Reinforced Concrete

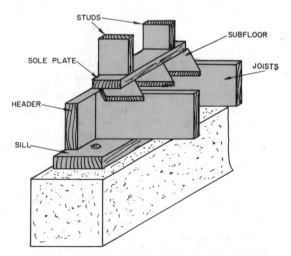

Fig. 16-17. Box Sill Used in Platform Construction

The dead weight of a roof covered with asphalt shingles is 10 lbs./sq. ft., but this is affected by the slope of the roof. Slopes under a pitch of 3″ in 12″ have 20 lb. dead load with asphalt shingles. Roofs with a slope greater than 3/12 are figured with a load of 15 lbs./ sq. ft. Local building codes should be referred to before calculating weight loads.

The dead weight of the wall includes studs, sheathing, plaster, etc., and is figured as 20 lbs./sq. ft.

Material	Lbs./Cubic Ft.
Concrete	150
Concrete blocks	80
Brick	120

Figuring the load for a single floor building on one lineal foot of footing (Fig. 16-16A) is as follows:

			lbs./ft.
Roof live load	40 lbs.	Northern × 12 =	660
Roof dead load	15 lbs.		
Attic live load	20 lbs.	× 5 (½ span) =	200
Attic floor dead load	20 lbs.		
First floor live load	40 lbs.	× 5 =	400
First floor dead load	20 lbs.		
Partition	20 lbs.		

Concrete wall $150 \times 7.5 \times 8/12$ = $\underline{750}$

Total weight on footing per foot $\overline{2010}$

Weight of footing $150 \times \dfrac{16}{12} \times \dfrac{8}{12}$ = $\underline{133}$

$\overline{2143}$

Total weight of footing per sq. ft. bearing on soil $2143 \times \dfrac{12}{16} = 1607$

Referring to Table 28 of *Safe Loading of Soil Types*, it is found that this weight is well under any load bearing type. Therefore, a wall of 8″ concrete with a footing 8″ deep and 16″ wide will be adequate.

Concrete Forms

It is common building practice today to rent forms for footings and/or foundations or to hire a contractor who does nothing but this type of work. These forms are usually made of a special exterior plywood, which is either plastic-coated or treated with oil to prevent the wood from absorbing water from the concrete. The forms are reusable. The plywood panels are available in the following sizes: 2′ x 4′, 4′ x 4′, 3′ x 8′, 2′ x 8′ and 4′ x 8′. These sizes fit the various lengths and heights of foundations and are made in ½″ and ⅝″ thickness. These panels are braced with 2 x 4's to make the form.

Footings (the base for foundation walls) are poured first, often with a keyway on the top to provide a better joint with the foundation walls. Generally, the footing should be as thick as the wall and at least twice as wide. (See Fig. 16-16.)

Spacer blocks are used throughout foundation forms to give proper thickness to the foundation. Wire or draw bolts are used to draw the two sides of the forms tightly against the spacer blocks. Openings for doors and windows and cavities for supporting ends of the girt or carrying timber must be provided for in the forms by blocking in.

Regardless of the type of form (footing, foundation, stairs, etc.), it should be firmly braced to offset the extreme pressure exerted by the weight of the concrete. The assembled form should be braced at the top, bottom, and corners.

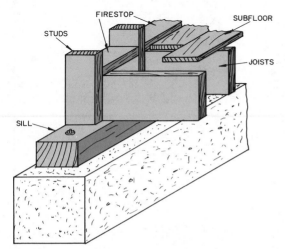

Fig. 16-20. Solid Sill Used in Balloon Frame Construction

Anchor Bolts

The frame structure should be fastened securely to the foundation and made into one solid unit. This is accomplished by "anchoring" the sill (to which the framing members are fastened) to the foundation.

Anchor bolts are set into the concrete foundation wall before it is hard. See Fig. 16-16. Forms must not be removed until the concrete sets; however, it is preferable to keep them on for three or four days. In curing, concrete increases in strength for a period of 28 days (provided it is kept damp) and increases in hardness for 7 years.

Sills
Box Sill

Used in platform construction, the box sill is anchored to the top of foundation wall. It is made up of a 2″ x 8″ sill and 2″ x 8″ header. The ends of the floor joists rest on the sill and are fastened in place by nailing through the header. The subflooring is laid on the upper edge of the floor joists. The sole plate is laid on top of the subflooring, and the lower ends of the studs rest on the sole plate. This is the most common type of construction for single-story buildings, because the walls can be assembled on the subfloor and then raised into position. See Figs. 16-17 and 16-18.

Solid Sill

Used in balloon frame construction, the solid sill is a 6″ x 8″ timber, anchored to the top of the foundation wall. The ends of the floor joists and the ends of the studs rest on the sill. A firestop of 2″ x 4″ material is fastened between the studs on top of the floor joists; this retards the spread of fire from one floor to another, by eliminating the "flue" or chimney effect which would otherwise be present between studs. The subfloor is laid on the top edge of the floor joists. See Figs. 16-19 and 16-20.

Girders and Joists
Factors in Determining the Size of Girders

Girders are the main structural members upon which the joists rest at the center.

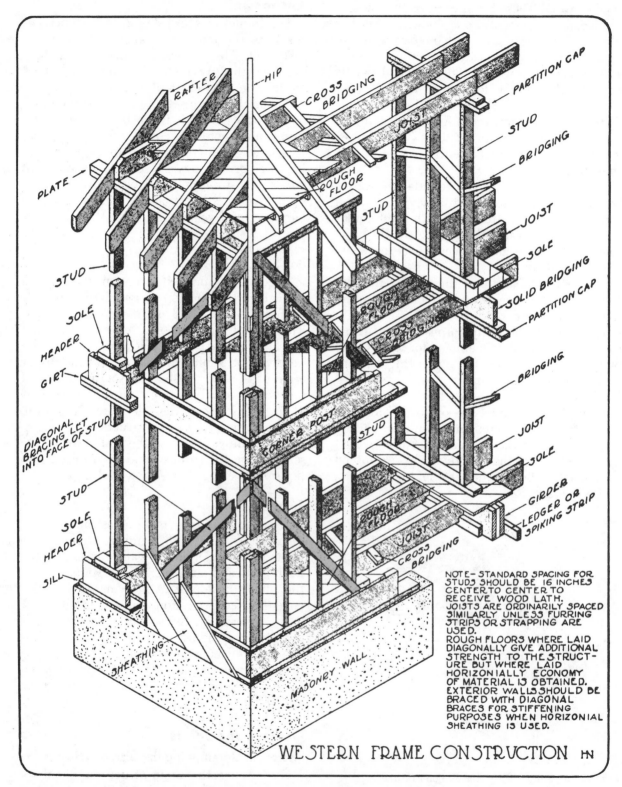

NOTE— STANDARD SPACING FOR STUDS SHOULD BE 16 INCHES CENTER TO CENTER TO RECEIVE WOOD LATH. JOISTS ARE ORDINARILY SPACED SIMILARLY UNLESS FURRING STRIPS OR STRAPPING ARE USED.
ROUGH FLOORS WHERE LAID DIAGONALLY GIVE ADDITIONAL STRENGTH TO THE STRUCTURE BUT WHERE LAID HORIZONIALLY ECONOMY OF MATERIAL IS OBTAINED. EXTERIOR WALLS SHOULD BE BRACED WITH DIAGONAL BRACES FOR STIFFENING PURPOSES WHEN HORIZONIAL SHEATHING IS USED.

WESTERN FRAME CONSTRUCTION

Fig. 16-18. Western Frame Construction (Courtesy National Lumber Mfr's. Assn.)

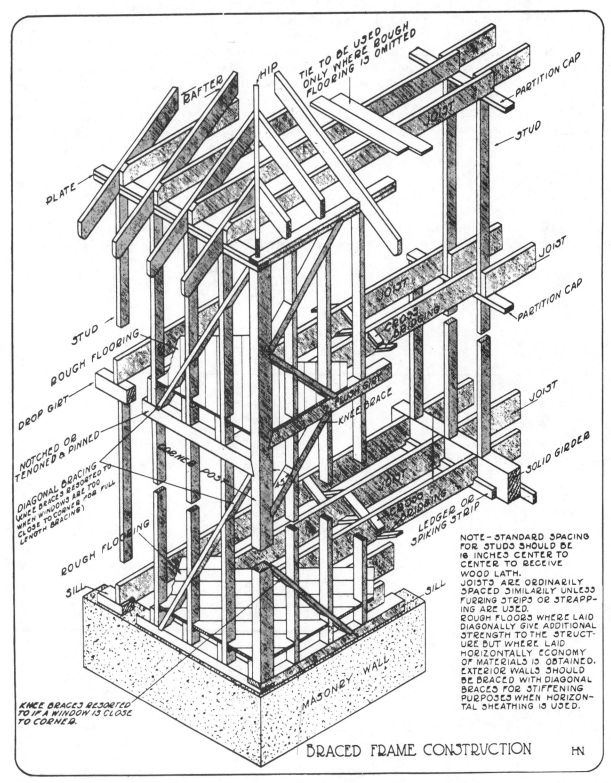

Fig. 16-19.   Braced Frame Construction (Courtesy National Lumber Mfr's. Assn.)

Girders are required when the span of the building is too great a distance for the joists to go from sill to sill. Girders may be of solid wood or built up by nailing or bolting several 2″-thick members together to form a single unit. Built-up girders have less bearing strength due to the smaller size of dressed material. A solid 6″ x 8″ would measure 5½″ x 7¼″ while a built-up girder of three 2″ x 8″ would measure 4½″ x 7¼″ (new structural lumber sizes). Built-up girders should be joined only over bearing posts.

The size of the girder will depend on the weight to be supported and the distance the girder must span. The greater the span, the heavier the girder must be. It is common practice to use steel columns (steel pipe filled with concrete) to bear weight at even intervals to decrease the length spanned and to decrease the size of the girder. Girders are supported at intervals so that the deflection caused by the weight of the building will not be greater than $\frac{1}{360}$ of the length of the span. This is to insure against cracking of plaster and sagging floors. By the use of shorter spans, the girder size may be decreased, thus giving more head room in the basement.

There are tables that give the strength of the various woods from which the girders are made. These may be expressed in modules of elasticity or the fiber stress in pounds per square inch working limits. See Table 29.

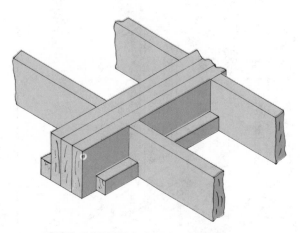

JOIST NOTCHED OVER LEDGER STRIP

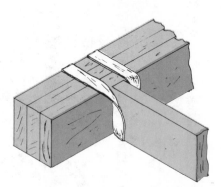

JOIST IN IRON STIRRUP

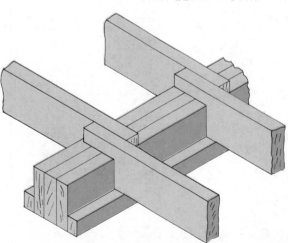

OVERLAPPING JOIST NOTCHED OVER GIRDER

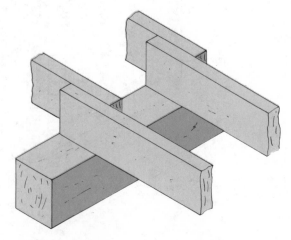

JOIST BEARING ON GIRDER

Fig. 16-21. Methods of Joining Floor Joists to Girders

Table 29

Fiber Stress of Woods for Girders

Wood	Lbs./Sq. In. Fiber Strength
Eastern Hemlock #1 common	1100
Western Hemlock #1 common	1450
Douglas Fir common structural	1450
Southern Pine #1 common	1450
Eastern Spruce standard structural	1200

To determine the size of the girder, assume that the girder is 30' long. The total area supported by the girder will be one-half the floor load each side of the girder multiplied by the length of the span between columns plus the weight of the attic floor and partition wall. See Fig. 16-16A.

To find the total floor load:

Attic floor live load	20 lbs.	$\times$ 10 ft. =	400
Attic floor dead load	20 lbs.		
Partition wall	20 lbs.	=	20
First floor live load	40 lbs.	$\times$ 10 ft. =	600
First floor dead load	20 lbs.		
		Total weight =	1020

Span of columns 7 feet 1020×7 ft.   = 7140 lbs.

Next, select the type wood to be used in the girder. This will indicate whether to use the 1200 lbs./sq. in., 1400 lbs./sq. in., or the 1600 lbs./sq. in. table. Reading the table figures to the right of the stepped line will cause a bending of more than $\frac{1}{360}$ of the span. This is to be avoided.

If a wood girder is to be of 1600 lbs./sq. in. fiber stress, a 6" x 8" would be used; 1400 lbs./sq. in. fiber stress, use a 6" x 10", or 8" x 8"; and for 1200 lbs./sq. in. fiber stress, use 8" x 8".

If a built-up girder is to be used made up of 2" milled stock, a factor number is used with the table reading to allow for loss of material. If two 2" pieces make up a 4" girder, multiply by .897; if three 2" pieces make up a 6" girder, multiply by .887; if four 2" pieces make up an 8" girder, multiply by .867. Thus, a 6" x 8" girder table reading from 1600 pounds fiber stress per square inch is 7260 x .887 (three 2" stock) = 6938 lbs./sq. in. This load bearing is just below the 7140 lbs./sq. in. of the bearing on the girder, so it cannot be used. The next size is a 6" x 10" or an 8" x 8".

$6'' \times 10'' = 9160 \times .887 = 8067$

This will satisfy the load of 7140.

To figure another example using a fiber strength of 1400 lbs./sq. in., the reading for an 8" x 8" girder is 8630 x .867 = 7482 which will satisfy the load of 7140.

Steel girders may be used in place of wood girders and their sizes may be found in tables available from the steel companies or structural handbooks.

Columns that bear the weight of the girder must have adequate footings. The area of the footing must be large enough to support this weight and is figured by the same method as the footing for the wall.

Table 30

Span of Solid Wood Girders with 1200 Fiber Stress Lbs./Sq. In.

Size	7 ft.	8 ft.	9 ft.	10 ft.	11 ft.	12 ft.	14 ft.
2 x 6	961	837	738	660	595	541	454
2 x 8	1605	1503	1331	1191	1075	980	827
2 x 10	2020	2020	2020	1912	1730	1578	1336
2 x 12	2435	2435	2435	2435	2435	2328	1973
4 x 6	2144	1866	1647	1471	1327	1206	1012
4 x 8	3570	3340	2953	2643	2388	2175	1836
4 x 10	4500	4500	4500	4267	3864	3520	2981
6 x 6	3111	2708	2389	2134	1924	1747	1467
6 x 8	5420	5064	4481	4011	3625	3300	2786
6 x 10	6830	6830	6830	6473	5860	5341	4524
8 x 8	7390	6905	6110	5464	4941	4500	3799
8 x 10	9320	9320	9320	8827	7980	7284	6179

Table 31

Span of Solid Wood Girders with 1400 Fiber Stress Lbs./Sq. In.

Size	7 ft.	8 ft.	9 ft.	10 ft.	11 ft.	12 ft.	14 ft.
4 x 6	2507	2184	1930	1726	1559	1418	1194
4 x 8	4165	3904	3456	2906	2800	2552	2160
4 x 10	5265	5265	5265	4992	4520	4125	3500
6 x 6	3638	3168	2800	2504	2260	2055	1731
6 x 8	6330	5924	5244	4698	4250	3873	3277
6 x 10	7990	7990	7990	7576	6860	6261	5312
8 x 8	8630	8078	7151	6406	5793	5281	4469
8 x 10	10920	10920	10920	10330	9351	8537	7244

Table 32

Span of Solid Wood Girders with 1600 Fiber Stress Lbs./Sq. In.

Size	7 ft.	8 ft.	9 ft.	10 ft.	11 ft.	12 ft.	14 ft.
4 x 6	2875	2505	2213	1981	1791	1630	1375
4 x 8	4770	4470	3960	3549	3212	2930	2484
4 x 10	6035	6035	6035	5419	5177	4731	4019
6 x 6	4165	3633	3211	2873	2596	2363	1995
6 x 8	7260	6783	6008	5386	4875	4446	3768
6 x 10	9160	9160	9160	8680	7862	7179	6100
8 x 8	9880	9247	8193	7344	6646	6063	5139
8 x 10	12500	12500	12500	11835	10720	9790	8318

Sizes of Floor Joists

The size of the floor joist is determined by the live load, the length of the span, and the spacing between joists.

Joists are used in thickness of 2″ and widths of 6″, 8″, 10″, and 12″. A joist should be able to support the live load with sufficient stiffness to prevent vibrations which cause walls and ceiling plaster to crack. The two tables following indicate the size of joists and spacing required for a live load of 40 pounds per square foot, generally adequate for house construction.

Table 33

Safe Spans of Floor Joists Which Carry
40 Lbs. Live Load

Size	Spacing on Centers	Span Limit
2 x 6	12″	10′ - 2″
	16″	9′ - 3″
2 x 8	12″	13′ - 6″
	16″	12′ - 4″
2 x 10	12″	17′ - 0″
	16″	15′ - 6″
2 x 12	12″	20′ - 5″
	16″	18′ - 9″

Table 34

Safe Spans of Ceiling Joists Which Carry
20 Lbs. Live Load

Size	Spacing on Centers	Span Limit
2 x 6	12″	11′ - 6″
	16″	10′ - 6″
2 x 8	12″	15′ - 2″
	16″	13′ - 11″
2 x 10	12″	19′ - 1″
	16″	17′ - 6″

When selecting the joist to lay in position, sight along the length of the joist and place it in position so that any crown is to the top. The weight of the floor will tend to even them out.

All joists under bearing walls should be *doubled*. If the wall is to contain heating or plumbing connections, space these joists to give an opening for the size of the units. Blocking between these joists with material of the same dimensions at frequent intervals will tie them together.

Fig. 16-21 shows several methods of joining floor joists to girders. The strongest method is that in which the joists bear directly on the girder, but headroom in the basement is sacrificed when this construction is used. The other methods shown are compromises to secure headroom and sufficient strength.

In Fig. 16-22 is shown the application of bridging between joists. Bridging helps to minimize twisting or warping of joists, to maintain a more level floor, and stiffen the floor framing.

The method of framing around an opening such as a stairway or chimney is shown in Fig. 16-23. The joists forming the width of the opening are secured in place. These need not be in the standard spacing of the rest of the floor joists. Along these two joists, lay out the position of the opening for the double head-

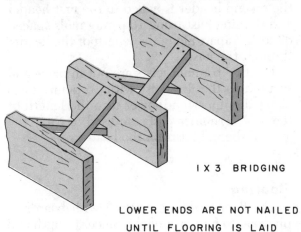

I X 3 BRIDGING

LOWER ENDS ARE NOT NAILED
UNTIL FLOORING IS LAID

Fig. 16-22. Bridging

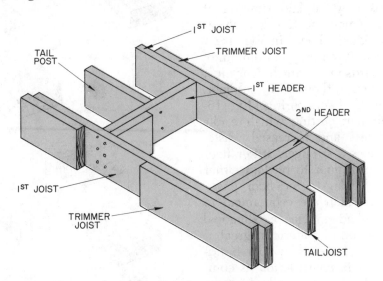

Fig. 16-23. Framing Around an Opening

ers. Note that the first header put in place should leave space so the second header added to the opening will be correctly spaced.

The first header is secured in place at each end of the opening with three 20 penny nails through the joist. In positioning these headers, check with a framing square for squareness, both horizontally and vertically to the opening.

The tail joists are cut and put in place, spacing them 16″ on center with the joist spacing pattern of the floor. Secure them with three 20 penny nails driven through the header.

When all tail joists are secured in place, the second header is nailed to the first header and framing joist using 16 penny nails spaced 8″ to 12″ apart along the length of the header through the joist.

The two trimmer joists are put in place and secured to the first joist with 16 penny nails along the upper and lower face the length of the joist. Trimmer joists are used to carry the load of the tail joists on the headers.

Flooring

The floor joists are covered with boards or plywood to form a subfloor. Since strength and stiffness are the prime considerations, the material does not have to be of finish grade. The subflooring boards may be laid running at right angles or diagonally to the floor joists. The right-angle method, shown in Fig. 16-20 is the fastest to lay as it requires a minimum of cutting, but the boards in the finish floor must be laid at right angles to those in the subfloor. The diagonal method of subflooring (Fig. 16-17) requires much more cutting, which results in higher labor costs and increased waste. However, it produces a stronger, stiffer floor and permits the finish floor to be laid either parallel or perpendicular to the floor joists. Plywood subfloors, which are economical to lay, have the same advantages as diagonal subflooring, but the cost of material is greater.

A more recent development in floor building, called *stressed skin construction*, is composed of covering plates of plywood which are glued to both surfaces of a wood framework to form what is essentially a box girder; thus the skin and the frame form a structural unit which permits much longer spans between supports.

Corner Posts

Corner posts are the built-up members located at the outside corners of a building. These usually consist of three 2″ x 4″′s, so positioned as to provide both interior and exterior nailing surfaces for adjacent walls. There are several types in common usage as shown in Fig. 16-24. If a solid corner post is used, it is customary to use a 4″ x 4″, with a 2″ x 4″ nailed to it on each adjacent inside corner to provide for interior nailing surfaces. Occasionally, in heavy construction, a 4″ x 6″ is used; in this case, only one 2″ x 4″ needs to be added to provide for interior nailing surface at that corner.

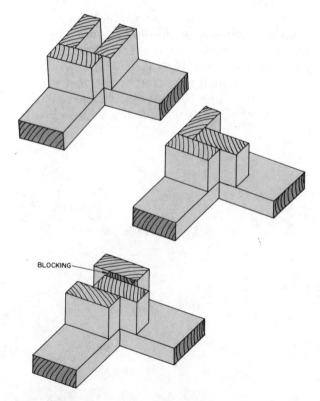

BLOCKING

Fig. 16-24. Corner Post Construction

Topic *148.* Framing a Wall

Classification

Framing

Procedure

Three Common Methods

1. Frame in all full-length studs before laying out and cutting any openings.
2. Mark the openings by laying out on the shoe or sole plate. Fasten full length studs in place. Frame in the openings.
3. Lay out a wall frame on the sub-floor or ground. Fasten full length studs in place. Frame in the openings. Raise the wall to the vertical position. Plumb and fasten.
4. Since methods 1 and 2 can be adapted from method 3, the latter only is described in detail below.

Framing Door Openings

1. Lay out and mark position of full length studs. Studs are commonly 16″ on centers (o.c.) in house construction. Depending upon types of structures and locality, studs are also spaced 20″ and 24″ on centers. See Fig. 16-25.
2. Cut and fasten full-length studs to the top plate and sole plate.
3. Cut two 2 x 4's and fasten in position for the header. To figure the height of a header — to the height of the finished door, add one inch for the thickness of the casing, add three-fourths of an inch for the thickness of the threshold, add one inch for the "horns" of the side of the casing.

    To figure the width of the door opening for framing, add three inches to the width of the door. This will allow for the thickness of the casing and wedging between the casing and trimmer studs.

4. Cut and fasten the trimmer and cripple studs above and below the header. Cripples are usually 16″ on center.
5. Cut and fasten the cripple studs between the plate and header.
6. Wide door openings or those which will support heavy overhead loads should be trussed.
7. Cut out the sections of the sole within the door opening.

Framing Window Openings

The procedure described below is for all types of windows. See Fig. 16-25. For specific size of rough openings and installations see manufacturers' specifications obtainable from your lumber or building supply dealer.

1. Lay out and mark the position of the full-length studs on the sole.
2. Cut and fasten full-length studs to the top plate and sole plate.
3. Cut four 2 x 4's for the double sill and header and fasten in position. To figure the height of a window opening, compute the glass height in the top and bottom sash, and add ten inches. To figure the width of a window opening add ten inches to the width of the glass.
4. Double headers should be placed on edge for greater strength. These headers should be securely nailed together with spacer blocks between so that their outer faces will be flush with the thickness of the studs. The F.H.A. recommends the following header sizes for openings:

    Spans up to 4′ in length, two 2 x 4's on edge

    Spans 4′ to 5½′ in length, two 2 x 6's on edge

    Spans 5½′ to 7′ in length, two 2 x 8's on edge

    Spans more than 7′ in length, two 2 x 10's on edge

5. Cut and fasten trimmer studs on each side of the opening.

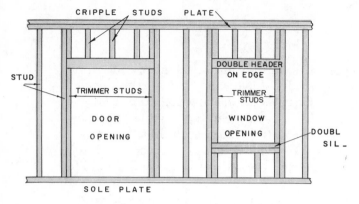

Fig. 16-25. Framing for Windows and Doors

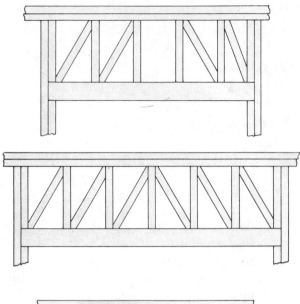

Fig. 16-26. Trusses for Wide Windows and Door Openings

Fig. 16-25A. Staging

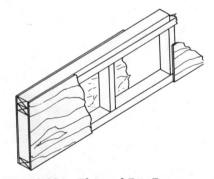

Fig. 16-26A. Plywood Box Beam

These hollow structural units are made from lumber and plywood. The 2″ x 4″ frame carries most of the bending forces and the plywood skin absorbs the shear stress. This type of beam construction provides lighter weight for spanning wide openings, such as garage doors.

6. Cut and fasten cripple studs above and below the header and sill. These are usually placed 16″ O.C.

Framing Wider Openings

1. Wide openings in bearing walls which will support heavy overhead loads, such as bathrooms and kitchens, should be trussed, Fig. 16-26.
2. Another method of spanning wide openings is the use of a plywood box beam. (See Fig. 16-26A.)

Standards and Results

1. Openings should be the correct height and width and in the specified location.

2. Studs should be plumb (vertical) and headers and sills level (horizontal), See Topic 145.
3. Each stud should be secured with specified size nails.

Safety Considerations

1. Observe all safety precautions in the use of hand and machine tools.

2. Avoid dangerous working positions.

3. Be careful in lifting and carrying lumber.

Topic *149*. Plumbing a Wall or Corner

Classification

Aligning and squaring

Procedure

Plumbing a Corner

1. A straightedge set with spacer blocks and a level is shown (#1 in Fig. 16-27). The corner is moved and held at the point where both the upper and lower bubbles read between the hair lines. In this position the corner post must be plumb.
2. A corner brace is temporarily nailed in place to hold the corner plumb (#2A, Fig. 16-27).
3. Repeat step 1 on adjacent side of corner post and nail corner brace (#2B, Fig. 16-27).

Aligning the Plate and Wall

1. A line and three blocks equal in thickness are used.
2. Two of the blocks are tacked at opposite ends of the plate. A line is drawn taut over these blocks.
3. A third block is placed under the string at spaced intervals along the length of the plate to test its position (#3, Fig. 16-27).
4. To move the plate (and wall) in or out for alignment, a board is tacked to the floor and plate.
5. Driving the board toward the wall will move the plate out (#4, Fig. 16-27).
6. To move the plate in, a short brace is placed under the board in order to make a bow in it, thus drawing the wall in (#5, Fig. 16-27).

7. These braces may be left in place until the ceiling joists and sheathing have been nailed in place.

Standards and Results

1. Walls should be plumb and straight.

2. Studs should be vertical.

Safety Considerations

Observe all safety precautions in use of hand tools.

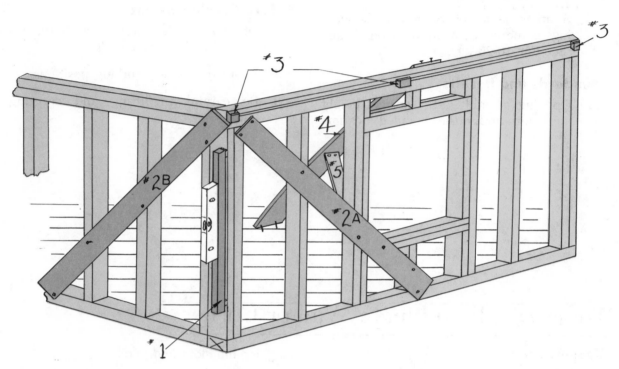

Fig. 16-27. Plumbing a Corner

Topic *150*. Roofs

The primary function of any roof is protection from the elements. The type of the roof is determined, therefore, by climatic conditions and architectural style. In some regions roofs must be designed to shed and bear the weight of snow and ice. Such roofs, therefore, usually have pronounced pitch or curvature.

Roof overhangs are designed to serve several purposes. They may add to the appearance of a building and serve to protect the upper walls from moisture. Overhang on ranch style buildings may provide shelter and shade for outdoor walks. When the house is properly oriented and the roof pitch and overhang correctly figured with respect to the height of the sun in the respective seasons, the winter sun will provide warmth to the rooms, yet the direct rays of the summer sun will be deflected. See Fig. 16-28.

The *shed roof* is the simplest form of roof construction. It has one slope, usually to the rear of the building, and a greater overhang at the front. Shed roofs have added simplicity and attractiveness to modern architectural styles.

A recent trend in roof construction is the *butterfly style*. In reality this is two shed roofs which slope to the center of the building, with the low point in the center. Extensive overhang on the front and back may be designed to provide both protection and benefit from the sun.

The *gable roof* is probably the most common type of roof because it serves several practical purposes and is easily constructed. The gable roof has two surfaces sloping away from the ridge. The slope varies from nearly flat to a steep pitch.

The *hip roof* has four surfaces slanting from a peak or ridge. The visual effect of this style of roof is a shortening of the length of the building. The hip roof is widely used in modern ranch houses.

The *gambrel roof* has two surfaces, each of which slopes on two separate planes. The upper slope forms about a 30° angle and the lower is approximately 60°. This type of roof is common in Dutch Colonial houses and in barn construction. It provides greater head room in the loft or uppermost story.

The *mansard roof* is another form of double sloped construction. The upper section has only a slight slope, about 15°. It is more or less flat. The lower slope approaches the vertical. This type of roof makes it possible to have attic rooms.

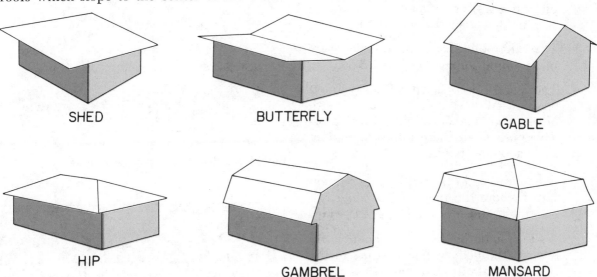

SHED   BUTTERFLY   GABLE

HIP   GAMBREL   MANSARD

Fig. 16-28. Types of Roofs

Topic *151.* Reading a Rafter Table to Figure the Length of a Common Rafter

Classification

Computing, laying out, and testing

Procedure

A common rafter is one that extends from the plate (1 in Fig. 16-29) to the ridge board (2). The length is figured along the center line which runs from the outside edge of the plate to the center line on the width of the ridge board.

1. To find the pitch of a roof divide the rise (4 in Fig. 16-29) by the span (3). The pitch of the roof in Fig. 16-29 is ⅜ since the rise is 8′ and the span is 21′: 8 ÷ 21 = .381 or ⅜.

2. To find the rise per foot run, multiply the rise (4) by 12 (to convert feet to inches) and divide by the run (5).

$$\frac{8 \times 12}{10.5} = 9''$$

The rise per foot run is always the same for any given pitch, and for ordinary pitches they can be easily remembered. A ½ pitch has a 12″ rise per foot run; a ⅓ pitch has an 8″ rise per foot run; a ¼ pitch has a 6″ rise per foot run and a ⅙ pitch has a 4″ rise per foot run.

3. The rafter table is found on the blade of a framing square. See Fig. 16-30.

4. The length of common rafters is found on the first line, indicated as "Length of common (main) rafters per foot run." There are 17 of these tables beginning at 2″ and continuing to 18″.

Example: Find the length of a common rafter where the rise is 9″ per foot run or ⅜ pitch and the building is 21′ wide:

First, find the inch line on the top edge of the body which is equal to the rise per foot. In our case this would be 9″.

On the first line below the figure 9 is the number 15. This number, 15, is determined in the following manner: The figure 9 on the body of the square is the rise or the altitude of a right triangle. The figure 12 on the tongue is the base, or one foot of run. The shortest distance between these two points, the hypotenuse, actually measures in this case 15″, which is interpreted as 15″ per foot run.

Multiply this by the run of the rafter, *i.e.*, 15″ × 10.5 = 157.5″ or 13′ 1½″. That is the length of a common rafter of ⅜ pitch with a 10′ 6″ run as shown in Fig. 16-29.

5. To lay out the bottom cuts of a common rafter, use the 12″ mark on the body of the square and the rise per foot on the tongue of the square. With the square in this position (see Fig. 16-31 and Fig. 16-32), lay out the cut for the plate by drawing a line along the body of the

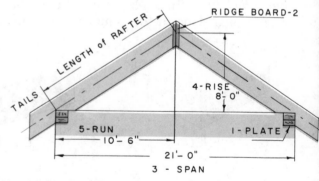

Fig. 16-29. Roof Framing Nomenclature

Fig. 16-30. Rafter or Framing Table (Courtesy Stanley Tool Co.)

square for the horizontal cut. Draw a line along the edge of the tongue of the square for the vertical cut.

6. To lay out the peak or ridge cut, move the square to the opposite end of the rafter, keeping the square in the same relative position. Draw a line along the edge of the tongue of the square for the vertical cut.

7. Remember the length of the rafter as figured from the tables is to the center line of the ridge board; therefore the thickness of one-half the ridge board must be subtracted from the total length. This is done by measuring at right angles to the plumb cut. See Fig. 16-31. The heel cut starts from the length of the common rafter on the center line, Fig. 16-32. The amount of overhang desired, called the tail or eave, should be added to the total length of the common rafter.

8. Lay out one rafter by this procedure and use it as a pattern to mark out the number required.

Standards and Results

1. All figuring should be accurate.
2. Lines should be sharp.
3. Check all figures and lines before making any cuts.

Safety Considerations

Observe all safety precautions in the use of tools and materials. See topic on safety.

Additional Reading

Stanley Tool Company, *Stanley Framing and Rafter Square*

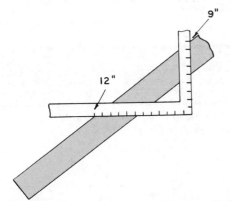

Fig. 16-31. Vertical Cut on Common Rafter at Ridge

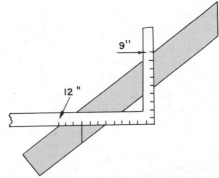

Fig. 16-32. Layout of Bird's-Mouth Cut for Top Plate

Topic *152.* Reading a Rafter Table to Lay Out the Length of Hip and Valley Rafters

Classification

Computing, laying out, and testing

Procedure

A hip rafter extends from the plate at an outside corner of a building diagonally to the ridge. (See Fig. 16-33.)

A valley rafter extends from the plate at the inside corner of a building and runs diagonally to the ridge. (See Fig. 16-33.)

1. The lengths of hip and valley rafters are found on the second line of the rafter table just under the line labeled "Length of main rafters per foot" on the blade of a framing square. (See Fig. 16-34.)

2. If we have a 10′ 6″ run and an 8′ rise, the rise per foot run will be $\frac{8 \times 12}{10.5}$ $= 9″.$

3. Example: Find on the framing square the length of a hip or valley rafter when the rise per foot is 9″ and the building is 21′ wide. Look on the second line below the 9″ mark and you will find 19.21 which is the length of a hip or valley rafter per foot run of 9″ rise. Since the run is 10′ 6″ or 10.5, multiply this by 19.21. The length of the hip and valley rafter is 201.705 inches, or 16.8 feet or 16 feet 10 inches.

4. The length of all hip and valley rafters is figured along the center of the top edge. To this dimension the length of tail or eave must be added and one-half the thickness of the ridge board must be subtracted. This measurement is made at right angles to the plumb mark.

5. To layout the top and bottom cuts, use 17″. Since all hip and valley rafters are in effect the diagonal of a cube, the ratio between the diagonal of a 12″ cube (17″) and the rise per foot of run establishes the angle of the cut. The 17″ on the body of the square will give the seat cut, and 9″ on the tongue in the given problem will give the ridge or top cut. See Fig. 16-35.

Fig. 16-34. Rafter or Framing Table (Courtesy Stanley Tool Co.)

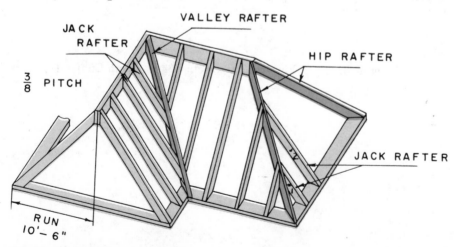

Fig. 16-33. Roof Framing Members

6. Hip and valley rafters require side cuts as well as top and bottom cuts. The table for these side cuts is found on the

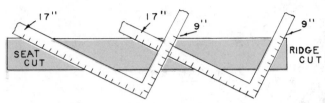

Fig. 16-35. Seat and Ridge Cut on Hip or Valley Rafter

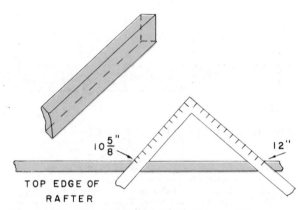

Fig. 16-36. Top and Bottom Side Cuts on Hip or Valley Rafter

bottom line of the rafter table. On the blade locate the rise per foot run, in this case 9″, and directly below this figure, on the line marked "Side Cut of Hip or Valley," find the number 10⅝″. Lay the square on the top edge of the rafter so that 10⅝″ on the blade and 12″ on the tongue are even with the ridge mark, Fig. 16-36. Then mark the side cut along the tongue. This is the layout for the side cut at the ridge for hip and valley rafters.

Standards and Results

1. All computations should be accurate.
2. Cutting lines should be sharp.
3. Check all figures and lines before making any cuts.

Safety Considerations

Observe all safety precautions prescribed in the use of tools and materials. See topic on safety.

Additional Reading

Stanley Tool Company, *Stanley Framing and Rafter Square*

Topic *153*. Reading a Rafter Table to Lay Out the Length of Jack Rafters

Classification

Computing, laying out, and testing

Procedure

A jack rafter is one that runs from the plate to a hip or from the ridge to a valley. Jack rafters lie in the same plane as common rafters; hence, they have the same rise per foot run as common rafters. (See Fig. 16-37.)

1. The lengths of jack rafters are located on the third and fourth lines of the rafter table found on the blade of a steel square. The third line reads "Difference in length of jacks 16 inches on centers." The fourth line reads "Difference in length of jacks 2 feet on centers." (See Fig. 16-34.)
2. The figures in the table indicate the length of the first or shortest jack. This

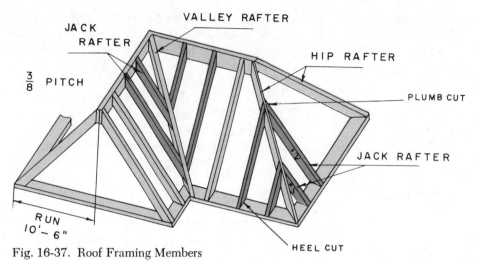

Fig. 16-37. Roof Framing Members

figure is also the difference in length between the first and second jack, the second and third jack, and so on.

3. Jacks are numbered in order, the shortest being #1, the next #2, next #3, and so on. To find the length of a jack rafter, multiply the figure in the table by the number of the position of the jack and subtract one-half the thickness of the hip or valley rafter. This measurement must be made 90° to the plumb cut.

4. If we have a 10' 6" run and an 8' rise, the rise per foot run will be $\dfrac{8 \times 12}{10.5} = 9''$. If the rafters are 16" on centers, look on the third line under 9 and you will find 20. If it is the first jack, it will be 20"; if it is second, it will be $2 \times 20'' = 40''$; the third, $3 \times 20'' = 60''$, and so on.

If the jacks are spaced 24" on center, look on the fourth line under 9 and locate the figure 30, which is the length in inches of the first jack; the second would be $2' 6'' \times 2 = 5'$.

5. To lay out the top and bottom cut of jack rafters, use 12" on the blade and the rise per foot run on the tongue as in cutting common rafters. The blade will give you the seat or heel cut, and the tongue the plumb cut, Fig. 16-38.

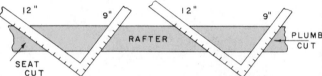

Fig. 16-38. Seat and Plumb Cuts for Jack Rafters

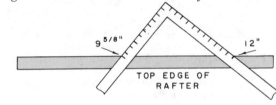

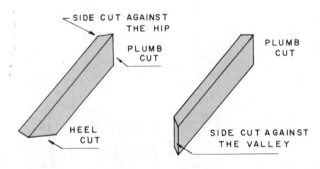

HIP JACK   VALLEY JACK

Fig. 16-39. Hip or Valley Jack Rafters

6. Jack rafters also require side cuts; hip jacks require them on the plumb cut and valley jacks require them on the seat cut. Find the figure under 9 on the fifth line labeled "Side cuts for jacks." In our case this would be 9⅝. With this

figure on the blade and 12″ on the tongue, lay out the side cuts as in Fig. 16-39. Subtract one-half the thickness of the hip or valley rafter. This measurement should be made at right angles to the plumb cut.

Standards and Results

1. All figuring should be accurate.
2. All cutting lines should be sharp.
3. Check all figures and lines before cutting.

Safety Considerations

Observe all safety precautions prescribed in the use of tools and materials. See topic on safety.

Additional Reading

Stanley Tool Company, *Stanley Framing and Rafter Square*

Topic *154.* Trusses and Their Use

When a long span, bridge, or roof is not supported by intermediate columns or partitions, a built-up frame, known as a truss, is usually used rather than a solid beam or girder. Trusses are used to distribute load, stiffen the structure, and build up strength. In designing a structural truss, any one or a combination of the basic truss patterns may be used. In actual practice, engineers determine the bearing load that must be supported

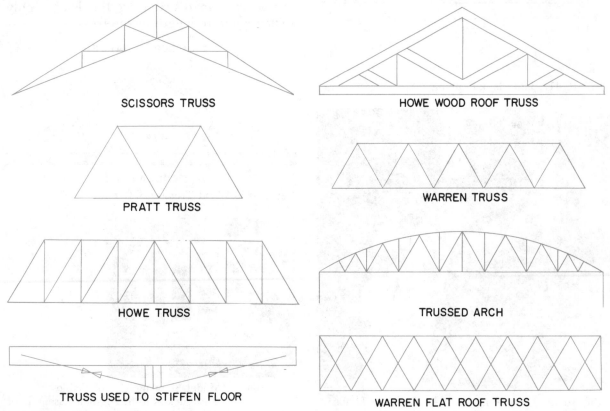

Fig. 16-40. Types of Trusses

and design a truss suitable for carrying such a load. See Fig. 16-40.

A truss is put together in a series of triangles. Since a triangle cannot change shape without changing the length of at least one side, the truss is strong and rigid. The use of roof trusses in construction provides for pre-

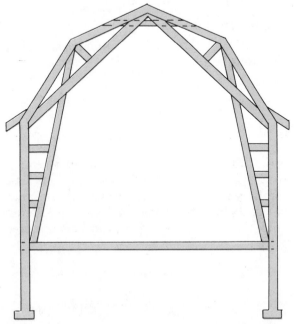

Fig. 16-41. Barn Plank Framing

Fig. 16-42. Laminating an Arch (Courtesy Timber Structures Inc.)

assembly and flexibility of the enclosed span as well as strength and rigidity. Many of the arrangements used to divide a span into different shaped trusses can be compared to the bridge truss.

In trussing over an opening such as doors and windows the load of the thrust is distributed along the direction of the brace from top to bottom, Fig. 16-26. This principle is also used in the straightening of sagging doors and gates and in the use of draw bolts to straighten and align beams and carrying timbers. Bridging, properly inserted between floor joists, forms a truss with the sub-flooring to stiffen and align the floor joist and distribute the load, Fig. 16-22. Collar ties between pairs of rafters of a hip roof act in the same manner. Ceiling joists (if tied in at the heel end of a rafter) and the bracing on concrete forms are additional applications of the truss.

In the truss, connectors are used to tie in the bearing area of joining members. The high compressive strength of short lengths of lumber aid in distributing the load evenly over the entire length of the truss.

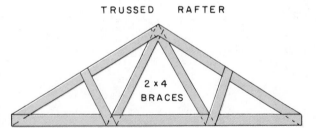

Fig. 16-43. Wood Trussed Rafter

Fig. 16-43A. Model Showing Use of Cables and Turnbuckles to Strengthen Assembly of Sill, Studs and Rafters

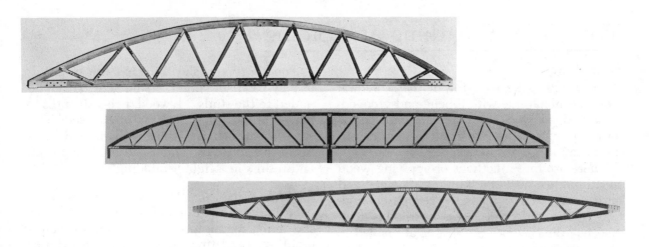

Fig. 16-43B. Various Truss Designs

Topic *155.* Sheathing and Siding

Sheathing

Sheathing is the covering of the structural members of a frame with tongue-and-grooved, square-edged stock or manufactured board, for the purpose of strength and insulation, but not necessarily for appearance.

There are three methods of applying wood sheathing to a wall of a building. The first and most common is to place the boards horizontally on the studs. The second method is diagonal boarding, where the boards are nailed to the studs at an angle of 45°. This construction eliminates the need for corner bracing and is much stronger, but it is more expensive because there is greater waste and it takes longer to apply.

The third method, called hurricane construction, is a combination of the above two types. Sheathing from the outside corners is run diagonally through the first four studs; the center section is covered horizontally.

Another type of sheathing is sheets or panels of plywood or other manufactured board nailed to the studs. Plywood, five-sixteenths to five-eighths inches thick, is often used. This type sheathing is stronger than boards, is faster to apply, has greater nail-holding power, and results in a tighter building.

Siding

Siding is the finished covering applied over sheathing, for the primary purposes of waterproofing, insulating, and giving the exterior an attractive appearance.

Probably two most common types of wood siding are clapboards and shingles. In laying out a wall to be covered with either of these types of siding, it is well to divide the height into three sections, *e.g.*, below the windows, beside the windows, and above the windows. If it has previously been decided to show a certain amount of siding exposed to the weather (as an example 4″), divide the distance from the base of the wall (usually slightly below the sheathing) to the bottom of the window by 4. The nearest whole number is the number of courses. Next, divide this whole number into the distance from the base to the bottom of the window casing. This gives the exact amount each course is exposed to the weather.

Fig. 16-44. Cutting Shingles with Froe and Mallet
(Courtesy National Park Service)

Fig. 16-45. Early Shingle-Making Machine

A. Masonite Provincial Lap Siding

B. Rough Sawn Plywood Siding

D. Masonite Barkridge Lap Siding

C. Masonite Ruf-X Lap Siding

E. Rough Sawn Shingle Siding

F. Patterned Masonite Lap Siding

Fig. 16-45B. Various Siding Designs Used for Modern Exterior Protection

Example: The distance from the base of the wall to the bottom of the window is 41"; $41 \div 4 = 10$; $41 \div 10 = 4\frac{5}{64}''$. If ten courses were used, each course would expose $4\frac{5}{64}''$ to the weather. If 9 courses were used, the exposure on each course would be $4\frac{1}{2}''$, and if 11 courses were used, $3\frac{11}{16}''$ would be exposed on each course.

It is considered good design to have a full course show at both the top and bottom of windows. In addition, it requires less cutting.

To make the layout of the entire wall, it is more efficient to use a *story-pole*. This is a piece of 1" x 1" or 2" by any convenient length (up to ten feet), with the markings on the edge indicating the amount that each course of siding is to show to the weather. Pencil marks are transferred from the story-pole to the wall near each end of the building, and a chalk line is run between these marks and then snapped.

Applying Siding

In applying clapboards, if the worker proceeds from top to bottom, the entire side of a building may be laid off at one time. Starting at the corner board, the first course of clapboards is cut, fitted and then nailed *at the top*. For the remaining courses, nails should be driven about one-half inch up from the butt edge; thus the nail holds the butt edge of one clapboard and the thin edge of the next one. Nails should not be driven home until the under course has been laid. Starting again at the corner board, the courses are begun by slipping a clapboard under the butt of the clapboard above, until the second butt coincides with the chalk line. The first course is then nailed at the bottom, which secures the lower clapboard in place. The entire side of the building is done in this manner. It is good practice to stagger the joints in clapboards by at least four inches, to minimize the possibilities of leaks.

The application of wood shingles, shakes, or composition shingles is very similar to that of clapboards, except that shingles are applied from the bottom up and a chalk line must be snapped after each course is laid. To shed water at the base of a wall, a double course of shingles is laid. Narrow-course shingles are not usually nailed at the butt, but, instead, are nailed slightly above the weather line. Wide-course shingles are nailed above the butt to prevent curling. To speed the application of shingles, a straightedge is often tacked along the chalk line, and the butts of the shingles are rested on the edge, thus being held in the proper place before being nailed. To insure a watertight wall, the joints should be staggered.

To give a wider shadow line, a double layer of shingles is often laid. The butt of the top layer is spaced one-half inch below the layer directly under it.

Some types of siding can be applied directly over the studs, eliminating sheathing. Novelty siding is usually used on camps or unheated buildings. It is molded for decoration, usually is tongue-and-grooved, and acts both as a sheathing and a siding. It is applied horizontally over the studs.

Also, many types of textured plywood patterns are available. These act as both sheathing and siding. Tests show that this type construction is stronger than, and insulates as well as inch boards.

Prefinished pressed wood, aluminum, and vinyl siding have become quite popular.

Fig. 16-46. Modern Shingle-Making

Shingle saws range from 36" to 50" in diameter. They are wedge-shaped saws with the body heavier than the cutting edge. They are made either right- or left-hand with the teeth pointing in the direction of rotation.

The cutting process slices the shingle so that it is cut with the grain and the width of the shingle is wedged out with the body of the saw (Courtesy Simonds Saw & Steel Co.)

Topic 156. Laying Out Straight-Run Stair Jacks

Classification

Computing and laying out

Procedure

If stairs are planned to run from an uncovered concrete slab to the first floor, all risers are of equal height except the bottom and top risers. To determine the height of the *bottom* riser, one must subtract the thickness of the tread from the height of the other risers. To determine the height of the *top* riser, deduct the thickness of the tread from the combined thicknesses of the sub floor and finish floor, then deduct this from the height of the regular riser.

As an example, assume that the thickness of the tread used is 1"; the height of the regular riser is 7"; the sub floor is $\frac{5}{8}$" thick; and the finish floor is $\frac{25}{32}$" thick. Calculations for the bottom and top risers would be:

Bottom riser: $7'' - 1'' = 6''$ height

Top riser: $\frac{5}{8}'' + \frac{25}{32}'' = \frac{45}{32}''$ or

$$1\frac{13}{32}'' - 1'' = \frac{13}{32}''$$
$$7'' - \frac{13}{32}'' = 6\frac{19}{32}'' \text{ height}$$

The following general procedure, although flexible, is a good guide for figuring stair risers.

1. Determine the perpendicular distance from the surface of the first floor to the top surface of the second floor.

2. The number of risers needed may be found by dividing the total height from floor to floor, in inches, by the desired height of the riser. (The riser is usually $6\frac{1}{2}$" to 7" high.) Dividing the number of risers required into the total height in inches will give the exact height of the individual risers. See Fig. 16-47.

Example: Total height equals 8' or 96 inches

Desired height of riser 7"

$96 \div 7 = 13\frac{5}{7}$. 13 or 14 risers will be needed.

$96 \div 13 = 7.384''$ or $7\frac{3}{8}''$, which may be too high.

$96 \div 14 = 6.857''$ or $6\frac{7}{8}''$, which may be more desirable.

3. The run of the stairs may be limited to a fixed distance. In this case the tread must be figured by the same method as the height of the riser. The length of each tread is as near to 10" as possible. The total of the tread plus the riser is equal to 17 or 18". It must also be remembered that there will be one less tread than the number of risers, because the top floor forms a tread.

Example: Total run equals 11 ft., or 132 inches

12 equals one less tread than risers

$$\frac{132}{12} = 11'' \text{ length of tread}$$

or, if 14 risers were preferred

$$\frac{132}{13} = 10.154'' \text{ or } 10\frac{1}{8}'' \text{ length of tread}$$

4. If the riser is $7\frac{3}{8}''$ and the tread is 11", lay the framing square so that the $7\frac{3}{8}''$ mark on the blade and the 11" mark on the tongue fall on the edge of the jack as shown in Fig. 16-48. Start the layout a sufficient distance from the edge to form the bottom riser which will be $6\frac{3}{8}''$

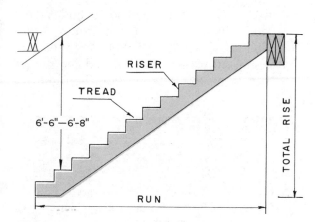

RISER

TREAD

6'-6"—6'-8"

TOTAL RISE

RUN

Fig. 16-47. Stair Nomenclature

high (allowance for the thickness of the tread).

5. Draw lines along the outside edges of the square indicating the tread and the riser.

6. Reverse the square to draw lines *AB* and *BC*. *AB* = 6⅜".

7. Mark out the number of treads and ris-ers required as in step number five.

8. The top riser should be modified accord-ing to the materials used in flooring, EF is square with DE.

Standards and Results

1. All risers should be of equal length ex-cept the bottom which is one inch less to allow for the thickness of the tread.

2. All treads should be of equal length.

3. All treads should be level and risers perpendicular, except on outside stairs whose tread has a slight forward pitch.

Safety Considerations

1. Observe all safety precautions in the use of hand tools. See topic on safety.

2. Select clear, straight-grained stock.

Additional Reading

Stanley Tool Company, *Stanley Framing and Rafter Square*

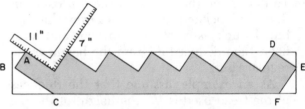

Fig. 16-48. Laying Out Stair Jacks with Framing Square

Topic *157.* Figuring Board Measure by the Use of the Essex Scale

Classification

Computing

Procedure

On most framing squares the Essex board measure table is facing you on the blade when the tongue is down and to your left. As the name indicates, the table gives the number of board feet in any piece of lumber from 2" to 24" wide and from 8' to 30' long.

1. Each number on the outer edge of the blade represents the width of lumber in inches (2" - 24"). Since 12" is the unit of width in figuring board measure, the number 12 on the outside edge of the blade is the focal point in using the table. Each number in the column of figures under the number 12 is a given length of a board in feet and the board feet for that particular length board, 12" wide.

2. To find the board feet of stock of widths other than 12", start with the number under 12 which corresponds to the board length and then move to the left or right to the correct width.

3. As an example, if you desire to find the number of board feet in a piece of stock 10" wide and 14' feet long, find 14 in the column under 12; then follow that line to the left until you are directly under 10 where you will find the num-ber 11 on the left and 8 on the right of

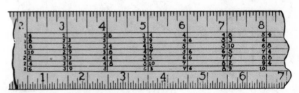

Fig. 16-49. Essex Board Measure Table (Courtesy Stanley Tool Co.)

the vertical line. This is read as 11⁸⁄₁₂ or 11⅔ board feet.

4. The figures given in the table are for 1″ stock. To find the board measure for other stock, multiply the figure found on the table by the standard, rough-stock dimensions of that particular thickness.

Standards and Results

Ability to figure board feet by the use of the Essex table.

Additional Reading

Stanley Tool Company, *Stanley Framing and Rafter Square*

Topic *158.* Fitting and Hanging a Door

Classification

Joinery and assembly

Procedure

Prior to hanging, the door should be properly fitted with an allowance of a minimum of ⅛″ clearance at the top and at each side, and with enough clearance at the bottom to clear the finished floor, carpeting, threshold, etc. when the door is open. After the door has been properly fitted, the edge opposite to the hinged side and away from the swing of the door should be planed on a 2° to 3° bevel.

The following general rule, although flexible, is a good guide for locating hinges. For built-up or flush doors, the top of the upper butt is located 6″ down from the top of the door. The bottom of the lower butt is located 8″ to 10″ from the bottom of the door. On panel doors, the top hinge is generally placed just below the upper rail and the lower hinge just above the lower rail. The hinges should not be opposite a rail because of the mortise and tenon joint. Heavy doors should have three hinges, with the third one usually centered between the upper and lower hinges.

On cabinet work, the top and bottom hinges are spaced an equal distance from the opposite ends of the door. The distance from the end of the door to the center of the butt is usually about ⅛ the length of the door. As an example, the centers of the top and bottom hinges on a 2′ door would be 4″ from the respective ends of the door.

Setting a Butt Hinge

1. Locate the position of the top edges of the hinges on the frame and mark with a sharp knife.

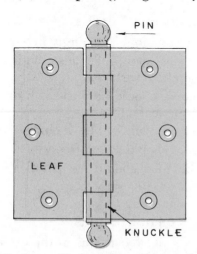

Fig. 16-50. Loose Pin Butt Hinge Nomenclature

Fig. 16-51. Cutting a Gain with a Mallet and Chisel

2. Place the door in position, keeping it tight against the top and hinge side. This may be done with shingles or other wedge-shaped pieces.

3. Project the position of the hinges on the door and mark with a sharp knife.

4. Remove the door. Using a knife and square extend the marks made on the face onto the edge of the door. Mark on the frame, with a knife and square, short lines which indicate the length of the butt.

5. Set a butt gauge or a marking gauge equal to the width of the leaf, not including the knuckle (see Figs. 4-18 and 4-19). The knuckle should project beyond the frame of the door to allow it to swing freely. Mark the width of the leaf on both the door and frame.

6. Extend the mark indicating the length of the butt to the line indicating the width of the butt. Do this with a knife and square.

7. Set the other spur of the butt gauge, or another marking gauge, to the thickness of the leaf and mark on the face of the door and the edge of the frame. Care should be taken not to mark beyond the lines marking the length of the butt.

8. On the lines indicating the ends of the butt score the ends of the gains with a chisel and mallet, keeping the bevel side of the chisel toward the waste.

9. Cut the gain by making a series of feather cuts with the chisel, bevel side down, as shown in Fig. 16-51.

Fig. 16-52. Cutting a Gain with a Chisel

10. Remove the surplus by paring toward the gauge line as shown in Fig. 16-52.

11. Repeat Steps 9 and 10 for all gains on the door and the frame.

12. Place the hinges in position on the door and mark the position of the screws. Use an awl and mark slightly back from the center of the holes. This will draw the leaf tightly to the back of the gain.

13. Repeat the above operation on the gains on the frame.

14. If installing loose-pin butts, remove the pin and separate the leaves. Drill the hole nearest the center of each leaf on both the door and the frame. Fasten each leaf with one screw so that the pin opening is up. If tight-pin butts are used, fasten the butts to the door. Hold the door up to the frame in the opened position and fasten the leaves to the frame starting at the top.

15. Check to see that the door opens and closes properly. A door should stay in any position if properly hung. If it has a tendency to swing open, it may be hinge bound; that is, the gains are too deep. This may be remedied by padding the gains with cardboard or a thin piece of wood. When all adjustments are made, drive the remaining screws.

Standards and Results

1. Leaves should fit snugly in gains.
2. Leaves should fit flush with the surrounding surface.
3. Screws should be flush with the surface of the leaf.
4. Gains should not have chipped edges.
5. Door should swing freely.
6. The pins should be parallel with the face of the door.

Safety Considerations

Observe all precautions in the use of hand tools. See topic on safety.

Topic 159. Installing a Cylindrical Lockset in a Door

Classification

Cutting, boring, and fitting

Procedure

Some locksets do not have a deadlocking plunger, and locksets for inside doors are without the locking function in the knobs. Most manufacturers provide a template with the lock, indicating size and position of all bored holes, mortises, and gains for latch front and strike plate. (See Fig. 16-53.)

Locate Center

1. Place the template on the face of the door and locate the hole for the cylindrical case. The distance from the floor to the center of the knob is usually between 34″ and 36″, and the distance in from the edge of the door is 2¾″.
2. Select the proper bit size, as indicated in the manufacturer's instructions, and bore through the face of the door. Care must be taken not to split out the stock on the inside face of the door. (See Topic 91).
3. Using the template, locate the center of the hole on the edge of the door.
4. Select a bit of the size recommended by the manufacturer, and bore a hole from the edge of the door, to house the latchtail. This latchtail hole is bored to meet the hole bored in the face of the door. (See step 2 above.)
5. Insert the latchtail in the hole just bored.
6. With a sharp knife, mark around the latch front for the size of gain.
7. Using a mallet and chisel, remove the waste material within the marked area to a depth equal to the thickness of the latch front.
8. Insert latch into hole and attach with screws.

Locate and Install Strike Plate

1. From the front edge of the jamb, measure back a distance equal to one-half the thickness of the door. This is the center line for the layout of the strike plate.
2. Place the strike plate over the latch and close the door until it comes to the jamb. Mark the top and bottom edge of the gain for the strike plate.
3. Place the strike plate in the proper position and mark around the plate with a thin-bladed, sharp knife.
4. Remove the stock from within the lines to a depth equal to the thickness of the plate. This may be done with a chisel, and mallet.
5. Some strike plates have a cutout in them. Others have a built-in receptacle to receive the latch. The slope in the receptacle should be opposite the swing of the door.
6. In either type, a deeper cavity must be cut to receive the full depth of the latch.
7. Fasten the strike plate in position with screws.

Insert Lockset in Door

1. Remove the inside knob, rose, and retaining sleeve from the lockset.
2. See manufacturer's specifications for distance between outside rose and cylinder case. This varies with the thickness of the door.

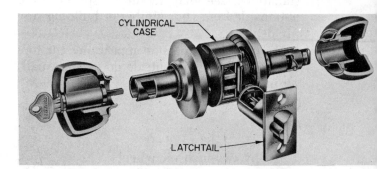

Fig. 16-53. Cylindrical Lock (Courtesy Independent Lock Co.)

3. From the outside of the door, insert the lockset and knob into the large hole on the face of the door. Make sure that the edges of the opening in the cylindrical case properly engage the prongs on the latch. See also that the latchtail is properly interlocked with the reactor. Test the action by turning the knob.
4. Attach the inside knob by sliding it onto the spindle.
5. Fasten the two parts together.
6. Turning either knob and releasing it should move the latch in and out.

Standards and Results

1. Hole for the lockset and latch case should be the proper size and in the correct location. There should be no chipping around the hole.
2. Hole for the latchtail should be the proper size and in the correct location.
3. Strike plate should be in the proper position and flush with the surface of the door jamb, so that the latch easily engages.
4. Turning either knob should unlatch the door.
5. Key should turn easily to lock or unlock the door.

Safety Considerations

Observe all safety precautions in the use of hand tools. See topic on safety.

Additional Reading

Manufacturers Catalogs

Topic 160. Standards Pertaining to Structural Elements

Windows

Many styles, patterns, and sizes of windows are manufactured and used in the various types of house architecture and are adapted to all forms of construction.

For specific size of rough openings and installations, see manufacturers' specifications obtainable from your lumber or building supply dealer.

For a balanced outside appearance the tops of the windows and outside doors are usually set in line.

Doors

Exterior
Width: 2' - 8" to 3' - 0"
    by two-inch increments
Length: 6' - 8" to 7' - 0"
    by two-inch increments

Interior
Width: 2' - 0" to 3' - 0"
    by two-inch increments
Length: 6' - 6" to 7' - 0"
    by two-inch increments

Ceiling Heights

	Minimum	Maximum
First floor	7' - 0"	8' - 0"
Second floor	7' - 0"	8' - 0"
Basement	7' - 0"	9' - 0"

Allowance should be made in basement ceiling heights to provide adequate head room where air conditioning or warm-air heating ducts are to be installed.

Yard Lumber and Timber Sizes

A "Simplified Practice Regulation" by the U.S. Department of Commerce (in effect March 1, 1970) sets the standards by which structural lumber will be cut. It includes three requirements:

1. All lumber sold "dry" must have a moisture content of no more than 19%.
2. Lumber dressed to the new standards must be milled when the moisture content is no more than 19%.
3. Rough dressed lumber must be of sufficient oversize so that its dressed use matches the standard dimensions.

There will be loss of lumber size, but it is not considered great enough to change lumber strength or framing specifications.

Example of table use:

A 2″ x 4″ would be 1⁹⁄₁₆″ x 3⁹⁄₁₆″ dressed green

1½″ x 3½″ dressed dry to 19%.

Table 35

New Table of Minimum Lumber Sizes
(Given in Inches)

Normal Size	Dressed Green	Dressed Dry Moisture 19%
1	¹⁵⁄₃₂	¾
2	1⁹⁄₁₆	1½
3	2⁹⁄₁₆	1½
4	3⁹⁄₁₆	3½
5	4⅝	4½
6	5⅝	5½
8	7½	7¼
10	9½	9¼
12	11½	11¼

Topic *161.* Boat Construction

The Frame

In boat construction, a "skin" of planking or plywood is fitted over a framework, to make the boat watertight. The frame provides structural shape and strength. See Fig. 16-54. The longitudinal members — keelson and stem — form the backbone and, with the chine and sheer batten, give shape to the length of the boat. The ribs or frames and transom run at right angles to the keelson and provide the width and beam. This transverse network forms a strong skeletal framework. The skin ties this framework together into one structural unit.

Fasteners

Obviously, more skill and care in fitting are required for this construction than in the car-pentry of a building. Great care must be taken in securing the various frame members together and securing the skin to the frame. Standard methods of nailing used in house construction are not adequate for a boat. The type and position of each fastener must be selected to gain the maximum strength. Rust-resistant, screw-type nails, screws, bolts, and rivets are used in place of common nails, along with a waterproof adhesive. A rigid frame minimizes the movement of the skin under the twisting and working of the boat in the water.

Frame Forms

There are two general types of frame forms. The built-up frame used in V-bottom boats consists of straight frame sections, tied together at the chine section with gussets. The

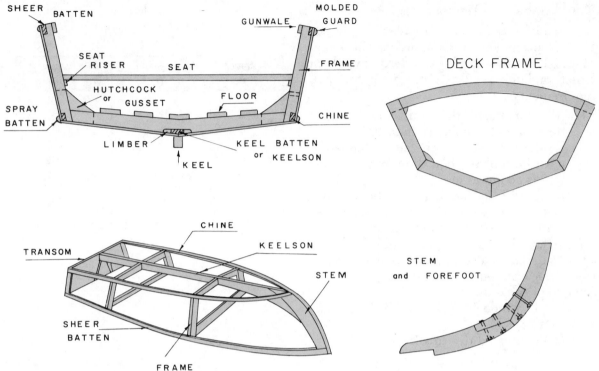

Fig. 16-54. Boat Construction

steam-bent ribs used in round-bottom boats require a forming process. Although the latter type provides lighter weight construction, a properly constructed built-up frame is considered stronger.

Woods Used

The material used in boat construction must be straight-grained, durable when exposed to moisture, very strong, free of knots and other defects, and must hold its shape. It should not be too dry; otherwise, it will swell excessively when the boat is in the water. For this reason, only air-dried heartwood, the most durable portion of the tree, should be used. Quarter-sawn boards shrink and warp less, so are desired for planking.

White oak is the most common wood used for the skeletal members, where great strength is required. It is the best wood for keels, stems, frames, sheer battens, centerboards, and rudders.

Mahogany is a very durable wood, and because of its interlocking grain pattern, it is fairly strong. It shrinks and swells little and is moderately light in weight. This makes it one of the best woods for all-round boat construction. It is the most used wood for exterior and interior finished surfaces.

White cedar is a lightweight wood with a fine, straight grain. Although not particularly strong, it is used for planking because of its durability. It is expensive because of its scarcity.

Some species of spruce, particularly Sitka, are known for their light weight, straight grain, and resistance to bending. In light boat construction, it is used for keelson, chines, and bent frames. It is one of the best materials for spars.

Cypress is a medium-weight, straight-grained wood that is very durable. It is used in large boat construction for planking, floors, and bulkhead work.

White pine is a substitute wood not generally recommended because of its weaker characteristics. It is easily worked and, if used, should be only that which is quarter-sawed.

White ash, like oak, is heavy; has a coarse, straight grain; and is very durable. It is more elastic than oak and is used as a substitute in frame members. It is the preferred wood for oars.

Two grades of plywood are used in boat building. *Marine plywood* is made up of a core and crossbanding of solid plies, so that each layer is free of defects and voids; *exterior plywood* requires only that the two face plies be free of defects and voids. Both types are glued up with the same waterproof adhesive.

In building a boat, the amateur craftsman should select the materials which best suit his purposes in terms of strength, appearance, weight, and cost. He should not attempt to design his own boat without extensive experience in this area; it is far safer to rely on proven plans which are available commercially.

Topic *162.* Glossary of Structural Terms

Abutment — that part of a pier or wall from which an arch is suspended; the support at either end of an arch, beam, or bridge.

Anchor bolt — the bolt which anchors the sill to the foundation. (See Fig. 16-16.)

Apron — the inside trim below a window stool.

Baluster — small vertical pillars which frame the opening beneath the handrail, usually used in stair and porch construction.

Baseboard or skirting — a finish trim at the base of a wall.

Batten — narrow strip of wood used as a reinforcement or covering for a joint.

Batter-board — temporary framework from which the level lines are run in establishing guides for the positioning, layout, and erection of a foundation. (See Figs. 16-12, 16-13, 16-14.)

Beam — horizontal timber supporting bearing load. (See Fig. 16-21.)

Bearing walls — those walls which serve as partitions and support the roof and upper stories.

Bracing — the ties and rods used for strengthening and reinforcing framework of the building. (See Fig. 16-18.)

Bracket — a triangular brace used as a support for a shelf or projection.

Bridging — furring strips crossed in pairs between floor joists, forming a truss which

Bulkhead — a partition or enclosure on a boat or a cover to a below-ground, outside basement entrance.

stiffens the floor and distributes the load.

Camber — slight curvature of a beam or surfaces of boats, planes or other conveyances.

Canopy—a roof-like structure projecting from a wall and supported on pillars.

Cantilever — a bracket-like projection unsupported at one end.

Casement — a type of hinged or pivoted window which swings open along its entire length.

Casing — the trim around a door or window.

Chine—the exterior horizontal strip on a boat which extends from the transom to the bow and ties together the ribs. (See Fig. 16-54.)

Clapboard—a standard siding, shingle-shaped in cross-section.

Cleat — a strip of wood used for fastening and as a support.

Collar beam — a horizontal member which serves to tie together and stiffen two opposite common rafters.

Corner post — a member which provides for exterior and interior nailing at corners. (See Figs. 16-24, 16-27.)

Cripple stud — a stud running from either the sole plate to the sill in a window opening or from the header to the top plate.

Cupola — a small structure built on top of a roof for ornamentation, ventilation, or observation.

Cornice — crowning members at the top of interior or exterior walls.

Door frame — the finished frame which forms a door opening.

Dormer — a projection upwards and outwards on a section of a roof to provide light, ventilation, style, and interior head room.

Ell — an extension of a building at right angles to the main structure.

Fascia — horizontal flat member of a cornice.

Fire stop — horizontal obstruction of wood or masonry filling opening between studs at floor level to prevent spread of fire by draft.

Flashing — sheet metal used around openings and valleys in roof and wall construction to prevent seepage of moisture.

Footing — an enlarged course of either concrete or stone placed under foundations or columns to provide a larger weight-bearing surface. (See Fig. 16-16.)

Framing — the skeleton framework of a building including walls, floor, and roof. (See Figs. 16-18, 16-25, 16-29.)

Furring — two- or three-inch strips nailed to the rough framing to build up an even surface and to provide nailing surface at desired intervals.

Gable — the projection of the roof which terminates in a triangular vertical wall above the eaves. (See Fig. 16-28.)

Gambrel roof — a symmetrical roof with two different pitches on each side, the lower of which is often 60° and the upper 30°. (See Fig. 16-28.)

Girder — the main carrying timber used to support the interior ends of the floor joists. (See Fig. 16-21.)

Girt — a horizontal strip set in the studs to support floor joists, generally used in balloon framing.

Grounds — strips of wood ¾″ in thickness, fastened around openings and at the base of surfaces to be plastered and to which plaster is leveled and finished and to which trim is nailed.

Gusset — a thin piece of material fastened as a plate to the face of two or more structural members to secure or reinforce a joint.

Gunwale or gunnel — the uppermost, inside, horizontal reinforcing member running the full length of a boat, tying the individual frames into one unit. (See Fig. 16-54.)

Hanger — a "U"-shaped, stirrup-like bracket used to support the end of a beam or joist at a masonry wall or girder. (See Fig. 16-21.)

Header — that member used in framing an opening which is fastened at right angles to full-length studs or joists and also supports cut-off members. (See Fig. 16-17.)

Heel — that part of any structural roofing member which rests on the wall plate.

Hip — the ridge formed at the point of intersection of two inclined roof surfaces at an exterior corner.

Jamb — the finish trim on an opening in which a door is hung.

Joist — one of a series of parallel, horizontal structural pieces laid on edge and used to support the floor or ceiling. (See Fig. 16-21.)

Keel — an exterior, longitudinal member running from stem to stern through the center of the bottom of a boat. It supports frame and skin, provides balance, and stabilizes direction of movement. (See Fig. 16-54.)

Keelson — the inner part of the keel which supports and ties together the frames. (See Fig. 16-54.)

Knee — an angular reinforcement between two or more structural members. (See Fig. 16-54.)

Lally column — a vertical member, usually of tubular steel filled with concrete, used to support a girder or beam.

Lath — wood strip, expanded metal, or composition material fastened to the frame of a building as a foundation for plaster.

Ledger strip — bearing strip nailed along the side of the main carrying girder, forming a seat to support the joists.

Lintel — a supporting horizontal structural member spanning window and door openings.

Louver — a slatted device fitted into an opening to provide ventilation while excluding rain or snow.

Mansard, French, or curb roof — a roof with a double slope on the four sides; the lower slope is very steep and the upper slope is relatively flat. (See Fig. 16-28.)

Mullion — a pier separating pairs of windows.

Muntin — slender divider between panes of glass in a window.

Newel — the center post about which a circular staircase is built, or the main supporting posts at the extreme ends of a hand rail.

Parting strip — a dividing retaining strip set into a window frame of a double-hung sash.

Pilaster — a built-in projecting column used to reinforce a straight wall.

Pile — heavy timber driven into the earth as a supporting foundation.

Pitch — angle or degree of the slope of a roof, usually expressed as a ratio between the rise and the span (Fig. 16-29).

Plancher — horizontal piece of trim forming a part of the cornice closing in the lower protruding ends of the rafters.

Plate — uppermost horizontal member of a framed wall (Fig. 16-29).

Plinth block — a rectangular block at the base of a casing or column to which the baseboard is butted. This block is usually slightly thicker than either the casing or baseboard.

Purlin — a horizontal supporting timber running from truss to truss and forming a bearing surface for the rafters.

Rafters — the members which form the skeletal, rib-like framework of a roof (Fig. 16-29).

Ridge pole, ridge board, or saddle board — the uppermost horizontal member of the roof framework which ties the rafters into one unit on gable and gambrel roofs (Fig. 16-29).

Rise — the vertical distance from the top of the plate to the peak of the roof in roof construction, or from one floor to the next in stair construction (Figs. 16-29 and 16-47).

Run — the horizontal distance which the rafters span in roof construction or the horizontal distance which the jacks span in stair construction (Figs. 16-29 and 16-47).

Sash — the framework of a window in which the glass is bedded.

Scaffold or staging — a temporary platform used in construction.

Sheathing — the material used to close in the skeletal framework.

Sill — the lowest supporting member of a structural framework as in a building or bridge or in window openings (Figs. 16-18, 16-25).

Sleeper — wood strips placed in or on concrete or on dirt as a base for nailing floor joist, sub-flooring, or finished flooring.

Shiplap — a type of siding whose molded edge forms a tight, water-shedding joint.

Shoring — timbers used for bracing to prevent sagging or bowing.

Soffit — the under side of a large cornice or arch.

Span — the distance between vertical exterior points of structural supports. (See Fig. 16-29.)

Spar — a term applied to a mast, boom, or similar member on sailboats.

Stem — the shaped structural member forming the bow or prow of a boat, the lower member of which is usually attached to the keelson (Fig. 16-54).

Structure — a unified construction of interrelated parts.

Story-pole — a rod used in measuring heights such as ceilings, in laying out window and door openings, courses of shingles or siding, and stair jacks.

Stringer — a term sometimes applied to joists and stairjacks and other horizontal structural timbers (Fig. 16-47).

Stud — a supporting frame member running from the sole plate to the top plate.

Subfloor — rough flooring made of boards, matched lumber, or plywood and laid on joists to serve as a base for the finished floor.

Transom — the hinged window over a door in building construction; the flat stern of a boat in boat construction. (See Fig. 16-54.)

Tread — the step portion or horizontal part of a stair (Fig. 16-47).

Trim — decorated finish applied in corners and around openings. Examples of trim are baseboards, chair rails, moldings, etc.

Trimmer — doubling a stud, joist, or rafter used to frame an opening.

Truss — a triangular arrangement of members used in supporting and dispersing bearing load. (See Fig. 16-40.)

Valley — the angle formed where two roof slopes meet at an interior corner. (See Fig. 16-33.)

Wainscoating — interior trim paneling on the lower portion of a wall, usually to chair rail height.

Topic *163*. Patternmaking

In wood patternmaking, a model, which may be built up of one or more parts, is made to specifications. This model or pattern is used as the form around which a mold is made. Metal, plastics or other materials which are reducible to a molten or liquid state may then be cast in the mold and upon solidifying produce a counterpart of the pattern. Many objects are made first as wood patterns and these serve as the model from which castings may be produced singly or in quantity. Patterns vary in size and complexity from those used for casting such small objects as a handle to those for casting a large machine base or an engine block.

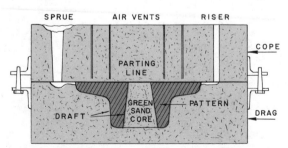

Fig. 17-1. One-Piece Turned Pattern and Method of Casting

One class of patterns are solid wooden models of the castings which will be made from them. Others are made in sections to facilitate the removal of the pattern from the mold or for castings which will have internal cavities. There are solid, one-piece patterns, sectional patterns, and patterns containing cores and core prints.

One-Piece Pattern

The one-piece pattern is almost an exact model of the object intended for casting. The pattern is made larger to provide for: (1) draft which facilitates removal from the mold, (2) shrinkage of the material to be cast, and (3) finishing. See Fig. 17-1.

Split Pattern

The split pattern is one which is made in two halves, with the split coming at the largest dimension of the pattern. The two sections are fitted very closely and are held together with either regular dowels or with dowel pins (male and female) made especially for this purpose. See Fig. 17-2.

Patterns with Cores

Where the casting is to contain an internal cavity, the patternmaker must make provision for the hollow or recess by making either a projection on the pattern or a recess or hole in the pattern. This process is called *coring*. In sand molds the core is a body of sand which projects into the cavity of the mold thus forming the opening in the casting. Some openings are such that the pattern may be constructed to leave its own core in the mold.

This part of the pattern usually has a greater degree of taper to facilitate removal of the pattern from the mold. See Fig. 17-4.

Shallow recesses, exposed cavities and shallow holes are cored out wherever possible by means of a *green sand core.* In such applications the cavity or hole will be made in the pattern and when the green sand is rammed in the mold it forms the core. See Fig. 17-1.

If the recesses and cavities are too deep or if they are too narrow to mold, they are generally cored out in the same manner as interiors of castings by means of a *dry sand core.* (A dry sand core is a body of sand which has been mixed with core oil and formed in an especially prepared box, called a *core box,* made to specified shape and dimension. This formed mixture is baked into a hardened, dry sand core. When the casting is poured, the dry sand core will provide the recess or cavity specified for the casting.) See Fig. 17-2.

Woods Used in Patternmaking

Common pattern woods are reasonably close-grained, easy to work, stay in place well, and do not expand or contract to any appreciable degree. Clear white pine is used for patterns which are to be used only a few times, mahogany for those to be used a greater number of times, and cherry for production work.

The particular characteristics of these woods are described in Section Three.

PATTERN HAVING LOOSE
PIECES THAT AID IN THE
REMOVAL OF PATTERN
FROM THE MOLD

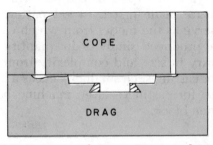

Fig. 17-3. Pattern with Loose Pieces and Method of Casting

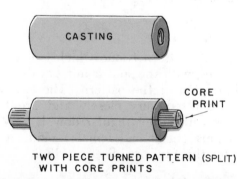

TWO PIECE TURNED PATTERN (SPLIT)
WITH CORE PRINTS

HALF SECTION OF FLASK, CAVITY
& DRY SAND CORE

Fig. 17-2. Two-Piece Turned Pattern and Method of Casting

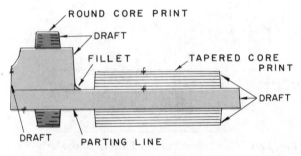

CASTING

ROUND CORE PRINT

DRAFT

FILLET   TAPERED CORE
PRINT

DRAFT

DRAFT   PARTING LINE

Fig. 17-4. Built-Up Pattern with Core Prints

Topic *164.* Considerations for Laying Out a Pattern

Classification

Providing allowance through measuring and laying out

Procedure

To the finished dimension of the object to be cast there must be added allowances for draft, shrinkage, and finish.

Draft Allowance

1. Draft is the name given to the slight taper on all vertical surfaces. This slope or taper extends from the parting line at the widest point to the section that will lie deepest in the mold. Draft facilitates withdrawal of the pattern from the mold, Fig. 17-4.

2. Draft is actually a dimension that is added to the finished size. An outsized dimension of ⅛″ to ⅜″ taper per foot is added at the parting line and tapers to the finish dimension at the base of the pattern.

Shrinkage Allowance

1. All metals expand when they undergo a change from a solid state to a liquid, and shrink when they change back to a solid state, but each metal expands and contracts differently. The cavity in the mold, therefore, must be larger than the finished casting will be. This oversize allowance is made by using the shrink rule for the particular metal to be cast.

2. In laying out patterns to be cast of iron, which shrinks ⅛″ to the foot, the actual measurements on the pattern stock would be made with the ⅛″ shrink rule. The same casting made of brass or bronze would be laid out with the 3⁄16″ shrink rule. For aluminum the ¼″ shrink rule would be used. See Topic 34A.

Finish Allowance

Since the casting will be rough as it comes from the mold, allowance must be made for finishing by removing stock through filing or machining.

1. The allowance for machine finish is usually a minimum of ⅛″, although greater allowance may be made.

   Machine finish is indicated on the drawing by the letter "f".

2. The allowance for finish by filing is usually $\frac{1}{32}$″. File finish is indicated on the drawing by an "ff" or "v."

Standards and Results

1. All layout and measurements should be accurate.

2. All vertical surfaces should have the proper amount of draft.

3. Proper allowance should be made for types of finish to be obtained.

4. Proper allowance should be made for shrinkage according to the kind of metal to be used in casting.

Additional Reading

Smith, *Patternmaking and Founding*

Topic 165. Making a Simple Pattern

Classification

Measuring, laying out, and shaping

Procedure

A simple pattern is a one-piece pattern that is to be molded in the drag section of a flask. Fig. 17-1.

1. Determine the type of metal to be used in the casting and select the proper shrink rule.

2. Procure a piece of stock of the appropriate kind (see Topic 163, "Patternmaking" and discussion of woods used in patternmaking) an inch or so greater in length and width and slightly thicker than needed for the finished pattern.

3. Plane or joint one face true and smooth and square one edge with the face.

4. On this prepared surface, lay out the length, width, and shape of the pattern. If any surface of the casting is to have a machined or filed finish, proper allowance must be made, *i.e.*, ⅛″ for machined finish and ⅟₃₂″ for a filed finish. Draft of ⅛″ per foot to ⅜″ per foot must also be added to the dimensions of all vertical surfaces.

5. Surface opposite face to specified thickness.

6. Cut the pattern to shape. Both edges and ends of the pattern should form an 88° to 89° angle with the layout face to form draft. This may be done with hand tools or by tilting the saw table or blade on circular saws, band saws, or jig saws, or the fence on a jointer or disc sander.

7. Smooth all rough edges with a plane or file and sandpaper.

8. If two or more pieces are to make up the pattern, such as ribs to strengthen the casting, they must also have draft.

Fig. 17-4A. Cornering Tool Used for Breaking Arrises (Courtesy Stanley Tool Co.)

9. Ribs and bosses should be attached with glue and brads. Brad heads should be set below the surface.

10. All arrises (sharp corners) except those on the parting surface should be rounded by sanding.

11. Seal all surfaces with a coat of shellac.

12. Apply fillets to inside corners and fill all nail holes.

13. Apply necessary coats of finish complying with patternmaker's practice. (See Color Code Glossary of Patternmaking Terms.)

Standards and Results

1. The pattern should be of proper shape and dimension.

2. The pattern should have draft on all vertical surfaces.

3. Surfaces to be machined should have proper allowance.

4. All fillets should be smooth.

5. All nail holes and blemishes should be filled with wax or wood filler.

6. The patternmaker's color code should be followed.

Safety Considerations

Observe all precautions in the use of hand and machine tools and heating devices. See topic on safety.

Additional Reading

Smith, *Patternmaking and Founding*

Topic *166.* Laying Out and Shaping a Cylindrical Split Pattern

Classification

Measuring, laying out, and shaping

Procedure

Some patterns would be impossible to withdraw from the mold unless they were made of two or more pieces. Cylindrical patterns are usually made in two pieces. One part of the pattern will be in the drag and the other half will be in the cope section of the flask, Fig. 17-2.

1. Select two clear pieces of stock of the appropriate kind (see Topic 163, "Patternmaking" and discussion of woods used in patternmaking) about two inches longer and at least ⅛" wider than the required pattern, and at least ¹⁄₁₆" thicker than one-half the finished pattern.

2. Joint one face of each piece so that these surfaces match.

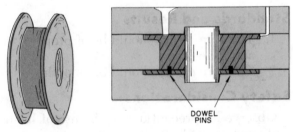

Fig. 17-5. Two-Piece Flange Pulley with Three-Part Flask

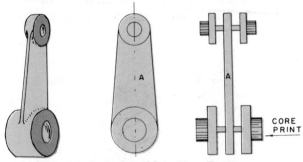

Fig. 17-6. Method of Building Up a Pattern

3. Determine the type of metal to be cast and select the proper shrink rule to lay out the full-size pattern.

4. Locate matching dowel holes toward each end and at points which will be of sufficient thickness after turning. (See Topic 113, "Reinforcing Joints with Dowels.")

5. If wooden dowels are used, one end of the dowels should be shaped like a blunt-nose bullet. Dowels should be cut to length so that they will protrude from the cope section of the pattern no more than ¼". They should be so fitted that they will keep the parts in register but do not bind when parts are separated, Fig. 17-5.

6. Glue the square ends of the dowels in the holes of the cope section. Metal dowels are screwed in with a special wrench.

7. Fasten the two pieces of stock together. If the pieces are under one foot long this may be done by using screws on each end. If the pieces are longer they should be spot glued with a piece of paper between as well as fastening with screws at each end.

8. Turn the pattern to shape on the lathe. (See Topic 102, "Spindle or Between-Center Turning.") Do not cut into the screws.

9. Remove the pattern from the lathe and cut off the extra stock.

10. Separate the cope half from the drag half of the pattern. If the glued paper method was used, hold one end upright and place a chisel along the glue line on the end grain. Force the two pieces apart.

11. Cut proper draft allowance on all vertical surfaces by filing or sanding.

12. Apply necessary coats of shellac to seal all surfaces.

Standards and Results

1. Turning should be of proper shape and dimensions.
2. Dowels should keep the two halves in register.
3. Two halves should separate easily.

Safety Considerations

Observe all safety precautions in the use of hand and machine tools. See topic on safety.

Additional Reading

Smith, *Patternmaking and Founding*

Topic 167. Laying Out and Constructing a Simple Cylindrical Core Box

Classification

Measuring, laying out, and cutting

Procedure

If the two sides of a core are identical in shape and size, it will be necessary to construct only one half of the core box. Two half-cores are made and their faces are cemented together with core oil.

1. Select a piece of surfaced stock of appropriate kind, approximately ⅜″ larger in width, thickness, and length than the finished dimensions. (See Topic 163, "Patternmaking," and discussion of woods used in patternmaking.)
2. Select the better face and draw a center line the full length of the piece.
3. Set compasses or dividers to the radius of the core, and with the centers located on the center line, scribe or layout a semicircle on each end of the stock.
4. Draw parallel lines along the face of the stock connecting the ends of the two half-circles. The material within these lines must be removed.
5. This material may be removed in one of three ways: (1) by making a series of depth cuts with a circular saw and removing the waste with a gouge; (2) by using a round molding plane the same size and shape as the core; (3) by using a core box plane. (See Topic 60, "Special Purpose Planes.")
6. Remove any rough imperfections by smoothing the surface with sandpaper held over a block of a slightly smaller radius than the core.
7. To provide proper draft for the removal of the core, saw one end at an angle of 87°-88° from the parting line.
8. Lay out the length of the core print and in a similar manner cut the opposite end.
9. Select two pieces of stock surfaced to ⅜″ thickness and large enough to cover each end of the box. Glue and brad in place, with the top edges flush with the parting line.
10. Apply coats of shellac as necessary to seal surfaces.

Standards and Results

1. The core cavity should be of proper size and shape.
2. The core cavity should be smooth.

Safety Considerations

Observe all precautions in the use of hand and machine tools. See topic on safety.

Additional Reading

Hanel, *Text in Patternmaking*, pp. 154-162
Smith, *Patternmaking and Founding*, pp. 35-40

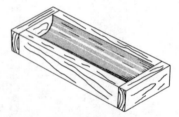

Fig. 17-6A. Cylindrical Core Box

Topic *168*. Fillets

Classification

Filler material used in patternmaking

Composition or Description

Sharp corners in a mold tend to crumble and wash away with the flow of molten metal. Rounding the inside corners with fillets permits the metal to flow more smoothly and actually adds strength to the casting. Eliminating sharp corners also reduces the occurrence of cracks and craters at the corners of castings, caused by the metal shrinking away from the sharp edges.

Fig. 17-7. Filleting Tool — Shapes of Fillets

Fillets are made from beeswax, paper, leather and plastic material. They are cove shape. (See Fig. 17-7.)

Properties

Fillets are pliable, relatively easy to form, retain their shape and are readily attached to wood.

Uses

Relatively narrow molding of pliable material used for filling out interior section of a corner. See Fig. 17-4.

Market Analysis

1. Fillets are commonly available in cove shape, in radii of ⅛″ to 1″ by eighths.
2. Standard lengths are 24″ and 36″.

Maintenance

Store flat in a cool place.

Topic *169*. Applying Fillets

Classification

Filling by rounding inside corners on a pattern

Procedure

Applying Wax Fillets

1. Apply a coat of shellac to the entire pattern.
2. Select the size of fillet to be used and the size of filleting tool to fit that fillet.
3. Secure an alcohol lamp or other suitable heating unit to provide low, constant heat.
4. Measure and cut a length of fillet material and fit it into a corner of the pattern.

5. Heat the ball end of the filleting tool so that it will be warm enough to smooth out the fillet but not melt the wax. Slowly move the filleting tool over the fillet, pressing and shaping it into the corner. (See Fig. 17-7.)
6. Work the warm filleting tool back and forth, making sure that the thin edges of the fillet adhere to the pattern and that the radius is uniform throughout.
7. Repeat the above steps and continue to fill all inside corners of the pattern. Remove excess wax from the surrounding surface by scraping.
8. Apply a second coat of shellac to seal the fillet and the entire pattern.

Applying Paper, Leather, and Plastic Fillets

Leather fillets should be softened in water to make them more flexible.

1. These fillets are usually bonded to a pattern with hot glue or shellac. If hot glue is used, the pattern should not be given a coat of shellac until all fillets are applied.
2. Apply a thin film of fast-setting glue to the corner and quickly place the fillet in position.
3. Heat the ball end of the filleting tool so that it will be warm enough to smooth out the fillet and keep the glue soft and tacky. Slowly move the filleting tool over the fillet, pressing it into the corner.
4. Continue to fill all corners of the pattern. Work the warm filleting tool back and forth, making sure that the thin edges of the fillet adhere to the pattern and the radius is uniform throughout.
5. Apply at least two separate coats of shellac to seal the pattern.

Standards and Results

1. All fillets should be smooth.
2. The edges of fillets should be bonded to the pattern.
3. Fillets should be of proper size for the pattern. Unless there is a special reason, large patterns require large fillets.

Safety Considerations

1. Care should be exercised in the use of heating equipment.
2. Filleting tool should not be overheated.

Additional Reading

Hanel, *Text in Patternmaking*, pp. 51-52
Smith, *Patternmaking and Founding*, pp. 12-13, 17

Topic *170*. Glossary of Patternmaking Terms

Boss — a built-up section of a pattern which provides a raised section in the casting to add strength where machining is to be done.

Chaplet — a specially designed shape of the same metal to be cast, which is so arranged in the mold as to support the core where the core seating is inadequate.

Color code —
   a. Black — Surfaces which are to be left unfinished.
   b. Red — Surfaces which are to be machined.
   c. Red stripes on yellow background — Seats of loose pieces.
   d. Yellow — Core prints and seats for loose core prints.
   e. Diagonal black stripes on a yellow base — Stop-offs (ribs which strengthen the pattern but which are not cast).

Cope — the upper section of the flask; the top half of a split pattern which contains the dowel pins.

Core — a core is a body of sand which projects into the cavity of the mold, forming an opening in the casting. There are two types of cores, *e.g.*, *green sand cores* and *dry sand cores*. A green sand core is a projection formed in the mold by the pattern itself. A dry sand core is a body of hardened sand which will be the recess or cavity in the casting. Core sand is coarse sand, free from clay, having a large percentage of silica mixed with water and core oil and baked.

Fig. 17-8. Split Patterns, Core Boxes, Pattern Mounted on Molding Board and Finished Grinder Head

Fig. 17-9. Patterns of Lathe Parts

Split patterns are made for headstock, bed, and toolrest holder; solid patterns for two sizes of tool rests and face plate.

Core oil may be a commercial brand or made of linseed oil. A good substitute for core oil in the school shop is one part polyvinyl-acetate glue to five parts water.

Core box — an especially prepared box into which sand is pressed to shape and dimension to form a core.

Core print — a projection on a pattern which forms a recess in the mold to seat and support a dry sand core.

Drag — the lower section of the flask; the lower half of a split pattern containing the dowel holes.

Draft — a slight bevel or taper ranging from ⅛″ to ⅜″ per foot on all vertical parts of patterns to facilitate their removal from the molded sand. The lesser amount of draft is used for those surfaces which are to be finished.

Fillet — a filler material (one quarter inside curve shape) of ⅛″ radius and upwards added to inside corners of patterns to minimize the danger of craters, cracks, washing of sand; to facilitate the flow of molten metal; and to provide added strength to the casting.

Finish — an increase in the size of a pattern to allow for working the casting to dimen-

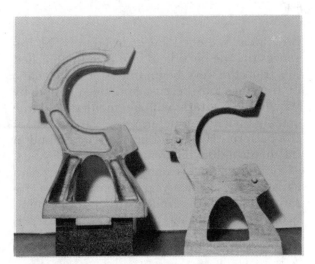

Fig. 17-10. Split Pattern of Lathe Steady-Rest—Cope on Right, Drag on Left

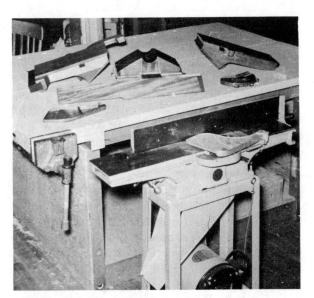

Fig. 17-11. Jointer Patterns on Bench — Jointer in Foreground

sions. The usual allowance is ⅛″ for machine finish and ⅟₃₂″ for file finish.

Flask — an open rectangular or circular frame in which sand molds are made for casting. Flasks are made of wood or pressed metal. They consist of two fitted sections; viz. the lower which is called the *drag* or *nowel* and the upper which is called the *cope*.

Match plate — a match plate is an assembly of small patterns mounted on a reinforced, flat board with the drag section attached to one face and, if there is a cope section, it is attached to the opposite face of the board with corresponding parts in alignment. It is essentially a split pattern with a board between the sections.

Many small patterns (a gang) may be attached to a board of this type by connecting the patterns with gates. Gates are channels in the mold forming a path for the flow of metal.

Parting line — the largest dimensions of a split or solid pattern.

Pattern — a wood, metal, plastic, or plaster model made in one or more parts, from which a sand mold is made for casting the part in molten metal.

Ribs — thin strips of wood attached to a pattern which strengthen the casting.

Shrink rules — patternmaker's rules made with graduations scaled larger than a standard rule in accordance with the rate of shrinkage of specified metals. See Topic 34, "Rules" and Topic 164, "Considerations for Laying Out a Pattern."

Tail print — an extension of a core print to the parting line of the pattern to permit withdrawal from the mold.

Topic *171.* The Patternmaker

Patternmaking is the trade in which materials are shaped or models constructed, from which molds are made to cast parts of metal or plastic. In addition to making new patterns, a patternmaker is often required to repair and redesign stock patterns that have been previously used and stored.

Patternmaking requires all-around skill and technical knowledge in the shaping of wood and metal. A patternmaker uses all common woodworking machines plus some special types developed particularly for the trade. He also uses all the common woodworking hand tools as well as shrink rules, core box planes, and filleting tools.

The patternmaker must be able to interpret ideas sketched by a designer. This requires that he be able to visualize the finished job from the very beginning, since the shape of the object to be cast and the method by which the pattern will be molded and the casting machined determines the design of the pattern. He should have a background in mechanical drawing to make accurate layouts.

Patternmaking is one of the highest paid skilled trades. A five-year apprenticeship is required to learn the trade. Although the number of patternmakers in modern industry is relatively small, almost every industry has need for this craft. Patternmaking is essential for development work in the construction of new models.

Topic 172. Finishing

Wood finishing is the application of selected stains, fillers, varnishes, lacquers, paints, enamels, oils, waxes, and transfers to wood. These materials may be applied by brushing, spraying, dipping, wiping, rolling, rubbing, and tumbling.

There are numerous purposes for finishing. Wood is a porous, absorbent material. Unfinished, it tends to absorb moisture, fumes, and oils which cause it to shrink, swell, check, warp, and discolor. It is also subject to fungi and insects. Under normal conditions it burns readily.

Selected finishes can retard or offset these tendencies. Finishes provide a protective coating which helps somewhat to set or stabilize the condition of a wood at the time of its finishing. Radical changes in moisture content are thus reduced. Some finishes are wood preservatives because they deter germs, fungi, and insects. There are finishes which will actually kill some bugs upon sufficient contact. Finishes improve sanitary conditions. Their use facilitates cleaning. Some finishes are fire and chemical resistant. The color in finishes has a psychological effect on people. Particular colors are used to suggest in varying degrees the presence and absence of space, weight, mass, heat, light, and emotion. Finishes enable artists or craftsmen to create desirable effects, match different kinds of wood, enhance the natural beauty of wood, or conceal its blemishes.

Stains provide transparent coloring to wood or accentuate the natural color. In general, stains may be classified as dyes, chemical stains, and pigment stains. Dyes derived from coal tar are the base of practically all modern stains. They may be divided into four groups depending on the solvents used. They are water stains, non-grain-raising stains, oil stains, and spirit stains. Chemical stains could be considered a fifth category. They are used sparingly in industry, usually to produce particular effects not obtainable by any of the other four methods. Chemical stains are tricky and often unpredictable. Those used are ammonia, chromates, and permanganates.

Varnishes give wood a relatively hard, though reasonably elastic, finish depending on the kind and grade. Varnishes may be classified as natural and synthetic. There are a great many natural gums on the market. They are derived from plants, insects, and vegetable matter, some of which have been buried for centuries and have fossilized. Natural gums are apt to be very hard and brittle.

The best-known synthetic resin used in varnishes is ester gum, made from rosin esterfied with glycerine. Practically all modern varnishes contain some synthetic resins. The name *synthetic varnish* has come to mean a quick-drying, hard, tough material that produces a film with high resistance to weathering, chemicals, and mechanical wear.

Varnishes may be divided into two types: *oleoresinous varnishes*, containing oil plus a natural or synthetic resin; and *spirit varnish*, containing solvents plus natural or synthetic resins. *Shellac* falls into the latter group. *Lacquer* is a synthetic, transparent, water-resistant finish which dries very rapidly by evaporation. Shellac added to lacquer improves adhesion and hardness, increases luster, but decreases water resistance as well as speed of drying.

Waxes provide an easy-to-apply surface coating. They are used as a type of rubbed finish, as a protection for a gum finish, and for purposes of providing and maintaining a polish. Waxes are divided into two classes: natural and synthetic. The three types of *natural wax* are paraffin, carnauba, and beeswax. *Synthetic waxes* are made by treating vegetable oil and fish oil with hydrogen.

Paint is an opaque finish which is used as a protective coating against the elements, insects, germs, fungi, water, acids, fire, dirt, oil, etc. Paints are of six main types: lead base, zinc oxide, titanium, lithopone, casein, and epoxy. The first four classes use oil, turpentine, and drier as a vehicle and binder. Casein paint is mixed with water, and may be of the oil-resin type or latex-emulsion type. The latex-emulsion type may be based on butadiene-styrene, polyvinyl acetate, or acrylic latex, which are basic plastics ingredients. Epoxy paints consist of a catalyst or hardening agent added to a pigment base. This group of finishing materials is rapidly changing and improving through industrial research.

The general properties of a good paint are: color consistency, color retention, brushability, leveling, running, covering, flooding, drying, initial gloss retention, durability, and package stability. There are special purpose paints such as metallic paints, crackle or wrinkle finish, luminous, plastic, sealers, waterproofing and many others.

Enamel is varnish paint. It is a mixture of varnish and paint pigment. It may be flat, medium gloss, or high gloss. Enamels have poor covering qualities and require undercoatings. They have most of the other properties of paint and provide a hard, long-wearing surface. Generally they are more brittle than paint.

Topic *173.* Preparing the Surface for Finishing

Classification

Leveling, smoothing and cleaning

Procedure

1. Carefully examine the article to be finished, noting and correcting defects.
2. If the surface is dented, raise the grain by (1) applying a drop of water to the dent; (2) placing a small cotton pad or absorbent paper soaked in warm water on the dent and allowing it to remain until the grain is raised, or (3) touching the pad with a hot soldering copper which changes the water to steam and causes the wood to swell quickly.
3. When the dent has been raised as much as possible or when it is raised above the surface of the wood, the surface is sanded until it is flat.
4. If there are shallow defects, scrape surface with hand scraper until all such defects are removed, or feathered out until they blend with the surface.
5. Remove grease and oil by sponging with naphtha, benzene, or lacquer thinner.
6. All traces of glue must be removed from surfaces to be finished by scraping or sanding.
7. Stains which are not removed by sanding may be bleached with oxalic acid or commercial bleaches.
8. Nail holes, checks, open joints, and large defects should be filled with patching material such as stick shellac, plastic wood, glue and sawdust, cabinet maker's cement, or putty. Patching materials should match the finished color of the wood as they will not accept wood stain. If the defect is large enough to patch

with an insert of wood, this technique is preferred.

9. Sand all surfaces, using 120 grit sandpaper and sandpaper block. Sand with the grain to remove all pencil marks and small scratches.
10. Brush surfaces thoroughly with a medium stiff brush to remove dust from the surfaces and from the pores of the wood. Excess dust may be removed with a vacuum or a tack rag, see Topic 187.

Standards and Results

1. The article to be finished should be free of all defects mentioned above.
2. Patching materials should match the finished color of the wood.
3. All pores should be free of dust.
4. The surfaces should be smooth but should not have a glazed appearance caused by using worn or too fine a grade of sandpaper, as this glaze will prevent stain from penetrating the surface properly.

Safety Considerations

1. Naphtha, benzene, and lacquer thinner should be applied in a well-ventilated room, as fumes have a toxic effect. They should be stored in a fireproof cabinet.
2. Rubber gloves should be worn when applying oxalic acid and commercial bleaches, and care must be taken to avoid splatters as bleach may burn skin or clothing.
3. When bleaches have dried, the surface should be neutralized. Surfaces bleached with oxalic acid should be neutralized with borax or baking soda; surfaces bleached with commercial bleaches should be neutralized with white vinegar. If bleaching agents come in contact with the skin, these neutralizers should be applied to the affected areas immediately.
4. Fire extinguishers of approved types should be provided in the finishing area. Safety containers should be used for cloths and rags.

Additional Reading

Soderberg, *Finishing Technology,* pp. 7-8, 167-8

Topic *174.* Paint Brushes

Classification

Bristle applicator for finishing materials

Application

Principle of Operation

The bristles of the paint brush hold the finishing material in the brush by the principles of adhesion and cohesion. The finishing material is transferred to the surface being finished by brushing with a back-and-forth motion.

Kinds and Uses

1. *Flat brushes* are used for general purpose finishing. The common flat brush is available in sizes ranging from ½″ to 4″. (Some special-purpose brushes do not fall within these limits; *e.g.,* artist's brushes are smaller than ½″, while calamine brushes may be as wide as 8″.) Some flat brushes are manufactured by arranging the bristles to form a chisel-shaped end, these are used for enameling and varnishing. Another flat brush

is made with the bristles arranged in a slanting ferrule so that one edge appears longer than the other; this brush, called a *sash tool*, is commonly used for painting window sash.

2. *Oval brushes* are used for applying paint and varnish on sash or trim. The shape permits more bristles to come in contact with the surface at any given time. This gives better spreading and a longer flow of the finishing material. Oval sash brushes (called *sash tools*) range in size from $\frac{7}{16}''$ to $1\frac{1}{2}''$, and oval trim and varnish brushes range in size from $1\frac{7}{8}''$ to $2\frac{3}{4}''$.

3. *Round brushes* have similar characteristics to those of oval brushes. They range in size from $\frac{11}{16}''$ to $1\frac{1}{16}''$ in diameter; round trim brushes range in size from $1\frac{7}{8}''$ to $2\frac{5}{8}''$ in diameter.

Principal Parts and Function of Each

1. *Bristles* are set in rubber, glue, or cement. They hold the finishing material and permit smooth application by brushing.

    Bristles are made in several categories, natural and nylon or a combination of each.

    The natural bristles are best suited for oil base paints, alkyds, varnish and shellac. Nylon bristles are best suited for water base, vinyl, acrylic, and latex paints. Natural bristles tend to go limp in water.

    A natural bristle should have what is called a flagged end (split bristle ends). This softens the brush tip and helps to spread the material more evenly.

    A good brush will have long, tapering bristles that will give a smooth flexing action that bends more at the tip than at the heel of the brush. Too stiff a brush will not smooth out the material readily and will leave brush marks on the surface.

    Natural bristles are made from hog's hair and horse hair, or the hair of other animals such as skunk, badger, mink, genet, Siberian squirrel, camel hair, etc.

    The nylon tapered monofilament is trademarked "Tynex." A new bristle called "Orel" developed by DuPont is said to possess the qualities of both the natural hairs and the tapered nylon. It has a deep brown color.

2. *Handles* are usually made of birch or maple, but in larger brushes a softwood is used to reduce weight. The handle is usually coated with a hard finish to prevent damage by finishing materials and solvents.

3. Metal or leather *ferrules* fasten the bristles securely to the handle. Together with the handle, the ferrule helps to determine the shape of the brush.

4. The *filler strip* is made of wood or hard rubber. It is used to separate the bristles, leaving a hollow space in the center of the brush to hold more paint and to give greater flexibility to the bristles. On large brushes more than one filler strip may be used.

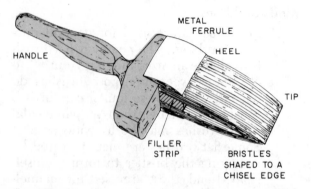

Fig. 18-4. Cut-Away View of Paint Brush

HANDLE

METAL FERRULE

HEEL

TIP

FILLER STRIP

BRISTLES SHAPED TO A CHISEL EDGE

Maintenance

Breaking-In New Brushes

A new paint brush should be soaked in linseed oil for approximately twelve hours to prepare the bristles for use. Paint pigments cling to bristles when not so treated, thus making cleaning more difficult.

Cleaning

1. Paint brushes may be cleaned by washing them in the solvent of the finishing material used. Use turpentine or mineral spirits to clean brushes used in oil paints, oil stains, and varnish (kerosene is sometimes used); alcohol to clean brushes used to apply shellac; lacquer thinner to clean brushes used to apply lacquer; and water to clean brushes used to apply water stains, latex-based paints, and other water-soluble materials.

2. Some finishers prefer to clean all brushes with soap and hot water.

3. Brushes may be cleaned in commercial brush cleaners.

Storing

Brushes should be wrapped in folds of absorbent paper after cleaning to preserve the shape of the bristles and to prevent entrance of foreign materials. They should be laid flat for storage. Brushes may be stored for short periods of time in a brush keeper or wrapped in folds of waxed paper to prevent the solvent from evaporating.

Additional Reading

Manufacturers catalogs

Topic 175. Paints and Enamels

Classification

Protective opaque coloring agent

Composition or Description

Paints and enamels are made of four ingredients: pigments, vehicles, thinners, and driers. There are three types of pigments used in paints and enamels: *white pigments* (one or more of the following — white lead, zinc oxide, lithopane, or titanium); *colored pigments* (derived from minerals or clay); and *extenders* (whiting, talc, and silica). There are two types of vehicles: *drying oils* (linseed oil, tung oil, soybean oil, or fish oil); or *varnish*. *Turpentine* and *mineral spirits* are considered the best all-round thinners, but *benzene gasoline* and other solvents may be used as well as many synthetic solvents. There are two types of driers: *oil driers* made from linseed oil or tung oil cooked with metallic drying salts and *Japan driers* made from resin varnishes cooked with metallic drying salts.

Properties

Paints and enamels produce opaque-colored finishes ranging from glossy to flat. They range from a hard brittle surface to a tough elastic surface. Paints and enamels should flow out or "float" on a surface without showing laps, brush marks, or sags. They should be of sufficient body to hide the substrate.

Uses

Paints and enamels are used to decorate, preserve, and protect wood, metal, and other materials. They may be applied for cleanliness, to make objects match, or harmonize with their surroundings, or to imitate other materials. *Oil paints* may be used on either interior or exterior surfaces depending on the composition of the paint. *Water-thinned, oil resin emulsion paints* may also be used on either the interior or the exterior. Paints are also made for special uses, i.e. paints used on toys are made with *lithopane* because it is nonpoisonous.

Market Analysis

Kinds

Paints and enamels are available as follows: gloss oil paints, eggshell or semigloss oil paints, flat oil paints, metallic paints such as aluminum, bronze, etc., oil resin emulsion paint, and luminous paint.

Sales Units

Paints and enamels are available in ¼ pints, ½ pints, pints, quarts, gallons, five gallons, and 55 gallon drums.

Maintenance

Storing

Paints and enamels should be stored in airtight metal containers and kept in a warm place. Containers which have been opened should be tightly sealed. Shaking the container after sealing or storing upside down may help to prevent the formation of a "skin" on the surface. Store paints in containers of approximate size for the quantity and label the containers.

Pour a thin film of linseed or tung oil over the surface of the paint or seal the top of the can with wax.

Reconditioning

If paint oxidizes in a can and a film is formed, this skin should be removed from the paint. Paint which contains undissolved particles is termed "lousy" in the trade and should be strained through nylon or cheesecloth. Colors of paints and enamels may be changed by the addition of appropriate type and shade of pigment mixed in oil or dryer.

Additional Reading

Soderberg, *Finishing Technology,* pp. 50-107

Manufacturers' catalogs

Topic *176.* Latex Emulsion Paints

There are three major types of latex paints: (1) butadiene styrene (B.D.S.); (2) polyvinyl acetate (P.V.A.); and (3) acrylic.

Classification

Protective opaque coloring agent

Composition or Description

Butadiene styrene is a colloidal dispersion in water of high molecular weight. With the evaporation of the water, the particles come closer together to form a clear, rubbery film. In pigmented paint, the butadiene styrene becomes the binder for the pigment film.

Polyvinyl acetate is a film former and pigment binder; water is the vehicle.

Acrylic latex is also a film former and pigment binder with water as the vehicle.

Properties

Butadiene styrene paint may be used on either interior or exterior surfaces of wood, concrete, brick, stucco, and asbestos. It may be applied by brush, roller, or spray. It dries quickly (two hours), covers well, and is washable with soap and water.

Acrylic paint may be used on either interior or exterior wood or masonry surfaces. But, when applied to new wood or wood which has been previously painted with an oil base paint, an organic solvent primer compatible with the paint (preferably made by the same manufacturer as the paint) must be applied before applying the acrylic paint. This type paint has excellent color retention, is a tough, durable finish which resists alkali and water. It has no paint odor, is fast drying, mildew resistant, and is easy to apply by either brush, roller, or spray. Equipment may be cleaned in cold water, but must be done immediately after using or every four hours, whichever comes first.

Acrylic fire-retardant paint will puff up in a fire and form a foam acting as insulation to the combustible surface underneath. This type paint has excellent hiding properties, may be applied by either brush, roller, or spray, and is available in light pastel tints. Thinning is not normally required, as it is applied while of the consistency of heavy cream, but it may be thinned with water if necessary. It dries in 30 minutes and may be recoated in two to three hours. It may be used at temperatures as low as 50°F. The surface to be painted must be free from dirt, grease, and loose paint. It may be applied over wood, metal, wallboard, cellulose board, acoustical tile, and plastic. Equipment must be washed immediately after use and may be cleaned in warm, soapy water.

Acrylic rubber base primer helps prevent cracking and checking which occurs from weathering and moisture on plywoods or solid stock. This primer may be used on either interior or exterior surfaces. It is a semi-transparent yellow which cannot be tinted. It may be top coated with either oil or latex paint, and may be applied by brush, roller, or spray at temperatures of 50°F. and above. It dries in ten to twenty minutes and may be recoated in two hours. The surfaces to be coated must be dry and free from dirt, grease, and foreign materials. Equipment may be cleaned with soap and warm water. This primer has excellent adhesion and greatly benefits the paint system used over it.

Acrylic concrete filler, surfacer, and drywall finish is used to waterproof exterior surfaces. It may be coated with oil, latex, or epoxy paints and may be applied by brush, spray, or squeegee on concrete or roller on drywall at temperatures above 45°F. Acrylic concrete filler may be tinted with universal tinting colors, dries in two hours, and can be recoated in twelve hours. It is a washable finish.

Polyvinyl acetate latex emulsion paint may be used as a sealer for indoor masonry or on exterior surfaces such as cement-asbestos shingles, brick, stucco, and concrete block. The paint covers well and dries quickly so a second coat may be applied the same day as the first. This paint applies easily with brush, roller, or spray gun, and soap and water may be used as cleaners.

Uses

Interior paints may be used on walls, woodwork, wallpaper, wallboard, drywall, brick, plaster, and plywood and may be applied over flat or semi-gloss oil paints.

Exterior latex paints may be used on shakes, shingles, clapboards, exterior wood surfaces, masonry, stucco, concrete, brick, asbestos, plywood, galvanized iron, and aluminum.

Market Analysis

Latex emulsion paints are available in flat and semi-gloss.

Sales Units

These paints are available in pints, quarts, gallons, and five gallon containers.

Maintenance

Storing

Latex emulsion paints should be stored in an air-tight metal container and should be kept at temperatures above 40°F.
CAUTION: Avoid getting latex paints on your skin and use only in well-ventilated area.

Additional Reading

Manufacturers' catalogs

Topic 177. Epoxy Finishes

There are three types of epoxy finishes: (1) two-component crystal clear finish; (2) epoxy two-component enamels; and (3) epoxy enamels ready to use without a catalyst.

Classification

Protective coating (transparent or opaque)

Composition or Description

Crystal clear two-component epoxy finish must be mixed in equal parts by stirring and allowing to stand for thirty minutes before using. It must then be used within twelve hours after mixing. Epoxy two-component enamels consist of one-third catalyst and two-thirds pigment base. It must be mixed by stirring, allowed to stand one hour before using, and must be used within twelve hours after mixing.

Epoxy finishes are a result of the reaction of biphenols with epochlorohydrin. Colored pigment may be added to achieve desired color of finish.

Properties

Epoxy clear finish is a hard, high gloss finish with good chemical and abrasion resistance. It dries in two hours, may be recoated in six hours, and reaches maximum hardness in seven days. It is non-yellowing and is heat resistant up to 350°F. It may be applied by brush, roller, or spray. It may be used on wood, metal, concrete, and drywall.

Epoxy two-component enamel may be used on either interior or exterior surfaces of iron, steel, galvanized iron, concrete, and brick at temperatures above 50°F. It dries to a high gloss in one to two hours, may be recoated in six hours, but surfaces to which the finish is applied must be clean and dry. It is heat resistant up to 275°F., chemical resistant after seven days, and is tough. It is available in many colors, but will chalk and/or change color. It may be applied with either a brush or roller. Equipment must be cleaned with a special cleaner every four hours.

Epoxy ready-to-use enamels do not require a catalyst. They are available in a great variety of colors, dry in two hours, and may be recoated in eighteen hours. They are heat resistant up to 250°F. These enamels may be applied by either brush or spray, but should be applied over a primer.

An epoxy coating has good adhesion and it is flexible. The coating resists abrasion, acids, alkalies, alcohol, detergents, water, waxes, and corrosion. It dries with a nontoxic, odorless film, but ventilation should be provided during application. Generally speaking, as the temperature increases, the time for setting decreases.

Uses

1. Epoxy two-component clear finish may be used on wood, metal, drywall, and concrete.
2. Epoxy two-component enamels may be used on iron, steel, galvanized iron, concrete, and brick.
3. Epoxy ready-to-use enamels may be used on steel, aluminum, galvanized iron, and masonry.

Market Analysis

Epoxy finishes are available in semi-gloss and high gloss.

Sales Units

Epoxy finishes are available in pints, quarts, gallons, and five gallon containers. Two-component epoxies must be purchased in two packages.

Maintenance

Storing

Epoxy finishes should be stored in air-tight metal containers at warm temperatures.

Topic *178.* Oil Stain

Classification

Transparent coloring agent

Composition or Description

1. Pigment stains are made with color ground in raw linseed oil, a solvent, and japan drier. Solvents include turpentine, linseed oil, benzene, mineral spirits, and others.
2. Preservative stains are made of pigments (chrome green, red and brown iron oxides) and creosote. Linseed oil, turpentine, benzene, and japan drier are often added.
3. Penetrating oil stains, or volatile oil stains, are made from oil-soluble coal tar colors and a solvent (turpentine, naphtha, benzene, or benzol).

Properties

Oil stains are the easiest types of stains to apply. They do not raise the grain of the wood, and if properly wiped, they do not show laps and streaks. They are especially recommended for staining to be done by amateurs.

Oil stain is a slow-drying coloring agent with limited penetrating qualities (particularly when used on hard woods), possessing the following general properties:

1. Coloring varies according to body consistency of the stain to a degree, on the number of applications and its ability to penetrate the wood.
2. Color changes in drying but is restored when finish is applied.
3. Penetrating oil stains are easy to apply by rag or brush, but they do not provide for a permanent color (fade in the sun). They must have a sealer coat to prevent bleeding.

Uses

Oil stains preserve the wood and bring out the beauty without raising the grain. They produce a uniform tone or color.

1. Pigment oil stains are used in blending colors in furniture and to give highlight effects. They have a tendency to mask out the beauty of the grain.
2. Penetrating oil stains work better on softwoods than hardwoods because of greater depth penetration. They are also used to color paste wood fillers.
3. Preservative oil stains are used for the protection of an exterior wood surface such as siding, porch floors, fencing, and any wood surface in contact with the ground.

Market Analysis

Kinds

1. Pigment oil stain.
2. Preservative oil stain.
3. Penetrating oil stain.

Sales Units

Oil stain may be purchased ready-mixed, or ingredients may be purchased and mixed as required. Available in half-pints, pints, quarts, half gallons, and gallons.

Maintenance

Storing

1. Containers must be airtight. Waxed paper spread over the top of the can before the cover is pressed into place will prevent air getting into the can and will facilitate removal of the top when the can is next used.
2. Oil stains should not be stored in strong light.

Additional Reading

Soderberg, *Finishing Technology,* pp. 125-126.

Manufacturers Catalogs

Topic *179.* Applying Oil Stains

Classification

Staining

Procedure

1. The surface to be stained should be clean, smooth, dry, and free of oil, wax, and glue.

2. Select a suitable brush. Almost any clean brush may be used but one with moderately soft bristles is preferred, especially when using penetrating oil stains. A piece of lint-free rag may be used also.

3. Dip the bristles of the brush about one-fourth to one-half their length into the stain.

4. Brush the stain on the wood. Start at the bottom of a vertical surface and work up to prevent runs. Also work from the least conspicuous to the most conspicuous part. Oil stain may be applied in any direction as the wood will absorb only limited amounts of the colored oil, and the excess which remains on the surface may be wiped off without leaving laps or streaks.

5. Allow the stain to set from a few minutes to twenty minutes (follow the manufacturer's recommendations for the brand being used). Using a soft, lint-free, absorbent material, wipe off stain in the direction of the grain. This removes excess stain before it dries on the surface and muddies or hides the grain of the wood.

6. The manufacturers of some penetrating oil stains (blonde and modern finishes) recommend that these stains be applied evenly and lightly and that they be permitted to dry on the surface, partially obscuring the grain of the wood to give uniformity of color.

7. Successive applications of oil stain normally will cause no appreciable change in color unless the preceding coat has been washed with naphtha or carbon tetrachloride to permit penetration of the next coat of stain.

8. Oil stains should be permitted to dry (at about 70° F.) for at least 18 hours before other finishes are applied.

9. It is advisable to apply a sealer coat of shellac prior to varnishing a surface that has been oil stained, to prevent lifting or bleeding through of color.

10. Oil stains may also be applied by spraying or dipping.

11. Preservative stains are not wiped.

Standards and Results

1. Oil stain should be rubbed off evenly to prevent streaks.
2. Stained surfaces should have a clear color tone; they should not have a muddy appearance.

Safety Considerations

Rags used to wipe off excess stain are highly flammable and should be deposited in a self-closing safety can for disposal as soon as possible.

Additional Reading

Soderberg, *Finishing Technology*, pp. 193-194

Topic *180.* Water Stain

Classification

Transparent dye

Composition or Description

Mainly aniline or coal-tar powder dissolved in water.

Properties

A fast-drying coloring agent with excellent penetrating qualities; color does not fade appreciably in strong light, will not bleed through lacquer or varnish; raises grain on wood if wood is not sponged or sized and sanded prior to applying stain.

Uses

Water stains are used to bring out the beauty of the grain in wood, to secure more uniform tone or color, and to color wood to harmonize with other finishes for matching, contrast, or imitation purposes.

Market Analysis

1. Colors purchased in tablets or powder form by the ounce or by the pound.
2. Water stain is the cheapest stain for school shop use.

Maintenance

Cleaning

After mixing powdered color with hot water, the solution should be filtered or strained to remove undissolved powder and impurities.

Storing

1. Powders should be stored in a moisture-proof container.
2. Solutions should be stored in covered glass or earthenware containers to prevent evaporation and chemical action of stain on metal containers.

Reconditioning

1. Color may be changed by addition of the same type of water-soluble powder.
2. Shade may be changed by addition of another color of the same type water-soluble powder or by addition of more water.

Additional Reading

Soderberg, *Finishing Technology*, p. 125

Topic *181.* Applying Water Stain — Brush Method

Classification

Staining

Procedure

Water stain is best applied by spraying, but good results may be obtained by brushing or by dipping. It is difficult to apply because of its thin consistency. It tends to drip and run, producing dark streaks.

Preparations

1. The surface to be finished should be clean, smooth, dry, and free of oil and wax.
2. When water stain is applied to wood, it tends to raise the grain, producing a fuzzy surface. This condition may be minimized by one of the following methods:

Apply glue size to the surface to be stained. This raises the grain and stiffens the raised fibers so they may be cut smooth by light sanding after thoroughly dried. A glue size may be mixed by blending a tablespoon of animal glue to a quart of warm water.

Sponge the surface to be stained with water and allow to dry. This raises the grain. Apply a wash coat of shellac (7 parts alcohol to 1 part 4-pound-cut shellac) and allow to dry. This stiffens the fibers so they may be cut smooth by sanding. Either of these operations decreases penetration but makes a smoother surface for staining.

3. Sand lightly with 120 grit sandpaper to cut smooth the stiffened, raised fibers.
4. Aniline or coal tar powder should be dissolved in warm water. Determine the approximate amount of water needed. Slowly add small portions of the selected powder or powders until the desired shade is obtained. Several light coats of water stain are better than one heavy coat because successive coats color the wood more uniformly and laps and streaks are less noticeable. Vinegar may be added to secure deeper penetration in hard woods. Ammonia may be used for this same purpose on woods that do not contain tannic acid. Test for color on a scrap piece of the same wood as that used in the project.
5. Select a brush with moderately stiff, clean bristles. It is difficult to apply water stain evenly, particularly on open-grained woods, with a soft brush.

Applying the Stain

The procedure for staining should be such that hidden areas and inaccessible parts are stained first and the most conspicuous parts stained last. This will facilitate handling and checking results.

1. Dip the bristles about half to two-thirds their length into the stain. Apply the stain to the *least* conspicuous part of the article first (for example, bottom, back, and under portions are stained first while top or front is stained last, depending on which will be seen most.) Start from the base of a vertical surface to prevent runs.
2. End grain absorbs more stain than surfaces and edges, resulting in a darker shade. This condition frequently occurs when staining sapwood. Therefore in order to secure an even tone, it is necessary to do one of the following:

   Sponge sapwood or end grain with water and then apply water stain while wood is still moist.

   Glue-size sapwood or end grain before applying water stain.

   Dilute the stain used on sapwood or end grain.
3. Apply water stain with the grain of the wood, working quickly so that the edge or end of one stroke does not dry before the next stroke is applied. Tipping the working surface of the object slightly permits the stain to flow to the lower edge of the brush stroke, thus keeping the working edge wet until the next stroke is applied. Sometimes it is advisable to brush from the bottom upward to prevent runs and streaks.
4. Care should be taken that stain does not run over edges or on surfaces as streaks will be seen in the stained surface. Care should also be taken to prevent stain from dripping from brush on work.

Standards and Results

1. The article being stained should be uniform in color with no appreciable difference in color of ends, heartwood, and sapwood unless highlights are desired.
2. There should be no holidays, brush marks, or laps in the stained surface.
3. The stained surface should be reasonably smooth.

Additional Reading

Soderberg, *Finishing Technology*, pp. 193-194

Topic *182.* Sealer

Classification
Transparent gum finish

Composition or Description
A sealer is a penetrating finish which preserves the natural beauty of the wood, helps to control grain raising, and increases moisture resistance. One coat completely soaks into the wood, leaving little or no surface film. The ingredients of sealer are: Soya or linseed oil, alkyd-ester resin, and mineral spirits.

Properties
Sealers dry fast (2 hours), do not darken woods, are not dust catchers and do not make floors slippery. They make an excellent base for all types of varnish, including polyurethane. When sanded, they do not gum up or load the sandpaper. They are heat resistant up to 140° F. They minimize unsightly color streaks on the grain of fir plywood, and reduce the tendency of grain to show through paint or enamel. Most sealers can be tinted with universal tinting colors. Ease of sanding is one of the features of sealers.

Uses
Sealers may be used as a base for other types of gum finishes on all types of interior finish, such as woodwork, floors, furniture and paneling; or they may be used as a clear gum finish when several coats are applied. They are also used on metals to prevent oxidation and on concrete to seal the surface.

Sanding sealers seal the surface porosity of woods, permitting greater buildup of finish.

Market Analysis

Sizes
Sealers are available in quart, gallon and five-gallon containers.

Kinds
Concrete sealers, sanding sealers, wood sealers.

Maintenance
Sealers should be stored in air-tight metal containers and should be kept at approximately 70° F.

Additional Reading
Manufacturers Catalogs

Topic *183.* Paste Wood Filler

Classification
Paste for filling pores of open-grained wood

Composition or Description
Oil base paste wood filler is made of silex, linseed oil, japan drier, and turpentine. Color is sometimes added for various shades. It is easy to rub off because of the lubricating qualities. Synthetic resin base filler is quick-drying, but hard to rub off the surface.

Properties
Deposits of non-volatile ingredients of the filler dry in the pores of open-grained woods, filling them and producing a smooth surface for shellac, varnish, or lacquer.

Uses
Used to fill the pores of oak, ash, chestnut, hickory, mahogany, walnut, and other open-

grained woods in order to produce a smooth surface for finishing. Two-toned effect may be secured by using a filler of contrasting color to the final finish.

Market Analysis

Grades

1. According to degree of fineness.
2. Colored or neutral.
3. Fast and slow drying.

Sales Units

Ready-mixed available in half pints, pints, quarts, and gallons.

Formula for Oil Base Filler

2 qts. linseed oil (boiled linseed oil is recommended).
1 qt. japan drier.
½ pt. turpentine.
Enough silex to produce a thick paste.
Dilute with turpentine to a creamy consistency.

NOTE: Silex should be suspended in oil several weeks in advance of use.

Maintenance

1. Store in airtight glass or metal containers.
2. Containers which have been opened should be covered tightly.
3. Homemade fillers should be made well in advance of actual use and stored until ingredients have properly mixed.
4. Filler may be softened or thinned by adding turpentine or linseed oil to oil base and a synthetic resin vehicle to the alkyd type.

Additional Reading

Deniston, *The Science of Modern Wood Finishing*, pp. 105-132
Soderberg, *Finishing Technology*, pp. 126-128

Topic *184.* Applying Paste Wood Filler

Classification

Filling of pores

Procedure

Applying Oil Vehicle Paste Wood Filler

1. Surface should be smooth.
2. Clean wood with a stiff brush, vacuum, or tack rag.
3. If paste filler is too thick, it should be thinned with turpentine to a creamy consistency. (See Topic 183, "Paste Filler.")
4. Apply paste filler by brushing evenly with or across the grain.
5. When filler becomes dull-looking (indicating that it has begun to set), it is rubbed with a piece of burlap or comparable material. This rubbing is done across the grain to prevent filler from being lifted out of pores of the wood. Some finishers follow this step by rubbing with the heel of the hand to compact the filler in the pores.
6. Final rubbing is done with a clean, soft cloth to remove all surplus oil and filler.
7. Clean out all corners with a hard wood pointed stick.
8. Allow to dry at least 12 hours. (Some fillers, particularly those which are colored, may take as long as 48 hours to dry.)
9. If pores are not completely filled, a second coat of filler may be applied. Second

coat may be thinned depending on the size of the pores to be filled.

10. When filler is dry, if necessary, the surface should be sanded lightly with 120 grit sandpaper.

Standards and Results

1. Pores should be completely filled, and a smooth, even surface should result.
2. Colored fillers accent the natural grain of the wood.
3. Surface should be clear.
4. All corners should be clean.

Safety Considerations

1. Liquids used in paste filler are flammable and should be kept away from an open flame.
2. Material used to wipe off excess filler should be placed in safety can and disposed of as soon as possible.
3. Fillers should be applied in a well ventilated room.

Additional Reading

Soderberg, *Finishing Technology*, p. 128

Topic *185.* Shellac

Classification

A spirit varnish

Composition or Description

Denatured alcohol and gum shellac.

Properties

Shellac dries dust-free in a few minutes and hardens to a pleasing luster. It can be rubbed to a fine finish, does not scratch white, and if damaged can be easily repaired. Moisture causes it to turn white and heat softens it. Orange shellac is more elastic and longer wearing than white shellac. Some finishers maintain that it has a special quality of bringing out the tone of the dark woods such as walnut and mahogany. White shellac darkens when exposed to strong light, air, or unlined metal containers. Shellac prevents oils and saps from bleeding through a finish.

Uses

Shellac is used as a finish on furniture, floors, and interior work. It is used as a sealer to prevent oils, stains, and sap from bleeding through other types of finish and as a liquid filler. Shellac is also used in the manufacture of playing cards, sealing wax, pencils, shoe polish, and numerous other articles. It is used in straw, felt, and wool hats.

Stick shellac is used as a patching material.

Market Analysis

Shapes

Flake, powder, liquid, and stick.

Grades

Shellac is sold according to the amount of shellac gum dissolved in one gallon of alcohol. Four pounds of shellac gum dissolved in one gallon of alcohol is known as "four-pound cut." Four-pound cut is the most common shellac sold.

Kinds

1. Orange shellac is partially refined shellac dissolved in alcohol. It is used where color is desired or where it is not objectionable.
2. White shellac is bleached shellac gum dissolved in alcohol. This produces a very light-colored shellac.
3. Colored shellac — colors soluble in alcohol are added to the shellac to produce the required color.
4. De-waxed shellac has had the wax removed to produce a perfectly clear shellac.
5. Stick shellac — hard sticks of shellac are available in various color shades for filling defects in wood. The shellac is softened and smoothed, using an alcohol torch and a knife.

Sales Units

Shellac can be bought in 2-, 3-, 4-, 5- and 6-pound cut in liquid measure; also pounds and sticks. Liquid shellac is available in half pints, pints, quarts, gallons and five gallon drums.

Maintenance

1. It is recommended that shellac be stored in an airtight wood container, lead-lined can, or glass container and protected from light.
2. Poor drying results when white shellac is kept longer than one year and orange shellac longer than two years.
3. Used shellac should not be poured back into the new mixture.

Additional Reading

Soderberg, *Finishing Technology*, pp. 41-44

Zinsser and Company, *The Story of Shellac*

Topic *186.* Varnish

Classification

Transparent gum finishing material

Composition or Description

1. Oil varnishes are manufactured by dissolving fossil gums or resins in oil, turpentine, or mineral spirits and driers.

   The percentage of oil in varnish has a marked effect on its properties. Varnish which has a high percentage of oil, such as spar varnish, is classed as a long-oil varnish and is highly resistant to water and alcohol and forms a fairly elastic film. Varnish which has a small amount of oil, such as cabinet rubbing varnish, is classed as a short-oil varnish which rubs well but is quite brittle. Medium-oil varnish, such as floor varnish, is an all-purpose varnish which is reasonably tough and elastic.

2. Spirit varnishes are manufactured by dissolving gums or resins in turpentine, alcohol, or benzol.

Properties

Oil Varnish

1. Good durability and hardness.
2. May be applied with brush or spray gun.
3. Transparent.
4. Drying time varies from 45 minutes to 48 hours, although 4-hour varnish is most commonly used.
5. Oil varnish is moisture resistant.

Spirit Varnish

1. Quick drying.
2. Shellac is an excellent seal to prevent oils and resins from bleeding through finish.
3. Transparent.
4. Poor exterior finish.

Uses

Varnish is used as a finish for furniture, floors, woodwork, boats, musical instruments, etc.; as insulation for electrical conductors; in the making of enamels; as a vehicle for artists' oil colors. See Market Analysis for specific use.

Market Analysis

Grades and Kinds — Oil Varnish

1. Rubbing — furniture finishing.
2. Spar — interior and marine finishing.
3. Floor — floor and general interior finishing.
4. Mixing — enamel vehicle.
5. Flat — dull interior finish.
6. Spraying — proper consistency for spraying.

Grades and Kinds — Spirit Varnish

1. Shellac — filler, sealer, or interior finsh.
2. Dammar — light, quick-drying finish; also used in lacquer.
3. Mastic — vehicle for artists' oil paints.

Sales Units

Half pints, pints, quarts, gallons, 5 gallons and 55-gallon drums.

Costs

Varies greatly because of variety of types and grades.

Storing

1. Containers must be airtight.
2. Should be kept at temperature of approximately 70°.
3. Small portions of varnish should be poured into a small container for use. Any excess that is left over should not be poured back into the supply.
4. Containers which have been opened should be tightly covered.

Reconditioning

Varnish which is not clean (called "lousy" in the trade) should be strained through cheesecloth or nylon which has been made lint-free by dipping it in a very thin solution of shellac or glue and allowing the cloth to dry before straining the varnish.

Additional Reading

Soderberg, *Finishing Technology*, pp. 27-31

Topic *187.* Applying Varnish — Brush Method

Classification

Flowing and spreading to cover a surface

Procedure

Preparations

1. The varnish, surface to be finished, and the room should all be at a temperature of approximately 70° F.
2. The room should be reasonably dust-free, or dust should be settled by sprinkling the floor with water. Room should be well ventilated.
3. Good light should shine on the surface from the opposite side from which you are working.
4. The working surface should be cleaned with a "tack rag" made by applying turpentine to a damp rag and sprinkling liberally with varnish until it is slightly sticky.
5. Select a well-made, clean chisel-type brush with fine bristles and dip one-third to one-half its length of bristles in varnish, removing surplus with a slight tap of the brush in the can.

Applying Oil Varnish

1. A small quantity of varnish (approximately the amount needed for the job) should be poured into a clean container and thinned with about 25% turpentine for the first coat. Succeeding coats need not be thinned. Left-over varnish should not be returned to the can.
2. Varnish is flowed onto the surface in the direction of the grain, brushed out across the grain and finished with long, even strokes in direction of the grain, using tip ends of bristles to smooth out the varnish.
3. Dust specks, loose bristles, and other imperfections may be removed from the wet varnished surface with the tip of the brush or by some other convenient means.

Applying Spirit Varnish

1. The surface should be wiped dust-free before applying finish.
2. Small quantity of spirit varnish (shellac most common) should be poured into a glass or porcelain container and thinned with proper solvent. For first coat, 4-pound-cut shellac is thinned to half strength, i.e., one part of shellac to one part alcohol; for second coats, two parts shellac to one part alcohol; and for successive coats, it is used without thinning.
3. Flow light film of spirit varnish on surface with grain, always keeping the working edge wet. Work quickly, because spirit varnishes dry quickly and will not permit repeated brushing.

Standards and Results

1. The coating should be smooth and even and should be free of imperfections (dust, loose bristles, lint, brush marks, sags, laps, crawls, blooms, pits, holidays, and fat edges).
2. A sufficient number of coats should be applied to build up a good body.

Safety Considerations

1. Some solvents can be harmful and should be handled with care. Keep away from your mouth and open cuts.

2. Reasonable care should be taken in the disposal of "tack rags."

3. The room should be well ventilated because of the toxic effect of the fumes from many varnishes.

4. Most solvents are flammable and should be kept away from open flame.

Topic 188. Polyurethane Varnish

Classification

Transparent plastic finish

Composition or Description

Polyurethane varnish is made of polyhydric alcohol esterified with oleic, linoleic, palmetic, and stearic fatty acids and modified with tolylene diisocyanate and mineral spirits. It is moisture curing and is oil free.

Properties

Polyurethane varnish is a very tough, hard, flexible finish which has superior resistance to chipping, abrasion, and dirt retention. It resists solvents, detergents, acids, alkalis, and hot and cold water. It dries to the touch in 20 minutes, is hard in 4 to 5 hours, and requires no sealer. It is the only transparent finish that can be used over polyethylene glycol 1000, which is a wood stabilizer. It must be used between 30% and 90% relative humidity to cure properly. Out of this humidity range, the finish may bubble.

Uses

Polyurethane varnish is used on furniture, paneling, boats, and floors in warehouses, industrial plants, gymnasiums, offices, department stores, cafeterias, and schools.

Market Analysis

Kinds

Clear gloss and semigloss.

Sales Units

Pints, quarts, half gallons, five gallons and 55-gallon drums.

Maintenance

When in use, keep away from heat and open flame.

Caution

Avoid prolonged breathing of fumes.

Additional Reading

Manufacturers catalogs

Topic *189.* Lacquer

Classification

Synthetic transparent or opaque gum finishing material

Composition or Description

Oriental Lacquer

Oriental lacquer, the earliest known lacquer finish, was made from the sap of lac trees, but this is not generally considered to be a true "lacquer" as the term is now used.

Clear Lacquer

Clear lacquer consists of:
1. Nitrocellulose (cotton treated with nitric and sulphuric acids).
2. A solvent (acetone, amyl-acetate, butyl-acetate, ethyl-acetate, etc.) which will dissolve nitrocellulose.
3. Varnish resins.
4. A diluent (toluene considered best, but benzene, etc., are also used) which will dissolve the varnish resins.
5. Plasticizers or softeners (derivatives of phosphoric and phthalic acids) which make a more elastic finish.

Tinted Lacquer

Tinted or opaque lacquers are made of the same ingredients as clear lacquer, but a pigment (color ground in japan) is added. (Color ground in oil is not suitable.)

Properties

Lacquer produces a hard, celluloid-like finish which dries very quickly. It may be brushed or sprayed on either wood or metal, although spraying is the preferred method of application. Lacquer should not be applied over oil stain, spirit stain, paste wood filler, paint, enamel, or varnish surfaces because the ingredients of lacquer are similar to those found in paint and varnish removers and they will lift these finishes. The viscosity of lacquer may be lowered by heating, a method used extensively by industry but not recommended for school shop use, because lacquer is highly flammable.

Lacquer dries rapidly to a hard finish; and once it has dried, all chemical action ceases. It produces a finish which is durable, moisture-resistant, alcohol-resistant, and is not appreciably affected by ordinary temperature changes or reasonable amounts of heat. Lacquer does not change color while drying.

Dust specks in the finished surface of lacquer are minimized by rapid drying. Its quick-drying properties shorten the time necessary to completely finish an article. Thinners made by one company are not recommended for lacquer made by another company because of the wide variety of chemical formulas used. To be reasonably sure of good results, it is best to purchase colored or tinted lacquers rather than trying to color or tint clear lacquer.

Uses

Lacquer is used as a finish on furniture, toys, jewelry, hardware, models, novelties, electric light fixtures, automobiles, items of sports equipment, etc. Clear metal lacquer is the recommended finish for articles of copper and brass to prevent tarnishing (oxidation). Lacquer sticks are used to patch defects.

Market Analysis

Kinds

1. Clear gloss lacquer
2. Clear flat lacquer
3. Water white lacquer
4. Bronzing lacquer
5. Brushing lacquer
6. Dipping lacquer
7. Shading lacquer
8. Novelty lacquer
9. Bar-top lacquer
10. Shellac mixing lacquer
11. Tinted lacquer
12. Padding lacquer
13. Lacquer sealer
14. Lacquer based primer
15. Dope or model making lacquer

Sales Units

Available in 27-cc., 70-cc., 113-cc., ¼-pint, ½-pint, pint, quart, and gallon containers, and 55-gallon drums. Also available in ½-pint aerosol cans (self-contained spray). Lacquer sticks are also available in colors for patching.

Maintenance

1. Lacquer should be stored in airtight metal containers in a room with a temperature of approximately 70° F.
2. It may be thinned by addition of a thinner recommended by manufacturers or by heating.

Additional Reading

Soderberg, *Finishing Technology*, pp. 38-41
Manufacturers Catalogs

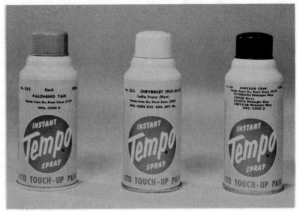

Fig. 18-2. Aerosol Cans of Lacquer (Courtesy Tempo Products Co.)

Topic *190.* Applying Lacquer

Classification

Flowing and spreading to cover a surface

Procedure

Lacquer is applied best by spraying, but it may be applied by brushing, dipping, or by padding.

Preparations

The surface to be finished should be clean, smooth, dry, and free of oil and wax. It may have an undercoat of shellac or lacquer sealer, but lacquer should not be applied directly over paint, enamel, paste filler, oil stains, or oil finishes because the ingredients of lacquer are similar to those of paint remover and will lift these finishes.

Applying by Spraying

1. If sprayed while at room temperature, lacquer should be thinned with the particular thinner specified by the manufacturer of the lacquer being used. Proportions of two parts lacquer to three parts thinner will produce a good consistency for spraying.
2. A much thinner consistency of lacquer may be applied by heating the lacquer to a temperature ranging from 80° to 160° F. Special facilities will be needed.
3. The spray gun pressure should be between 35 and 70 pounds per square inch.
4. Adjust the nozzle of the spray gun until the desired spray is obtained.

5. Squeeze and hold the trigger of the spray gun, and with a slow, sweeping motion apply the spray along the entire length of the article being sprayed. Swing past the end of the surface and release the trigger at the end of each stroke.

6. The nozzle should be held from 6 to 12 inches away from the surface to be finished. When the most effective distance has been determined, the nozzle should be kept at this distance for the entire length of each and every stroke. The body should move with the motion of the spray gun. Each successive stroke should be lapped sufficiently to blend in with the previous coat.

7. Successive coats may be applied without the sanding of preceding coat, but a sufficient time should be allowed between coats for lacquer to dry thoroughly.

8. Lacquer is available in pressurized spray containers for use in shops which do not have spray equipment.

9. Some shops use an insecticide gun to spray lacquer on small projects, but best quality results are difficult to obtain by this method.

Applying by Brushing

1. Apply brushing lacquer with a good quality, soft bristle brush, flowing lacquer on the surface. The lacquer should be reasonably thin.

2. It is necessary to work fast, keeping the working edge wet because of the quick-drying properties of lacquer.

3. A minimum amount of brushing should be done to prevent lapping and to avoid lifting previous coats.

Applying by Dipping

This is an industrial method which does not lend itself to the school shop unless the object is extremely small, in which case it may be dipped into a jar or can into which a small amount of lacquer has been poured. Suspend the object to dry.

Applying by Padding

1. Padding lacquer is applied to a lint-free pad which is rubbed on the surface to be finished. Rubbing may be done with a straight or with a circular motion, using light pressure and squeezing the pad to keep the surface wet.

2. Care must be taken in applying successive coats not to rub too long or with too much pressure in order to prevent the lifting of previous coats.

3. The use of padding lacquer is almost entirely restricted to patching defects in lacquer surfaces.

Standards and Results

1. The coating should be smooth and even and should be free of imperfections (bubbles, pinholes, blisters, runs or sags, orange peel, fat edges, bridging, granular effects, dust, loose bristles, brush marks, laps, holidays, etc.).

2. A sufficient number of coats should be applied to build up a good body.

Safety Considerations

1. A mask should be worn while spraying lacquer to prevent inhalation of fumes because they have a toxic effect.

2. The mask should be wiped with medicinal alcohol prior to using in order to prevent transmission of germs from one user to another.

3. Lacquer should be applied in a well ventilated room because of the toxic effect of fumes.

4. Lacquer must be kept away from open flame. Special equipment should be used to apply heated lacquer.

Additional Reading

Soderberg, *Finishing Technology*, pp. 144-158

Topic *191.* Super Finishes

Classification

Protective opaque or transparent finishes

Super finishes are synthetic coatings that cure (dry) by a chemical reaction. There are two types: (1) *catalyzed synthetic lacquer* and (2) *catalyzed synthetic varnish*.

Composition or Description

Catalyzed synthetic lacquer is made of *nitro cellulose and a chemically reactive converting resin.*

The composition of catalyzed synthetic varnish is usually *alkyd resins in combination with urea formaldehyde* and/or *melamine formaldehyde resins*. These cure (harden) by converting or polymerizing, and require 110° to 160°F. for 60 minutes.

Properties

Catalyzed synthetic lacquer is superior to conventional nitrocellulose lacquer. It is highly resistant to wear, marring, water, alcohol, and detergents. It can be pigmented (colored) like any conventional finish and is available from low luster to high gloss. It rubs well. The pot life after the catalyst is added is fourteen days. It must be applied by spraying.

Catalyzed synthetic varnish is a two-coat clear finish. It has excellent resistance to marring, abrasion, water, alcohol, detergents, and other household cleaners. It is more difficult to spray than conventional finishes and a special undercoat is required. The pot life varies from eight hours to twenty-one days depending on the catalyst used. Some catalyzed synthetic varnishes will air dry at room temperature, others need heat (120° to 140°F. for 20 to 30 minutes). It rubs well. This finish may be dipped or curtain coated.

Both of these finishes are impervious to foods, fruit juices, ammonia, cleaning fluids, bleach, nail polish, and nail polish remover.

Uses

Super finishes are used on household and institutional furniture, kitchen cabinets, and wall paneling. Because of equipment required for application and drying, it is not normally used in school shops.

Maintenance

Storing

Super finishes should be stored in separately packaged, air-tight metal containers and should be kept at 70°F. or above.

Additional Reading

Paint manufacturers' technical pamphlets

Topic *192.* Spray Gun

Classification

Controlled pressure atomizer for applying finishing materials

Application

Principle of Operation

Spray guns (in common use) depend on a stream of compressed air or a pressure pump which atomizes the liquid being sprayed so that a controlled, uniform coating of finishing material may be applied to the surface.

The material to be sprayed must be thin so that atomization will allow even application, yet set quickly enough to prevent sagging. Solvents used for thinning must be compatible with the base material so the cohesiveness of the finish is not altered. An ideal solvent will blend in with the base, but evaporate before most of the paint particles reach the surface. The remaining solvent keeps the paint wet enough to form a nonsagging film.

The use of too much solvent or over-thinning can change the chemical and physcial characteristics of the finishing material. This may result in too thin a film, which will cause such problems as orange peel, solvent bubbles, or dry spray.

Temperature and humidity enter into the evaporation or drying of the paint particles. Cold increases drying time, while humidity decreases evaporation.

Kinds and Uses

Spray guns are used to spray paints, lacquers, stains, liquid fillers, sealers, varnishes, and other liquids.

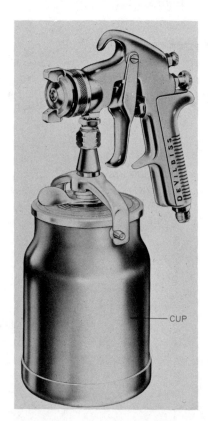
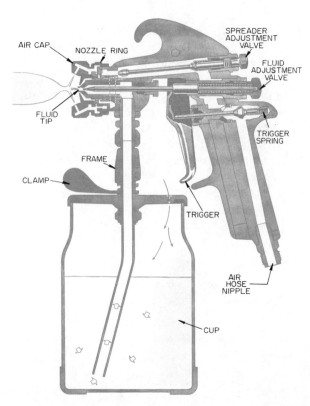

Fig. 18-3. Spray Gun and Diagram of External Mix Operation (Courtesy DeVilbiss Co.)

Types of nozzles produce various shapes of spray such as round, oval, and fan. Forty-five degree nozzles for overhead spraying are available in the above shapes.

Spray guns are of several types with different systems of forcing material to the nozzle, mixing, and controlling flow of the air or the material. The size is designated by the capacity of the container.

1. Suction type — material to be sprayed is siphoned up to the nozzle.
2. Pressure type — material to be sprayed is forced to the nozzle by air pressure.
3. Internal mix type — the material to be sprayed is mixed with compressed air inside the nozzle.
4. External mix type — the material to be sprayed is mixed with air outside the nozzle.
5. Bleeder type — compressed air flows continuously through the nozzle and only the material being sprayed is controlled by the trigger.
6. Non-bleeder type — the trigger controls the flow of both compressed air and the material being sprayed.

Principal Parts and Function of Each

1. *Container or cup,* made from an aluminum alloy, which holds the spraying liquids.
2. *Cap* to which is attached a fluid tube through which liquid flows to the nozzle.
3. *Frame* which contains passages for air flow.
4. *Trigger and needle valve* for regulating flow of air or material, or both.
5. The hardened steel *fluid tip* through which liquid flows when needle is drawn back.
6. *Spring* for closing needle valve and holding trigger forward.
7. *Nozzle* which determines whether air and liquid will mix internally or externally, and through which air and liquid are projected from the gun.

8. *Nozzle lock-ring* which holds the nozzle in fixed position.
9. *Drain cap* — some spray guns have a small reservoir to collect moisture which condenses within the gun. This moisture may be drained off by removing this cap.
10. Threaded *air hose nipple* to which the air pressure hose is connected.

Maintenance

Cleaning

1. Remove the cap from the container and pour out the liquid.
2. Partially fill the container with solvent of the material just sprayed and replace the cap.
3. Spray solvent through using steady flow and then intermittent spurts for cleaning the nozzle.
4. With a lint-free cloth saturated in solvent, wipe off nozzle and other parts.
5. Remove cap and pour out remaining solvent.

Lubrication

Lubricate trigger assembly periodically.

Market Analysis

Capacity

Spray guns used in schools and home workshops usually have a one-pint container but quart, half-gallon, and gallon sizes are available. Industrial types spray directly from drums of larger sizes.

Additional Reading

Soderberg, *Finishing Technology,* pp. 158-162

Manufacturers Catalogs

Topic *193.* Abrasive Flours — Pumice and Rotten-stone

Classification

Fine powdered abrasive

Composition or Description

1. Pumice is a light, porous substance obtained from volcanic lava. The word itself means foam, and indicates that it is caused by the expansion of water vapor in an eruption of lava under water. This solidified foam is ground into a very fine abrasive powder which is grayish-white in color.
2. Rottenstone is made from decomposed limestone ground into a very soft, greenish-gray abrasive powder which is finer than pumice.

Properties

1. Pumice is a sharp cutting agent which smooths and polishes by abrading while causing fine, hairlike scratches.
2. Rottenstone is a sharp cutting agent, finer than pumice, which smooths and polishes although leaving very fine scratches (practically invisible).

Uses

1. Pumice is used with water, paraffin oil, or various rubbing oils to produce an extremely smooth, polished surface on finished objects. The degree of luster is determined by the lubricant.
2. Rottenstone is used with water, paraffin oil, or various rubbing oils to produce a smoother polished or lustrous surface after the finished object has been rubbed with pumice.

Market Analysis

1. Both pumice and rottenstone are available in powder form.
2. Pumice is available in F (floated), FF (double floated) and FFF (triple floated).
3. Rottenstone is available in but one grade.
4. Both pumice and rottenstone are sold by the pound or multiples thereof.

Maintenance

1. Both pumice and rottenstone are often kept in shakers for ease of application and to prevent foreign grit from getting into the flours.
2. Should be stored in a dry place.

Topic 194. Waxes — Liquid, Paste

Classification

Protective and polishing film.

Composition or Description

Waxes are vegetable, animal, or mineral fat-like substances which are harder and not as greasy as fats.

Vegetable Waxes

1. Carnauba wax — cream-colored wax obtained from the leaves of the carnauba palm of Brazil.
2. Candelilla wax — obtained from a Mexican plant.
3. Japan wax — obtained from berries of Japanese and Chinese sumac trees.

Animal Waxes

1. Beeswax — amber-colored wax secreted by the honeybee to form the honeycomb.
2. Shellac wax — exuded by the lac bug.
3. Chinese wax or insect wax — secreted by insects found on certain evergreen trees in China.
4. Spermaceti — obtained from the oil of the sperm whale and the dolphin.

Mineral Waxes

1. Paraffin wax — opaque white wax, a petroleum distillate.
2. Montan wax — obtained from peat and lignites.
3. Ozocerite — colorless or white mineral wax.

Synthetic Waxes

Ceresin or ceresino wax.

Properties

Waxes are dissolved in turpentine, mineral spirits, gasoline, and kerosene. They are only partially soluble in alcohol and are insoluble in water. Some waxes will turn white when they come in contact with water, and most waxes may be removed from a surface with hot water. They may be colored by adding color ground in japan to the natural wax. Carnauba wax is the hardest of the waxes and has good polishing qualities. Because of these properties, most commercial waxes contain some carnauba wax mixed with other kinds of waxes.

Uses

Wax is used to produce a hard, tough film on a surface. This film of wax protects the surface, making it water repellent and abrasion resistant. It is widely used on furniture, floors, automobiles, and plastic products. It is used when etching to prevent acid from coming in contact with surfaces which are not to be etched. Wax fillets are used in pattern-making, and melted beeswax is sometimes used to flatten varnishes and enamels. Waxes are used to reduce friction on sliding surfaces such as drawer slides and skiis. It is also used on tool and machine parts as a lubricant and to prevent rust. (NOTE: It is not interchangeable with oil lubricants for bearings.) More wax is used in the making of candles than for any other purpose.

Market Analysis

Shapes

Wax is available in paste, liquid, cake, fillet, flake, and powdered form.

Sizes

Fillets ⅛″, ³⁄₁₆″, ¼″, ⁵⁄₁₆″, ⅜″ and ½″ radius.

Sales Units

1. Paste wax is sold by the pound (and fractions and multiples of a pound).

2. Liquid wax is sold in pint, quart, ½-gallon, gallon, and 5-gallon containers and 55-gallon drums.
3. Cake wax is sold in one-pound cakes.
4. Wax fillets are sold in boxes which contain a number of two-foot lengths, the number varying with the radius of the fillet.
5. Flake and powdered waxes are sold by the pound.

Maintenance
Waxes may be softened by heating in hot water.

Additional Reading
National Paint, Varnish, and Lacquer Manufacturers Association, *Tales of the Genie of the Paint Pot*

Topic *195.* Preparing and Applying a Wipe-on Gum Finish

Classification
Building up a gum finish by wiping on successive coats of film

Procedure
A suitable wiping finish can be made by mixing 25% *boiled* linseed oil and 75% four-pound-cut white shellac or 25% *boiled* linseed oil, 25% mixing lacquer, and 50% four-pound-cut shellac. Either mixture should be shaken well before applying. The latter is more water resistant.

1. Cut a piece of lint-free cotton cloth about eight inches square. Make a wad of cotton waste about two inches in diameter and place it in the center of the cotton cloth.
2. Saturate the ball of cotton waste in the solution. Wrap the saturated ball in the piece of cotton in such a way that the loose ends are gathered at the top.
3. Rub the mixture on the surface of wood in a back-and-forth motion, following the direction of the grain. Keep enough mixture on the rag so that the entire surface is evenly coated.

4. After coating the entire surface three or four times, let dry for twenty-four hours and repeat process until a satisfactory body is built up. Sanding between coats is not usually necessary although light sanding may be done if irregularities appear.
5. If a high luster is desired, the object may be waxed after the final coat is dry.

Standards and Results
1. The coatings should be smooth, even, and free from laps and streaks.

Safety Considerations
1. Finish should be applied in a well ventilated room.
2. Saturated rags should be disposed of or kept in an airtight, safety container.

Additional Reading
Manufacturers Catalogs

Topic 196. Finish Schedules for Close and Open Grain Woods

Finish Schedule for Close Grain Woods

1. Surface preparation is very important on close grain woods. Make sure all sanding scratches have been worked out by the use of fine grit papers. (Topic 173.)
2. On softwoods it is recommended that a non-grain raising stain be used, such as an oil stain. On hardwoods such as maple or birch, a water stain will give better tone quality.
3. Oil stains may be applied to the surface without other preparation. Water stain will raise the grain so the surface must be either sponged or glue sized prior to staining. (Topics 179 and 181.)
4. If surface is to be of a natural finish, steps 2 and 3 are omitted.
5. Apply a sealer coat (Topics 182-185). Dry according to specifications. A thinned coat of lacquer or varnish may be used as a sealer coat if succeeding coats are of the same material. (Topics 186-190.) Sand lightly using 220 grit paper.
6. Apply the synthetic finish. Be sure the finish and sealer coat are compatible. (Topic 187.) Dry 24 hours. Sand lightly with 220 grit paper to produce a level surface.
7. Apply a second coat of finish. Dry 24 hours.
8. Inspect the surface to be sure necessary buildup of finish is adequate. Several more coats may be necessary to produce leveling. Proceed with each coat as in step 7. Lightly sand between coats.
9. Apply final coat.
10. Final coat is rubbed with #400 grit, wet or dry, abrasive paper using water as a lubricant. A *stearate paper* may also be used dry. Remove all lumps or irregularities on the surface.
11. To produce a high gloss finish, rub the surface with pumice stone and oil, followed by rottenstone and oil. (Topic 193.)
    NOTE: Some finishers use steel wool between coats for smoothing the surface. This is not recommended. Small particles of the steel remain in the surface to rust and cause imperfections.
12. A coat of rubbed down paste wax over the finished surface will protect and make cleaning easier.

Finish Schedule for Open Grain Wood

1. Surface preparation is very important for any finish. (Topic 173.)
2. Select a water stain to match the color tone of the wood or the desired shade.
3. Apply a glue size or a shellac wash coat to stabilize the wood fibers, lightly sand smooth with worn 120 grit paper. (Topic 181.)
4. Apply stain to the least noticeable surfaces first. (Topic 181.) Dry 12 hours.
5. Apply a wash coat of shellac to seal in the stain. Dry one-half hour to one hour.
6. Apply paste filler colored to match tone desired. (Topic 183 and 184.) Dry 24 hours.

7. Apply a sanding sealer. (Topics 182-185.) Dry according to specifications. Sand lightly with 220 grit paper being careful not to remove any stain.

8. Apply synthetic finish. Be sure that the finish and sealer are compatible. (Topic 188.) Dry 24 hours. Sand with 220 grit paper to level the surface.

9. Apply second coat of finish. Dry 24 hours.

10. Inspect the surface to be sure buildup of finish is adequate. Several more coats may be necessary to produce leveling. Proceed with each coat as in step 9. Lightly sand between coats.

11. Final coat is rubbed with #400 grit, wet or dry, abrasive paper using water as a lubricant. A stearate paper may also be used dry. Remove all lumps or irregularities on the surface.

12. To produce a high gloss finish, rub the surface with pumice stone and oil, followed by rottenstone and oil. (Topic 193.) (Some finishers use steel wool between coats for smoothing the surface. This is not recommended. Small particles of the steel remain in the surface to rust and cause imperfections.)

13. A coat of rubbed-down paste wax over the finished surface will protect and make cleaning easier.

Topic *197.* Decalcomania Transfers — Decals

Classification

Surface decoration

Composition or Description

A special coated decalcomania paper, or unsized paper which is coated with starch or glue, is covered with a coat of clear lacquer or varnish. A design is printed, silk-screened, drawn, or painted on this finished surface. When the decal is soaked in water, the starch or gum coating is softened, making it possible for the lacquer or varnish film on which the design is imposed to slide off and adhere to the surface of the object to be decorated.

Properties

Most decals are made in colorful designs which, if used appropriately, serve as a simple and effective way to decorate an object. The backing of varnish or lacquer is so clear and transparent as to be practically invisible when the decal is applied.

Uses

Decals are used to decorate china, novelties, trays, windows, canister sets, children's furniture, toys, models, and games. They are also widely used on luggage and car windows in the form of letters and other insignias.

Market Analysis

Sales Units

1. Decalcomania paper is available in sheets 25″ x 36″.

2. Commercial decals are usually sold in sheets 4¾″ x 3¾″ and approximately 8″ x 6″. Many of the larger size sheets have several designs on each sheet.

Maintenance

1. No special maintenance is required.

2. If no protective coating is applied over the decal, it may be removed from a

surface with a special decal liquid remover, or a damp cloth may be applied to the decal and allowed to remain for approximately 30 minutes at which time the decal may be lifted from the surface.

3. Decals should be stored in a cool, dry place.

Additional Reading

Manufacturers Catalogs

Topic *198.* Glossary of Finishing Terms

Abrasive — a graded grit in the form of flour, compound, or a coating on paper or cloth used in cutting and smoothing.

Acrylic resins — a thermo polymer resin soluble in acetone and methyl ethyl.

Adhesion — the mechanical or molecular affinity of one material to another as in paints.

Air bubbles — a defect in finishes caused by air vapors or gasses trapped in the surface resulting in bubbling, pitting, and blistering.

Alligatoring — a pattern of cracks in a finished surface caused by an uneven expansion and contraction of separate coats of finish.

Aniline dyes — soluble colors made from aniline oils or coal tar derivatives and used in the manufacture of fast-color dyes and stains.

Banana oil — a common name for amyl acetate, a colorless liquid used as a solvent and vehicle for lacquers and bronze powders.

Bite — the quality of a finishing material which tends to soften or partially dissolve the preceeding coat.

Bleach — a chemical solution used to blanch or permanently lighten the coloring of the wood.

Bleeding — the seeping of colors through a finish.

Blending — a uniform mixing of liquids and colors.

Blushing — a milky, cloudy effect in clear finishes, caused by excessive humidity or improper solvent balance.

Body — the weight or thickness of a film or the viscosity of a finishing material.

Boxing — the intermixing or blending of the ingredients of finishing materials by pouring back and forth from one container to another.

Burning-in — the process of patching by melting a stick shellac into a surface defect or scratch.

Casein — a base for water soluble paints derived from milk and soya beans.

Checking — small pattern of cracks due to uneven surface drying or film failure.

Cohesion — the molecular affinity of the molecules of the same material to each other.

Crawling — the formation of patches of globules of finishing materials caused by either excessive surface tension of the material or lack of bite with the under surface.

Crinkling — a shriveling of thick edges of finishing materials caused by too heavy a coating or improper bonding.

Cut — the term used to designate the number of pounds of shellac resin per gallon of solvent, as 4-pound-cut shellac.

Drier — a liquid with high oxidizing properties added to finishing materials to accelerate drying and hardening and for mixing of colors.

Earth pigments — dry, finely ground, colored, mineral matter used for coloring in paints.

Egg shell — a term used to denote a low gloss, hard finish.

Elasticity — a property in flexible film finishes which permits bending and contracting of materials without damaging the finish.

Enamel — an opaque, relatively glossy, pigmented, varnish-paint mixture used to color and coat a surface.

Extender — a filler substance used to increase coverage in paint or enamel.

Fat edges — built-up finish on an edge due to overlapping.

Filler — a finishing material used to fill open grain or minor defects to obtain a level, compact wood surface.

Flow — the property of a liquid to spread or level to an even film.

French polish — a high gloss finish obtained by applying with a pad a solution of shellac and alcohol mix and adding a few drops of linseed oil for lubrication.

Glue size — a thin glue solution applied to a wood surface to raise and stiffen the fibers prior to finish sanding, also used to partially seal end grain.

Grain raising — the swelling and lifting of the short, surface wood fibers.

Gum finish — a gum material dissolved and suspended in an oxidizing or evaporating liquid.

Holiday — a trade expression to describe that section of the finish surface which was missed by the finisher.

Lacquer — a finishing material with a nitro-cellulose base which dries by evaporation of the solvents.

Lap — to extend or overlay one coat over the edge of another coat.

Leveling — the property of a material to flow evenly, free of brush marks, runs, sags, or fat edges.

Linseed oil — a prepared vegetable oil, raw or boiled, used as a vehicle and a binder in paints. It dries by oxidation.

Lousy — a condition of small foreign particles in paint materials or brush.

Mineral spirits — a by-product of the distillation of petroleum, used as a solvent or thinner.

Oil rubbing — the process of smoothing and leveling by rubbing with abrasives (fine sandpaper, fine pumice, and rottenstone) and one of the mineral oils to produce a dull finish.

Opacity — the quality of a pigment to cover or hide a surface.

Orange peel — a pebbled surface condition caused by rapid drying or improper application.

Paint remover — a finish dissolving or destroying compound.

Pigment — coloring matter used in the preparation of finishing materials.

Pumice — a porous volcanic lava which has been finely pulverized into a graded abrasive flour used in smoothing, polishing, and cleaning.

Resin — natural or synthetic gums with properties especially suited to the preparation of varnishes and enamels.

Retarder — a solvent used to slow the drying or hardening rate of a finish.

Rottenstone — a soft, greenish-gray limestone clay, pulverized into very fine abrasive flour and used for smoothing and polishing. Rottenstone is finer than the finest grade of pumice.

Rubbed finish — a smooth, flat, built-up, uniform body of gum produced by the application, leveling, and toothing of successive coatings.

Rubbing oil — any one of several kinds of mineral oil used as a lubricant with fine abrasives in rubbing down a finish.

Sheen — the luster of a rubbed surface.

Shellac — a natural resin which is soluble in alcohol to form a sealer or gum finish.

Silex — graded, powdered quartz used as a base for paste filler.

Silicate — a finely ground (floured) powder of quartz.

Solvent — a thinner used to dissolve a finish to assist in oxidizing and to give brushing and flowing quality.

Stain — a coloring substance or dyestuff with a water, oil, or spirit base used to obtain defined tones, shades, and colors.

Substrate — the unfinished base material to which finish is applied.

Thinner — a liquid used in finishes to extend the vehicle or gum.

Titanium dioxide — is a white pigment derived from a mineral composed of iron, titanium, and oxygen. It has been processed to resist chalking and has better color retention than any other known pigment.

Vehicle — the liquid in which the base material is suspended.

Wash coat — a thin solution of shellac, lacquer, or other gum finishing material

Reference List

Books

Boerhave, Beekman W., *Wood Dictionary.* Vol. 1, *Commercial and Botanical Nomenclature of World Timbers, Sources of Supply,* 1964. Vol. 2, *Production, Transport and Trade,* 1965. Vol. 3, Industry and Applications, 1966. New York: American Elsevier Publishing Company.

Brown, H. P., A. J. Panshin, and C. C. Forsaith, Textbook of Wood Technology. Vol. 1, *Structure, Identification, Defects and Uses of the Commercial Woods of the U.S.,* 1949, 2nd Ed. by A. J. Panshin and DeZeeuw, 1963. Vol. 2, *Physical, Mechanical, and Chemical Properties of the Commercial Woods of the U.S.,* 1952. New York: McGraw-Hill Book Company.

Capron, J. Hugh, *Wood Laminating.* Bloomington, Illinois: McKnight & McKnight Publishing Company, 1962.

Clark, W., *Veneering and Wood Bending in the Furniture Industry.* Long Island City, New York: Pergamon Press, 1965.

Cramlet, Ross C., *Woodwork Visualized.* Milwaukee: Bruce Publishing Company, 1950.

Dahl, Alf, and J. Douglas Wilson, *Cabinet Making and Millwork.* Chicago: American Technical Society, 1956.

Deniston, G. L., *The Science of Modern Wood Finishes.* Research Press, Inc., 1949.

Douglass, J. H., *Woodworking With Machines.* Bloomington, Illinois: McKnight & McKnight Publishing Company, 1960.

Durbahn, Walter E., and Elmer W. Sundberg, *Fundamentals of Carpentry,* Vol. II. Chicago: American Technical Society, 1963.

Feirer, John L., *Advanced Woodwork and Furniture Making.* Peoria: Chas. A. Bennett Company, 1963.

————, *Industrial Arts Bench Woodworking.* Peoria: Chas. A. Bennett Company, 1965.

————, *Industrial Arts Woodworking.* Peoria: Chas. A. Bennett Company, 1965.

————, *Woodworking for Industry.* Peoria: Chas. A. Bennett Company, 1963.

Feirer, John L., *Cabinetmaking and Millwork,* Peoria: Chas.A. Bennett Company, 1967.

Fryklund, Verne C., and Armand J. LaBerge, *General Shop Woodworking.* Bloomington, Illinois: McKnight & McKnight Publishing Company, 1963.

Furniture Development Council. *Design Manual for Cabinet Furniture.* Long Island City, New York: Pergamon Press, 1959.

Graham, F. D., and T. J. Emery, *Audel's Carpenter's and Builder's Guide.* New York: Theodore Audel and Company, 4 vols., 1963.

Groneman, Chris H., *General Woodworking.* New York: McGraw-Hill Book Company, 1964.

Groneman, Chris H. and Everett Glazener, *Technical Woodworking,* New York: McGraw-Hill Book Company, 1966

Gunerman, Milton, *How to Operate Your Power Tools,* New York: Home Craftsman Publishing Corporation, 1950.

Hackett, Donald F. and Patrick E. Spielman, *Modern Wood Technology,* Milwaukee: The Bruce Publishing Company, 1968.

Hanel, Alexander B., *Text in Patternmaking.* Milwaukee: Bruce Publishing Company, 1949.

Highland, Harold J., *Painting and Decorating Manual.* New York: Theodore Audel and Company, 1963.

Hillis, W. E., ed., *Wood Extractives and Their Significance to the Pulp and Paper Industries.* New York: Academic Press, 1962.

Hjorth, Herman, and William F. Holtrop, *Operation of Modern Woodworking Machines.* Milwaukee: Bruce Publishing Company, 1959.

————, *Principles of Woodworking.* Milwaukee: Bruce Publishing Company, 1961.

Klenke, William W., *The Art of Wood Turning.* Peoria: Chas. A. Bennett Company, 1954.

Koch, Peter, *Wood Machining Processes,* New York: The Ronald Press Co., 1964.

Lammey, W. C., *Power Tools and How to Use Them.* Chicago: Popular Mechanics Press, 1950.

Ludwig, O. A., *Metalwork Technology and Practice.* Bloomington, Illinois: McKnight & McKnight Publishing Company, 1962.

Mix, Floyd M., and Ernest H. Cirou, *Practical Carpentry.* Homewood, Illinois: Goodheart-Willcox, 1963.

Newell, Adnah C., and William F. Holtrop, *Coloring, Finishing, and Painting Wood.* Peoria: Chas. A. Bennett Company, 1961.

O'Neill, James M., *Early American Furniture.* Bloomington, Illinois: McKnight & McKnight Publishing Company, 1964.

Panshin, Alex J., and others, *Forest Products.* New York: McGraw-Hill Book Company, 1962.

Pelton, B. W., *Furniture Making and Cabinet Work.* Princeton, New Jersey: D. Van Nostrand Company, 1961.

Ramsey, Charles G. and Harold Sleeper, *Architectural Graphic Standards,* New York: John Wiley & Sons, October, 1966.

Smith, Robert E., *Machine Woodworking.* Bloomington, Illinois: McKnight & McKnight Publishing Company, 1958.

————, *Patternmaking and Founding.* Bloomington, Illinois: McKnight & McKnight Publishing Company, 1954.

Soderberg, George A., *Finishing Technology,* Bloomington, Illinois: McKnight & McKnight Publishing Company, 1969.

Spence, William P., *Architecture: Design-Engineering - Drawing,* Bloomington, Illinois: McKnight & McKnight Publishing Company, 1967.

Tierney, William F., *Modern Upholstering Methods.* Bloomington, Illinois: McKnight & McKnight Publishing Company, 1965.

Towers, Whitney K., *Cabinet Maker's Manual.* New York: Home Craftsman Publishing Corp., 1957.

Townsend, Gilbert, *The Steel Square.* Chicago: American Technical Society, 1947.

Wagner, Willis H., *Modern Carpentry,* Homewood, Illinois: Goodheart-Wilcox Co. 1969.

————, *Modern Woodworking,* Homewood, Illinois: Goodheart-Wilcox Co., 1967.

Waring, Ralph G., *Modern Wood Finishing.* Milwaukee: Bruce Publishing Company, 1963.

Periodicals

Woodworking Digest, Hitchcock Publishing Co., Hitchcock Building, Wheaton, Illinois.

Government Publications

Department of Agriculture, Washington, D.C.
Identification of Furniture Woods, The, Circular No. 66.
Trees, Yearbook 1949.

Department of Agriculture, Forest Products Laboratory, Madison, Wisconsin.
Bending Solid Wood to Form.
Blood Albumin Glues.
Casein Glue.
Effect of Nail Points on Resistance to Withdrawal, The.
Important Factors in Gluing with Animal Glue.
Occurrence and Removal of Glue Stains.
Some Methods of Gluing Light Laminated or Plywood Curved Shapes from Veneer.
Strength of Commercial Liquid Glues.
Strong and Weak Glue Joints.
Vegetable Glue.
Wood Handbook.

Department of Agriculture, Forest Service, Washington, D. C.
Hardwoods of the South.
Useful Trees of the United States:
    Birch, No. 22.
    Cedar, No. 14.
    Eastern Hemlock, No. 10.
    Oak, No. 20.
    Redwood.
    Sweetgum, No. 28.
    Western Hemlock, No. 11.
    White Ash, No. 18.

Department of Commerce, Superintendent of Documents, Washington, D.C.
American Hardwoods and Their Uses.
American Southern Pine.

Housing and Home Finance Agency, Washington, D.C.
Technique of House Nailing.

Association and Industrial Publications

Adjustable Clamp Company.
Clamps.
American Plywood Association, Tacoma, Washington.
Softwood Plywood Grades
Architectural Wood Institute
A Guide to Wood Specie Selection
Atkins Saw Division, Borg-Warner Corporation, Indianapolis, Indiana.
Saw Sense.
Behr-Manning Company, Troy, New York.
How to Sharpen.
Sandpaper — Why and How.
Cincinnati Tool Company, Cincinnati, Ohio.
A Clamp for Every Purpose.
Delta Power Tool Division, Rockwell Manufacturing Company, Pittsburgh Pennsylvania.
Getting the Most Out of Your Abrasive Tools.
Getting the Most Out of Your Band Saw and Scroll Saw.
Getting the Most Out of Your Circular Saw and Jointer.
Getting the Most Out of Your Drill Press.

Getting the Most Out of Your Lathe.
Di-Noc Company, Cleveland, Ohio.
Transveneer Plastic Veneer.
Fine Hardwoods Association, Chicago, Illinois.
A World of Fine Hardwoods
Hardwood Plywood Manufacturers' Association, Arlington, Virginia.
Hardwood Plywood Grades

Henry Disston & Sons, Inc., Philadelphia, Pennsylvania.
Disston Saw, Tool and File Manual.
Grinding Wheel Institute, 2130 Keith Bldg., Cleveland, Ohio.
Use, Care, and Protection of Abrasive Wheels.
Mahogany Association, Inc., 75 Wacker Drive, Chicago, Illinois.
Mahogany Book, The.
National Casein Company, Chicago, Illinois.
Gluing Guide for Woodworking
National Glue Manufacturers Association, New York.
Animal Glue in Industry.
National Hardwood Lumber Association, Chicago, Illinois.
Grading Rules for Hardwood Lumber
National Paint, Varnish, and Lacquer Manufacturers Association, 1500 Rhode Island Avenue, Washington, D.C.
Tales of the Genie of the Paint Pot.
National Particleboard Association, Washington, D.C.
Proceedings of First Symposium on Particleboard
Pullman, Washington, 1967.
Nicholson File Company, Providence, Rhode Island.
File Filosophy.
Norton Company, Worcester, Massachusetts.
Handbook on Abrasives and Grinding Wheels, A.
How to Sharpen.
Philippine Mahogany Association, 111 West 7th Street, Los Angeles, California.
Philippine Mahogany for American Industry.
Philippine Mahogany for the Building and Furniture Industry.
Philippine Mahogany for Churches.
Simonds Saw and Steel Company, Fitchburg, Massachusetts.
File Facts.

Southern Hardwood Producers, Inc., Memphis, Tennessee.
Southern Hardwoods, The.

Southern Pine Association, New Orleans, Louisiana.
Southern Pine Story, The.

Stanley Tool Company, New Britain, Connecticut.
How to Use the Stanley T-Bevel.
How to Work With Tools and Wood.
Stanley Framing and Rafter Square.
Stanley Tool Guide.
Using Your Router.

Timber Structures, Inc., Portland, Oregon.
Engineering in Wood

The Veneer Association, 600 South Michigan Avenue, Chicago, Illinois.
Veneers — The Industry and Its Salesmen.
Veneers — Their Manufacture.

Walnut Manufacturers Association, Chicago, Illinois.
Of Course It's Walnut.
Walnut Book.
Working Wonders With Walnut.

Western Pine Association, Veon Building, Portland, Oregon.
Facts About Engleman Spruce.
Facts About Larch and Douglas Fir.
Facts About Ponderosa Pine.
Facts About White Fir.
White Fir.
Woodcarving for Pleasure.

Yates-American Company, Beloit, Wisconsin.
Short Talks on Wood.

William Zinsser and Company, New York.
Story of Shellac, The.

TELEPHONE NIGHT TABLE

This project is taken from pages 79 and 81 of **Early American Furniture** by James M. O'Neill, published by McKnight & McKnight Publishing Company, Bloomington, Illinois, 1963.

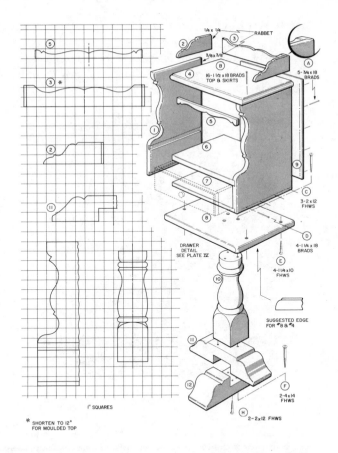

1/4 x 1/4 RABBET

3/8 x 3/8

16-1 1/2 x 18 BRADS TOP & SKIRTS

5-3/4 x 18 BRADS

3-2 x 12 FHWS

4-1 1/4 x 18 BRADS

4-1 1/4 x 10 FHWS

SUGGESTED EDGE FOR #8 & #4

DRAWER DETAIL SEE PLATE IV

2-4 x 14 FHWS

2-2 x 12 FHWS

1" SQUARES

* SHORTEN TO 12"
FOR MOULDED TOP

OPEN EIGHT-PIECE TABLE LAMP

This project is taken from pages 110-112 of **Contemporary Lamps** by Wallace W. Holbrook, published by McKnight & McKnight Publishing Company, Bloomington, Illinois, 1968.

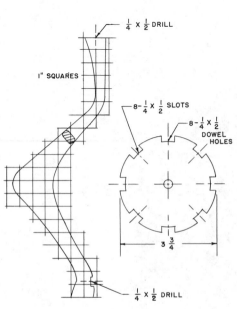

1/4 X 1/2 DRILL

1" SQUARES

8-1/4 X 1/2 SLOTS

8-1/4 X 1/2 DOWEL HOLES

3 3/4

1/4 X 1/2 DRILL

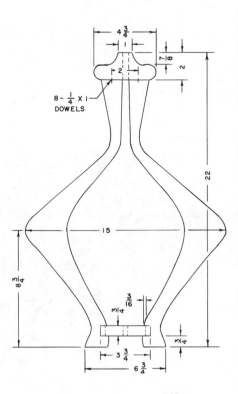

4 3/4

7/8

2

8-1/4 X 1 DOWELS

22

15

8 3/4

3/16

3/4

3/4

3 3/4

3 3/4

6 3/4

HUTCH TABLE

This project is taken from pages 107 and 109 of **Early American Furniture** by James M. O'Neill, published by McKnight & McKnight Publishing Company, Bloomington, Illinois, 1963.

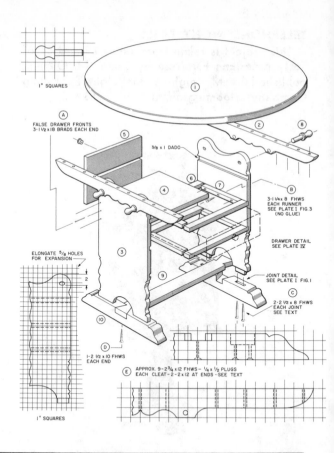

FALSE DRAWER FRONTS
3-1½ x 18 BRADS EACH END

1" SQUARES

3/8 x 1 DADO

3-1¼ x 8 FHWS
EACH RUNNER
SEE PLATE I FIG. 3
(NO GLUE)

DRAWER DETAIL
SEE PLATE IV

JOINT DETAIL
SEE PLATE I FIG. 1

2-2 ½ x 8 FHWS
EACH JOINT
SEE TEXT

ELONGATE 5/8 HOLES
FOR EXPANSION

1-2 ½ x 10 FHWS
EACH END

APPROX. 9-2¾ x 12 FHWS – ¼ x ½ PLUGS
EACH CLEAT – 2-2 x 12 AT ENDS – SEE TEXT

1" SQUARES

TRAYS

This project is taken from pages 117 and 122 of **Woodturning** by Eldon Rebhorn, published by McKnight & McKnight Publishing Company, Bloomington, Illinois, 1970.

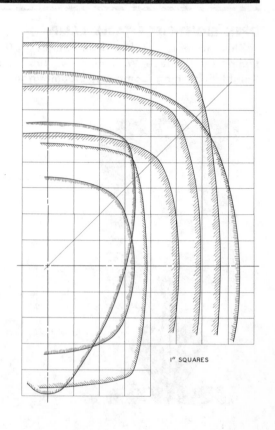

1" SQUARES

444

DRY SINK HUTCH

This project is taken from pages 131, 133, and 134 of **Early American Furniture** by James M. O'Neill, published by McKnight & McKnight Publishing Company, Bloomington, Illinois, 1963.

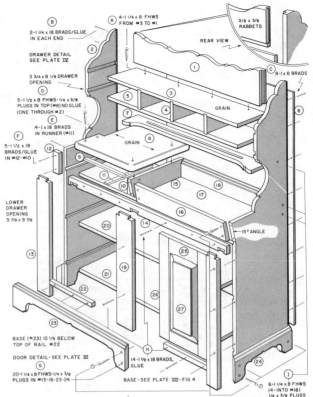

A 4-1 1/4 x 8 FHWS FROM #3 TO #1

B 2-1 1/4 x 18 BRADS/GLUE IN EACH END

3/8 x 3/8 RABBETS

REAR VIEW

DRAWER DETAIL SEE PLATE IV

3 3/4 x 8 1/8 DRAWER OPENING

C 8-1 x 8 BRADS

D 5-1 1/2 x 8 FHWS-1/4 x 3/8 PLUGS IN TOP (#8) NO GLUE (ONE THROUGH #2)

GRAIN

E 4-1 x 18 BRADS IN RUNNER (#11)

GRAIN

F 5-1 1/2 x 18 BRADS/GLUE IN #12-#10

LOWER DRAWER OPENING 3 7/8 x 9 7/8

15° ANGLE

BASE (#23) IS 1/8 BELOW TOP OF RAIL #22

DOOR DETAIL-SEE PLATE III

G 20-1 1/4 x 8 FHWS-1/4 x 3/8 PLUGS IN #13-16-23-24

H 14-1 1/2 x 18 BRADS, GLUE

BASE-SEE PLATE VII-FIG 4

I 6-1 1/4 x 8 FHWS (4-INTO #18) 1/4 x 3/8 PLUGS

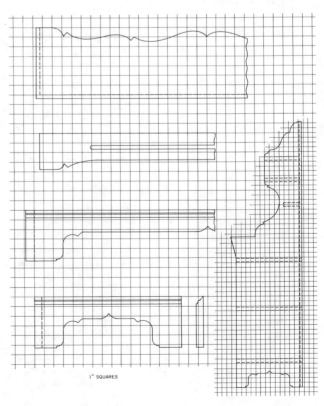

1" SQUARES

445

SHAPED BOWL

This project is taken from pages 115' and 116 of **Woodturning** by Eldon Rebhorn, published by Mc-Knight & McKnight Publishing Company, Bloomington, Illinois, 1970.

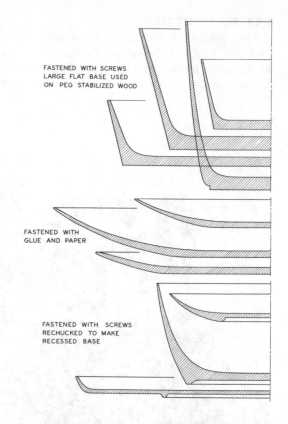

FASTENED WITH SCREWS
LARGE FLAT BASE USED
ON PEG STABILIZED WOOD

FASTENED WITH
GLUE AND PAPER

FASTENED WITH SCREWS
RECHUCKED TO MAKE
RECESSED BASE

PICNIC TABLE

This project is taken from page 247 of **Projects in Wood Furniture** by J. H. Douglass, published by McKnight & McKnight Publishing Company, Bloomington, Illinois, 1967.

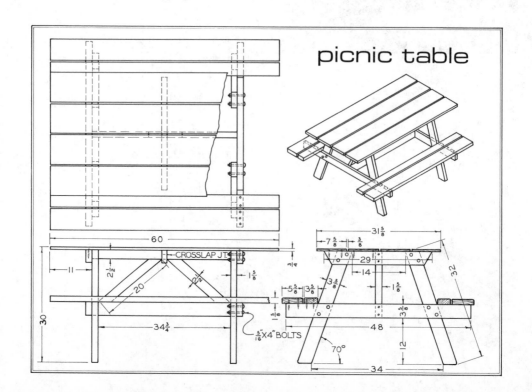

picnic table

SALT AND PEPPER SHAKERS

This project is taken from pages 100 and 101 of **Woodturning** by Eldon Rebhorn, published by McKnight & McKnight Publishing Company, Bloomington, Illinois, 1970.

GUN RACK

This project is taken from page 245 of **Projects in Wood Furniture** by J. H. Douglass, published by McKnight & McKnight Publishing Company, Bloomington, Illinois, 1967.

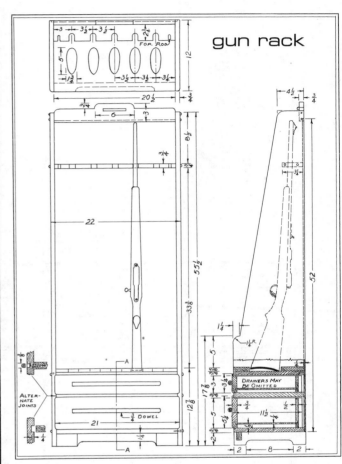

gun rack

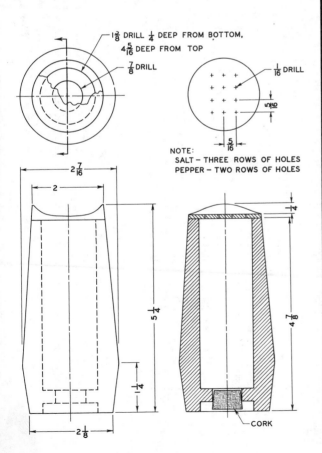

$1\frac{3}{8}$ DRILL $\frac{1}{4}$ DEEP FROM BOTTOM, $4\frac{5}{16}$ DEEP FROM TOP

$\frac{7}{8}$ DRILL

$\frac{1}{16}$ DRILL

NOTE:
SALT – THREE ROWS OF HOLES
PEPPER – TWO ROWS OF HOLES

CORK

STEREO-TV CABINET

This project is taken from pages 235 and 239 of **Projects in Wood Furniture** by J. H. Douglass, published by McKnight & McKnight Publishing Company, Bloomington, Illinois, 1967.

stereo-tv cabinet

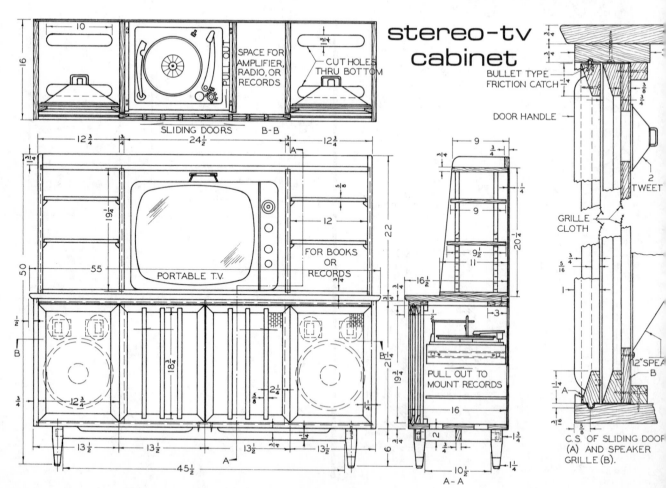

Index

Abrasive flours, 432
Abrasives, 213-215
  closed coat, 214
  open coat, 214
  table of numbers and uses, 215
Abrasive wheels, of grinder, 174
Acrylic latex paint, 412, 413
Actual load, 359
A-frame house, 355
Air, as drying process, 21
Allowances, in patternmaking, 399
Aluminum oxide, 213
American sycamore, 37
Anchor bolts, 361
Angle divider, 98
Angles —
  for crosscutting, 111
  laying out and testing, 97-98
  for ripping, 110, 111
  table of, 98
Animal glue, 304, 305
  in coated abrasives, 213
Anti-kickback lever, on radial arm saw, 134
Appearance, in furniture design, 8
Apron, cutting fingered, 300
Arbors —
  on circular saws, 122, 123
  for wood lathe, 255
Arch —
  laminating, 380
  trussed, 379
Arcs, laying out on finger joints, 299
Arkansas stone, natural oilstone, 178
Arris, of joint, 272
Ash, 33
  white, 41
Assembling, industrial, 318
Assembly, of veneers, 342, 343
Attachments, *see* Name of machine or tool
Auger bits, 226, 227
  cutting action of, 104
Automatic stroke sander, 221
Axe, sharpening, 182

Backing, used for abrasives, 213
Back-knife lathe, 269
Back saw, 108
  using, 112
Balsa, 34
Band clamps, 313-316
Band saw, 143-150
  operator, 150
  using, 146-148
Bar clamps, 310-312
Basswood, 35
Batter boards, laying out, 358
Bayonet saw, 121, 122

Beading, with hand router, 200, 201
Beads, cutting with skew chisel, 263
Beech, 36, 37
Below grade, of lumber, 30
Belt guard, on jig saw, 117
Belt sander, 215, 216, 217
Bench rabbet plane, 154
Bench rules, 89
Bending, 347-352
  by laminating method, 351-352
  by steaming method, 348-351
Benzene gasoline, in thinning paints and enamels, 411
Between-center turning, 260-266
Bevel —
  cutting on circular saw, 132
  cutting on jointer, 189
  cutting on radial arm saw, 137
  of wood joint, 272
Bevel ripping, on radial arm saw, 138
Billet, defined, 27
Birch, 38
  yellow, 48
Bird pecks, defect in lumber, 28
Bit, and brace to bore holes, 231-233
Bit brace, 224-226
  application of wheel and axle, 85
Bit gauge, 230, 238
Bit stops, 232, 283
Black cherry, 40
Black tupelo, 44
Black walnut, 40, 69, 70
Black willow, 70, 71
Blade guides, on jig saw, 117
Blades —
  band saw, 145-146
  on circular saw, 123
  jeweler's and saber on jib saws, 118
  of jig saw, 115, 117
  jig saw selection (table), 120
  replacing band saw, 148-149
  saber for portable saws (table), 120
  selecting for circular saw, 125-127
  table of rip tooth sizes, 145
  table of saber tooth sizes, 146
  table of skip tooth sizes, 145
Blank, defined, 27
Blemish, classification of lumber surface, 28
Block planes, defined, 153
Blood albumin glue, 304, 305
Board —
  defined, 27
  sawing with hand saw, 110-113
  squaring by hand process, 158-162
Board foot, measure of lumber, 32
Board measure, 19
  figuring, 386

Boards —
  laying out batter, 358
  sawing types of, 19
Boats, construction of, 353, 391-393
Bolts, anchor, 361
Bond coat, on coated abrasives, 213
Boring, drilling, and mortising, 223-249
Bow —
  affects suitability of lumber, 28
  facing stock having, 101
Box hinge, 335
Box joint, 274
Box nails, 322
Box sill, 361
Braced frame construction, 363
Braces, corner, 333-334
Brad awl, 223
Brads, 322
Breast drill, 234, 235
Bridge, model covered, 354
Bridging, of joints, 367
Bristles, of paint brushes, 410
Brushes —
  breaking-in new, 410, 411
  cleaning and storing, 411
  paint, 409-411
Bull nose rabbet plane, 154
Butadiene styrene paint (B.D.S.), 412, 413
Butt chisel, 168
Butterfly roof, 373
Butt gauge, 91, 92
Butt hinges, 336
  to hang cabinet door, 338-339
Butt joint, 273

Cabinet clamps, 310
Cabinet hinges, 335, 336
Cabinetmaker's rabbet plane, 154
Cabinet paper, 214
Cabinet saw, 109
Cabinet scraper, 165
Caliper rules, 89
Cam, and pitman on jig saw, 117
Cant, 19
  defined, 27
Capacity, *see* Name of tool or machine
Carborundum, artificial oilstone, 178
Carpenter, skills of, 355-356
Carriage clamps, 313, 314
Carvings, sample, 173
Carving tools, 168-170
  using, 170-172
Casehardening —
  of cut wood, 16
  drying condition, 20
Casein glue, 304, 305
Casing nails, 322
Catalyzed synthetic lacquer, 429

Catalyzed synthetic varnish, 429
Cavity —
    cutting clearance, 301
    of wood cells, 19
C-clamps, 313-316
Cedar, 39, 42
    eastern red, 52
Ceilings, structural standards for
        heights, 390, 391
Cells —
    structure in wood sections, 16, 17
    types of wood, 17
Cellulose, 17
Cement, contact, 348
Center, locating, 260, 261
Chain mortiser, 248
Chair backs, gluing, 317, 318
Chairs, design features, 8
Chamfer —
    cutting on circular saw, 132
    cutting on jointer, 189
    of wood joint, 273
Check, defect in lumber, 28
Checking, of cut wood, 16
Cheek, of wood joint, 273
Cherry, 42, 43
    black, 40
Chevrons, 324
Chisels, 168-170
    to cut end grain, 170
    turning, 258-259
    using, 170-172
    using in face-plate turning,
        267, 268
    whetting, 180, 181
Chucks —
    nomenclature, of, 235
    on jig saws, 117
Circle, layout of, 100, 101
Circular plane, 156
Circular saw —
    to cut tenon, 292
    cutting stock to length with,
        128, 129
    operator, 134
    selecting blades for, 125-127
    table type, 122-125
    using, 128-133
Clamps, 310-316
Claw hammers, 319-320
Clearance, lip, 105
Climate, affects air seasoning, 21
Cloth, as backing for abrasives, 213
Clothing, and safety, 105
Collar and pin, to shape curved stock,
        205, 206
Combination blade, 126
Combination circular blade, cutting
        angles, 104
Combination plane, 155
Combination squares, 94, 96
Common grades —
    numbered for hardwoods, 29-30
    of softwoods, 31
Common nails, 321

Common rafters, 374-375
Common screwdrivers, 328
Compass saw, 109
Computers, used to grade lumber,
        30, 31
Concave saws, 124
Concrete forms, for footings or
        foundations, 360, 361
Cone pulleys, on jig saws, 117
Construction —
    boat, 391-393
    braced frame, 363
    classifications of woodworking, 2
    Western frame, 362
Contact cement, 348
Contour gauge, 298
Controlled-cut, on circular saw, 126
Coped joint, making, 298-299
Coping saw, 108, 109
    using, 112
Core box, laying out and constructing,
        402
Core box plane, 156
Cores —
    grades of lumber, 79
    in patterns, 397, 398
Corner, of wood joint, 273
Corner brace, 324
Corner irons, 333-334
Corner posts, 368
Corners, plumbing, 371-372
Counterboring, 233
Countersink holes, for screws, 332
Countersinking, 233
Cove, molding with router bits,
        200, 201
Crook —
    affects suitability of lumber, 28
    planing, 101
Crosscut saws, 107, 108, 126
    cutting angles of, 104
Crosscut teeth, on circular saw, 125
Crosscutting —
    with band saw, 147, 148
    with circular saw, 128
    on radial arm saw, 136
Crystolon, artificial oilstone, 178
Cup —
    affects suitability of lumber, 28
    in board, 194
    correcting stock having, 101, 102
Cup center, 253
Curves —
    cut by jig saw, 115
    cutting with band saw, 146
    filing convex, 211, 212
    laying out, 100
    sanding inside and concave, 220
Cut —
    finishing, 112
    making concave with chisel, 171
    making concave or cove, 264
    making inside, 119
    making V, 263
    smoothness of, 105
    starting, 110, 111

Cuts, table of radial arm saw, 135
Cutters, profiles of shaper, 205
Cutting —
    by hand tools, 152-183
    machine processes, 184-208
    in squaring process, 196
Cutting units, determining, 29, 30
Cypress, 43, 46

Dado blade, on circular saw, 127
Dadoes —
    cut with circular saw, 122, 132
    cutting on radial arm saw, 138
    cutting with hand router, 199
    wood joint, 273
Dado head chippers, 123
Dado head saws, 123
Dado joint —
    making by hand process, 278-279
    in table construction, 302
Dado plane, 155
Dado rabbet joints, 274, 275
Deacon's Masterpiece, 61
Dead load, 359, 360
Dead weight, of roof, 360
Decals, 436, 437
Decay, of wood, 17
Defects —
    and grading of lumber, 27-31
    standard, 28
Deflector, dust on sanders, 216, 217
Depth gauge, adjusting spindle travel,
        243
Depth stop, in miter box, 114
Design, 4-11
    beauty vs. function, 5, 6
    and function, 4
    in turning, 9-10
    and use of proper wood, 4
Diamond point chisel, 258, 259
Dielectric gluing, 305, 306
Dimensional lumber, defined, 27
Dimension Reference Chart, 12, 13
Dimensions, changes in wood
        determine usage, 26
Disk sander, 216, 217
Divider —
    angle, 98
    using wing, 100
Dogs, steel, 312
Doors —
    fitting and hanging, 387-388
    framing, 369, 370
    hanging cabinet, 338-339
    installing cylindrical lockset in,
        389-390
    structural standards for, 390
Double-end block planes, 155
Double pipe bar clamps, 310
Dovetailing, with hand router,
        201, 202
Dovetail joint, 274
    making by machine process,
        294-296
    in table or drawer construction, 302

Dovetails, laying out and cutting, 296, 297
Dovetail saw, 108
Dowel bit, 226, 227
Dowel jig, 232, 233, 282, 283
Dowel joint, in table construction, 302, 303
Dowels, 275
  reinforcing joints with, 282-284
  wood and metal, 281
Draft allowance, 399
Drawer, dovetailing with hand router, 202
Drawknife, 164
  sharpening, 182
Dresser, grinding wheel, 175
Drier, veneer, 343
Drilling, boring, and mortising, 223-249
Drill press —
  floor and bench models, 239-242
  nomenclature of, 242
  using, 242-247
  using attachments on, 240, 241
Drills, 234-247
  inserting in press, 242, 243
  size designations, 236
  sizes and speeds of electric (table), 238
Drop leaf, in table construction, 302, 303
Drops, in furniture design, 10
Drum sander, 222
Drying —
  air process, 21
  controlled process, 20
  forced air, 23
  by radio-frequency dielectric process, 23-24
  time factor of, 23
Drying oils, in paints and enamels, 411
Duplex rabbet plane, 155
Duplicator, turning, 254

Eastern pine, 62
Eastern red cedar, 52
Easy cut blade, 126
Eccentric clamps, 310
Edges —
  planing, 160
  sanding, 221
  of wood joint, 273
Edge-to-edge spring joint —
  making, 276
  used in table construction, 302
Edge trimming block plane, 155
Electric screwdriver, 329
Ellipse, laying out, 100
Enamels, 411-413
Enclosed hand drill, 234
End butt joint, in table construction, 302
End checks, removing, 102
Epoxy finishes, 414
Epoxy resin glue, 305

Equilibrium Moisture Content (E.M.C.), 25, 26
Essex scale, to figure board measure, 386, 387
Evaporation, control of, 19-20
Expansive bits, 226, 228
Extenders, in paints and enamels, 411
Extension rules, 89
Extensions, for bit braces, 224, 225
Eyes, and safety, 105, 106

Face —
  planing true and smooth, 158, 159
  testing for flatness, 159
Face-plate turning, 266-269
Facing, in squaring process, 196
Fans, used in forced air drying, 23
Fasteners —
  for boat construction, 391
  corrugated, 324
  for crate corners, 324
  nails, 320-325
Fastening, 304-339
Feather strip, used in ripping, 130
Feet, shapes of furniture, 9
Fence, testing for squareness, 187
Fiberboard plane, 156, 157
Fibers —
  as backing for abrasives, 213
  determine grain of wood, 18
  major wood cells, 17
Fiber Saturation Point (F.S.P.), 20
Fiber stress, of woods for girders, (table), 365
Fiddle bow drill, 230
Figure, classification of lumber surface, 27
File card, to clean file, 210, 211
Files —
  nomenclature of, 209
  oilstone, 178, 179
  using for shaping, 211-212
Filing, 209-212
Fillets, 403
  applying, 403-404
Finger joint, 274
Finger joints —
  making, 299-301
  in table construction, 303
Finials, in furniture design, 11
Finish, applying gum, 434
Finish allowance, 399
Finishes —
  epoxy, 414
  super, 429
Finishing, 407-442
  glossary of terms, 437-438
  introduction to, 407-408
  preparing surface for, 408-409
Finishing nails, 322
Finishing paper, 214
Finish sander, 218, 219
Finish schedules, for open and close grain woods, 435-436
Fir, 46, 47
Fire, safety rules to prevent, 106

Firmer chisel, 168
First grade, of lumber, 29, 30
First and Second grades (F.A.S.), of lumber, 29, 30
Fish glue, 304, 305
Fitting, of doors, 387, 388
Flint quartz, 213
Flitch, of lumber defined, 27
Flooring, 368
Flooring saw, 109
Floor nailing, 327
Fluting, with hand router, 200, 201
Fly cutter, 245
Fly rail, in finger joints, 299-301
Folding extension rule, 90, 91
Folding rules, 89
Footings —
  concrete forms as, 361
  factor determining size of, 359, 360
Force, determining hammer, 86
Fore planes, 152
Forest cruiser's sticks, 90, 91
Formulas —
  for computing lumber quantities, 32
  for determining force, 86, 87
  for determining loads, 360
Forstner bit, 226, 227
Foundation wall, factors determining size of, 359, 360
Frame, constructing boat, 391, 392
Framing —
  of houses, 359-368
  around openings, 367, 368
  of walls, 369-371
Framing chisel, 168
Framing squares, 94, 95, 96
Frog, on plane irons, 153
Fulcrum, of lever, 86
Furniture —
  combines wood and other materials, 7
  designs of, 6-11
  function and design, 8
  glossary of terms, 13-14
  mass-produced, 7, 8
  occupations in industry, 150-151
  shapes of legs and feet of, 9-11

Gable roof, 373
Gains, 273
  cutting, 387, 388
  cutting for inlay and insets, 345, 346
  laying out and cutting door, 338
  removing surplus stock when cutting, 171
  using hand router to cut, 199, 200
Gambrel, 373
Garnet, 213
Gauges, 91-93
  in measurement and layout, 88
  router, 200
Gears, see Name of tool or machines
Girders, 361-366
  fiber stress of woods for (table), 365
Glasses, in leveling tool, 356
Glazier's chisel, 169

Glossary —
　of finishing terms, 437-438
　of furniture terms, 13-14
　of patternmaking terms, 404-406
　of structural terms, 393-396
Glue —
　in coated abrasives, 213
　properties of (table), 308
　types of, 304-305
　in veneering, 342-344
　see also Wood Glue
Glue gun, 306
Gluing —
　dielectric, 305-306
　of joints, 317-319
　in veneering, 342, 343
Gouges, 168-170, 258
　using, 170-172
　using in turning, 261, 262
　whitting, 181
Grades —
　of lumber, 29-31
　see also Name of Species
Grading, and defects of lumber, 27-31
Grain —
　classification of lumber surface, 27
　cutting end with chisel, 170, 171
　determine direction to plane, 159
　filing end, 212
　shaping end, 207
Grinder, bench, floor models, 174-175
Grinding, of tools, 176-177
Grit cloth, as backing for abrasives, 213
Grooves, 273
　cutting on circular saws, 122, 132
　cutting on radial arm saw, 139
Guards —
　on circular saw, 124
　plastic on lathe, 250, 261
　for portable electric saw, 142
　on radial arm saw, 134
Guide blocks, of band saw, 143
Guide post, on jig saw, 117
Guides, in miter box, 113
Gum finish, preparing and applying, 434
Gumwood, 50, 51
Gun, spray painting with, 430, 431

Half-back saw, 109
Half lap joint, 274
Hammers —
　claw, 319-320
　position in driving nails, 326
Hand drill, 234-235
Hand planes, 152-153
Hand saws, 107-110
Hand scraper, 165
　cutting action of, 104
Hand screws, 309
Hanging, of doors, 387, 388
Hardboard, 71, 80-81
Hardwoods —
　source, 16
　types of porosity in, 18, 19

Headers, 367, 368
Heads —
　of nails, 323
　of screws, 330
Hemlock, 51, 53
Hexagon, laying out, 100
Hickory, 53, 54
　true, 41
Hinges, 335-337
　cutting gains for, 199, 200
　in hanging doors, 387, 388
Hip rafters, 376-377
Hip roof, 373
Holes —
　boring dowel in apron, 243
　boring with bit and brace, 231-233
　defect in lumber, 28
　drilling with drill press, 244
　drilling in irregular shaped stock, 243
　drilling procedure with hand drill, 237
　grub, 28
　pinworm, 28
　rafting pin, 28
　for screws, 332
　selecting tool to cut (table), 223
　shapes of arbor, 141
　shot worm, 28
　spot worm, 28
Hole saw, 245
Hollow chisel mortiser, 247-249
Hollow chisels, 248
Hollow ground blade, 126
Honeycombing, of cut wood, 16
Honing, 180-183
Hook and eye, hinge, 335
Hook rules, 89
Hook scraper, 165
Hook stave rules, 89
Hot-melt adhesives, 304
Houses —
　A-frame, 355
　building model, 353
　design, 354
　framing, 359-368
　scale models of, 353
Howe truss, 379
Humidity, affects wood dimensions, 23, 26
Hydraulic bending press, 349, 350

I-bar clamps, 310, 311
Idler pinion gear, 235
Inboard face-plate turning, 266-268
Inclined plane, classification of tool, 85, 86
Indexing head, on wood lathe, 255
India stone, artificial oilstone, 178
Injuries, reporting, 106
Inlay, 344
　applying, 345-346
Inline sander, 218
Insets, 344
　applying, 345-346

Inside gouge, 168
Inspection, visual for grading lumber, 30

Jack plane, 152
Jack rafters, 377-379
Japan driers, in paints and enamels, 411
Jaws, on bit braces, 224
Jeweler's blade, on jig saws, 118
Jigs, using during boring holes, 232, 233
Jigsaw, 115-117
　blade and speed selection (table), 120
　using, 118-120
Joiner bar clamps, 311
Joinery, 272-303
Jointer, 184-185
　aligning rear table, 186, 187
　cutting action of, 104
　to smooth surface, 187-190
Jointer planes, 152
Jointing, in squaring board, 195
Joints —
　common wood, 273-275
　definition of wood, 272
　gluing, 317-319
　making coped, 298-299
　making dado by hand process, 278-279
　making dovetail by machine, 294-296
　making an edge-to-edge spring, 276-277
　making finger, 299-301
　making lap, 277, 278
　making miter, 284-287
　making mortise and tenon by hand, 288-290
　making mortise and tenon by machine, 291-293
　making rabbet, 280
　reinforcement of wood, 272
　reinforcing with dowels, 282-284
　types of wood, 272
Joists, 366-368

Kerf, in relation to saw teeth, 107
Keyhole saw, 108, 109
　using, 112
Kiln, to dry lumber, 21, 23
Knife, sharpening, 181
Knife wedge, cutting action of, 103
Knives, setting jointer, 186-187
Knots —
　defect in lumber, 28
　eliminating, 102

Lacquer, 426-427
　applying, 427-428
Laminating, 347-352
　method of bending, 351-352
Laminator, to make manufactured board, 78

Lap joints, making, 277-278
Latex emulsion paints, 412-413
Lathe —
  back-knife, 269
  face-plate turning on, 266-269
  in fluting and beading, 200
  the Mattison, 270
  primitive examples of, 256, 257
  shaping circular forms on, 250-271
  using to turn wood, 250
  veneer, 340
  wood, 252-257
Layer, S_2 in wood, 19, 20
Layout, 85, 99, 101, 102
  of batter boards, 358
  of patterns, 399-402
Leaves, table, 299-303
Leg, dovetail on pedestal, 296-298
Legs, shapes of furniture, 9, 10
Length, cutting to, 161
Level, in breast drill, 235
Leveling tools, 356-357
Lever —
  classification of tool, 85, 86
  hammer as, 85
Lignin, binds fibers, 17
Limba (Korina), 49, 55
Linear measure, 88
Line level, 356
Lip clearance, 105
Lithopane, 411
Live center, 253
Live loads, 359, 360
Loads —
  determining, 359, 360
  on girders and joists, 365-367
Locks, column, yoke, and swivel, 134
Lockset, installing cylindrical in door, 389-390
Log rules, 90
Logs —
  determining measure, 19
  sawing considerations, 19
Lumber —
  classifications of manufactured, 27
  computing quantities, 32
  minimum sizes (table), 391
  seasoning of, 19-20
  slash sawn shrinkage, 20
  surface characteristics of, 27
  terms, defects, and grading, 27-31
  wood and trees, 15-84
Lumber cores, grades of, 79
Lumberman's board rule, 89, 90
Lumtape, 90

Machine bit, 228
Machines —
  safety rules in using, 106
  tools as, 85
Machinists' clamps, 313, 314
Magnetic-type jig saw, 116
Mahogany, 55, 56
  Phillippine, 52-57
  tropical American, 49

Maintenance, see Name of species, tool, or machine
Mallets, types, 172
Mansard, 373
Manufactured board, 71, 72-82
Maple, 58, 59
  sugar, 48
Marking gauges, 91, 92, 93
Mathematics, instruments of, 88
Mattison lathe, 270
Mauls, wood, 172
Melamine formaldehyde, in wood glues, 304
Mending plates, 333-334
Meters, moisture, 24, 25
Microfibrils, 17
Mineral spirits, in thinning paints and enamels, 411
Mirror, used in turning, 10
Miter —
  cutting with circular saw, 129, 130
  cutting on radial arm saw, 137
Miter box, 113-115, 285
  in making coped joint, 298
  motorized, 114, 115
Miter box saw, 109-113
Miter clamps, 313-316
Miter gauge, on circular saw, 122, 129
Miter joints, 273
  making, 284-287
Miter machine, 287
Miter square, 94
Miter vise, 285
Model maker's plane, 156
Moisture —
  effect on cut wood, 16
  measuring content of lumber, 24, 25
Molders, 208
Molding, 347-352
  with hand router, 201
Molding comb, 298
Molding head, of circular saw, 124, 126
Moldings, furniture types, 11
Mortise —
  cutting, 289, 291
  cutting in end of pedestal, 244
  layout of, 289
  removing surplus stock when cutting, 171
Mortise chisel, 168
Mortise gauges, 92
Mortiser, vertical hollow chisel, 247-249
Mortise and tenon joints, 274
  in table construction, 302
  making by hand process, 288-290
  making by machine process, 291-293
Mortising —
  drilling, and boring, 223-249
  using attachment on drill press, 244, 245
Motor —
  of jig saw, 117

reversible on portable electric saw, 141
  see also Name of machine
Multiple spindle drill, 244
Multi-spur machine bit, 228, 229

Nails, 320-325
  driving, 325-327
  factors affecting holding power, 326, 327
  special purpose, 325
  withdrawing, 326
National Hardwood Lumber Association, 29
Newspaper, in veneering, 342, 343

Oak, 59, 60
  red and white, 45
Occupations —
  of carpenter, 355, 356
  in furniture industry, 150-151
  of patternmaker, 406
  wood turning, 271
Offset screwdrivers, 328
Offset shank chisel, 169
Oil stains, 415
  applying, 416
Oilstone, 178-179
  for whetting, 180
One-piece pattern, 397
Open gear hand drill, 234
Open ratchet bit brace, 224
Operator —
  band saw, 150
  of circular saw, 134
Orbital sander, 218
Outboard face-plate turning, 266-268
Outside gouge, 168

Paint brushes, 409-411
Paints, 411-413
Panel gauges, 92
Panel saw, 108
Paper, as backing for abrasives, 213
Parallel gauges, 92
Parallelism, principle of, 88
Parenchyma, function of, 17, 18
Paring chisel, 168, 170
Particle board, 71, 81-82
Parting tool, 258, 259
Paste wood filler, 419-420
  applying, 420-421
Patternmaker, skills of, 406
Patternmaker's gauge, 92, 93
Patternmaking, 397-406
  glossary of terms, 404-406
Patterns, 397-406
  laying out, 399, 401
  making simple, 400
  transferring, 99
Pedestal leg, cutting dovetail on, 296-298
Pedestals, patterns, 10
Phenol resin, in wood glues, 304
Phillippine mahogany, 52, 57
Phillips screwdrivers, 329

Pigments, in paints and enamels, 411, 415
Piling clamps, 311
Pilot holes, for screws, 332
Pine —
    eastern, 62
    ponderosa, 63
    yellow or hard, 64, 65
Pinion gear, 235
Pins, of dovetail joints, 294, 295
Pitch pocket, defect in lumber, 28
Pith, defect in lumber, 28
Pivot support, in table construction, 302
Plain bit brace, 224
Plane blade, cutting action of, 103
Plane iron, squaring edge of, 176
Planer, single surface, 191-194

Planer blade, 126
Planes —
    hand, 152-153
    special purpose, 154-158
Planks —
    defined, 27
    sawing lumber to, 19
Plastic laminates, 347
Plastics, as backing for abrasives, 213
Plow cut, with radial arm saw, 138
Plow plane, 155
Plug cutter bit, 226, 228
Plumb bob, 356, 357
Plumbing, of walls or corners, 371, 372
Plunger, of jig saw, 117
Plunger-type jig saw, 115, 116
Plywood, 71, 72-79
    classifications of species (table), 74
    grade-use guide for appearance of (table), 75
    grade-use guide for engineered (table), 76
    hardwood grades, 74, 78-79
    softwood grades, 72-74
    summary of veneer grades used (table), 77
    typical constructions, 73
Pocket level, 357
Points, of nails, 323
Polyethylene glycol, agent to stabilize wood, 26
Polyurethane varnish, 425
Polyvinyl acetate paint (P.V.A.), 412-413
Ponderosa pine, 63
Poplar, yellow, 64, 66
Pores, types in hardwoods, 18, 19
Portable electric drill, 238-239
Portable electric saw, 140-142
Portable electric saber saw, 121-122
Portable hand router, 196
    using, 199-203
Portable sanders, 218, 219
Pneumatic screwdrivers, 329
Pratt truss, 379
Presser foot, on jig saw, 117

Protractor, used in laying out, 97
Pulley, classification of tool, 86, 87, 88
Pumice, abrasive flour, 432
Pump drill, 230
Push shoe, 188
Push stick, used in ripping, 130

Quadrant, in miter box, 113

Rabbet joint, making by hand process, 280
Rabbet plane, 154
Rabbets —
    cutting on circular saw, 122, 132
    cutting with hand router, 199
    cutting on jointer, 188
    cutting on radial arm saw, 139
Radial arm saw, 134-140
    table of cuts, 135
    using, 136-140
Radio-frequency dielectric drying, 23-24
Rafters, 374-379
Rafter tables, reading, 374-379
Rake angle, during cut, 105
Rasp, 209-211
    using for shaping, 211, 212
Ratchet screwdriver, 328
Rays —
    major wood cell, 17, 18
    medullary, 16, 20
Razor, sharpening angle, 182
Reaction wood, defined, 18
Red oak, 45
Redwood, 66, 67
References, 439-442
    see also Additional Readings under each topic
Reinforcements, 333-334
Relief cuts, on band saw, 147
Replaceable bit screwdriver, 329
Resawing, 273
    with band saw, 146
    on circular saw, 131
Resin —
    in coated abrasives, 213
    in glues, 304, 305
Resorcinal formaldehyde glue, 304
Rings, annual of trees, 15
Rip fence, on circular saw, 122, 128, 129
Ripping —
    with band saw, 147, 148
    on circular saw, 130
    on radial arm saw, 137
    in squaring process, 195
Ripsaw, 107, 108, 109, 126
    cutting angles of, 104
Rip teeth, 108, 109
    on circular saw, 125
Rip tooth blade, table of sizes, 145
Rocker arm jig saw, 116
Roller marking gauges, 92, 93
Roof loads, 359, 360
Roofs, 373-379
Rottenstone, abrasive flour, 432

Rough lumber, defined, 27
Roundnose chisel, 258
Router —
    multiple spindle, 204
    portable hand, 196-198
    using attachment on drill press, 246
Router bits, shapes and uses, 197
Router plane, 154
Routing, with radial arm saw, 138, 140
Rule joint, in table construction, 302
Rules, 89-91

Saber blades, 118, 120
Saber tooth blades, table of sizes, 146
Safety, 105-106
    in applying lacquer, 428
    in applying varnish, 425
    in band saw operation, 148
    in bending wood to form, 352
    in boring holes, 233
    in circular saw operation, 133
    with chisels, gouges, carving tools, 172
    when cutting board, 110, 111, 113
    in drill press operations, 247
    in driving nails, 327
    in driving screws, 333
    in face-plate turning, 268, 269
    with file and rasp, 212
    in finishing, 409
    in framing openings, 371
    in gluing joints, 319
    in grinding edge tools, 177
    in hand drilling, 237
    in hand router operations, 203
    in jointer operations, 189, 190
    in making joints, 277, 278, 279, 280, 284, 286, 290, 293, 301
    in planing, 162, 187, 194
    with portable electric saw, 140
    with radial arm saw, 140
    with sanders, 219, 222
    in setting knives of jointer, 186, 187
    in shaper operations, 208
    in sharpening scrapers, 167
    in spindle turning, 265, 266
    in squaring a board, 196
    in use of jig saw, 119
    in whetting and honing, 182
Sales units, see Name of species
Sanders, 215-219
    portable, 218-219
    using, 220-222
Sanding, 213-222
    in spindle turning, 265
Sanding disk, for lathe, 253
Sanding drum, for lathe, 254
    using on drill press, 246
Sandpaper, 214
Saw horse, 110, 112
Saw kerf, as method of bending, 352
Saws —
    crosscut cutting angles of, 104
    cutting stock with, 103, 151
    hand, 107-110
    maintenance of, 109

portable electric, 140-142
portable electric saber, 121-122
saber blades for portable (table), 120
sawing board with hand, 110-113
selecting blades for circular, 125-127
table type circular, 122-125
types to cut logs, 21, 22
Sawyers, 19
Scale, of drawings, 99
Scanning device, to grade lumber, 31
Scarf joint, 273, 274
Scissors truss, 379
Scraper plane, 156
Scrapers, 165-166
  sharpening, 166-167
Scraping, in spindle turning, 261, 262, 264
Screen hinge, 335
Screw, classification of tool, 85, 86, 87
Screwdrivers, 328-330
Screw mate, 229
Screws, 330-331
  hand, 309
  and holes (table), 331
Scrub plane, 157
Sealer, 419
Seasoning, of lumber, 19-20
Second grade, of lumber, 29, 30
Selection, of proper stock, 101-102
Selects, grade of lumber, 29, 30
Self-cleaning cloth, 214
Self-cleaning paper, 214
Shake —
  defect in lumber, 28
  ring, 28
  wind, 28
Shank holes, for screws, 332
Shaped stock, terms applied to, 27
Shaper, 203-205
  cutter shapes, 205
  multiple spindle, 204
  using, 205-208
  using attachment on drill press, 245
Shapes, see Name of species
Shaping —
  with miter gauge and hold-downs, 207
  on radial arm saw, 139
  with use of fence, 205
  with use of template, 206
Sharpening, by whetting or honing, 180-183
Shearing, in spindle turning, 261, 262, 264
Sheathing, 382-384
Shed roof, 373
Sheet, of lumber defined, 27
Shellac, 422
Shells, furniture design, 11
Shields, eye, 175
Shingles, 382, 384
Ship carpenter's bevel rule, 90
Shoemaker's rasp, 210
Shoor, defined, 27
Shop lumber, defined, 27

Shoulder, 273
Shrinkage —
  comparisons of, 25
  of cut trees, 15, 16,
  of slash and quarter sawn lumber, 20
Shrinkage allowance, 399
Shrink rules, 89
Side rabbet plane, 155
Siding, 382-384
  applying, 384
Silicon carbide, 213
Sills, 361
Single surface planer, 191
  using, 193, 194
Size coat, on coated abrasives, 213
Sizes —
  of hand saw blades, 110
  of jig saws, 116
  see also Name of species
Skew chisel, 258
  cutting action of, 103
  using in turning, 262, 263
Skew cutter rabbet plane, 155
Skip tooth blade, table of sizes, 145
Slab, defined, 27
Slicer, veneer, 340, 341
Slip stone, to sharpen gouge, 181
Sloyd knife, 182
Smooth planes, 152
Sockets, of dovetail joints, 294, 297
Socket slick chisel, 169
Softwoods —
  grading, 31
  source, 16
Soil, bearing quality of (table), 359
Solid sill, 361
Song of Hiawatha, 84
Soss hinge, 337
Sound wormy, grade of lumber, 30
Spade bit, 229
Span —
  of girders determined by fiber stress, 365, 366
  safe floor joint (table), 366
Speed —
  selecting for drill size, 243
  selecting jig saw (table), 120
Spikes, 322
Spindle sander, 215, 216
Spindle turning, 260-266
Spiral ratchet screwdriver, 329
Splines, 275
  in making miter joint, 285, 286
Split patterns, 397, 398
  laying out and shaping, 401, 402
Splitter, on circular saw, 124
Spoke caliper rules, 89
Spoke shave, 163
  sharpening, 182
Spray gun, 430-431
Spring clamps, 313-316
Spring joint, making edge-to-edge, 276-277
Spring set, 125
Spruce, 67, 68
Spur center, 253

Square, of lumber defined, 27
Squareness, testing end to edge, 162
Squarenose chisel, 258
Squares, 94-96
  attachments for, 96
  to layout and test angles, 97
  in measurement and layout, 88
  proportional to layout irregular designs, 99
Squaring —
  on crosscut saw, 128
  hand process of, 158-162
  on the jointer, 188
  by machine process, 194-196
Stabilization, of wood, 26
Staging, 370
Stains, oil, 415
  water, 417
Stair builder's saw, 109
Stairs, laying out, 385-386
Standards —
  see Name of machine or process of operation
  of structural elements, 390-391
Stave, defined, 27
Steaming, method of bending, 348-351
Steel rules, 89
Steel squares, 94
Stickers, in drying lumber, 21, 22
Stock —
  cutting with saws, 103-151
  getting out, 101-102, 195
  removing surplus, 171
  securing to table to drill hole, 243
  shaping curved, 205
  shaping straight, 205
Stop, depth in miter box, 114
Stop block, used on circular saw, 128, 129
Stop boring, 232
Stop grooves, cutting on circular saws, 132
Storage, see Name of species of tool
Straightedge, to check surface during planing, 159
Straight gauge, 198, 199
Straight shank drill, 236
Stretchers, turned, 10
Structural lumber, defined, 27
Structure, cellular of wood sections, 16, 17
Structures, 353-396
  glossary of terms in, 393-396
  introduction to, 353, 354
  standards of elements, 390, 391
Stubby screwdrivers, 328
Studs, in framing wall openings, 369, 371
Sugar maple, 48
Sunbursts, in furniture design, 11
Surfaced (dressed) lumber, defined, 27
Surface hinges, 336
Surface measure, of board, 29, 30
Surfacers, see Planer

Surfaces —
  characteristics of lumber, 27
  filing concave, 212
  planing on jointer, 188
  preparing for finishing, 408-409
  sanding convex and small, 220
  sanding flat, 220, 221
  smoothing on jointer, 187
  veneering, 342-344
Surfacing, 193, 194
  in squaring process, 195
Surform, 209, 210
Swaged hinge, 336
Swage teeth, 126
Sweet gum, 44
Swelling, of cut trees, 15, 16
Sycamore, 68, 69
  American, 37

Table —
  adjusting drill press, 243
  joints used in construction, 302-303
Tails, of dovetail joints, 294, 295
Tape, in veneering, 343
Tapering jig, adjustable and fixed, 131
Tapers, cutting, 131, 189, 264, 265
Tapes, steel, 89
Taylor clamps, 317
T-Bevel, using, 97, 231
Teeth —
  on circular saw, 125
  of crosscut saw, 107
  of ripsaw, 107, 108
  of saws, 104
Temperature, in drying lumber, 23
Template —
  finger, 202
  to make coped joint, 299
  used to shape stock, 206
  used with router, 200
Tenoning jig, 292
Tenons —
  cut with circular saw, 122
  cutting, 290, 292
  laying out, 288, 289
Tension, of band saw blade, 143
Tension sleeve, on jigsaw, 117
Texture, classification of lumber
    surface, 28
Theory, of cutting tools, 103-105
Thickness —
  planing to, 162
  surfacing to, 195
T-Hinge, 336
Throat plate —
  of band saw, 143
  on jig saw, 117
Through boring, 231
Thrust wheels, of band saw, 143
Tie bar, in miter boxes, 114
Timber, defined, 27
Toe nailing, 326
Tolerance, accuracy in, 88
Tongue and groove joint, 273
Tongue and groove plane, 155, 156
Tool rests, 255

Tools —
  classifications of, 85, 86
  grinding edge, 176-177
  for laying out, 85-88
  leveling, 356-357
  safety with hand, 106
  selecting to cut hole, 223
  theory of cutting, 103-105
  understanding woodworking, 2-3
  whetting or honing, 180-183
Torpedo level, 356
T-plates, 333-334
Trammel points, to layout circle, 100
Transveneer, 340-341
Trees —
  growth of, 15, 16
  wood and lumber, 15-84
Triangle, laying out in circle, 101
Trimmer, wood, 287
Trimming, with chisel, 171
Tropical American mahogany, 49
True hickory, 41
Trunnions, table, 191
Trusses, 370, 379, 381
Try squares, 94, 95
  to check squareness, 231
Tupelo, black, 44
Turkey stone, natural oilstone, 178
Turning —
  design in, 9-10
  industrial, 269-270
  samples of, 251, 252
  spindle, 9, 10
  spindle or between-center, 260-266
  use of mirror in, 10
Turning chisels, 258-259
Turning saw, 109
Turning square, of lumber defined, 27
Turpentine, in thinning paints and
    enamels, 411
Twist drill, 236

Uniplane, 190-191
Universal saw, 122
Urea, in wood glues, 304
Uses, see Name of species, tool, or
    machine

Valley rafters, 376-377
Variety saw, 122
Varnish, 423, 424
  applying, 424, 425
  in paints and enamels, 411
  polyurethane, 425
V-Block, used with drill press, 242
V cuts, making, 263
Vegetable glue, 304, 305
Veneer, 340-341
  applying to surfaces, 342-344
Veneering, 340-342, 344-346
Veneer saw, 108, 109
Veneer sheets, to make plywood, 71
Vertical hollow chisel mortiser, 247
Vessels, or pores as major wood cell, 17
Viscosity, testing glue for, 305

Vise —
  application of screw, 85
  drill press 243
  to hold board for cutting, 110

Walls —
  framing, 369-371
  plumbing, 371, 372
Walnut, black, 40, 69, 70
Wane, defect in lumber, 28
Waney edge, planing, 101
Warp —
  and shrinkage, 16
  squaring board with, 194-196
Warren truss, 379
Washita stone, natural oilstone, 178
Water, in seasoning wood, 19
Water stain, 417
  applying, 417-418
Waxes, 433-434
Wedge, classification of tool, 85, 86
Wedges, cutting tools as, 103
Western frame construction, 362
Wheel and axle, classification of tool,
    85, 86, 87
Wheels —
  dressing grinding, 175
  standard grinding, 174
  tilting and hand on circular saws,
    123
Whetting, 180-183
White ash, 41
White oak, 45
Width, planing to, 161, 162
Willow, black, 70, 71
Wind —
  affects suitability of lumber, 28
  in board, 194
  facing stock having, 101
Windows —
  framing, 369, 370
  structural standards for, 390
Wing divider, using, 100
Wire nails, 322
Withe, defined, 27
Wood —
  as art medium, 4, 5,
  bending to form, 348-352
  for boat construction, 392
  compression, 18
  decay of, 17
  effects of cutting green, 19, 20
  fiber stress of girders (table),
    365
  for inlays and insets (table), 344
  finish schedule for close grain,
    435, 436
  nature of, 15-19
  nonporous softwood, 18
  reaction, 18
  stabilizing dimensions, 26
  summary of properties of selected
    (table), 83

tension, 18
 testing strength of, **17**
 trees, and lumber, 15-84
 used in patternmaking, 398
Wood bits, 226-230
Wooden spiral hand drill, 230
Wood file, 209-211
Wood glues, 304-307
Wood joints, *see* Joints
Wood lathe, 252-257

Wood screws, 330-331
 driving, 332-333
Wood turner, occupation of, 271
Wood turning, 250-252
Wood twist bits, 226, 229
Woodware, 6
Woodworking —
 categories of, 1
 in education, 1-3
 learning principles of operation, 3

Worked lumber, defined, 27
Wright, Frank Lloyd, 336

Yard lumber, defined, 27
Yellow birch, 48
Yellow or Hard pine, 64, 65
Yellow poplar, 65, 66

Zig-zag rule, 90, 91